International Conference on River Flood Hydraulics

International Conference on River Flood Hydraulics

Edited by

Dr W. R. White
Hydraulics Research Limited
Wallingford, Oxon OX10 8BA, UK

Published on behalf of
HYDRAULICS RESEARCH LIMITED, WALLINGFORD
by
JOHN WILEY & SONS
Chichester · New York · Brisbane · Toronto · Singapore

The selection and presentation of material and the opinions expressed in this publication are the sole responsibility of the authors concerned. The papers have been reproduced by offset printing from the authors' original typescript to minimise delay.

Library of Congress Cataloging in Publication Data:

International Conference on River Flood Hydraulics (1990 :
Wallingford, England)
International Conference on River Flood Hydraulics / edited by
W.R. White.
p. cm.
"Papers presented at the International Conference on River Flood
Hydraulics held at Wallingford, England, 17–20 September 1990
organised and sponsored by Hydraulics Research Limited"—P. v.
Includes bibliographical references.
ISBN 0-471-92713-9 (Ppc.)
1. River engineering—Congresses. 2. Floodplains—Congresses.
I. White, W. R., Dr. II. Hydraulics Research (Firm) III. Title.
TC530.I625 1990 90–12701
627'.4—dc20 CIP

British Library Cataloguing in Publication Data:

International Conference on River Flood Hydraulics (1990 ;
Wallingford, England)
International Conference on River Flood Hydraulics.
1. Floods. Hydraulics
I. Title II. White, W. R. III. Hydraulic Research
Limited
551.48

ISBN 0-471-92713-9

Printed and bound in Great Britain by
Courier International Ltd, Tiptree, Essex

Papers presented at the International Conference on RIVER FLOOD HYDRAULICS held at Wallingford, England : 17–20 September 1990. Organised and sponsored by Hydraulics Research Limited and co-sponsored by: International Association for Hydraulic Research, National Rivers Authority (Thames Region), Institution of Water & Environmental Management, Overseas Development Administration, British Hydrological Society.

Acknowledgements

The valuable assistance of the UK Organising Committee, the International Organising Committee and Panel of Referees is gratefully acknowledged.

UK Organising Committee

International Organising Committee

Contributors

Contact addresses for correspondence

Prof. W. J. R. Alexander (A1), *University of Pretoria, Dept. of Civil Engineering, 0002 Pretoria, South Africa*

Mr J. M. Bartlett (N4), *Binnie & Partners, Grosvenor House, 69 London Road, Redhill, Surrey, RH1 1LQ, UK*

Prof. A. Betamio de Almeida (G3), *CEHIDRO, Dept. of Civil Engineering, Avendida Rovisco Pais, 1096 Lisboa Codex, Portugal*

Mr G. R. Bezzola (J2), *Laboratory of Hydraulics, Hydrology and Glaciology, Swiss Federal Institute of Technology, ETH Zentrum, CH−8092 Zurich, Switzerland*

Prof. S. P. Chee (E1), *University of Windsor, Dept. of Civil & Environmental Engineering, 401 Sunset, Windsor, Ontario, Canada, N9B 3P4*

Mr P. B. Clark (K4), *Binnie & Partners, Grosvenor House, 69 London Road, Redhill, Surrey, RH1 1LQ, UK*

Mr C. Dobson (M5), *NRA − Severn Trent Region, Sapphire East, 550 Streetsbrook Road, Solihull, B91 1QT, UK*

Mr R. Faeh (C1), *Laboratory of Hydraulics, Hydrology and Glaciology, Swiss Federal Institute of Technology, CH−8092 Zurich, Switzerland*

Mr P. C. Fernandez (C3), *Centro Regional Andino, Instituto Nacional de Ciencia y Tecnica Hidraicas, Belgrano 210−3er Piso, Casilla de Correo No 6, 5500−Mendoza, Argentina*

Prof. T. Fukuhara (E2), *Fukui University, Dept of Civil Engineering, Bunkyo 3−9−1, Fukui Shi 910, Japan*

Prof. S. Fukuoka (D2), *Tokyo Institute of Technology, Dept of Civil Engineering, O-Okayama, Meguro-Ku, Tokyo 152, Japan*

Mr J. L. Gardiner (M3), *NRA − Thames Region, Kings Meadow House, Kings Meadow Road, Reading, Berks, RG1 8DQ, UK*

Mr M. D. Gill (C4), *Tatopani Small Hydel Project, PO Box 126, Kathmandu, Nepal*

Mr K. Hasegawa (J3), *Hokkaido University, Dept. of Civil Engineering, North 13 West 8, Sapporo 060, Japan*

Dr J. G. Herbertson (H2), *The University, Dept. of Civil Engineering, Rankine Building, Glasgow, G12 8LT, UK*

Mr N. N. J. Higginson (L2), *Dept. of Agriculture for Northern Ireland, Room 462 Hydebank, 4 Hospital Road, Belfast BT8, Northern Ireland, UK*

Mr L. Iritz (J1), *Uppsala University, Dept. of Hydrology, S-75220 Uppsala, Vastra Agatan 24, Sweden*

Dr M. N. R. Jaeggi (C2), *Laboratory of Hydraulics, Hydrology and Glaciology, Swiss Federal Institute of Technology, CH-8092 Zurich, Switzerland*

Mr G. P. G. Johnson (N2), *NRA – Thames Region, Kings Meadow House, Kings Meadow Road, Reading, Berks, RG1 8DQ, UK*

Dr J. M. Jordaan (F4), *Department of Water Affairs, Directorate of Design Services, Private Bag X313, Pretoria 0001, South Africa*

Mr Gerard Kiely (F3), *University College Cork, Department of Civil Engineering, Cork, Eire*

Dr D. W. Knight (G1 and G4), *University of Birmingham, School of Civil Engineering, PO Box 363, Birmingham, B15 2TT, UK*

Dr P. Y. Ko (G2), *Shawinigan Lavalin Inc., 1100 Rene Levesque Blvd, West Montreal, Quebec, H3B 4P3, Canada*

Mr N. Kouwen (M2), *University of Waterloo, Dept. of Civil Engineering, Waterloo, Ontario, N2L 3G1, Canada*

Mr T. Larsen (F1), *University of Aalborg, Dept. of Civil Engineering, Sohngardholmsvej 57, DK 9000 Aalborg, Denmark*

Mr M. J. Le Gouais (N1), *Scott Wilson Kirkpatrick, Scott House, Basing View, Basingstoke, Hants, RG21 2JG, UK*

Prof. U. Maione (N3), *Istituto di Idraulica, Politecnico Di Milano, Piazza Leonardo da Vinci 32, 20133 Milano, Italy*

Mr A. V. Metcalfe (A2), *University of Newcastle upon Tyne, Dept. of Engineering Mathematics, Stephenson Building, Claremont Road, Newcastle upon Tyne, NE1 7RU, UK*

Mr P. Mignosa (D1), *Istituto di Idraulica, Politecnico Di Milano, Piazza Leonardo da Vinci 32, 20133 Milano, Italy*

Mr D. N. Mills (B2), *NRA – Thames Region, Kings Meadow House, Kings Meadow Road, Reading, Berks, RG1 8DQ, UK*

Mr R. J. Moore (A3), *Institute of Hydrology, Wallingford, Oxon, UK*

Dr W. R. C. Myers (L1), *University of Ulster at Jordanstown, Dept. of Civil Engineering & Transport, Newtonabbey, Co Antrim, BT37 0QB, Northern Ireland, UK*

Prof. M. D. Newson (D3), *The University, Dept. of Geography, Newcastle-Upon-Tyne, NE1 7RU, UK*

Prof. M. Nouh (K3), *Sultan Qaboos University, Dept. of Civil Engineering, PO Box 32483 Al-Khod, Muscat, Sultanate of Oman*

Dr G. Pender (L3), *University of Glasgow, Dept. of Civil Engineering, Rankine Building, Oakfield Avenue, Glasgow, G12 8LW, UK*

Mr P. Prinos (E4), *Aristotle University, Faculty of Engineering, Dept. of Energy, 54006 Thessaloniki, Greece*

Prof. K. G. Ranga Raju (L4), *University of Roorkee, Dept. of Civil Engineering, Roorkee 247667 U P, India*

Dr C. E. Reeve (H1), *Hydraulics Research Ltd, Wallingford, Oxon, OX10 8BA, UK*

Dr B. Sackl (B1), *Graz University of Technology, Institute of Hydromechanics, Hydraulics and Hydrology, Mandellstrasse 9/1, A-8010 Graz, Austria*

Dr P. G. Samuels (K1), *Hydraulics Research Ltd, Wallingford, Oxon, OX10 8BA, UK*

Prof. Wang Shiqiang (H3), *Tsinghua University, Dept. of Hydraulic Engineering, Beijing, China*

Mrs J. E. Slade (K2), *Hydraulics Research Ltd, Wallingford, Oxon, OX10 8BA, UK*

Mr P. Treadgold (M4), *Flynn and Rothwell, 45-47 South Street, Bishop's Stortford, Herts, CM23 3AG, UK*

Dr H. F. P. van den Boogaard (B3), *Delft Hydraulics, PO Box 177, 2600 MH Delft, The Netherlands*

Mr J. B. Wark (E3), *University of Glasgow, Dept. of Civil Engineering, The Rankine Building, Oakfield Avenue, Glasgow, UK*

Mr D. C. Watkins (M1), *Hydraulics Research Ltd, Wallingford, Oxon, OX10 8BA, UK*

Prof. B. B. Willetts (F2), *University of Aberdeen, Dept. of Engineering, King's College, Aberdeen, AB9 2UE, UK*

International Conference on

RIVER FLOOD HYDRAULICS

17-20 September, 1990

CONTENTS

Paper		Page
C4	An historical perspective and analysis of flooding in the upper reaches of the Kali Gandaki River Valley, Nepal. M.D. Gill, Tatopani Small Hydel Project, Nepal.	93
D1	2D mathematical model for flood simulation and drainage design. U. Maione, P. Mignosa and M.G. Tanda, Politecnico di Milano, Italy.	103
D2	Prediction method of flow resistance in rivers with compound channels and application to river course design. S. Fukuoka, Tokyo Institute of Technology and K. Fujita, National Institute for Research Advancement, Japan.	113
D3	The geomorphologically effective flood and vertical instability in river channels - a feedback mechanism in the flood series for gravel-bed rivers. M.D. Newson and M.G. Macklin, University of Newcastle-upon-Tyne, UK.	123
	HYDRAULICS OF FLOOD FLOWS	
E1	Conveyance distribution in multi-section streams. S.P. Chee and S. Ray, University of Windsor, Canada.	143
E2	Discharge assessment in compound channel with floodplain roughness. T. Fukuhara, Fukui University and A. Murota, Osaka University, Japan.	153
E3	A practical method of estimating velocity and discharge in compound channels. J.B. Wark and D.A. Ervine, University of Glasgow, P.G. Samuels, Hydraulics Research Ltd, UK.	163
E4	Turbulence modelling of main channel - flood plain flows with an algebraic stress model. P. Prinos, Aristotle University of Thessaloniki, Greece.	173
F1	Discharge/stage relations in vegetated Danish streams. T. Larsen, J-O Frier and K. Vestergaard, University of Aalborg, Denmark.	187
F2	Model studies of overbank flow from a meandering channel. B.B. Willetts and R.I. Hardwick, University of Aberdeen, UK. and A.G. Maclean, Grampian Regional Council, U.K.	197
F3	Overbank flow in meandering compound channels - the important mechanisms. G. Kiely, University College, Cork, Eire.	207
F4	Hydraulic phenomena associated with recent disastrous floods in South Africa. J.M. Jordaan and D. Van Bladeren, Department of Water Affairs, South Africa.	219
G1	Mathematical models of flow in two or multi-stage straight channels. K. Shiono and D.W. Knight, University of Birmingham, UK.	229

Preface

Our understanding of river flood hydraulics is increasing rapidly thanks to worldwide research efforts into the various complex flow phenomena which contribute to the subject. It is the purpose of the present conference to promulgate these new ideas and to bring together international experts in the field.

From ancient times floods have been a threat to life and property, yet man has sought to exploit the fertility of river flood plains and use rivers as corridors of communication. The importance of river management has increased steadily alongside the need to take a broad view of the catchment as a whole. Floods vary from year to year in their severity and often cannot be predicted sufficiently well to avoid severe economic loss and human suffering.

The fluid mechanics of river flow are complex, with processes having a wide range of time and length scales from those of turbulence to those of morphological and climatic change. With suitable simplifying assumptions, physical and computational models can be developed to study many practical and theoretical problems in river hydraulics. The aim of the conference is to link current experimental and analytical research to the needs of engineering practice. The topics selected for the conference cover areas of international research interest and practical importance with a view to providing a forum for advancing the art of river engineering.

One major initiative in the UK has been the development and use of the large scale test facility sponsored by the Science and Engineering Research Council and Hydraulics Research Ltd with additional finance from the Water Industry. This facility is located at Hydraulics Research and is being used to study, on a large scale, the interaction between channel and flood plain flows for straight and meandering channels including sediment movement. Wallingford is thus an appropriate venue for the conference.

The major topics covered by the conference are:

- flood analysis and prediction
- field data
- hydraulics of flood flows
- sediment transport and morphological effects
- physical and numerical modelling
- engineering design, maintenance and operation of schemes

I should like to acknowledge the contribution made by the members of the National and International Organising Committees, particularly for the conscientious way in which they reviewed the submitted abstracts and papers. My gratitude also goes to Dr Paul Samuels and other colleagues at Hydraulics Research who have worked so hard for the success of the conference. Finally, I should like to thank Jacqueline Watts, our Conference Organiser for the efficient and enthusiastic way in which she has carried out her many duties.

RODNEY WHITE
Hydraulics Research, Wallingford

Preface

Flood Analysis and Prediction

PAPER A1

International Conference on
RIVER FLOOD HYDRAULICS
17-20 September, 1990

FLOOD PEAK-FREQUENCY CHARACTERISTICS AND REGIONAL MAXIMUM FLOODS IN SOUTHERN AFRICA

by

Z.P. Kovâcs* and W.J.R. Alexander**

* Directorate of Hydrology, Department of Water Affairs, South Africa
** Department of Civil Engineering, University of Pretoria, South Africa

ABSTRACT

Over-conservatism in design flood estimation procedures can result in diminished potential net benefit of water supply projects in arid and semiarid regions. For this and other reasons the probable maximum flood concept is inappropriate for design maximum flood estimation. Rare, extreme meteorological phenomena produce flood peaks which preclude the application of standard direct statistical analysis and deterministic methods for small annual exceedance probability estimates.

The development of the regional maximum flood method for estimating design maximum floods, and regional direct statistical analysis methods that can accommodate abnormal conditions are described.

It is concluded that the flood peak magnitude-frequency relationship is discontinuous for annual exceedance probabilities greater than about 1:50 to 1:100 in many regions of southern Africa. The regional maximum flood method is appropriate for design maximum flood estimation, and regional direct statistical analysis methods can be used with confidence for estimates of flood peaks having annual exceedance probabilities of up to about 1:50. Both methods can be used for estimates in the range 1:50 to the regional maximum flood but the results must be interpreted with care.

INTRODUCTION

In arid and semiarid regions of southern Africa water resource development projects are often only marginally economic but nevertheless they may have greater potential benefit to the community they serve than similar projects in well-watered regions which are less dependent on surface water storage projects. Because of the greater variability in annual flood peak maxima in these regions, extreme floods have values relatively much greater than the mean annual values, and consequently the costs of the flood control works are much higher.

In this situation the price to be paid for over-conservatism in design flood estimation procedures is a reduction in potential net benefit from the proposed project. In the worst case the project may no longer be economically viable and the potential increase in the welfare of the community may not be realized.

SPECIFICATION OF THE DESIGN FLOOD

The method for determining the design flood should meet the following criteria:

1. The method should be such that a balance can be achieved between the economic benefit to the community served by the project on the one hand, and the threat to life and property should the structure fail on the other.
2. The responsibility for determining the degree of conservatism inherent in the method should rest with an acknowledged authority and not with the individual users of the method.

International Conference on River Flood Hydraulics, edited by W.R.White

3. Different users of the method should get answers that are in close agreement when it is applied to the same problem.

THE PROBABLE MAXIMUM FLOOD

The most used method for maximum flood estimation is the estimation of the probable maximum flood (PMF).

We share the view of Bouvard (1988) and others who believe that the annual flood peak maxima are unbounded. This does not preclude the use of this method as a design tool provided that the users and their clients are aware that the answers obtained are not absolute maximum values. It should also be appreciated that the implementation of this method is a *policy decision* and not a hydrological reality.

The method does not meet the first and third requirements specified above. There are a number of other objections to the use of the PMF as a method for determining the design maximum flood in southern Africa. These include the need for meteorological expertise in the determination of the associated probable maximum precipitation (World Meteorological Organization, 1986) which is not available in this region; the large measure of subjective judgment in determining the time and space distribution of the storm rainfall; and the assumption that the antecedent catchment moisture status which includes river channel and overbank storage, has to be at some unquantifiable maximum possible value at the commencement of the causative rainfall.

Any reduction in these very stringent and highly unrealistic requirements requires an estimate by the analyst of what is reasonable as it is very difficult to specify these situations in a policy formulation. Where the analyst has to exercise his judgment he places himself at risk and the natural consequence is to over-estimate the magnitude of the design event with the resulting adverse economic consequences.

The PMF method featured in the interim guidelines on dam safety issued by the South African National Committee on Large Dams (1986) but has been excluded in the final guidelines (1990).

THE NATURE OF THE SERIES OF FLOOD PEAK MAXIMA

If the annual flood peak maxima are not upper bounded then the form of the magnitude-frequency relationship has to be determined, and a point on this relationship selected for the design of the structure.

The problems that arise when attempting to determine the appropriate probability distribution at low exceedance probabilities have been described by many authors. However, the conclusions reached are often based on analyses of synthetically generated, *identically distributed* data sets. In our view there is mounting hydrological and meteorological evidence that the annual maxima are the result of a mixture of the dominant population of annual events, and several other, different, multi-year meteorological phenomena (Alexander and Kovàcs 1988). These events are frequent enough to be of importance to the designer, yet not sufficiently frequent at any one site to permit statistical analyses based on mixed populations. As these anomalies are also present in the rainfall data, deterministic methods which assume that the exceedance probability of the flood event is the same as that of the storm rainfall do not overcome the difficulty.

We have followed two different approaches to the problem, both of which are user orientated.

Kovàcs (1988) developed the empirical Regional Maximum Flood method which provides a single maximum flood value, while Alexander (1990) developed a suite of regional direct statistical analysis programs which derive the conventional flood peak-frequency relationship.

DIRECT STATISTICAL ANALYSIS METHODS

Micro-computer programs were developed to carry out regional direct statistical analyses. Details are provided in Alexander (1990). This publication includes the theoretical background, sources of information used for developing the programs, and disks containing the programs and a number of representative data sets from South Africa, Lesotho and Botswana.

The four distributions included in suite of programs are:

- Log normal using conventional moments
- Log Pearson 3 using conventional moments
- General Extreme Value using probability weighted moments
- Wakeby using probability weighted moments

The programs make provision for the exclusion of zero discharges and low outliers by applying conditional probability algorithms, the inclusion of historic data by applying historical weighting algorithms, and parameter adjustments by applying regional weighting algorithms to the distribution moments.

The main conclusions reached when these methods were applied to a range of data sets from southern African were:

- All four methods produced results which were in fair agreement for annual exceedance probabilities within the range 1:2 to 1:100 years *except* at sites where anomalous high outliers were present.
- The results of the five-parameter Wakeby and three-parameter General Extreme Value distributions were generally in close agreement, probably due to the use of the same moment estimators. Initial conclusions were that there appeared to be little justification for using the more complex iterative procedures of the Wakeby distribution which require a measure of subjective intervention on the part of the user, in preference to the procedures used in the General Extreme Value distribution which do not require this intervention and consequently produce consistent results (third requirement above).
- For obvious reasons the three-parameter log Pearson 3 and General Extreme Value distributions provided better visual fits to skewed data sets than the two-parameter log normal distribution. However, there were cases where the log normal distribution provided more acceptable results. This was generally the case where upstream development during the period of record resulted in abnormally low annual maxima occurring in dry years, and a diminishing effect in years with higher rainfall. The negative skewness produced by these low outliers results in a serious underestimate of flood peak maxima for low annual exceedance probabilities where they are most needed. The recommended procedure in this situation is either to use the log normal distribution if this provides a better visual fit, or to exclude the low values based on a visual examination of the plotted data and make use of conditional probability adjustments to calculate the desired value.
- The studies carried out to date were not sufficient to permit an assessment of the relative merits of the log Pearson 3 and General Extreme Value distributions.

A disturbing feature that became apparent during the analyses was the large number of data sets that contained one or more abnormally high outliers which were associated with meteorological phenomena that were either abnormal in intensity (eg tropical cyclones or cut-off low pressure systems) or abnormal in duration (prolonged seasonal rainfall over a large region). These were of sufficient magnitude and spatial frequency of occurrence to preclude the assumption that they were part of the same statistical population as the remaining observations, yet were not sufficiently frequent at any one site to allow the application of mixed population statistical analyses. This raised doubts about the appropriateness of direct statistical analysis methods for the estimation of small annual exceedance probability flood peak maxima.

While deterministic methods allow the user to explore the effects of these anomalous conditions on peak discharges, annual exceedance probabilities cannot be assigned to the results because the depth-area-duration-frequency relationships of rainfall produced by these conditions are unknown, as is the probability structure of the rainfall-runoff process.

EMPIRICAL APPROACH : THE REGIONAL MAXIMUM FLOOD

A detailed description of this method is contained in a report published by the Department of Water Affairs, Pretoria (Kovács, 1988).

The Francou-Rodier method of flood peak classification. The basis chosen for the development of the regional maximum flood (RMF) estimation procedure was the Francou-Rodier method of flood peak classification (1967).

The equation for determining the Francou-Rodier K-value is:

$$K = 10 [1 - (\log Q - 6) / (\log A - 8)]$$

where Q is the largest flood observed at the site in m^3/s, and A is the effective catchment area in km^2.

The principle of this method is shown in Fig 1. The upper envelope K_e-values converge at a point having an area of 10^8 km^2 and a discharge of 10^6 m^3/s which are equivalent to the the total drainage area and total mean flow of all rivers on the earth respectively. Within the storm zone the upper limit of rainfall intensity is 800 mm/h which is the world record point rainfall intensity, and the lower limit is the minimum rainfall intensity that will cause runoff. The boundaries between the zones can be adjusted if necessary.

In Fig 2 world recorded maximum flood peaks prior to 1960 and 1984 respectively (Rodier and Roche 1984), and South African recorded maxima prior to 1960 and 1988 respectively, are plotted against respective catchment areas on a log-log scale. The K-values for the recorded world maxima appear to have stabilized between K=6.0 and K=6.5. The envelope of South African peaks shifted upwards from K=5.2 to K=5.6 between 1960 and 1988, not the least because of the substantially enlarged data base (Table 1). The important conclusion is, however, that the trends of both data sets are similar in the flood zone as well as the transition zone, and the observations are well aligned with the direction of the K=constant lines. In the flood zone the peak discharge depends upon both storm rainfall (intensity, area and duration) and catchment processes, while in the transition zone the peak discharge becomes increasingly dependent on the maximum rainfall intensity alone with decrease in catchment size. This is clearly evident for catchment areas between 100 km^2 and 200 km^2.

Catalogue of maximum recorded flood peaks. The gathering of the information commenced in 1985 and was completed in 1988 after the extraordinary regional floods over the interior of southern Africa. The catalogue contains 519 peaks observed in seven countries of the subcontinent. The earliest peak was recorded in 1856. The geographic distribution of the data is shown in Fig 3.

For each peak the corresponding coefficient K was calculated from the Francou-Rodier equation. Each peak was also assigned a representative period N. This represented the length of record if there was one, or the number of years that had elapsed since the historic maximum value. Although the value of N is not the same as the return period T, the assumption that the mean values of N and T should converge if calculated from a greater number of events, is realistic. The knowledge of N was not essential for the determination of the regional maximum flood, but was used for the development of the method for the estimation of flood peak magnitudes with annual exceedance probabilities between 1:50 and the RMF.

Tables 1 and 2 contain some statistics abstracted from the catalogue.

TABLE 1 : Dates of events

Country	Number of events	Date of events			
		before 1900	1900-29	1930-59	1960-88
South Africa	355	6	50	85	232
Lesotho	12	-	-	-	12
Swaziland	7	-	-	-	7
Namibia	64	-	-	17	47
Botswana	14	-	-	-	14
Zimbabwe	54	-	8	17	29
Mozambique	13	-	-	2	11
Total	519	6	58	121	333

TABLE 2 : Method of measurement and accuracy

Method	Number	Probable error		
	of events	< 10%	< 30%	unknown
Gauging station	209	44	63	102
Slope-area	151	11	100	40
Bridge contraction	27	4	20	3
Dam spillway	54	24	26	4
Other	78	2	10	66
% of total	100	17	42	41

The conclusion from Table 2 is that the accuracy of the two indirect methods i.e., the slope-area and bridge contraction, compares well with that of gauging weirs. This is important because by far the greatest number of really extreme peaks were obtained by indirect methods.

In Table 3 the maximum recorded *K*-values in seven countries of southern Africa are listed.

TABLE 3 : Maximum observed *K*-values

Country	Region	River	Catchment (km²)	*K*
South Africa	Highveld	Rietspruit	752	4.81
	Karoo (arid)	Willem Nels	32	5.03
	South Coast	Loerie	147	5.27
	East Coast	Mfolozi	9 216	5.55
Lesotho	Highland	Senqu	7 950	4.72
Swaziland	Lowveld	Great Usutu	15 350	5.11
Namibia	Windhoek	Oanob	100	4.92
Botswana	North-east	Ntshe	800	4.52
Zimbabwe	Central	Munendi	130	5.15
Mozambique	Beira-inland	Lucite	1 980	5.54

Delimitation of maximum flood peak regions. The *K*-values of flood peaks were plotted on 1:1 000 000 scale topographical maps. In delimiting regional boundaries consideration was given to individual *K*-values, the number and accuracy of data in a particular area, maximum recorded 3-day rainfall, topography, catchment orientation with respect of dominant storm-producing weather systems, soil permeability, and the presence of dams large enough to influence the downstream maximum flood.

The outcome of the analyses is shown in in Fig 4 where eight RMF regions are distinguished by using the corresponding Francou-Rodier *K*-envelope values (refer to the next subheading). In regions with sparse information the boundaries are shown as dashed lines.

Establishment of regional envelope curves. For each region the flood peaks listed in the catalogue were plotted against respective catchment areas (see Fig 1). In the flood zone the K_e=constant envelope line was traced close to the highest observed *K*-value. In regions of moderate and high extreme flood potential the lower limit of the flood zone was set at A=100 km². In the relatively flat and dry regions of the subcontinent the separation between the flood zone and the transition zone had to be shifted towards larger catchment areas. The reason is that even under such conditions comparatively high flood peaks can be generated by intense, short duration (less than four hours at most) storms. In the transition zone the envelope lines are tentative and at A=1 km² they indicate the discharge which is associated with the respective maximum recorded 15-minute point rainfall (no storm loss is allowed).

The corresponding regional RMF equations and their area range of application are listed in Table 4.

TABLE 4 : RMF equations for use in southern Africa

Region	Transition zone		Flood zone	
	Area (km²)	RMF (m³/s)	Area (km²)**	RMF (m³/s)*
2.8	1 - 500	$30\ A^{0.262}$	500 - 500 000	$1.74\ A^{0.72}$
3.4	1 - 300	$50\ A^{0.265}$	300 - 500 000	$5.25\ A^{0.66}$
4.0	1 - 300	$70\ A^{0.340}$	300 - 300 000	$15.9\ A^{0.60}$
4.6	1 - 100	$100\ A^{0.380}$	100 - 100 000	$47.9\ A^{0.54}$
5.0	1 - 100	$100\ A^{0.500}$	100 - 100 000	$100\ A^{0.50}$
5.2	1 - 100	$100\ A^{0.560}$	100 - 30 000	$145\ A^{0.48}$
5.4	1 - 100	$100\ A^{0.620}$	100 - 20 000	$209\ A^{0.46}$
5.6	1 - 100	$100\ A^{0.680}$	100 - 10 000	$302\ A^{0.44}$

* Francou-Rodier equation
** The upper limits refer only to South Africa

Notes on the application of RMF method. The map shown in Fig 4 and the equations listed in Table 4 enable the rapid determination of RMF once the geographic position of the site and its effective catchment area are known. The method is expected to provide the best results for catchment sizes approximately between 300 km² and 20 000 km². In both the small and large catchments one is confronted with the inherent weakness of all regionally based methods, namely that the particular characteristics of these catchments cannot be easily expressed by one common regional factor, in this case K_e.

The following recommendations may help solve various problems in the application of the method.

1. As a general rule, a site located in a given region is characterized by the K_e line of that region even if parts of the catchment extend into other regions. At sites located close to regional boundaries, the average K_e value or, where particularly justified, the higher of the two values may be adopted.

2. Small and medium catchments (A < 5 000 km^2). K_e may be reduced if more than the half of the area is very permeable, dolomitic or afforested, or the 1-day maximum observed rainfall is markedly lower than in adjoining areas, or the catchment is very flat. However, the reduced K_e should not be lower than the K_e-value of the next lower numbered region.
3. K_e may be increased only in exceptional cases such as a very steep catchment or much higher maximum observed 1-day rainfall than in the surrounding area. The increase in K_e should not exceed 0.2.
4. Large rivers which flow across several RMF regions have their own characteristics which may differ substantially from those of the regions through which they flow. In lower reaches of large rivers the most important features of extraordinary floods are the flood volume and duration rather than the flood peak. In practice the peak often has a fairly well defined upper limit because of the attenuating effects of flood plain storage.
5. As a rule of thumb RMF should not be reduced because of upstream dams except in rare occasions when the dam capacity is larger than the RMF flood volume associated with long duration (3-day and longer) storm rainfall.

Comparison of RMF and PMF in South Africa. The RMF and the PMF are two different concepts. The PMF is a theoretically based estimate of the maximum flood that *can be expected at the site* whereas the RMF is an empirically based estimate of the maximum floods that *have been observed within the region* within which the site is located. Nevertheless, a comparison of the results obtained when applying the two methods is of interest.

Analyses were undertaken for 75 large dams where the PMF was estimated by the synthetic unitgraph method which is the most widely employed technique for this purpose in South Africa (Midgley, 1972). The mean ratio PMF/RMF was 1.82, with a minimum of 0.54 and a maximum of 4.49.

As expected, the PMF values were higher on average than the RMF values. However, the inconsistency of PMF estimates is manifest in Table 5 where the regional K_e values are compared with the means of the K-value equivalents of PMF estimates (K_{PMF}) in six RMF regions.

TABLE 5 : Comparison of K_e and K_{PMF}

K_e	Number of dams	K_{PMF}
4.0	1	5.34
4.6	17	5.51
5.0	41	5.47
5.2	8	5.60
5.4	6	5.39
5.6	2	5.90

Note that K_{PMF} does not increase progressively from region 4.6 where the extreme flood peak potential is moderate through to region 5.4 where extremely high peaks are fairly frequent. The causes of inconsistency of PMF estimates are given earlier in this paper.

The consequence of this weakness is that the error may reach the magnitude of PMF itself in the more arid regions. For instance, the earlier quoted maximum PMF/RMF ratio of 4.49 was associated with a dam having a catchment area of 2 452 km^2. The estimated PMF is equivalent to a Francou-Rodier K-value of 6.41 which is higher than all known world record values except the Amazon River (Rodier and Roche 1984). The occurrence of an event of such a relative magnitude is impossible in southern Africa under the present climatic conditions.

Reliability of the RMF method. As is the case with all empirical methods, their ability to provide sound estimates depends principally on the representativeness of their data base. In the more humid eastern and southern parts of southern Africa including Swaziland and Lesotho as well as south-eastern Zimbabwe and central Namibia the present data base is fairly extensive (Fig 3) and future revisions of K_e and regional boundaries are expected to be modest. In the drier western half of southern Africa greater future modifications are possible because of the as yet inadequate data base. Consequently the regional boundaries and K_e values are only tentative and might require substantial changes in the future.

CONCLUSION

The RMF is the accepted method for maximum design flood estimation in South Africa. The advantages over the PMF method are its simplicity, consistency, and, in our opinion, its sounder logical basis for application in conditions where over-conservatism can have significant adverse consequences on the welfare of the community that the project is to serve.

Regional direct statistical analysis methods can be used with confidence for estimates of flood events having annual exceedance probabilities of up to about 1:50.

An unresolved issue is the probability that the flood magnitude-frequency relationship is discontinuous for annual exceedance probabilities somewhere in the range between 1:50 and 1:100 over most of the sub-continent due to the presence of severe, abnormal, multi-year meteorological phenomena. This precludes the application of direct statistical analysis methods which are based on the assumption of either single populations or mixed populations of annual events.

Designers requiring estimates of flood magnitudes with annual exceedance probabilities between 1:50 and the RMF should be aware of the shortcomings of all currently available analytical procedures in this range.

REFERENCES

Alexander, W.J.R. (1990). Flood hydrology for southern Africa. South African National Committee for Large Dams. Pretoria.

Alexander, W.J.R. and Kovàcs Z.P.J. (1988). Lessons learnt from exceptional floods in southern Africa. Proceedings of the Sixteenth Congress of the International Commission on Large Dams. San Francisco.

Bouvard, M. (1988). Design flood and operational flood control. Report of the Rapporteur-General. Proceedings of the Sixteenth Congress of the International Commission on Large Dams. San Francisco.

Francou, J. and Rodier, J.A. (1967). Essai de classification des crues maximales. Proceedings of the Leningrad Symposium on Floods and their computation, Vol. 1, IASH-UNESCO-WMO.

Kovàcs ZPJ, (1988). Regional maximum flood peaks in southern Africa. Technical Report TR 137, Department of Water Affairs, Pretoria.

Midgley, D.C. (1972). Design flood determination in South Africa. University of the Witwatersrand. Johannesburg.

Rodier, J.A. and Roche, M. (1984). World catalogue of maximum observed floods. IAHS Publication No. 143, Wallingford.

South African National Committee on Large Dams (1990) Guidelines on safety related to floods. South African National Committee on Large Dams. Pretoria

World Meteorological Organization (1986). Manual for the estimation of probable maximum precipitation. Report WMO-No. 332. Geneva.

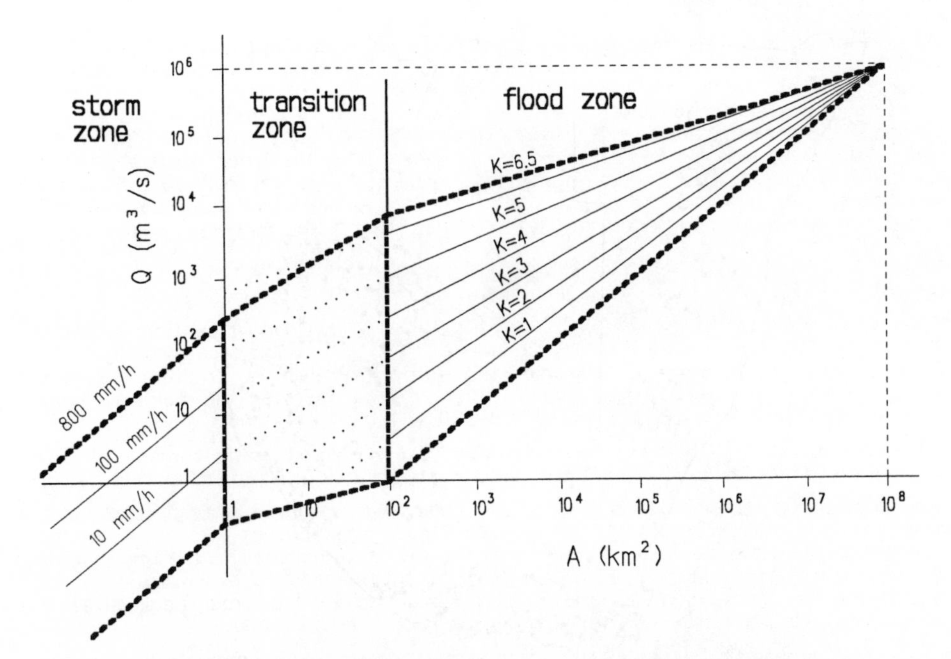

FIGURE 1 : Francou-Rodier flood peak classification method

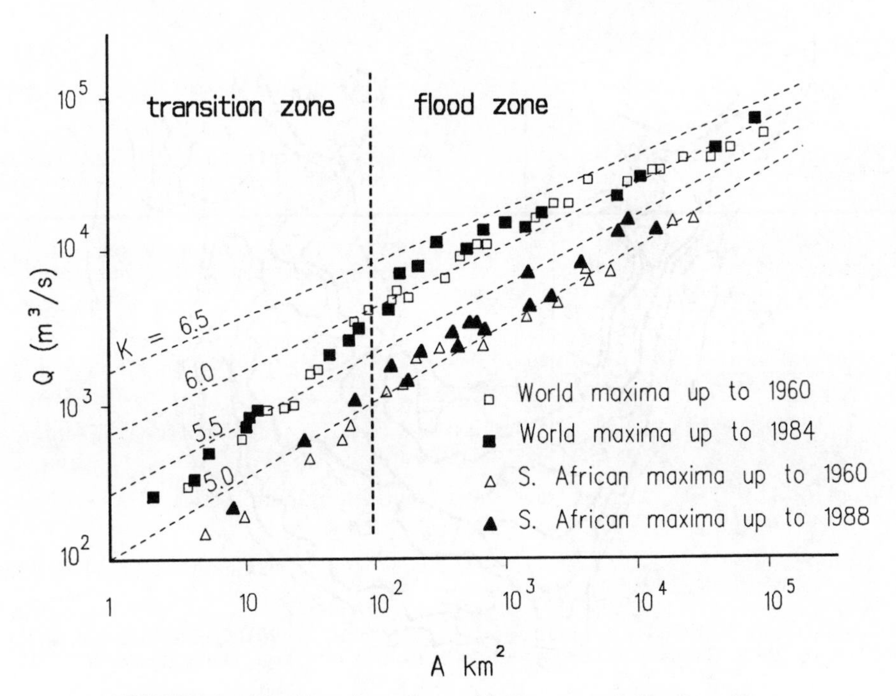

FIGURE 2 : World and southern African record flood peaks

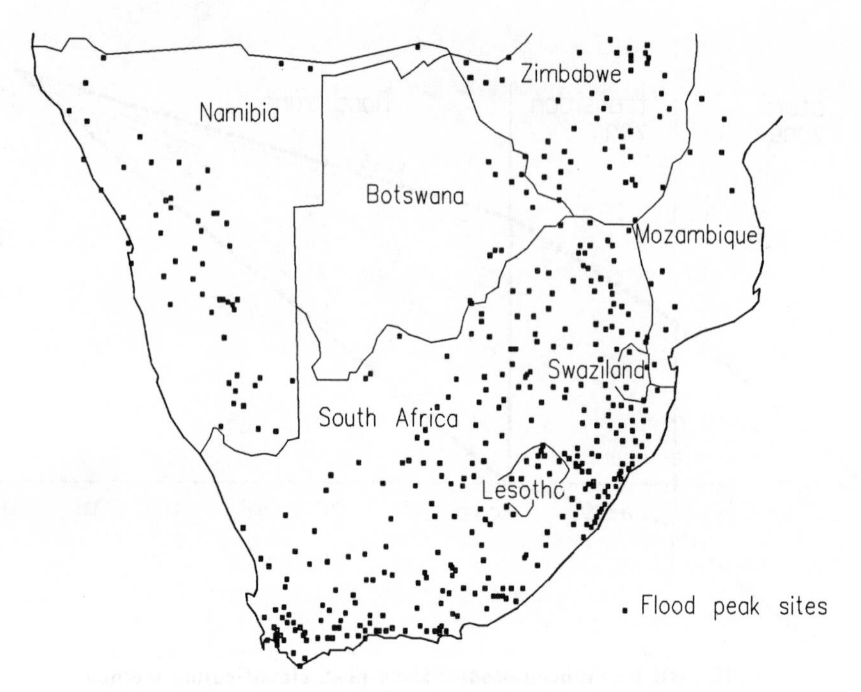

FIGURE 3 : Geographical distribution of flood peak maxima

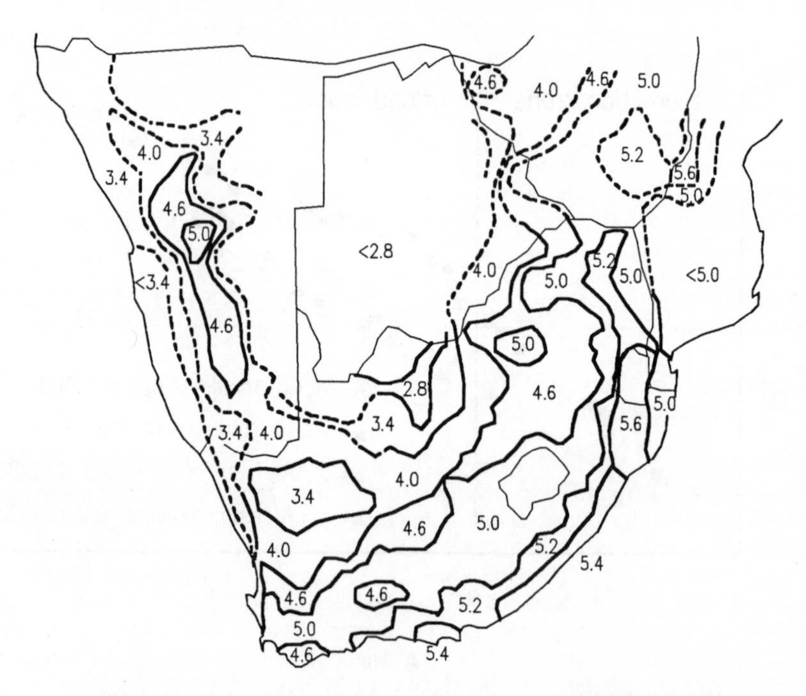

FIGURE 4 : Maximum flood peak regions in southern Africa

International Conference on
RIVER FLOOD HYDRAULICS
17-20 September, 1990

RISK OF FLOODING DEPENDENT ON PREVAILING CATCHMENT CONDITIONS

M. FUTTER, J.A. MAWDSLEY and A.V. METCALFE.
Department of Civil Engineering and Department of Engineering Mathematics, The University, Newcastle upon Tyne, England, U.K.

ABSTRACT

Seasonal variation in both the number and magnitude of peakflows has been observed by many researchers, and models which incorporate seasonal variation will give more accurate estimates of flood risk. Two recently published models also allow prevailing catchment conditions to be used for short–term estimates. The model proposed by Ettrick *et al.* (1987) is based on conditional probability distributions, while Smith and Karr (1986) relate the rate of exceedance of the critical level of interest to relevant covariates. One thousand years of simulated daily peakflows, baseflows and rainfall allow a comparison to be made between the two models for 30 day ahead flood risk estimates. Both models perform well for the winter period. In the summer, the Ettrick *et al.* model tends to over predict the flood risk, whilst the Smith and Karr model under predicts it. Reasons for these findings are proposed. The results show how sensitive the flood risk is to antecedent conditions at the start of the 30 day period.

INTRODUCTION

Seasonal variation in both the number and magnitude of peak flows has been observed by many research workers, for example Archer's (1981) investigations of flooding in North East England. If this feature of hydrological processes is ignored the probabilities of high flows during the summer months, when flood risk is usually relatively low, will on average be overestimated. Furthermore, if the distributions of annual maxima or peaks over some threshold are modelled without allowing for seasonal changes, winter flood risk estimates will be subject to two sources of error. The mean of the distribution of winter floods will tend to be underestimated and the variance will tend to be overestimated. Whilst these effects do at least work in opposite directions, it is rather optimistic to rely on their cancelling out!

Several methods for modelling seasonal variation have been proposed. Todorovic (1978) modifies peak over threshold methods by allowing the rate of exceedance and the distribution of exceedances to change with time of year. Ghani (1988) reduces the threshold to include all peaks and uses data from the required season only. This has the advantage of releasing more data, but the drawback that they cannot be considered independent. He circumvents this problem by using spectral analysis on the time series of midday observations. Tawn (1988) takes a more direct approach and presents an extreme–value theory model for dependent observations. Models which incorporate seasonal variation will give more accurate estimates of the flood risk which are valuable for long term decisions concerning the levels of flood protection, or for the design of storm sewers. It may be that they are even more valuable to Civil

International Conference on River Flood Hydraulics, edited by W.R.White

Engineers when the risk of flooding in the near future is of prime interest. For example, contractors working in or near rivers, on a dam face, from barges or with floating cranes on a river will benefit from accurate estimates of flood risk. Water Engineers responsible for reservoir operation who need to balance the requirements of flood control, provision of domestic and industrial water supply, public amenity, and effluent dilution will also benefit from up to date estimates of the risk of occurrences of high flows. However, in all these cases a knowledge of the risk of flooding over a short period into the future influenced as it is by the prevailing catchment conditions and weather forecast, is likely to be of more relevance than the average seasonal variation provided by the models referred to earlier. In this paper two recently developed models which incorporate catchment conditions, and have the potential to incorporate precipitation forecasts, are compared using a synthetic time series of 1000 years duration. The comparison is made on the basis of risk estimates for the next 30 days. The first model, proposed for immediate flood risk by Smith and Karr (1986), is extended to cover short term predictions and relates the rate of exceedance of the critical level of interest to relevant covariates. The second model, presented by Ettrick *et al.* (1987) is based on conditional distributions. A simple analogy may help clarify the main conceptual difference between the methods. If a record of annual maximum flows over a number of past years is available, the probability of a future annual maximum exceeding some critical level can be estimated in two ways. One method is to estimate the probability by the sample proportion of exceedances. The other is to assume some imaginary distribution of all such flows, estimate its parameters from the sample and hence estimate the probability. The first method would be preferred if the sample was very large, but only the second would be feasible with a small sample. There is, however, more to the comparison described in this paper than is apparent from the analogy, and the investigation has revealed potential problems with both models and ways around these.

THE DATA

The data used in this study were provided by the Institute of Hydrology, Wallingford, UK, and are 1000 years of daily triplets consisting of daily peakflow (cumecs), daily low flow (baseflow) (cumecs) and daily rainfall total (mm). The rainfall values were generated by a seasonal (summer/winter) simulation model (Acreman 1988) and input to a probability distributed rainfall–runoff model (Moore and Clarke 1981). To calculate an immediate empirical flood risk, the baseflow on each day (t) was put into one of several consecutive ranges. Then the peakflow on day t+1 was compared with the peakflows on the preceding and following day to ascertain whether it was a maximum of the daily series. If it was, and also exceeded the critical flow threshold of 16 cumecs the peakflow was classed as an event. The 16 cumecs threshold is equivalent to runoff of 0.4mm/hr/km^2 for the simulation catchment. This resulted in an average of 1.7 events per year. The immediate flood risk, conditional on base flow, was taken as the number of events in each baseflow range divided by the number of days in the range. To find the empirical 30 day ahead risk, the start of month baseflows, defined as the lowest simulated flow on the last two days of the previous calendar month, were categorised by range and season. The risk, conditional on season and start of month baseflow, was found by dividing the number of events in the appropriate category by the number of months in that category.

THE MODELS

The Smith and Karr Model. Smith and Karr (1986) proposed the use of the Cox regression model, which was presented by Cox (1972) in the context of survival times, to estimate 'immediate' flood risk. They defined an event as a peak flow which exceeded the critical flow level of interest. They modelled the rate of occurrence of such events by the product of a season varying parameter, a(t),and the exponential of some linear combination of m covariates $z_1(t), ..., z_m(t)$, such as rainfall and catchment wetness. That is

$$\lambda(t) = a(t) \exp(b_1 z_1(t) + ... + b_m z_m(t)) \tag{1}$$

where a(t) is the seasonally varying 'baseline' intensity, and $b_1, ..., b_m$ are constant (regression) coefficients. All of $a(t), b_1, ..., b_m$ have to be estimated from the available data. Flood peaks are assumed to be random and indepen–dent, which was defined as at least two days between events. The average time of concentration of the synthetic catchment was the main factor used to formulate this definition of independence. It should be noted that it is quite feasible to do this with field data (Futter 1990). In the case of multipeaked events the associated value of the covariate process was taken relative to the first crossing of the critical level. When applying the Smith and Karr model to the simulated data, only one covariate was considered, namely baseflow. This was used as a measure of catchment wetness. This decision was taken because rainfall cannot, usually, be adequately forecast. However, the influence of rainfall is not neglected as its average seasonal pattern is included in the baseline intensity a(t). Ettrick *et al.* explicitly introduce an average seasonal distribution of rainfall, but it is subsequently integrated out. Thus, in both models, the flood risk estimates are conditioned on catchment wetness, with rainfall being included with 'seasonality' in the Smith and Karr formulation and explicitly accounting for seasonality in the Ettrick *et al.* model.

In Cox's (1972) paper the regression coefficients were estimated by comparing the covariate values at time of death of a patient with the covariate values of all the patients alive at that time, who were therefore 'at risk'. In the hydrological application patients are replaced by years, and this leads to complications. If a patient dies he or she is no longer 'at risk' and is therefore no longer a member of the risk set. Furthermore, 'time' is measured from the beginning of the follow up study. In contrast to this, 'time' in the hydrological application ranges over one calendar year and the starting point is arbitrary. Also a year remains 'at risk', whether or not a peak has already exceeded the critical level. It would, of course, be possible to ignore this last point and drop a year from the risk set if a peak exceeded the critical level, but this would have two disadvantages. The estimates of the regression coefficients would differ with different starting points during the year and the baseline intensity would be estimated from fewer data as t increases through the year. An improvement would be to repeat the estimation procedure, starting at several equally spaced points throughout the year, and to average the results. An alternative approach, the 'exclusion method' is presented in this paper. Smith and Karr (1986) did not explicitly specify the risk set. In the 'exclusion method', a year has been brought back into the risk set two days after a peak flow exceeds the critical level. The two days allows the recession curve to drop back to a 'baseflow'. Cox (1972) recognised the problem of ties when two, or more, deaths occur in the same time interval. In the case of two people dying at the same time, the appropriate comparison is between the covariate values for this pair at time of death with those for all possible pairs chosen from the risk set. This modification was used to allow for 'exact' ties and the 'exclusion method' removed the problem of 'near' ties which would otherwise seriously prejudice the results.

To allow the Smith and Karr model to be used for flood risk estimation over longer periods, baseflows must be forecast; risks are then calculated for each day and combined under an assumption of independence once baseflow has been allowed for. That is,

$$\text{Pr (exceedance of the critical level within next 30 days)} = 1 - \prod_{k=1}^{30} (1 - \lambda(t_k)\Delta) \ , \tag{2}$$

where t_k is the day k days ahead, $\lambda(t_k)$ is the estimated risk per day on that day, and Δ is the time increment of 1 day. Two methods for modelling inter–event series were compared, a constant change and autoregressive schemes. In the former case a fixed amount was removed from, or added to, the mean corrected baseflow on day t to bring the value for day t+1 closer to the mean. In symbols, with w representing baseflow,

$$(w_{t+1} - \overline{w}) = (w_t - \overline{w}) + \delta w_t \tag{3a}$$

until it equals $\overline{w}$ when it remains at $\overline{w}$. In the latter case a fixed proportion was used,

$$(w_{t+1} - \overline{w}) = \alpha(w_t - \overline{w}) \quad \text{where} \quad 0 < \alpha < 1 \ . \tag{3b}$$

Conditional Distribution Model of Ettrick *et al*. The model proposed by Ettrick *et al.* (1987) starts with a distribution of peakflows (q) conditional on catchment wetness (w) and depth of rainfall (y) given that a chosen rainfall threshold has been exceeded (a rainfall event). This was then elaborated to provide 30 day ahead predictions, based on observed persistence of catchment wetness in several river basins. A distribution of baseflows, prior to rainfall events, for up to 30 days after, and conditional on, baseflow at time of prediction w_s was introduced. The conditional distribution for peak flows is,

$$F(q \mid w_s, y>y_o) = \int_o^q \int_{y_o}^{\infty} \int_o^{\infty} g(x \mid y,w,y>y_o)\, h(y \mid y>y_o)\, k(w \mid w_s, y>y_o)\, dw\, dy\, dx \ . \tag{4}$$

where it has been assumed rainfall is independent of catchment wetness. A Poisson model is assumed for exceedances of the rainfall threshold. For the synthetic data, log normal distributions provided satisfactory fits to the event peakflows and the baseflows. A Weibull distribution was used to model the depths of rainfall events. Parameters were estimated by maximum likelihood and the integrals were evaluated numerically. The peakflow and baseflow distributions were fitted to all events, whereas the rainfall model was fitted separately to the summer and winter data to account for the marked seasonality present in the data.

RESULTS AND DISCUSSION

Figures 1 and 2 illustrate the estimates of the risk of exceeding the critical flow threshold of 16 cumecs within the next 30 days for the summer (April to October) and winter (November to March) periods. These estimates were obtained using the Ettrick model, the Smith and Karr model with both the constant change and autoregressive models of baseflow, and empirical estimates from the 1000 year record. All estimates were obtained from 10 by 100 year subsets of data, and the results reported are the average values. The 95% confidence intervals for the empirical estimates were estimated and are shown for all prior baseflows for which sufficient data were available so that reliable estimates of those intervals could be made. These are based on the normal approximation to the distribution of proportions.

All the estimates, with the exception of the autoregressive version of the Smith and Karr model, show a significant variation in the risk with baseflow at the beginning of the 30 day period. For example, for the winter empirical results, the risk increases by 300% when the baseflow is increased from 1.0 to 3.3 cumecs.

In the summer period, the Ettrick model is tending to over–estimate the flood risk, while the Smith and Karr model, with both baseflow modelling options, is under–estimating the risk, compared with the empirical estimates. For the winter months, the Ettrick and constant change version of the Smith and Karr model have produced estimates comparable with the empirical values, and for higher start of the month baseflow values, well within the empirical 95% confidence intervals. The autoregressive baseflow version of the Smith and Karr model has produced estimates which do not reflect the sensitivity of the flood risk to the start of the month baseflow shown by the empirical estimates. This is due to the structure of the autoregressive model, as each baseflow series progresses exponentially and all approach the mean value within 10 days. Consequently, little of the influence of the baseflow at the beginning of the period persists through the full 30 days. The constant change model, however, continues to decrease, or increase, by the same amount for the full 30 days, (equation 3a), unless the base flow at the time of prediction is already close to the mean. An exponential decline is often assumed to fit baseflow recessions; however, during the inter–event periods, peakflows less than 16 cumecs may occur. These sub–critical events will produce increases in the inter–event baseflow series. In such circumstances, according to the empirical results, the constant change scheme appears to be the better model, at least for these data.

Both models produce poorer results in the summer season. For the Smith and Karr model, this is due to a lack of data. Although a large number of events exceed the critical flow threshold, they displayed a marked seasonality and few of them occurred in summer. This made the estimate of the seasonal parameter, the baseline intensity, poor in the summer period.

In the Ettrick model, the baseflow distribution (equation 4) was estimated using the data from the whole year, and was used for both the summer and winter seasons without change. The baseflows in the summer are generally smaller and it is likely that even for the same baseflow at the beginning of the 30 day period, the distribution in the summer conditional on this prior flow will have a smaller mean than for the same initial conditions in the winter. If this is true,

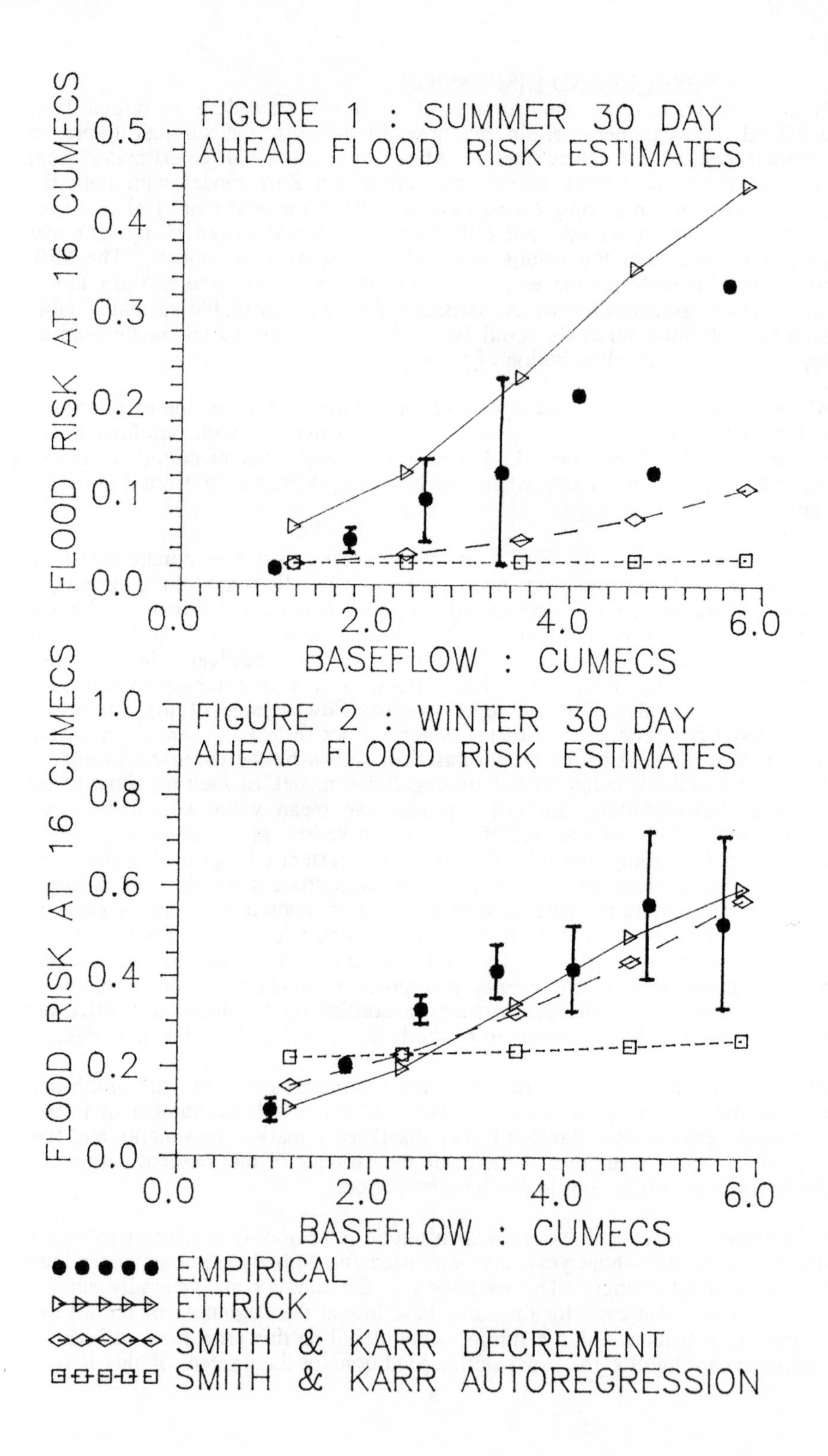
FIGURE 1 : SUMMER 30 DAY
AHEAD FLOOD RISK ESTIMATES
FLOOD RISK AT 16 CUMECS
0.0
0.1
0.2
0.3
0.4
0.5
0.0
2.0
4.0
6.0
BASEFLOW : CUMECS
FIGURE 2 : WINTER 30 DAY
AHEAD FLOOD RISK ESTIMATES
FLOOD RISK AT 16 CUMECS
0.0
0.2
0.4
0.6
0.8
1.0
0.0
2.0
4.0
6.0
BASEFLOW : CUMECS
EMPIRICAL
ETTRICK
SMITH & KARR DECREMENT
SMITH & KARR AUTOREGRESSION

then the risk estimates in the summer will tend to be too high, which is the result observed.

The use of the synthetic data has allowed a certain amount of model validation to be carried out. The Smith and Karr model would be expected to perform the better of the two models with a large amount of data because it makes no distributional assumptions. In fact, for these data, both models have a comparable level of performance. For the Ettrick model, the reasonable results suggests that adequate distributions were found, and also adequate relationships between the distribution parameters and covariates. The distributional assumptions associated with the Ettrick model become more important when using real data, which will be shorter in duration than those used here, and for many, they will be too short for the Smith and Karr model to be fitted with sufficient accuracy. In such circumstances, recourse has to be made to distributional assumptions.

In terms of ease of use, if the critical flow threshold of interest is altered, then for the Smith and Karr model, the regression coefficients and baseline intensity parameters need re–estimating. However, once the distribution parameters have been estimated for the Ettrick model, then only the numerical integration needs to be changed to the new threshold. Including a new covariate is easier in the Smith and Karr model, because of the lack of any distributional assumptions. In the Ettrick model, such an inclusion would mean finding a satisfactory relationship between distribution parameters and the new covariate. If a different time period of interest were required, this would relatively easy to do with the Smith and Karr model. For the Ettrick model, this would again mean checking the distributional assumptions, and altering them if need be.

CONCLUSIONS

The two models have very different structures but their accuracy is similar for the long synthetic data records to which they were applied, particularly in winter. The Smith and Karr model is perhaps the easier to apply, making it the preferred choice for short term flood risk estimation with long data records. However, with shorter data records, the situation for most field applications, it is likely that the Ettrick model will be more accurate. This is because the Ettrick model is based on a rainfall threshold, whilst the Smith and Karr model is based on a flow threshold, and the data record will be longer for the former. However, for either model it is interesting to see how the sensitivity of the flood risk varies with the baseflow at the beginning of the 30 day period. This observation confirms the results obtained earlier by the Ettrick model using field data from three rivers in the U.K. (Ettrick 1986). With changes in the risk of over 200%, the importance of models incorporating information about the catchment conditions is confirmed.

ACKNOWLEDGEMENTS

The authors would like to thank N.E.R.C. for some financial support during this work, and Dr. M.C. Acreman and Dr. R.J. Moore of the Institute of Hydrology for providing the data.

REFERENCES

Acreman, M.C., (1988) Catchment response and the flood frequency curve; Phase I : A simple hourly simulation model for point rainfall in southern Britain. Report to MAFF, Institute of Hydrology.

Archer, D.R., (1981) Seasonality of flood and the assessment of seasonal flood risk. Proc.Instn.Civ.Engs. Part 2 1023–1035.

Cox, D.R., (1972) Regression models and life tables (with Discussion). J.Roy.Stat.Soc. Series B, 34 187–220.

Ettrick, T.M., (1986) Seasonal flood risk. Ph.D. Thesis, University of Newcastle upon Tyne.

Ettrick, T.M., J.A. Mawdsley and A.V. Metcalfe, (1987) The influence of catchment antecedent conditions on seasonal flood risk. Wat.Resour.Res. 23(3) 481–488.

Futter, M.R., (1990) Winter flood risk. Ph.D. Thesis. To be submitted to the University of Newcastle upon Tyne.

Ghani, A.A.A., (1988) Spectral estimation of flood risk. Ph.D. Thesis, University of Newcastle upon Tyne.

Moore, R.J. and R.T. Clarke, (1981) A distribution function approach to rainfall–runoff modelling. Wat.Resour.Res. 17(5) 1367–1382.

Smith, J.A. and A.F. Karr, (1986) Flood frequency analysis using the Cox regression model. Wat.Resour.Res. 22(6) 890–896.

Tawn, J.A., (1988) An extreme–value theory model for dependent observations. J.Hydrol. 101 227–250.

Todorovic, P., (1978) Stochastic models of floods. Wat.Resour.Res. 14(2) 345–356.

International Conference on
RIVER FLOOD HYDRAULICS
17-20 September, 1990

A BASIN-WIDE FLOW FORECASTING SYSTEM FOR REAL-TIME FLOOD WARNING, RIVER CONTROL AND WATER MANAGEMENT

R. J. Moore and D. A. Jones
Institute of Hydrology, Wallingford, Oxon, UK

P. B. Bird
Logica Energy and Industry Systems, Leatherhead, Surrey, UK

M. C. Cottingham
NRA Yorkshire Region, Leeds, Yorkshire, UK

ABSTRACT

The paper describes the design and development of a real-time river modelling system for flood warning, river control, intake protection, and drought management. A modular design and flexible structure allows the addition of new forecast points, new measurement sites, and new model structures as the need arises. Indeed the design enables the system to be readily reconfigured to model any river network: the system is currently being implemented to provide flow and level forecasts at 200 sites throughout the NRA Yorkshire Region's 13,500 km^2 area of responsibility. A key feature of the design is an information control algorithm which uses the river network structure to automatically work out the sequence of chained-forecasts required to generate a forecast at a chosen point within the river basin. The modelling modules incorporated in the system model rainfall-runoff, snowmelt, and channel flow in gate-controlled, washland- and tidally-affected reaches. Forecasts are updated using recently telemetered river level measurements via state- and error-correction techniques. The river modelling components form the kernel within a program shell which handles data acquisition and information dissemination tasks: external data are polled over telephone lines by an independent regional telemetry system scheduled to coincide with the forecasting requirements. For example, when the system is being used to support flood warning and control decisions data at 15 minute intervals can be obtained for the whole region in near real-time.

INTRODUCTION

Research on flow forecasting has been concerned traditionally with the development of improved models which transform precipitation into basin runoff and upstream channel flow into downstream channel flow. With the increased availability of data acquisition systems based on telemetry, attention in the 1970's turned to the development of techniques which combine flow forecasts with recent observations of flow to produce more accurate "updated" forecasts. More recently, a threshold on improved model performance was recognised to be associated with the limited accuracy of areal average rainfall estimates derived from a sparse raingauge network: this has lead to recent work on the use of weather radar for real-time flow forecasting (Collinge and Kirby 1987; Cluckie et al 1987; Moore et al 1989a, 1989b; British Hydrological Society 1989).

All the above activities share the common goal of improving the performance of a flow forecasting model. However, the actual requirements of a real-time flow

International Conference on River Flood Hydraulics, edited by W.R.White

forecasting system extend far beyond the requirement to model streamflow. The main thrust of this paper is to outline the development of a River Flow Forecasting System (RFFS) and to focus, not on the model development, but on the requirements of a flow forecasting system and the system design which leads to these requirements being met. The requirements were established as part of a Systems Analysis following a Preliminary Requirements Specification produced by the National Rivers Authority Yorkshire Region. In broad terms, the requirements were to develop a region-wide flow forecasting system to support flood warning, river control, intake protection, and drought management. These requirements implied the need for full flow range forecasting at many points within a number of river basins and the need for lead times from less than 1 hour to several days. A particularly stringent requirement was for flexibility of design to allow the system to be configurable to any set of river basins and to readily accomodate new model structures.

The first section of the paper describes some design tools used in the specification of the RFFS which helped reduce a complex system requirement into a well structured system design. An Information Control Algorithm developed to meet the requirement for configurability is then outlined. The remainder of the paper reviews the modelling modules (paying particular attention to the treatment of missing values and forecast updating), the facilities for decision support and the functioning of the operational system. The System is currently being configured to provide forecasts at 200 forecast points within the National Rivers Authority Yorkshire Region's 13,500 km^2 area of responsibility. These forecast points are shown in Figure 1 which provides an impression of the complexity of the river model network.

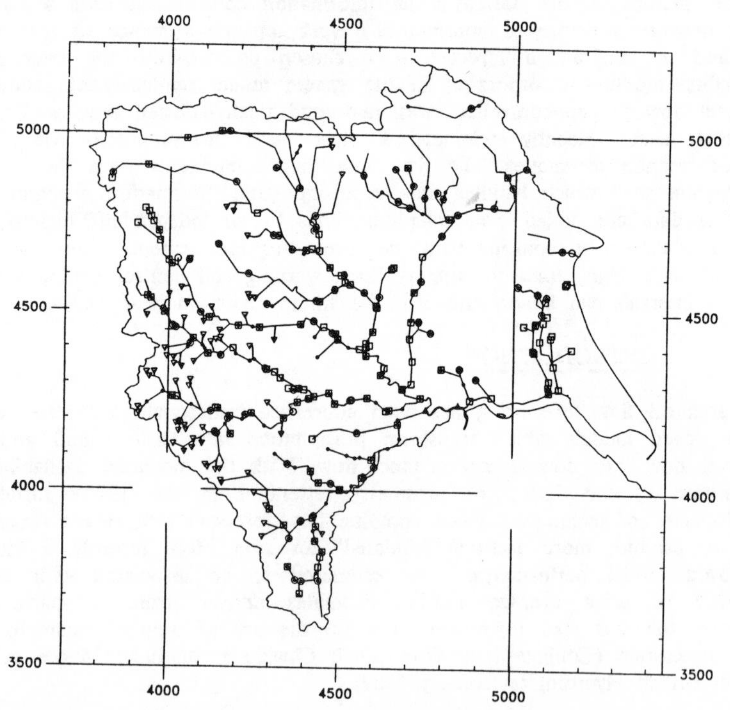

Figure 1 River Model Network for the Yorkshire region

SYSTEM DESIGN

The RFFS can be envisaged as consisting of a shell and kernel, the kernel being the modelling software and the shell handling data storage and transfer of data both external to the system and generated internally by the forecasting activities of the kernel. External data includes the acquisition of telemetry data, user transactions with the System and also report generation.

The two main system design tools used in the development of the RFFS were the Data Flow Diagram (DFD) and the Entity-Relationship Diagram (ERD). Details of these structured system design tools can be found in the book by Page-Jones (1988) and derive from methods popularised by Yourdon. The DFD was used to give structure to the RFFS requirements specification. It reveals the essential functions and data that must exist within the system. In particular, it serves to clarify the flow of data between data stores and data processing functions and the nature of the data interfaces. In the DFD processes are represented graphically by bubbles, data flows by arrowed lines, and data stores by open-sided boxes. Partitioning of the DFD allows a complex system to be described at a number of levels working from the top down. The Level 0 DFD shown in Figure 2 is particularly useful in highlighting the external data sources which form Local Input to the RFFS.

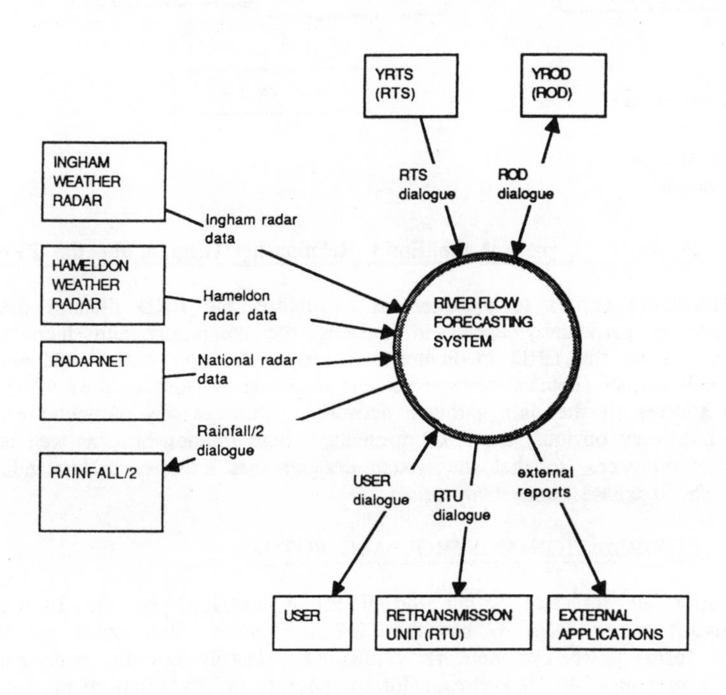

Figure 2 Level 0 data flow diagram for the RFFS

The stored data, or entities, involved in the system and the relationships between them can be depicted using the Entity Relationship Diagram (ERD). Boxes are used to denote entities and a coded line linking two boxes is used to signify the nature of the relationship. Any data mentioned in the DFD or ERD is defined in the data dictionary and in turn this is used as part of the structured relational database that features in the implemented system. A part of the RFFS's ERD is shown in Figure 3.

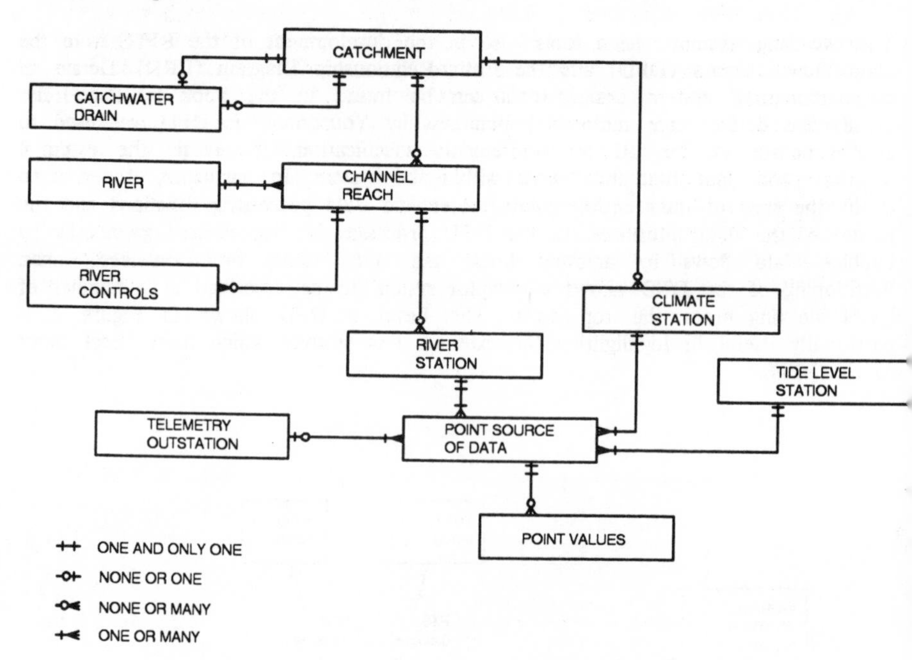

Figure 3 A part of the Entity Relationship Diagram for the RFFS

Whereas the DFD relates to program task structure, the ERD dictates database structure and is particularly useful in showing the complexity and hierarchy of relationships. Thus the ERD in Figure 3 shows a structure based predominantly on a hierarchy which depicts catchments encompassing outstation sites which link point data sources to the data gatherer network. Although any particular example may seem intuitively obvious, the ERD formalises these relationships, as well as less obvious cross-references, so that the system designer has a better understanding of when and why database connectivity arises.

INFORMATION CONTROL ALGORITHM

The generation of forecasts within the RFFS is managed by the Information Control Algorithm, or ICA. Within the ICA the model components are linked together to form a tree-like network configured primarily on the river network itself. For a user-specified downstream forecast point the algorithm works out the sequence of forecasts required for each forecast point upstream of it. This is done by working up the network one forecast point at a time and logging the model operation required to make forecasts for the user-specified forecast lead time. On completion, the forecasts are then generated by working down the tree, using upstream observed and forecast flows/levels, and other inputs, to forecast those downstream using the appropriate model component. Thus a downstream forecast is obtained by chaining together observed and forecast values upstream through a sequence of model components. In calculating the forecast requirement at each point account is taken of previous forecasts made and whether new data (eg. from telemetry) are available.

An information structure is used to reduce a complex basin-wide river flow forecasting problem to a larger number of simpler sub-problems which are easily managed. The structure describes the model network as a set of links (the model components) and nodes (the forecast points). It is comprised of a set of interlinked and cross-referenced lists: these lists contain information which allows the network to be traversed up and down along with details relating to the links and nodes (for example, the type of model component and data-input sources). Some nodes function as input-data points and control-structure points: these essentially supply information, available externally, to the ICA. They contrast with forecast point nodes which derive their information from model components. Figure 4 illustrates the information structure and how it fits within the wider framework of the RFFS.

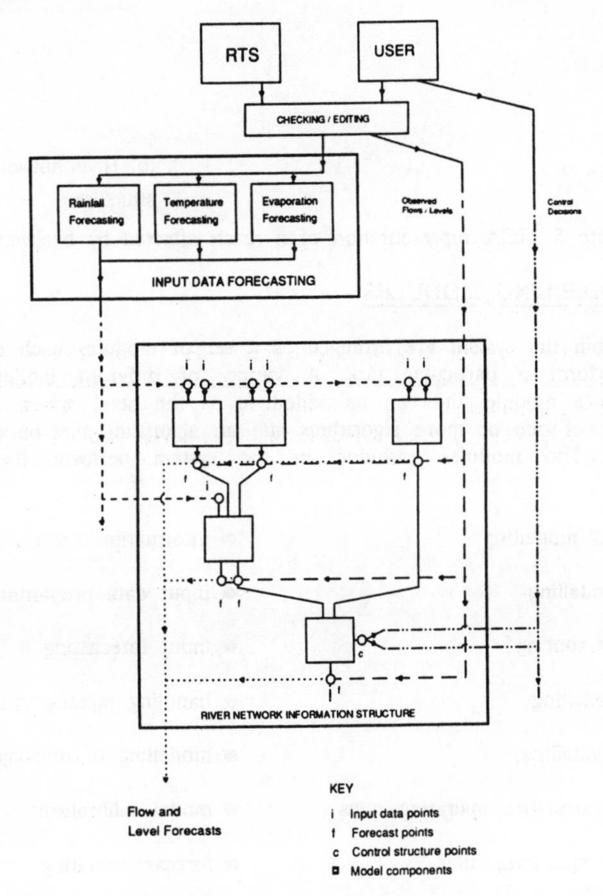

Figure 4 The information control structure of the RFFS

An assumption made of the information structure is that information flows are from the headwaters seawards. However, the structure is still capable of handling backwater effects in tidal, tributary or controlled reaches by incorporating an affected area within a single model component. This is illustrated in Figure 5 where forecast points 4 and 5 lie within the backwater area of forecast point 6 and are represented by a single model component with 4 and 5 forming "internal" forecast nodes.

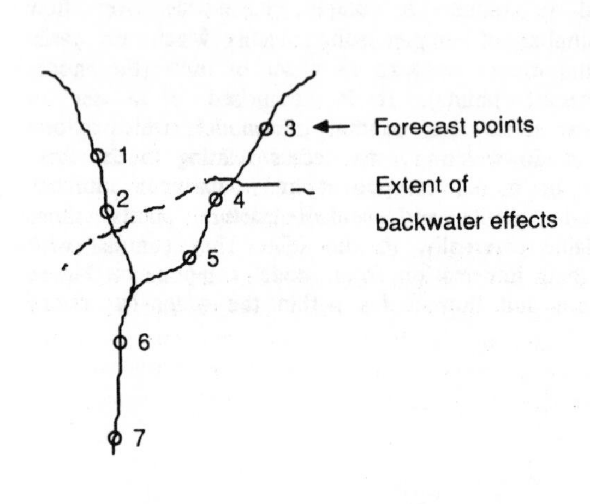

(a) River network and forecast points

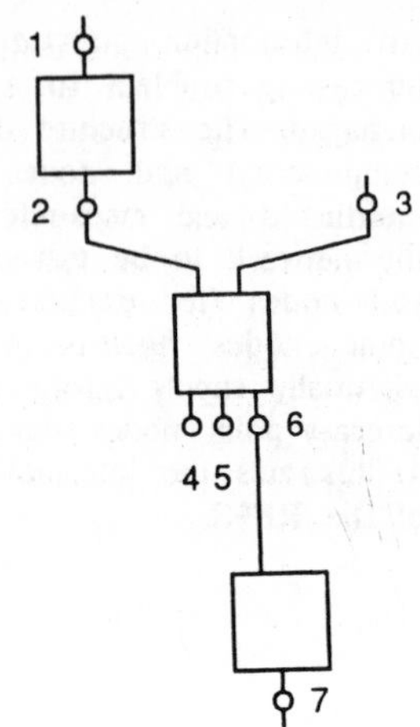

(b) River network information structure

Figure 5 ICA representation of a reach affected by backwater

MODELLING MODULES

The models within the system are arranged as a set of modules each of which is assigned to perform a particular task. A variety of different models may be contained within a module and can be added to as the need arises; a model is usually made up of one or more algorithms and an algorithm may be common to several models. The modules included in the system perform the following modelling tasks:

- rainfall-runoff modelling
- snowmelt modelling
- channel flow routing
- washland modelling
- tidal river modelling
- river control structure operating rules
- tidal barrage operating rules
- decision support facilities
- information control algorithm
- input data preparation
- input forecasting
- handling missing values
- modelling of ungauged basins
- model calibration
- forecast updating
- estimating forecast uncertainty

The models provided in the initial implementation include simple transfer function models (Box and Jenkins 1970; Moore, 1982), conceptual rainfall-runoff and snowmelt models (Moore 1985), hydrological channel flow routing models (Jones and Moore 1980), and simplified hydraulic-based channel and washland models suitable for real-time forecasting of levels in tidal, natural backwater and gate-controlled reaches. However, it is clear from the above list of tasks that the River Flow Forecasting System is much more than a set of model algorithms. Two particularly important features of the System are the ability to cope with data loss and to update model forecasts using the most recently available data on river levels, snow pack water equivalents, etc.

Missing Values. Missing values at interior points within the model river network are replaced by model forecast values, which in turn derive from observations upstream. Only at the extremities of the network do difficulties arise in infilling missing values, and in extreme cases the problem becomes analogous to providing input forecasts. However, more commonly recourse can be made to either temporal or spatial interpolation techniques. As a simple example, a set of different permutations of raingauge weighting factors defining a basin average rainfall for a headwater basin can be constructed to cope with data loss from one or more gauges. A hirearchy of options can be formulated, one of which may utilise radar rainfall data. In the case of more conservative data, such as potential evaporation, it is possible to use a value from a standard profile or from the previous day.

Forecast Updating. The term "updating" is used to describe the operation of using hydrological observations to improve model forecasts: most commonly the hydrological variable concerned will be river flow or level and the observation will be derived via telemetry. In the RFFS two techiques are used to update forecasts, one termed "error prediction" and the other "state correction"; reviews of these methods can be found in Moore (1986) and Reed (1984). The error prediction method takes the model forecast and attempts to predict future model errors by exploiting the dependence structure of past errors, using an autoregressive moving average (ARMA) structure. An updated forecast is obtained by summing the model forecast and the predicted error for a given time in the future. State correction provides a conceptually more appealing updating method by adjusting the state variables of a model (eg soil moisture content) to achieve concordance beteen observed and modelled flow. In particular, this method can compensate for errors in the rainfall input which accumulate in a model's moisture stores. Simple empirical state correction techniques, presented in Moore (1986), typically consist of a rule for weighting the amount of change made to different model states in order to match, or nearly match, the latest observations. These have been adopted within the RFFS in preference to more formal Kalman filter based state-correction methods (Jazwinski 1970) because the latter have no outstanding advantages and are considerably more complex to implement.

DECISION SUPPORT

The System incorporates information support tools to assist in real-time decision making. In addition to the System's primary function to support flood warning decisions it can be used as an interactive decision making tool for flood control. Specific attention, in implementation of the System to the Yorkshire region, has been placed on its use for controlling in-stream regulator gates and tidal barriers. A user of the System can select his preferred sequence of gate settings during a flood or tidal incursion and observe the forecasted impact on river levels upstream and downstream. In this way a sequence of "What if?" questions provides an informal means of arriving at an appropriate decision for implementation, even for a complex interconnected system of gates, overflow weirs and washland flood storages. Figure 6 illustrates a typical gate regulation simulation during a flood for a vertical lift gate on the River Rother in Yorkshire: level control is followed by flow control and the induced backwater behind the gate leads to diversion of flood water into washland storages, thereby mitigating the severity of flooding downstream.

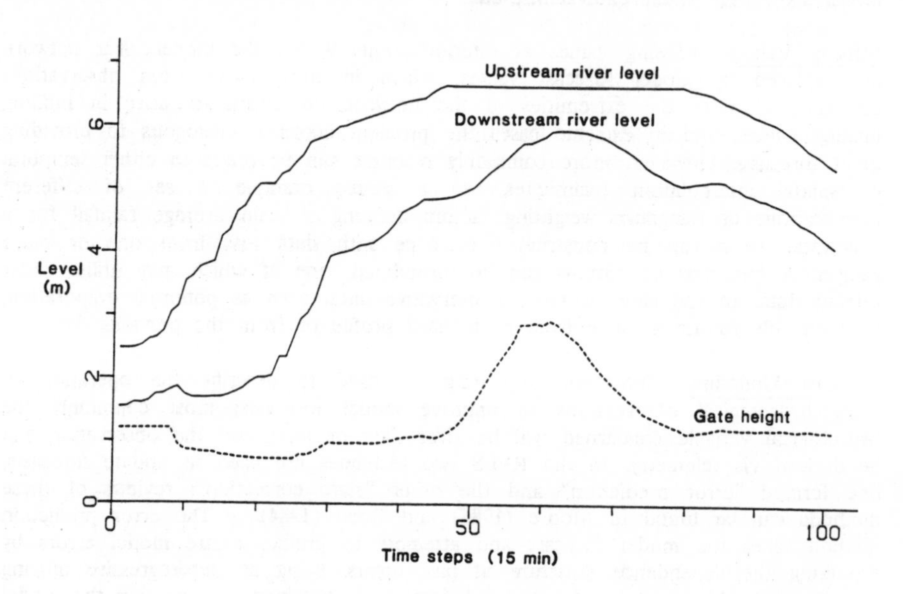

Figure 6 Simulation of the regulation of the Canklow vertical lift gate on the River Rother during a flood

THE OPERATIONAL SYSTEM

A separate Regional Telemetry System (RTS) consisting of a distributed network of data gatherer computers, is responsible for polling the outstations via PSTN (Public Switched Telephone Network), to gather hydrometric data required by the RFFS to make forecasts. During normal routine operation data are gathered for the whole region once a day between midnight and four o'clock. The frequency of data logging at the outstations is normally 15 minutes, but this is configurable; all the data collected by the outstations since the last poll are transferred to the data gatherer system during a call. Similarly, the RFFS is routinely run once a day, after the RTS polling schedule has been completed, and a routine daily report is generated. A fixed forecast lead time of five days is normally assumed and default input forecasts and gate operations are built into the system to allow the forecasts to be prepared without manual data entry. During a flood, or other event requiring more frequent updates, the RTS polling schedules are changed to gather data at more frequent intervals, depending on the nature and extent of the forecast requirement. The state variables of the model components are stored from a previous model run: this allows the models to make forecasts without needing to use a long history of past data for initialisation.

The Information Control Algorithm is such that the user can specify any forecast point within the model network as the "furthest downstream node" and only forecasts upstream of this point, and required for its generation, are calculated. This means that forecasts of flash-floods in headwater basins can be updated as frequently as, say, every 15 minutes, provided the RTS polling schedules have been set up appropriately. Of course, forecasting of all forecast points within the entire river basin, including the running of the hydraulic-based tidal model component, would not be required to be done so often.

CONCLUSION

The paper has demonstrated that the implication of developing a River Flow Forecasting System for operational use involves far more than the development of mathematical models to transform precipitation and upstream flows to produce forecasts at a point requiring a flood warning. There is a need to combine expertise in computer system design, communications technology and hydrological modelling with a knowledge of actual forecast requirements if a successfull operational system is to be realised. Such a pooling of expertise in this instance has lead to a River Flow Forecasting System which is configurable to any set of river basins and is extendable to incorporate new modelling routines, either as technological advances are made or new requirements are encountered.

REFERENCES

Box, G.E.P. and Jenkins, G.M., 1970. Time series analysis forecasting and control, Holden-Day, 553 pp.

British Hydrological Society, 1989. Weather Radar and the Water Industry: Opportunities for the 1990s. BHS Occasional Paper No. 2, 91 pp, Institute of Hydrology.

Cluckie, I.D., Ede, P.F., Owens, M.D., Bailey, A.C., and Collier, C.G., 1987. Some hydrological aspects of weather radar research in the United Kingdom, Hydr. Sci. J., 32(3), 329-346.

Collinge, V.K. and Kirby, C. (eds.), 1987. Weather radar and flood forecasting. J. Wiley, 296 pp.

Jazwinski, A.H., 1970. Stochastic processes and filtering theory. Academic Press, 376 pp.

Jones, D.A. and Moore, R.J., 1980. A simple channel flow routing model for real-time use. Hydrological Forecasting, Proc. Oxford Symp., IAHS-AISH Publ. No. 129, 397-408.

Moore, R.J., 1982. Transfer functions, noise predictors, and the forecasting of flood events in real-time, in Singh, V.P.(ed.), Statistical Analysis of rainfall and runoff, Water Resources Publ., 229-250.

Moore, R.J., 1985. The probability-distributed principle and runoff production at point and basin scales, Hydrological Sciences Journal, 30(2), 273-297.

Moore, R.J., 1986, Advances in real-time flood forecasting practice. Invited paper, Symp. on Flood Warning Systems, Winter Meeting of the River Engineering Section, The Institution of Water Engineers and Scientists, 24 January 1986, 23pp.

Moore, R.J., Watson, B.C., Jones, D.A., Black, K.B., Haggett, C.M., Crees, M.A., and Richards, C., 1989a. Towards an improved system for weather radar calibration and rainfall forecasting using raingauge datas from a regional telemetry system. New Directions for Surface Water Modelling, Proc. Baltimore Symp., IAHS Publ. no. 181, 13-21.

Moore, R.J., Watson, B.C., Jones, D.A., and Black, K.B., 1989b. London Weather Radar Local Calibration Study: Final Report. Institute of Hydrology, 85 pp.

Page-Jones, M., 1988. Practical guide to structured systems design. Yourdon Press Computing Series, Prentice-Hall International Editions, 2nd edn., 368 pp.

Reed, D.W., 1984. A review of British Flood Forecasting Practice. Report No. 90, Institute of Hydrology, 113 pp.

International Conference on
RIVER FLOOD HYDRAULICS
17-20 September, 1990

Influence of basin characteristics on flood hydrographs

B. SACKL
Institute for Hydromechanics, Hydraulics and Hydrology
Graz University of Technology
Mandellstr. 9/I, A–8010 GRAZ / Austria

ABSTRACT

Flood hydrographs of certain return periods are necessary for the dimensioning of many water constructions. But in most of all cases no runoff observations are available and the estimation of statistical flood hydrographs has to be done by regionalization methods. Different basin properties are used, which are relevant for the flood regime and which are describing the topography, geometry, river network, soil or vegetation. The contribution describes also the application of a digital terrain model (50m square grid raster) for the determination of topographical and slope characteristics, for which a computer program has been developed. Regional flood estimation formulas are achieved, which are calibrated by regional flood data, taken from a flood date base for water gauges of Austria. The data base consists of observed flood hydrographs and their characteristics like peak and volume of runoff, time and hydrograph shape parameters.

INTRODUCTION

Flood hydrographs for different return periods have to be available for the design of water constructions like for flood prevention (river regulation, flood detention basins or flood spillways of water power storages). But the number of observed water gauges is too low and there are no data for most of all relevant river sites, especially for small basins with a size up to 300 km^2. As in this case also the application of rainfall runoff models is almost not possible, the determination of T_r–years floods has to be done by regionalization methods. For a 'hydrological region' – which is nearly homogenious in its precipitation characteristic – all measured runoff samples are evaluated and the dependence to basin characteristics is analyzed. With the numerous estimation formulas, which we can find in literature, useful results are achieveable only for special regions. Most of all properties (e.g. the mean slope of the main valley) describe the basin characteristic only in a very simple and insufficient way. Therefore the aim of two research projects is to find the foundations for the developement of regional estimation formulas for different areas of Austria, not only for the

International Conference on River Flood Hydraulics, edited by W.R.White

determination of probability of flood peaks, but also for other flood characteristics, as the volume of direct runoff, time to peak, total duration and hydrograph shape. As a foundation a flood data base is installed, which allows a fast access to all observed floods and their characteristics at water gauges in Austria. With the increasing computer power and the more and more extensive geodata base it is possible, to use basin characteristics, which were not taken into account until now because of the high expense. As an example these are the mean slope of the basin and the river network and the application of a so called hypsogram, hypsoklinogram or orientogram. The hypsogram-curve describes, what area is above a certain altitude (Fig. 3), the hypsoklinogram-curve decribes, what area has a slope steeper than a certain value (Fig. 4). The orientogram is achieved by deviding the orientation into discrete intervals of for instance 10 degrees and determining the area, which has a corresponding orientation (Fig. 5). Further the basin area is devided into subsections, representing different classes of geology or vegetation. These data are taken from a data base too or they are digitized from maps.

FLOOD DATA BASE

Data input The input for the flood data base are analogous (from recording water gauges) and digital (from mass storages) measurements at water gauges in Austria. A flood hydrograph is taken into the data base, if the runoff peak is an annual maximum or if the peak exceeds a certain threshold HQ_{min}. The threshold follows from the condition, that the number N of floods is four times the number Y of observed years ($N = 4 \cdot Y$). An automatic computation of the threshold is done, if the hydrographs already exist in a digital form. The water level–runoff relation is stored as 3 analytical functions for different ranges of water level.

All of the more than 500 recording water gauges of the hydrographic survey of Austria will be analyzed, from which in a first testing phase 4 basins with a size from 65 to 7000 km^2 are evaluated.

Data base structure The data access is done by index files (water gauge code, river basin etc.). All computer programs (data evaluation, data base system, data analysis) are written in the language APL ('A Programming Language'). Therefore files are stored as APL–specific component–files, which allow a faster access and lower needed storage capacity. Flood hydrographs are stored as polygons, whereby the components contain the day of year, the second of day, the water level and the discharge for each point, the begin and end indices of hydrograph sections and eventually remarks in the case of later corrections.

Data analysis The begin and end of the direct flood runoff is determined automatically by a computer program at all hydrographs, which have been taken into the data base because of the selection criterions mentioned before. Simultaneous the base flow is seperated. The linear seperation is made by objective criterions, starting from the event peak, for instance by a constant ratio of direct runoff volume and the separates triangular volume below the direct runoff. Empirical investigations have shown, that the best results are achieved with a ratio 8:1 in most of all cases. A manual correction is considered. In table 1 the flood characteristics are shown, which are evaluated and can be called from the data base. For each single event a data sheet (Fig. 1) can be plotted.

TABLE 1 Flood characteristics.

total flood volume	V_T	$[m^3]$
height of total runoff	H_T	$[mm]$
volume of direct runoff	V_D	$[m^3]$
height of direct runoff	H_D	$[mm]$
peak of total runoff	Q_T	$[m^3/s]$
peak-rate of total runoff	q_T	$[m^3/s \cdot km^2]$
peak of direct runoff	Q_D	$[m^3/s]$
peak-rate of direct runoff	q_D	$[m^3/s \cdot km^2]$
initial base flow	$Q_{B,0}$	$[m^3/s]$
initial base flow-rate	$q_{B,0}$	$[m^3/s \cdot km^2]$
base flow at the end	$Q_{B,E}$	$[m^3/s]$
base flow-rate at the end	$q_{B,E}$	$[m^3/s \cdot km^2]$
time-characteristics:		
begin	T_b	date, time
peak	T_p	date, time
end	T_e	date, time
total duration	t_t	$[h]$
time to peak	t_p	$[h]$
standard parameters:		
standard volume	V_S	$[-]$
t_t/t_p	τ_t	$[-]$
standard filling line parameters	n, f	$[-]$
recession curve coefficient	k_i	$[h]$

For small basins (approximately $< 150\ km^2$ the hydrograph shape is simulated with the following two formulas (u = standard runoff, normalized by the peak discharge; τ = standard time, normalized by the time to peak):

$$u = \tau^a \text{ for } u \leq 1$$

$$u = \exp(-m\,\tau) \text{ for } u > 1$$

For larger basins a twoparametric analytical formula is used (SACKL, 1987), which describes both the increasing and decreasing tail of the hydrograph and which makes it possible to vary the hydrograph shape in a wide range:

$$u = \tau^{am} e^{m(1-\tau^{a})}$$

FLOOD DATA BASE Version 1.0 Inst.f.Hy.-TU Graz

WATER GAUGE: OBERWART A_E = 171.7 [km^2]	Gauge.No.: 210229
RIVER: PINKA	August 1987

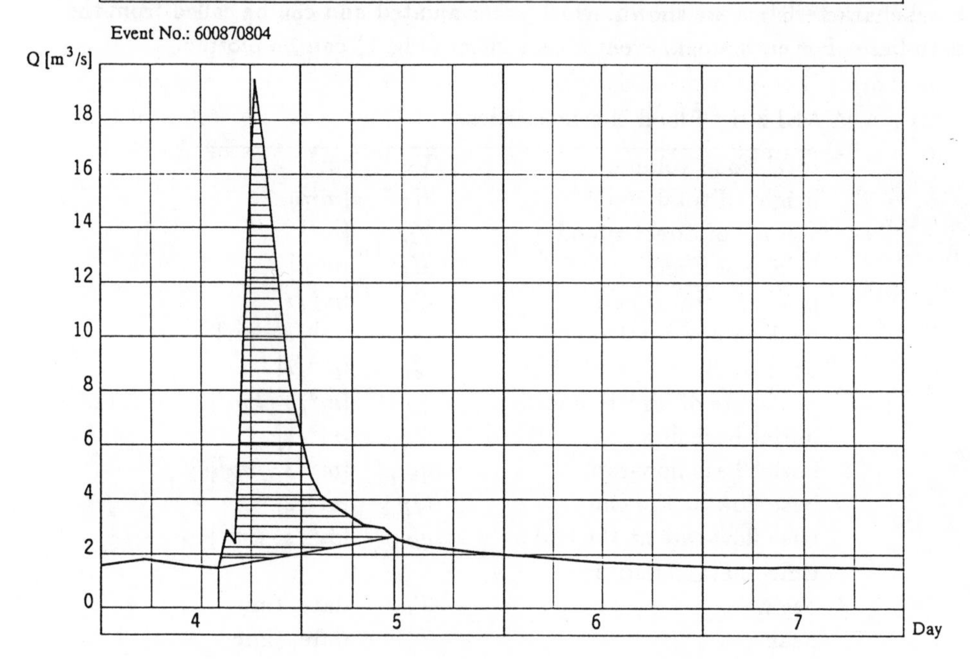

VOLUME		V	V-B0	V-B1	V-D
mass	[m^3]	506270	112913	43706	349650
depth	[mm]	2.9	0.7	0.3	2.0

DISCHARGE		Q-B0	Q-BS	Q-BE	Q-BM	Q-S	Q-D
discharge	[m^3/s]	1.50	1.75	2.66	2.08	19.47	17.72
flow rate	[l/s km^2]	8.73	10.19	15.49	12.11	113.42	103.23

TIME		Date/Hour
begin	T-0	08 04 / 14:00
peak	T-S	08 04 / 18:30
end	T-E	08 05 / 10:55

DURATION	[h]
t-a	4.51
t-e	16.41
t-ges	20.93
t-m	5.48

standard values	
VS	1.21
tau-max	4.64
N-f	2.349
B-f	4.09E-6

NOTES:

separation criterion: V-B1/V-D = 1 : 8.00

Fig. 1 Example for a flood event, called from the data base

Periodicaly every 5 years a statistical analysis is made. The exceedence probability of peak flow, volume of direct runoff, time to peak, total duration and mean initial base flow is determined, the standard parameters of standard hydrographs and filling lines are determined and the correlation between different characteristics is analyzed. From the Normal–, log.Normal– , 3-parameter-log.Normal–, Gumbel–, log.Gumbel–, Pearson-III–, log.Pearson-III–, Gamma– and log.Gamma-distribution type the best fitted curve is determined for both annual maximum series and partial duration series. Furthermore the 'log.-transformed Normal distribution' after SACKL (1987) is computed, which gives an excellent fit in almost all cases and which is relatively insensible to outliers. The sample is transformed logarithmically, so that the skewness becomes zero, then the normal distribution is computed and the values are retransformed into the 'original system'. As the plotting position formula the one after Chegodajev (CUNNANE, 1978) and as parameter estimation method the method of moments are used.

In a second step a bivariate statistical analysis of floods is made, whereby a 'log. transformed' binormal distribution (SACKL, 1987) is used. A flood is characterized by the pair of values V_D, Q_D, the volume and the peak of direct runoff. The lines of equal 'upper right probability' and with the help of a basin specific standard hydrograph shape T_r–years flood hydrographs are determined (Fig.2).

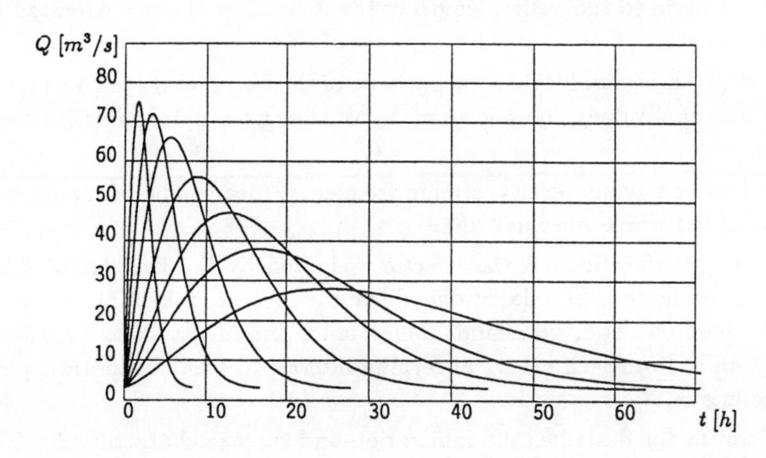

Fig. 2 Spectrum of T_r–years flood hydrographs

Data access The data access is done by many different criterions. The output occurs as tabular or graphics on the screen, a printer or plotter. It is possible to call from the data base: single events at a certain water gauge, events at different water gauges within a region, which are correlated in time, also single characteristics (volumes, peaks etc.), which are exceeding a certain threshold, for optional time intervals, or annual maxima.

EVALUATION OF BASIN CHARACTERISTICS

The flood data, which are available from the data base, are only sufficient for the dimensioning close by observed water gauges. For ungauged sites regional flood estimation formulas have to be developed, which are describing the dependence of flood parameters and their probability from basin characteristics. The flood data base is a comprehensive and fast available basis for the developement and calibration of such regional flood formulas.

Input data, maps, geodata base In the near future there will be available an environment–data base including also basin characteristics. For the entire area of Austria a digital terrain model in form of a 50-m square grid raster is already available for everyone. Most of all rivers are digitized as polygons and different simple vegetation classes are available for some regions, such as forest, fallow land, agricultural land and urbanized land. Where the data cannot be taken from an existing data base, they have to be digitized or scanned from special maps. This concerns geology, but also vegetation and the water devide.

Basin characteristics The basin properties, which are relevant for the flood regime are principally devided into the following groups:

a) Geometry: Basin area (real and projected area), circumference, distance from centre of basin to the outlet, length of the main river channel extented up to the water devide.

b) Topography (slope and height): mean slope of the basin, altitude (mean, minimal and maximal value), hypsogramm, hypsoklinogramm, mean orientation, orientogramm.

c) River network: stream density, stream frequency, mean slope of main river, mean slope of the whole river network.

d) Vegetation ('surface'): A surface factor weighted by the the size of different classes is evaluated. Simple, but significant classes are taken into account, such as the part of wood, grassland, fallow land, agricultural and urbanized area. They differ from each other concerning interception and evapotranspiration characteristic.

e) Soil: A soil factor describes the infiltration and storage characteristic. The soil classes are distinguished by the thickness and infiltration capacity.

f) Geology: Different geological subsurfaces like crystalline, tertiary or chalky, are taken into account.

g) Meteorology: The flood regime referring to the meteorological characteristic is described by the T_r-years height of precipitation for a certain duration, which is determined for instance as the time to peak in respect to the special problem.

Evaluation methods – Computer programs   Numerous characteristics cannot be simply taken out of maps. This concerns for instance the mean height of the basin, the mean slope of the basin and the river network, the mean orientation and the real basin area. A software package has been developed for the purpose to evaluate this characteristics for any basin out from the digital terrain model of Austria. Furthermore a program for the automatic determination of the orographic water devide will be developed. In figure 3 to figure 5 examples are shown for a hypsogram, hypsoklinogram and orientogram of a basin. The computer program allows also the graphical presentation of maps concerning altitude, slope and orientation (Fig.6) on screen or plotter (laserprinter), and the determination and plotting of profiles along single rivers or any other profile with the resolution of the 50-m square grid raster.

The determination of the part of different surface, geological or pedological classes becomes easier now by scanning colors from special maps or already existing data base. If this is not possible, the borders of different types are digitized and the types are marked by reference points. The border polygons are corrected automatically by a program in respect to their connections and converted into closed polygons, which allow an analytical computation of areas.

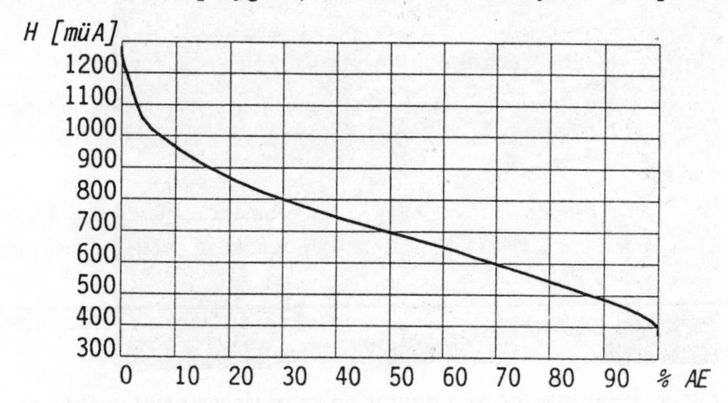

Fig. 3 Hypsogram of a basin (using a digital terrain model)

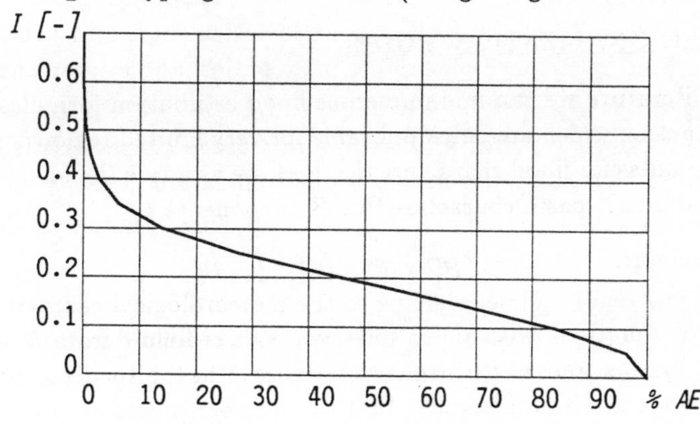

Fig. 4 Hypsoklinogram of a basin (using a digital terrain model)

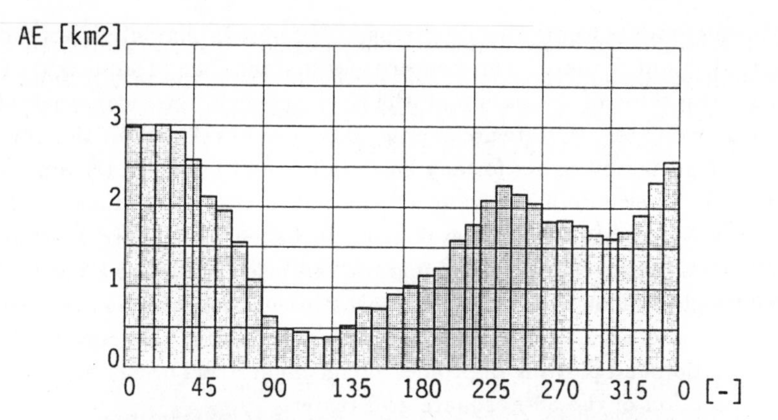

Fig. 5 Orientogram of a basin (using a digital terrain model)

Fig. 6 Example for an orientation map (laser printer output)

REGIONALIZATION MODEL

Method In literature we can find numerous flood estimation formulas, especially for flood peaks, which are only applicable for very limited regions. Regional estimation formulas for flood characteristics F_C have as a rule the following form (regional constant C, basin characteristics B_i, exponents p_i)

$$F_C = C \cdot B_1^{p_1} \cdot B_2^{p_2} \cdot B_3^{p_3} \text{.........} B_n^{p_n}$$

A system of N equations with $n+1$ unknown values follow from N observed and analyzed basins and n basin characteristics taken into account. For a convenient calibration it is necessary, that the number of basins is more than two times the number of characteristics. The equation system is linarized and solved by multiple linear regression. The fitting between the results from the empirical formula and the results from statistical analysis is called 'good', if the mean value from the deviations is lower than 5 percent.

Definition of a region In many cases it is not possible to evaluate all relevant basin characteristics. Therefore regions are defined, which are nearly homogenious concerning their meteorological or geological situation.

Relevant basin characteristics In a first step the 'relevance'of different basin characteristics is analyzed by correlation analysis. A low 'relevance' inside the region is further given, if the result of the regression analysis is a very low exponent. 'Reference basins' must have a certain variability concerning the relevant characteristics, since an extrapolation to other basins is not possible. Up to now the investiagations have shown the basin area, an index for the circularity of the basin, the mean slope of the basin and the river network and the stream density as the most relevant parameters inside a region beside the geology and vegetation (BERGMANN & SACKL, 1989). For instance the following flood formula has been developed for the subalpine region in Styria/Austria for the estimation of the 100–years flood peak discharge in basins of an area from about 5 to 300 km^2:

$$Q_{100} = 6.71 \cdot A^{0.542} \cdot C^{-0.219} \cdot \left(\frac{C_b}{L}\right)^{-0.33} \cdot S_L^{0.016} \cdot D_S^{0.236} \cdot Fo^{-0.169} \quad [m^3/s]$$

with:

A	$[km^2]$	basin area
C	$[-]$	circularity $= (2\sqrt{A/\pi})/L$
C_b	$[km]$	distance from basin centre to the outlet
L	$[km]$	length of the main river valley
S_L	$[-]$	slope referring to the length L
D_S	$[km/km^2]$	stream density
Fo	$[-]$	forested part of the basin

CONCLUSION

In the scope of two research projects a flood data base is installed for all recording water gauges in Austria, which allows a fast access to numerous flood characteristics for different purposes. The data base will be applied especially for the dimensioning of water constructions, but also for the analysis of changes in the flood regime of a basin and for scientific research. The data base is also a foundation for the developement of regional flood formulas for the estimation of flood characteristics and their probability, based upon basin properties. Computer programs are applied for the evaluation of basin characteristics, which allow the determination of much more significant basin properties as it was possible until now. Furthermore the developement of a flood concentration model is planned, based on a digital terrain model (50-m square grids) and defined parameters for each pixel. The results of this projects should bring a significant improvement in the applicability of rainfall runoff models even in unobserved catchments.

REFERENCES

CUNANNE C., 1978. Unbiased plotting positions – A review; Journal of Hydrology No. 37.

SACKL B., 1987. Determination of flood design hydrographs at gauged and ungauged sites; Graz University of Technology, Eigenverlag.

BERGMANN H., SACKL B., 1989. Determination of design flood hydrographs using a twodimensional approximation method based on regional hydrological data; In: New Directions for Surface Water Modeling, IAHS Publ. no.181, 1989.

International Conference on
RIVER FLOOD HYDRAULICS
17-20 September, 1990

FRQSIM - A FLOOD HYDROLOGY MODEL

A Vairavamoorthy BSc Eng.(Hons) Dip S.E. Delft Eng. MICE MIWEM
Consultant Hydrologist
W.D. Rylands BSc (Hons) MSC
Senior Flood Hydrologist, Thames Region NRA
D.N. Mills BSc Eng.(Hons) C.Eng MICE
Technical Support Manager, Thames Region NRA

ABSTRACT

The methodology and software referred to collectively as 'FRQSIM' (Frequency Simulation) was developed for design flood estimation in heavily urbanised catchments. It is based on synthetic unit hydrographs produced from time area information. A series of 250 rainfall profiles, representing one hundred years of flood producing rainfall, were developed for input to the model so that frequency analysis can be carried out on the resultant hydrographs at any chosen point in the modelled channel network.

FRQSIM has proved to be extremely flexible, easily tailored to specific study needs. It has been adapted to generate inflows for computational hydraulic models, and to investigate the effects of storage provision for new developments on river flows.

INTRODUCTION

In recent years rapid growth of urban areas and encroachment of developments on to the flood plains in the south-east has resulted in increased flood hazards requiring flood defence schemes to be undertaken in many urban catchments. At the same time, growing environmental concern has demanded that increased channel capacity should not be gained at the expense of all other attributes of the

International Conference on River Flood Hydraulics, edited by W.R.White

watercourse. Sensitive but effective engineering solutions were required and computational hydraulic modelling was introduced to aid design work.

Many of the models of urban watercourses required a large number of inflows from both sewered and 'natural' sub-catchments and contributing areas. No standard hydrological methods appeared to be very suitable for the provision of the input hydrographs. However, the FRQSIM model, which had been developed for the estimation of design flows in London catchments, appeared to have great potential. It was based on synthetic unit hydrographs, with separate ones produced for paved and open areas from time-area data. It also had the benefit of a series of rainfall profiles which could be used to simulate one hundred years of flood hydrographs at any chosen point on the modelled channel network. The model has been considerably refined and adapted to the needs of various studies over the past three years. In its present form hydrographs are produced from each of several sub-catchments by convoluting effective rainfall with the synthetic unit hydrographs. Different loss models are used to calculate effective rainfall for the open and paved areas, reflecting their different runoff characteristics. The total hydrograph from each sub-catchment is routed down the channel network until a storage or a design point is reached. Here the routed hydrographs from all upstream sub-catchments are added together. If it is a storage, the total hydrograph is routed through it and on down the channel to the next one, where it will be combined with the hydrographs from the down-stream sub-catchments. This process is repeated until the required design point is reached and the final hydrograph is produced.

CONSTRUCTION OF A CATCHMENT MODEL

The catchment to be modelled must first be broken down into sub-catchments by reference to topographic and sewer network maps. The model will produce a hydrograph for each sub-catchment which be assumed to enter the channel network at a specific node point. Where a sub-catchment is an amalgamation of several small inputs, consideration must be given to the location of storages, channel restrictions or design points to avoid confusion over their contributing area. The channel network is divided into branches, so that any node, storage or design point can be identified by a branch number and the time of travel to the downstream limit of the modelled catchment.

Each sub-catchment is further divided into small sub-areas. These may be either open (parks, playing fields, rural areas etc) or urbanised. The area of each is measured, and times of travel through the system are estimated to a five minute resolution as shown in Fig 1. Three times are required: from the upstream end of the sub-area to the node point; from the downstream end of the sub-area to the node point, and from the node point to the downstream limit of the modelled catchment. Times of travel in sewers are estimated along the longest pipe run in the sub-area using standard pipe flow tables (HRS 1978) assuming the sewers are running almost full. In open channels Mannings formula is used assuming the channel is about three-quarters full. Overland flow velocity calculations in open areas are based on Mannings formula and

fig 1 Time—area data

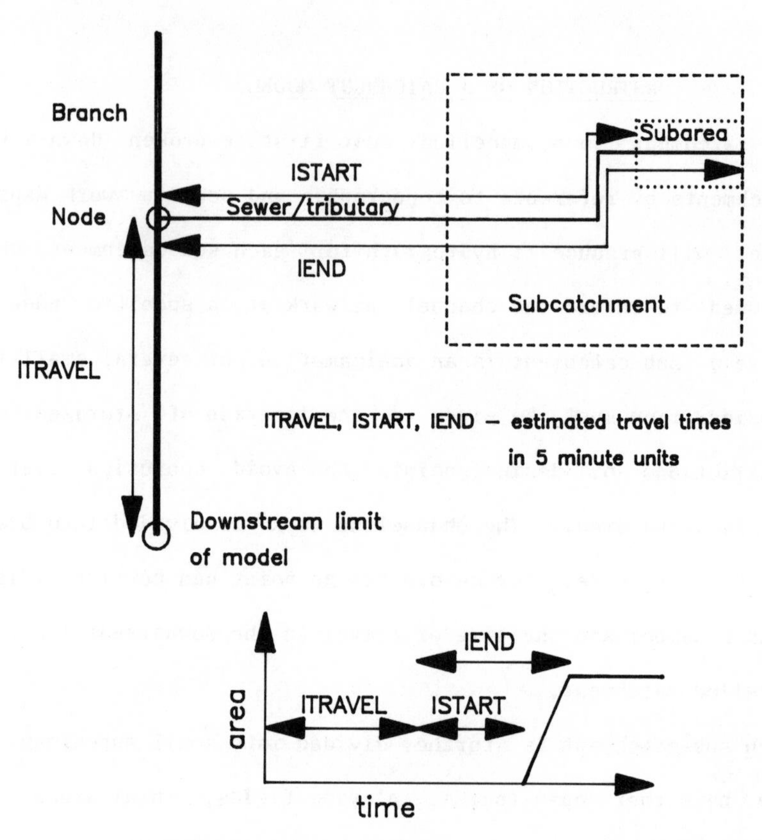

fig 2 Simple flow restriction and storage

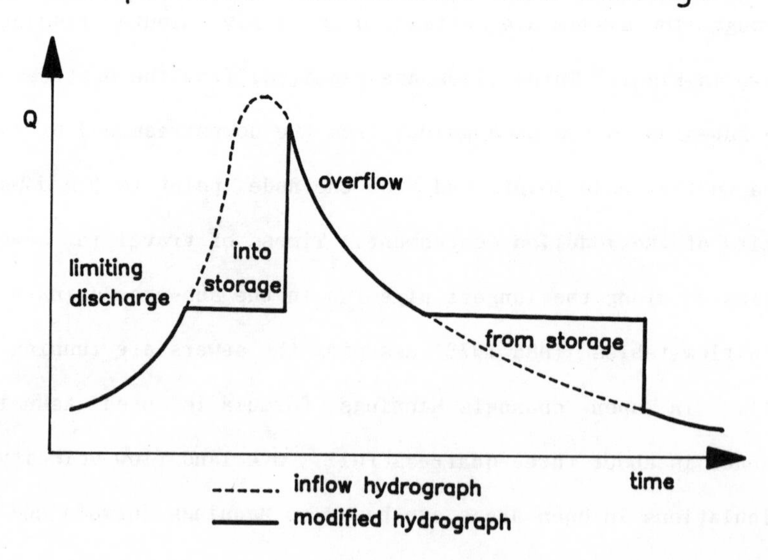

generally result in figures of about 0.05 m/s. For the urban sub-areas, the percentage that is paved is estimated from maps.

These data for all the sub-areas within each sub-catchment are transformed into synthetic unit hydrographs by the program UNIHYD. Two unit hydrographs, one for the open areas and one for the paved areas, are produced for each sub-catchment using different values of the routing parameter, k. A third unit hydrograph is produced when the model is run. This is based on the paved area unit hydrograph and represents the remaining open areas such as gardens and grass verges amongst the paved areas.

The storages in the channel network are detailed after the unit hydrograph data has been assembled. Two types of storage are commonly used. Where the depth-storage-discharge relationships of a storage pond or reservoir are known, standard reservoir routing is used. Where there is a restriction in the channel and the amount of water that can be taken into storage can be estimated, the hydrograph can be modified simply as shown in figure 2.

The soil factor, which can be global or specific to each sub-catchment, must be estimated from the Flood Studies Report map (NERC, 1975) and a channel routing parameter must be selected. A value of k of 0.33 is generally used for in banks flows, and 0.5 for out of bank flows.

RAINFALL LOSSES

Separate rainfall loss models for the paved and open areas are used to calculate the effective rainfall. Generally, a constant 70% runoff is assumed from paved areas, although for safety higher

values are assumed on small catchments for design purposes. On open areas, the total loss is calculated using the method described in Flood Studies Supplementary Report Number 16 (NERC 1985).
Part of this total goes as an initial loss, and the rest is distributed proportionally to the inverse of the Catchment Wetness Index of each half hour period. Alternatively a constant proportional loss may be used for greater compatibility with standard FSR methods.

MODEL CALIBRATION

Wherever possible, an attempt should be made to calibrate and verify models with the use of recorded rainfall and flow or level data from as many large events as possible. Half hourly and daily check gauge rainfall totals are used to produce weighted average rainfall profiles for each sub-catchment. The soil moisture deficit before the rainfall and the five days previous rainfall are required for open area rainfall loss calculations. Finally the recorded hydrograph from gauging stations within the catchment are included for comparison with the modelled results. Where there is a long and reliable gauging station record, the model can also be verified by comparing the frequency analysis of recorded peak flows with the analysis of the modelled peaks resulting from the 250 rainfall profiles (Fig. 3).

DESIGN FLOWS

When the model is considered to be working satisfactorily, it can be used to produce design flows at any chosen point on the channel.

fig 3 Model verification

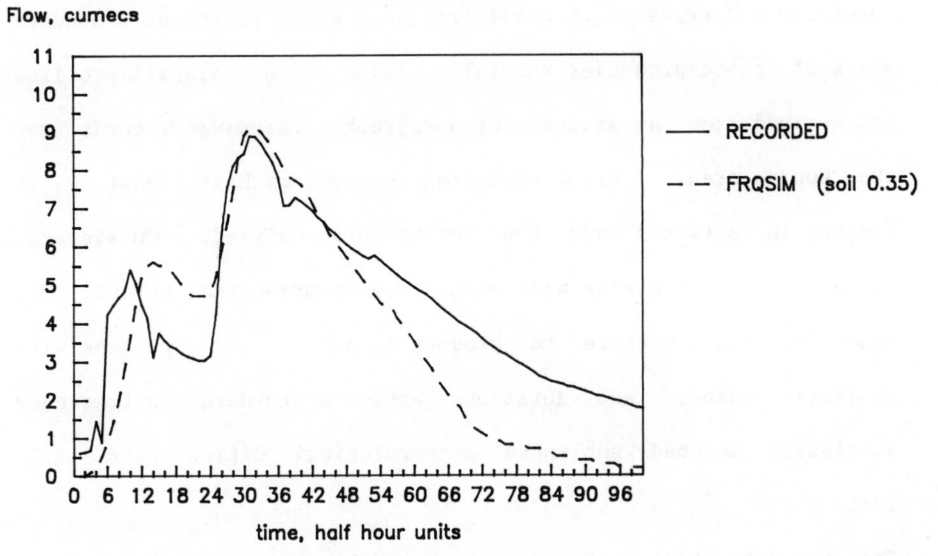

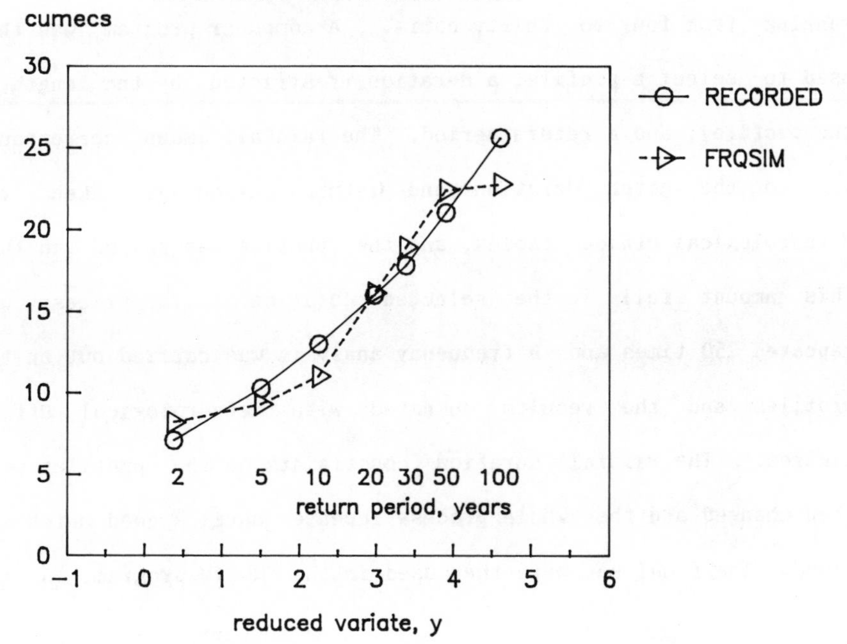

This can be done using a Flood Studies Report design rainfall profile of the appropriate duration. Alternatively, frequency analysis can be carried out on the peak flows resulting from inputting a series of rainfall profiles which represent a hundred years of flood producing rainfall. This set of rainfall profiles was derived from an analysis of autographic raingauge records from the London area. Flood producing storms with at least 25 mm falling in a twenty four hour period were analysed. On average, 250 events of this size will occur in a hundred year period. The objective was therefore to produce a set of 250 profiles with realistic shapes and durations whose depth-duration-frequency statistics matched published Meteorological Office data (M.O. 1968).

The recorded storm profiles were sorted by shape into ten groups. An average profile was produced for each group, with durations ranging from four to thirty hours. A computer program was then used to select a profile, a duration (restricted by the length of the profile), and a return period. The rainfall amount corresponding to the given duration and return period was taken from Meteorological Office tables, and the profile was scaled so that this amount fell in the selected duration. The process was repeated 250 times and a frequency analysis was carried out on the profiles and the results compared with Meteorological Office figures. The rainfall duration constraints on the profiles were then changed and the whole process repeated until a good match was found. The final set were then used in the FRQSIM program. A fuller description of the derivation of the rainfall profiles can be found in Butters and Vairavamoorthy, 1977.

FRQSIM APPLICATIONS

FRQSIM has been used in several Thames Region catchments for investigating a variety of problems. It has been used successfully on largely rural catchments such as the Cobbins Brook near Waltham Abbey where storage options were examined. It has frequently been used to provide input hydrographs for hydraulic models such as in the studies of Aylesbury and the Crane. Selection of design rainfall for a hydraulic model can be a problem. In the Crane, where design flows and levels were required from the headwaters down to its confluence with the Thames, a single design storm would not have been appropriate. However, although FRQSIM can process 250 events in a matter of seconds, the time required for a large hydraulic model to do the same thing might run to several days. A compromise was struck for the Crane where the thirty events which gave the highest flows were used. These would represent events with return periods greater than about three years. In Aylesbury, where the length of channel of interest through the town was relatively short compared to the size of the whole catchment, Flood Studies rainfall profiles could be used.

The operation of networks of storage ponds have been investigated in Stevenage and Bracknell. The effect of a proposed storage pond on flows downstream can be investigated both by looking at its effect on individual design hydrographs and by examining the effect on the frequency analysis of peak flows. However, the results must be viewed with caution. Normally, FRQSIM uses an EV1 straight line Gumbel plot to assess flows of different return period. Provision of a storage pond may dramatically reduce low return period flows, but leave high flows unaltered when it is overtopped. However, the fit of the whole line will be affected and cursory inspection of the figures may lead to the erroneous conclusion that the pond will influence flows throughout the range.

FRQSIM is well suited to investigate the effects of urbanisation and storage provision, since separate unit hydrographs are used for paved and open areas. An extra unit hydrograph can be introduced to represent additional paved area, with either of the two open area unit hydrographs reduced accordingly. The effects of storage provision on these new developments can be investigated easily. Restricting outflow from these new sites to a given number of litres per second per hectare can be simulated by restricting the effective rainfall intensity to an equivalent number of millimetres per half hour before convolution with the additional paved area unit hydrograph. The amount of storage required can then be calculated in terms of millimetres of rainfall or litres per hectare.

A study of this type was carried out on the Crane in London, resulting in the zoning of the catchment into areas where storage on new developments was essential and other areas where storage would not be beneficial.

CONCLUSIONS

FRQSIM has proved to be an extremely flexible tool, adaptable to a variety of design and catchment planning problems. At present it runs on an IBM mainframe but a shorter version, which only produces hydrograph inputs suitable for a hydraulic model without channel routing has been adapted for use on a PC.

ACKNOWLEDGEMENTS

The authors would like to thank B N Chea and Julie Lee of the Flood Hydrology Section of Thames NRA and all others who have helped with the development of the model.

REFERENCES

Butters K. and Vairavamoorthy A. 'Hydrological Studies on some river catchments in Greater London' in Proc. Instn. Civ. Engrs. Part 2, 1977, 63, June 331-361.

Hydraulics Research Station (HRS) (1978) Charts for the Hydraulic Design of Channels and Pipes. 4th ed HMSO

Meteorological Office 'Rain intensity frequency relationships in Britain' Appendix to Hydrological Memorandum 33, 1968

Natural Environment Research Council (NERC)(1975) Flood Studies Report

NERC (1985) Flood Studies Supplementary Report No: 16 The FSR rainfall-runoff model parameter estimation equations updated.

International Conference on
RIVER FLOOD HYDRAULICS
17-20 September, 1990

A CORRELATION ANALYSIS OF EXTREME RIVER MEDWAY DISCHARGES AND SHEERNESS STORM SURGES

H.F.P. van den Boogaard and R.J.H. Stive
DELFT HYDRAULICS
P.O.Box 177
NL-2600 MH DELFT

ABSTRACT

This paper deals with a technique for the assessment of dependency of extreme events in more than one time series. It is proposed to convert the time series into point processes and calculate auto- and cross-correlation densities. This approach has been applied to extreme upstream discharges and extreme downstream storm surges of the river Medway (UK).

KEY WORDS

Extreme value analysis, Correlation functions, Point processes, River Medway

1. INTRODUCTION

The tidal length of the river Medway is about 40 km and extends from the river´s mouth at Sheerness to the Allington Sluices, downstream near Maidstone.
On commission of SOUTHERN PROJECTS LTD, extreme tidal heigths in this estuary have been calculated by DELFT HYDRAULICS. This had to be done for several combinations of the river's discharge at the Allington Sluices and the storm surge at the port of Scheerness as boundary conditions. For the calculation of the Medway tidal heights, the 2 Dh option of the 3D curvilinear, numerical flow model TRISULA was used.

For this purpose it had to be investigated what surges and what discharges should be taken as ´extreme´, what are the statistical distributions of the extreme events, and is there any dependency of extreme surges and extreme discharges?

A well known method for the statistical description of extremes in a (univariate) time series is provided by the so called Extreme Value Analysis (EVA). See e.g. Haan [3]. In many cases the method is applied as follows. From all samples of the time series a selection is made for all those maxima that exceed some large, fixed value, the so called threshold. On this subset of peaks one more dilution is carried out: adjacent maxima must satisfy some minimum time-distance. The idea is that such adjacent exceedences of the treshold will not form independent events. If two peaks are closer than the minimum distance the smallest peak is considered as dependent on the larger peak and is deleted.

International Conference on River Flood Hydraulics, edited by W.R.White

In this way a set of independent peaks is obtained. The sizes of the peaks are considered as a set of independent samples from a probability distribution. It is common use to determine this distribution by probability plotting. In a probability plot the (empirical) distribution of the (ordered) extreme peaks is compared with some 'candidate' distribution of which the Generalized Extreme Value (GEV) distribution (and as a special case the Gumbel distribution) is most widely used, see e.g. Hosking et al. [4], Prescott and Walden [6], Smith [7] and Tawn [9]. The GEV forms a three-parameter distribution. In practice these parameters are chosen such that the GEV agrees best with the (empirical) distribution of the peaks. This leads to a parameter-estimation problem. For this a maximum likelihood estimation is often used, see e.g. Prescott and Walden [6], but alternative methods like e.g. probability weighted moments (see e.g. Hosking et al. [4]) can be used as well.

The approach described here is known as the 'Peak Over Threshold' (POT) method. See Petrauskas and Aagaard [5] for a more detailed discussion.
From literature slightly different methods are known, e.g. EVA based on all annular (or any other relevant period) maxima of the time series, or, even more generally, an EVA based on the r largest annual events. See e.g. Smith [7], Tawn [9].

In all these cases the goal of the EVA is the derivation of return periods of extreme events. For the derivation of a return period (RP) both the distribution of the extreme events, and, their frequency of occurrence must be used.

So far only univariate time series have been discussed. However, sometimes it is necessary to deal with the extremes of two or more time series as is the case with the discharges and surges of the river Medway. The remainder of this paper will exclusively deal with the analysis of the dependency of extreme surges and extreme discharges. The distribution of the extreme events of the individual time series will not be discussed.

For an analysis of the dependency of time series, correlation functions can be used. This approach is rather standard and it will be applied in Section 2.1. However, it is argued that this form of correlation is not very suitable to detect the dependency of extreme events.
Therefore a conditional form of the correlation function is introduced in Section 2.2 which lays special emphasis on extreme values in time series.
This form of correlation is further improved in Section 2.3 and leads to a point process approach for the investigation of the dependency of extreme events in time series.

2. CROSS-CORRELATION OF SURGES AND DISCHARGES

As already mentioned in Section 1 the dependency of surges and discharges was investigated by means of correlation functions.
For the calculation of these functions a set of simultaneous observations of Sheerness sea levels and Allington Sluices discharges was

used with a total length of about 13 years (1975-1987, hourly samples).
Apart from the observed sea levels also a prediction of the Sheerness astronomical tide was available. The surge is the difference of observation and prediction. Surges are mainly the result of wind. They have a noisy appearance, and can vary from a few cm ('normal' conditions) to values exceeding one or several meters (storm conditions). For an illustration of a Sheerness surge series see Figure 1. Figure 2 shows a typical example of an annual record of the discharge at the Allington sluices.

2.1 TIME SERIES CROSS-CORRELATION FUNCTION

The cross-correlation function of two time series $\{X(j),Y(j)|j=1,2,...,N\}$ can be estimated by

$$r_{XY}(k) = C_{XY}(k) / \sqrt{C_{XX}(0)\ C_{YY}(0)} \tag{2.1a}$$

where

$$C_{XY}(k) = \begin{cases} \frac{1}{N-k} \sum_{j=1}^{N-k} (X(j) - \bar{X})(Y(j+k) - \bar{Y}), \quad 0 \leqq k \leqq N-1 & (2.1b) \\ \frac{1}{N+k} \sum_{j=1-k}^{N} (X(j) - \bar{X})(Y(j+k) - \bar{Y}), \quad -N+1 \leqq k \leqq -1 & (2.1c) \end{cases}$$

See e.g. Chatfield [1]. The cross-correlation function assumes values between -1 and 1. A peak in the cross-correlation function at lag k indicates that one series is related to the other when delayed by time k. The more the peak approaches -1 or 1 the more the series are related.
Absence of dependency of the time series is recognised by a correlation function that is close to zero for all time lags.

For the Medway surges and discharges this 'standard' cross-correlation function has been calculated. The result is shown in Figure 3. It is seen that for all time lags the correlation is small and that on this basis no dependency of surges and discharges is found.

2.2 CONDITIONAL CROSS-CORRELATION FUNCTION

The cross-correlation function of Figure 3 is based on all the observations of surges and discharges. It is seen that this function does not reveal any mutual dependency.
However care must be taken not to conclude too soon that the series do not interact. By an example it will be shown that even if the 'standard' cross-correlation function is small the time series can nevertheless be dependent. This example is based on the following idea.

Imagine two time series where the large values tend to be synchronised whereas such synchronisation is absent for all other samples. Here 'large values' must be understood as values that significantly exceed the mean of the series.
The large samples form a small subset of the whole series. Since the 'standard' cross-correlation function is based on the complete set

of observations and the extreme values are only a small subset of these, it may easily happen that the correlation of the extreme values is masked.
In particular this will be the case when the samples are noisy and/or the number of correlated extremes is small.

In order to reveal the correlation of extreme events a conditional correlation function is proposed. In this conditional form the correlation function is evaluated on the basis of only the large samples of the series and the 'non-interesting' part of the data are thus discarded. In this procedure a decision must be made which values are large. Here it is chosen for thresholds. In a formula this leads to the following definition of the conditional correlation function:

$$r'_{XY}(k) = C'_{XY}(k) \;/\; \sqrt{C'_{XX}(0)\, C'_{YY}(0)} \tag{2.2a}$$

where

$$C'_{XY}(k) = \frac{1}{N'_k} \sum_j (X(j) - \bar{X}')(Y(j+k) - \bar{Y}') \,.\, 1_{[X(j)>T_X,\, Y(j+k) > T_Y]} \tag{2.2b}$$

and the indicator function $1_{[\;,\;]}$ is defined by

$$1_{[X(j) > T_X \,,\; Y(j+k) > T_Y]} = \begin{cases} 1 & \text{if } X(j) > T_X \text{ and } Y(j+k) > T_Y \\ 0 & \text{else} \end{cases} \tag{2.2c}$$

$$N'_k = \sum_j 1_{[X(j) > T_X \,,\; Y(j+k) > T_Y]} \tag{2.2d}$$

N'_k is thus the number of joint-super-threshold events at shift k.

By a simulation it is shown that this definition enhances the detectability of a correlation of extreme events. In this simulation the following stochastic time series $\mathbf{X}()$ and $\mathbf{Y}()$ are considered:

$$\mathbf{X}(k) = \mathbf{W}_X(k) + \sum_{j=1}^{N_P} P(k-k_j) \;,\; \mathbf{Y}(k) = \mathbf{W}_Y(k) + \sum_{j=1}^{N_P} P(k-k_j-T) \qquad k = 1, 2, \ldots, N \tag{2.3}$$

$\mathbf{W}_X()$ and $\mathbf{W}_Y()$ are independent white Gaussian noises. P() is a deterministic function. Here a Gaussian profile is chosen for P() with a peak of the order of the largest noise samples.
The series $\mathbf{X}()$ is defined as the superposition of the noise series $\mathbf{W}_X()$ and a series of P()-functions centered at times $\{k_j \mid j=1,2,\ldots,N_P\}$.
This construction is repeated for noise $\mathbf{W}_Y()$ however the k_j are subjected to an extra shift T. As a consequence the profiles P() in the $\mathbf{Y}()$-series are centered at times k_j+T.
It is obvious that the time series $\mathbf{X}()$ and $\mathbf{Y}()$ are not independent. Due to their construction this dependency is completely induced by

the P()-series and therefore the correlation can best be detected on the basis of the largest **X**() and **Y**() values.

Figure 4a and 4b show a realisation of the **X**() and **Y**() series. Here 1201 samples of a total of 10000 are shown. Both **X**() and **Y**() contain 10 equidistant 'pulses' P() with peak 3 and width σ=2. The time shift T of the **Y**()-pulses with respect to the **X**()-pulses is 5.
Figure 4c shows both the 'standard' cross-correlation function as defined by Eq.(2.1) (dashed line) and its 'conditional' form (solid curve) as defined by Eq.(2.2). It is readily seen that the conditional correlation function assesses the dependency of the extreme **X**() and **Y**() samples much better than the 'standard' correlation function.

The conditional form of the correlation function has also been calculated for the Sheerness surges and Allington discharges. The result is shown in Figure 5. This conditional correlation function has a noisy appearance and does not reveal a dependency of extreme events.

2.3 POINT-PROCESS CROSS-CORRELATION DENSITY

In its most compact definition a point process is a set of random times $\{ \ldots \mathbf{T}_{-2}, \mathbf{T}_{-1}, \mathbf{T}_0, \mathbf{T}_1, \mathbf{T}_2, \ldots \}$. It forms a mathematical description of (physical) phenomena with a repeated and very pulse like occurrence.
The individual occurrences ('events') are almost instantaneous, i.e. the events are highly localized in time with a duration that is significantly less than the time between the successive events. Examples of point processes are the occurrence times of earthquakes, discharges of nerve cells, and photon emission of radioactive material. For other examples and further introduction see Cox and Isham [2], Snyder [8].

Apart from the set of random times, a point process can also be represented by its counting process **N**(). **N**() is an integer valued function and gives the number of events that occured in the time interval [0,t). In this way **N**() has unit jumps at the occurrence times $\mathbf{T}_k$ and is constant in between.

As holds for time series, it is also possible for point processes to investigate their dependency by correlation functions. The cross correlation density of two point processes $\mathbf{N}_1()$ and $\mathbf{N}_2()$ is defined by:

$$h_{12}(t_1,t_2) = \lim_{\Delta t_1, \Delta t_2 \downarrow 0} \frac{\mathrm{Prob}[\Delta \mathbf{N}_1(t_1) > 0,\ \Delta \mathbf{N}_2(t_2) > 0] - \mathrm{Prob}[\Delta \mathbf{N}_1(t_1) > 0]\ \mathrm{Prob}[\Delta \mathbf{N}_2(t_2) > 0]}{\Delta t_1\ \Delta t_2} \qquad (2.4)$$

where $\Delta \mathbf{N}_1(t_1) = \mathbf{N}_1(t_1+\Delta t_1) - \mathbf{N}_1(t1)$ and $\Delta \mathbf{N}_2(t_2) = \mathbf{N}_2(t_2+\Delta t_2) - \mathbf{N}_2(t_2)$

It is remarked that due to this definition $h_{12}(,)$ must be called correlation density rather than correlation function.
If $\mathbf{N}_1()$ and $\mathbf{N}_2()$ evolve mutually stationary then $h_{12}(t_1,t_2)$ is a function of the time shift $t=t_2-t_1$ only. If the point processes evolve mutually independent then the cross-correlation density is zero.
In practice the cross-correlation density of two point processes can be estimated on the basis of cross-coincidence histograms.

Now the point process of extreme surges and the point process of extreme discharges must be defined. This definition is quite similar to the approach that lead to the collection of independent peaks in the POT method. Again for both time series a threshold is imposed and the independent peaks are selected. Recall that these peaks are the (local) maxima that exceed the threshold and, moreover, satisfy the condition that adjacent peaks are separated in time by some minimum distance. This distance is chosen on the basis of the ´standard´ auto-correlation function of the time series (auto-correlation time).

The so found occurrence times of the remaining peaks form the realisation of the point process. Note that in this construction only the occurrence times of the extreme events are considered. It is not accounted for the amount that these events exceed the treshold.

This approach was applied to the surge and discharge time series.
In the selection of the peaks a treshold of 0.75 m and a minimum peak-distance of 48 hours was used in the surge series. For the discharges these values were 20 m^3/s and 10 days respectively.
This leads to a surge point process with 128 events and a discharge point process with 94 events in 13 years.

For the surge- and discharge point process auto- and cross-coincidence histograms have been calculated (a binsize of 1 month was used). See Figure 6a, b and c for the results (note: the cross-correlation density is merely a scaled form of the cross-coincidence histogram).

From these figures it is seen that:
(1) All coincidence histograms show a yearly periodicity.
Apparently the extreme events do not occur completely at random throughout a year but tend to ´prefer´ some periods to others.
This conclusion is supported by the distribution of the extreme events over the year: see Figure 7a (surges) and 7b (discharges) that show the total number of events per month.
(2) The maxima at integer-year-time-shifts are practically of equal size.
The same is found for the minima in the coincidence histograms (the fact that at the large time shifts the coincidence histograms tend to decrease is inevitably due to the small number of events in both point processes).
In particular this holds for the cross-coincidence histogram of Figure 6c. This shows that the amount of correlation of simultaneous surges and discharges is the same as the correlation of surges and discharges that are 1, 2, 3, ... years

apart. This points at the absence of any dependency of extreme surges and discharges.

In order to demonstrate even more convincingly the independency of extreme surges and discharges a correction for periodicity in the cross coincidence histogram has been carried out. This is done by a transformation of time on the basis of the intensity-histograms of Figure 7.
The evolution of time has been adjusted in such a way that the intensity of extreme surges is made uniform over the year. The same has been done for the extreme discharges. In this adjustment $t \rightarrow t'$ of time, time t' evolves slower at times t where the intensity of the point process is large, whereas t' evolves faster where this intensity is small. The mean yearly intensity is however not affected in this adjustment of time.

Again the cross-coincidence histogram of the for seasonal influence corrected point processes has been calculated. The result is shown in Figure 8. It is seen that the cros-coincidence histogram is equalized. The absence of any correlation of the time adjusted point processes is evident.

Although not shown it also turned out that the auto-coincidence histograms of the adjusted extreme surge and discharge point process do not reveal any auto-correlation.

All this leads to the conclusion that the Medway extreme surges and extreme discharges evolve as independent (inhomogeneous Poisson) point processes. The (deterministic) intensities of these point processes show a yearly periodicity. Extreme surges and discharges tend to occur at the same time of the year (winter, see Figure 7), however this is purely a seasonal effect and is in no way a result of explicit mutual interaction.

REFERENCES

1. C. Chatfield, The analysis of time series: An introduction, Chapman and Hall, London, 1980.
2. D.R. Cox and V. Isham, Point Processes, Chapman and Hall, London, 1980.
3. C.T. Haan, Statistical Methods in Hydrology, The Iowa State University Press/Ames, 1979.
4. J.R.M. Hosking, J.R. Wallis and E.F. Wood, Estimation of the generalized extreme-value distribution by the method of probability weighted moments, Technometrics, 27-3, pp.251-261, August 1985.
5. C. Petrauskas and P.M. Aagaard, Extrapolation of historical storm data for estimating design wave heights. In: Offshore Technology Conf., Houston, Vol I pp.409-428, April 1970.
6. P. Prescott and A.T. Walden, Maximum likelihood estimation of the parameters of the generalized extreme-value distribution, Biometrika, 67-3, pp.723-724, 1980.
7. R.L. Smith, Extreme value theory based on the r largest annual events, Journal of Hydrology, 86, pp.27-43, 1986.
8. D.L. Snyder, Random Point Processes, Wiley, New York, 1975.

9. J.A. Tawn, An extreme-value theory model for dependent observations, Journal of Hydrology, 101, pp.227-250, 1986.

ACKNOWLEDGEMENT

The authors wish to thank SOUTHERN PROJECT LTD. for their kind permission to use the Sheerness surge- and Allington discharges data and the results of the performed analysis.

FIGURES

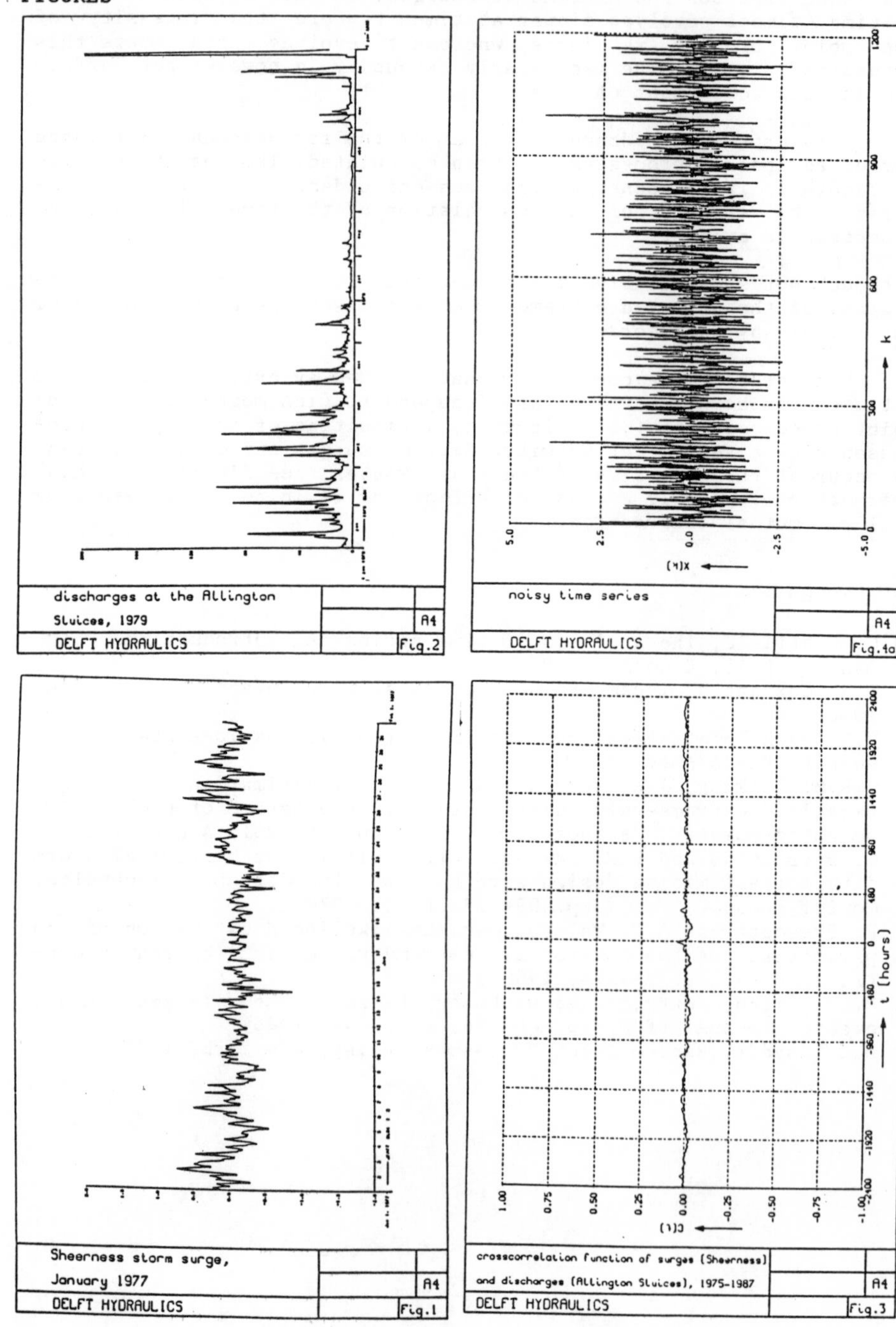

discharges at the Allington Sluices, 1979 — Fig.2

noisy time series — Fig.4a

Sheerness storm surge, January 1977 — Fig.1

crosscorrelation function of surges (Sheerness) and discharges (Allington Sluices), 1975-1987 — Fig.3

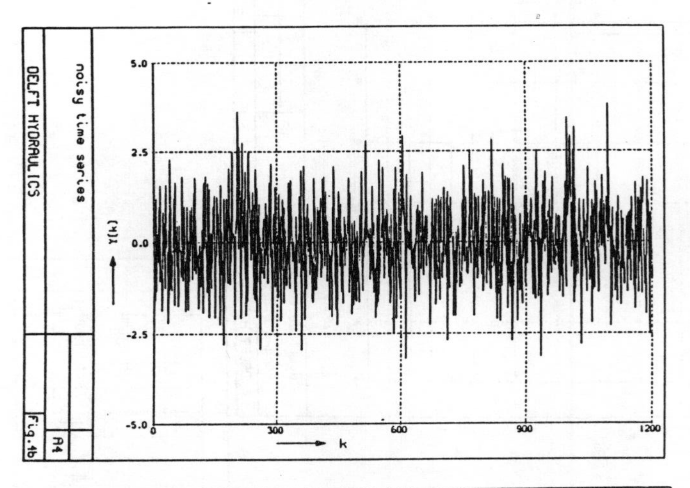
5.0
2.5
0.0
-2.5
-5.0
Y(k)
0
300
600
900
1200
k
noisy time series
A4
DELFT HYDRAULICS
Fig.4b

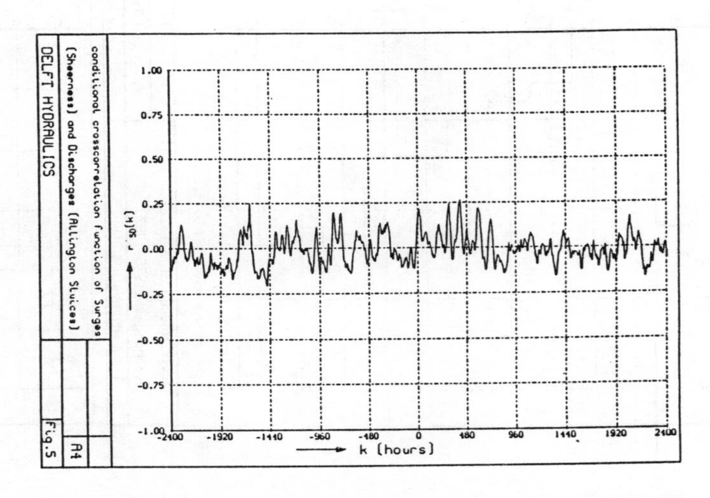
1.00
0.75
0.50
0.25
0.00
-0.25
-0.50
-0.75
-1.00
-2400
-1920
-1440
-960
-480
0
480
960
1440
1920
2400
k (hours)
conditional crosscorrelation function of Surges
(Sheerness) and Discharges (Allington Sluices)
A4
DELFT HYDRAULICS
Fig.5

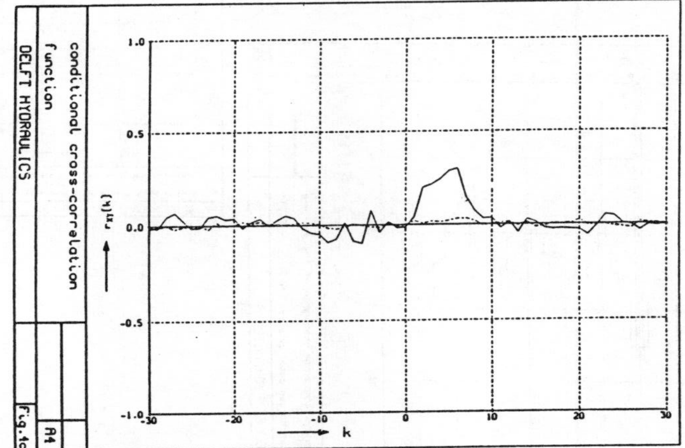
1.0
0.5
0.0
-0.5
-1.0
-30
-20
-10
0
10
20
30
k
conditional cross-correlation
function
A4
DELFT HYDRAULICS
Fig.4c

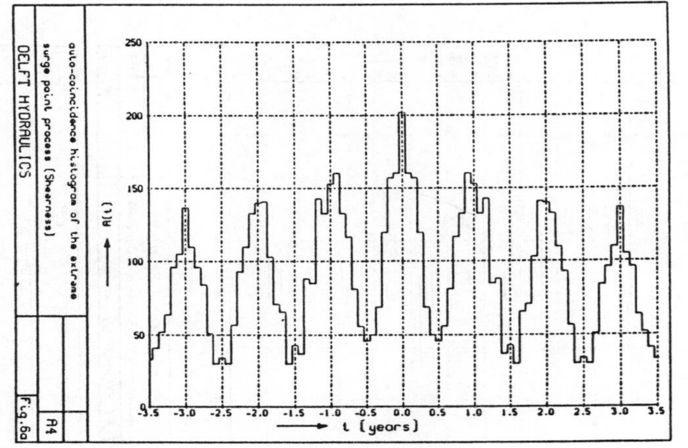
250
200
150
100
50
0
-3.5
-3.0
-2.5
-2.0
-1.5
-1.0
-0.5
0.0
0.5
1.0
1.5
2.0
2.5
3.0
3.5
t (years)
auto-coincidence histogram of the extreme
surge point process (Sheerness)
A4
DELFT HYDRAULICS
Fig.6a

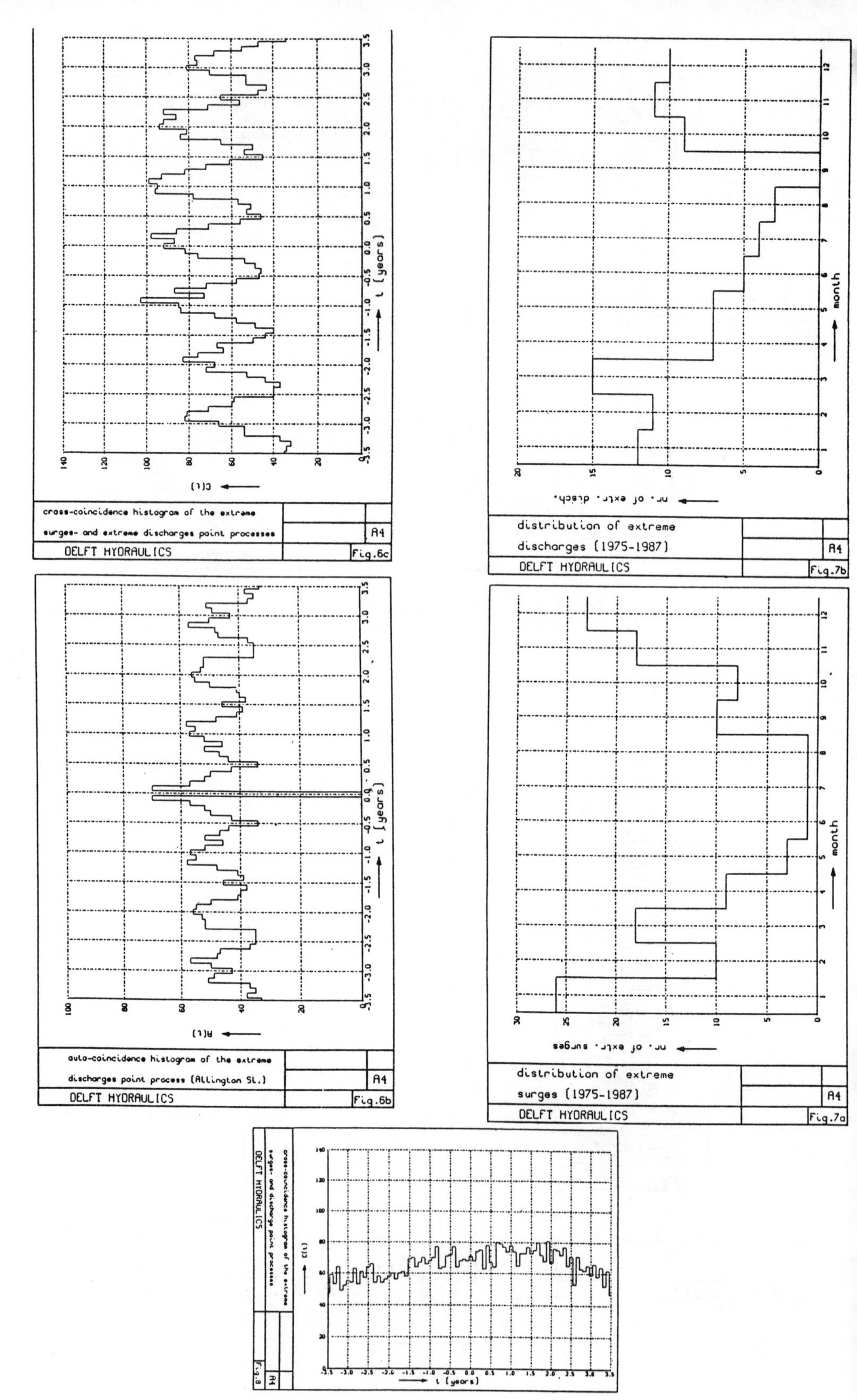
cross-coincidence histogram of the extreme
surges- and extreme discharges point processes
DELFT HYDRAULICS
A4
Fig.6c
C(t)
t (years)
distribution of extreme
discharges (1975-1987)
DELFT HYDRAULICS
A4
Fig.7b
nr. of extr. disch.
month
auto-coincidence histogram of the extreme
discharges point process (Allington Sl.)
DELFT HYDRAULICS
A4
Fig.6b
A(t)
t (years)
distribution of extreme
surges (1975-1987)
DELFT HYDRAULICS
A4
Fig.7a
nr. of extr. surges
month
cross-coincidence histogram of the extreme
surges- and discharge point processes
DELFT HYDRAULICS
A4
Fig.8
C(t)
t (years)

Field Data

International Conference on
RIVER FLOOD HYDRAULICS
17-20 September, 1990

The flood in the Reuss valley in August 1987: A computer aided reconstruction of a flood in a mountainous region

Roland Faeh, Elisabeth Koella and Felix Naef

Laboratory of Hydraulics, Hydrology and Glaciology, Swiss Federal Institute of Technology, CH-8092 Zurich; Switzerland

Abstract

On the 24/25 August 1987, an extreme flood causing extensive damage occured in the Reuss valley, in the center of Switzerland. A discharge of 800 m^3/s originated from the mountainous region, being far the greatest since 200 years.

To have a proper base for planning, the event was reconstructed. All the available data (rainfall and discharge measurements, radar pictures for the distribution of the precipitation, inflow to reservoirs, traces of the flood, eye witness accounts of the flood and of the breaching of the levees) was used as input to a mathematical model for unsteady flow for the Reuss river over a length of more than 40 km.

With the model a longitudinal profile of the discharge along the river of the 1987 event could be reconstructed and the effects of reconstruction works investigated.

1. Introduction

Through the Reuss valley, which is situated in the mountainous and historic center of Switzerland, runs the most important road and train connections between the northern and southern part of Switzerland.

After heavy precipitation on the 24/25 August 1987, an extreme flood of a magnitude never recorded before, hit the Reuss valley. In a few hours all the traffic connections were interrupted and houses flooded or washed away, causing damages of up to several hundert million Swiss Francs.

The planning of the reconstruction work needed a sound hydrologic base. Providing such a base was difficult, because from the 5 stream gauges along the 50 km long Reuss river, three had been washed away during the flood and the records of the two other gauges had been so affected, that the accuracy of the measurement is uncertain. But reliable estimates of the peak flow is essential for the statistical analyses to assess the return period and the design flood.

Only a few raingauges were situated in the 800 km^2 catchment area of the Reuss. Little was known of the rainfall distribution during the event and about the formation of the event in general. Many people were convinced that this extreme flood was caused or at least aggravated by human activities which influenced the runoff process

International Conference on River Flood Hydraulics, edited by W.R.White

like the construction of the highway through the valley, or the "dying of the forests" caused by air pollution.

To understand what happened during these few hours in the Reuss Valley and to provide a base for planning the flood protection work, it was decided to reconstruct the 1987 flood as accurate as possible, using every possible source of information as input or as verification for a mathematical model of the Reuss River. With the model, the events along the river could be analyzed and a longitudinal profile of the peak discharge along the river could be computed.

The Reuss Valley consists of several rather different sections. Each of them posed its own problems in modelling. The highest mountains in the catchment are well over 3000 m a.s.l. Within a few kilometers, the rivers drop to 1500 m a.s.l to join the 10 km long Urseren valley. This relatively flat valley was flooded during the event. Located at the end of the Urseren valley is Andermatt where the first, working gauging station is situated.

The next section in which the river falls 500 m within 20 km, was mainly affected by erosion. In the last section, before the river enters the lake of Lucerne near Seedorf, the Reuss flows between dams. This section is16 km long with a small slope. The adjoining plains build the most densly populated part of the canton Uri and when the dams along the river broke, the widespread flooding caused serious damage.

The second working stream gauge is situated in Seedorf. Above Seedorf, several million m^3 of water poured into the plain through three breaches in the levees. For the evaluation of the design flood, the size of the peak flow and the volume of the 1987 event at Seedorf which would have occured, if the levees had remained intact, was of interest. To estimate these values detailled knowledge was necessary about the time of the breaching and the discharge through the different breaches .

2. Reconstruction of the flood

The reconstruction of the flood was carried out in two steps. First, flood hydrographs for all the subcatchments had to be derived from hydro meteorological information. These were then used as input for the flood routing model of the main river.

2.1 Hydrologie

The hydrology is based on interpretation of data from rain gauges, stream gauges, estimated peak flows at selected sites, registration of water levels at the two large reservois, weather radar observations and eye witness accounts.

Only few satisfactory measurements of rainfall, waterlevels or discharge exist. During the heavy storm, several recordings were disturbed and some installations were damaged (Fig. 1). But the evolution of the rainfall can be observed on a film taken from the screen of a weather radar.

The key information for the reconstruction were the records from two gauging sites of the Reuss River at Andermatt and Seedorf. They were used for the calibration of the

mathematical model and to derive the "synthetic" hydrographs in the ungauged tributaries.
After the event, traces of flooding along the Reuss River and several tributaries were identified and surveyed. From these data which indicated the maximal water level during the flood, the maximum discharge could be derived in control sections from a backwater curve computation or an overfall formula (i.e. weirs of hydropower stations and natural river sections with well defined river bed) .

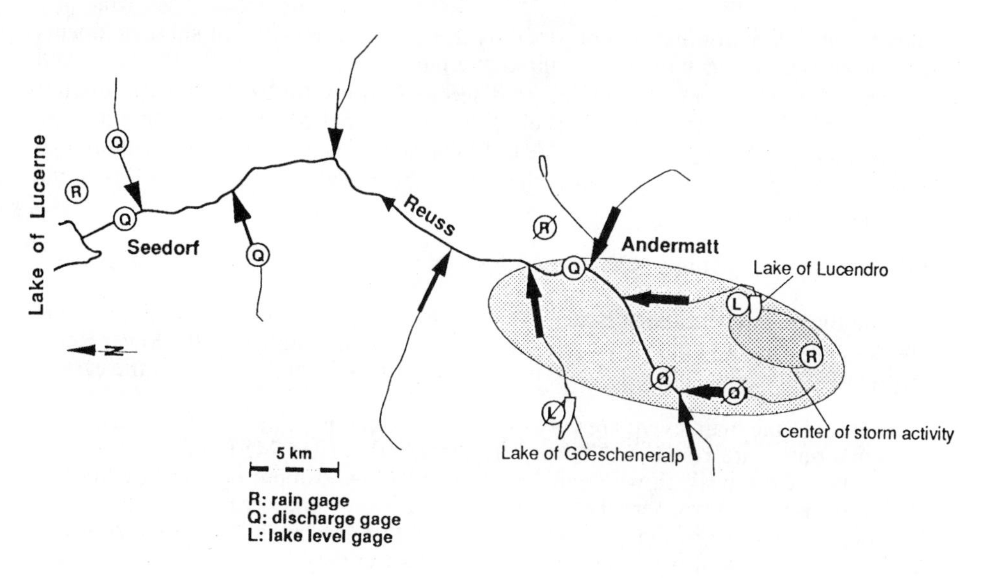

Figure 1 Geographical overview of the Reuss Valley: Location of gauging stations and the main tributaries which were considered in the hydraulic model.

In August 1987, the higher regions of the catchment were still covered with old snow. The weather was warm and dry and intense snow melting occured up to the highest regions, so that the saturation deficits of the slopes was already low at the beginning of the event. At about 10 o' clock in the morning on the 24th, the 3-week period of good weather ended with the beginning of a nationwide precipitation. Unusual for such an abrupt weather change, the relativly high zero-centigrade line didn't drop so that it rained also in the highest part of the Reuss catchment. The intensity of the rainfall with a duration of approximately 12 hours was fairly high in the upper part of the catchment (10 mm/h on the average). Such an event has a return period of some decades, according to frequency curves of nearby rain gauges.

A short rain shower of about two to three quarters of an hour, took place around midnight. The zone of maximum rainfall intensity was located again in the mountainous region of the catchment with a steep gradient to the East and to the North (Fig. 1). The rainfall intensity was about 40 mm/h. Such an event occurs every ten years but here it fell on already saturated soils and slopes and runoff coefficients were very high. In the catchment of the Lake of Lucendro, which was in the center of the storm, about 80% of the rainfall was recorded as direct runoff during the peak hour. At Andermatt, the Reuss rose within 90 minutes from 200 to 340 m^3/s.

In other words, if the precipitation event would have ceased before midnight, only an average flood would have occured in the Reuss River and its side streams . If there had only been this rain shower at midnight without the preceding rainfall, limited runoff would have been expected because of the high saturation deficit at the beginning of the event. But the combination of a long snow melting period followed by a moderate but lasting rainfall and finally a short but intense burst of rain, produced the observed extreme discharge.

As input to the flood routing model, flood hydrographs from different sub-catchments had to be reconstructed with very limited available information. Only the large and important tributaries were modelled as discrete inflows (m^3/s), whereas smaller tributaries and direct inflow from adjacent slopes are modelled as specific line inflows ($m^3/s/km$) along the Reuss. The arrows in Fig. 1 show the locations (and tributaries) where discrete inflow was considered, the size of the arrows give an indication on the size of the inflow.

The derivation of the hydrographs were based on the following simplified assumptions:

- During the main event (peak hour), the specific discharge is directly proportional to the rainfall. The rainfall intensity decreases from south to north. In the lower Reuss Valley specific runoff on the western side is significantly higher than on the eastern side.
- The peaks of the main event are very high. In the upper part, the steepest rise and the maximal runoff are assumed to occur between 23.30 pm and 24.00 pm.
- Estimates of the peak flows could often be made by computing the flow at well defined cross-sections where the maximum waterlevel was known.
- The depletion curve of the hydrographs is considered to be analog to the measured curves of the Reuss at Andermatt and Seedorf, respectively.

Some cross checks were also possible.

- The total volume of direct runoff of the tributaries in the upper part of the catchment (above Andermatt) had to coincide with the measured direct runoff volume at Andermatt. The same was valid for the lower part of the catchment with respect to the gauging site at Seedorf.

2.2 The mathematical model

For the flood routing, the computer program FLORIS (FLOod routing in RIverSystems) was used. This mathematical model is based on the full Saint-Venant equations for gradually varying unsteady flow in open channels (Kuehne and Faeh, 1983). The equations are integrated using an implicit finite difference scheme. At places where the Saint-Venant equations are not valid (weirs, bridges confluence of a tributary with the main river, dam breaks etc.) they are replaced by relations which describe the local flow conditions more accurately.

The application of the model to the River Reuss caused some numerical problems. The many transitions from sub- to supercritical flow and vice versa were difficult to handle. As the locations of the transitions depend on the discharge which varies with time, the reaches of the different states of flow had to be determined at the beginning of each time step. This is done - similar to a generalized water surface profile computation (Molinas and Chih, 1985)- by means of the energy and momentum equation. When the reaches of the different flow types are determined, the subsequent conventional computation procedure can go through hydraulic jumps without interruption. However, the distance between the cross-sections in the vicinity of the transition from one state of flow to another, must be smaller than usual. Otherwise sudden displacements of the hydraulic jump or the critical waterdepth from one cross-section to the other, lead to numerical oscillations which can not be dampened out. This normally results in a break-off of the computation.

The River Reuss has been modelled over a lenght of 45 km. The heavy variable topography of the river course and its flood plains has been described with about 400 cross-sections. Due to the requirementes of the mathematical model, the river has been divided into 35 branches (Fig. 2).

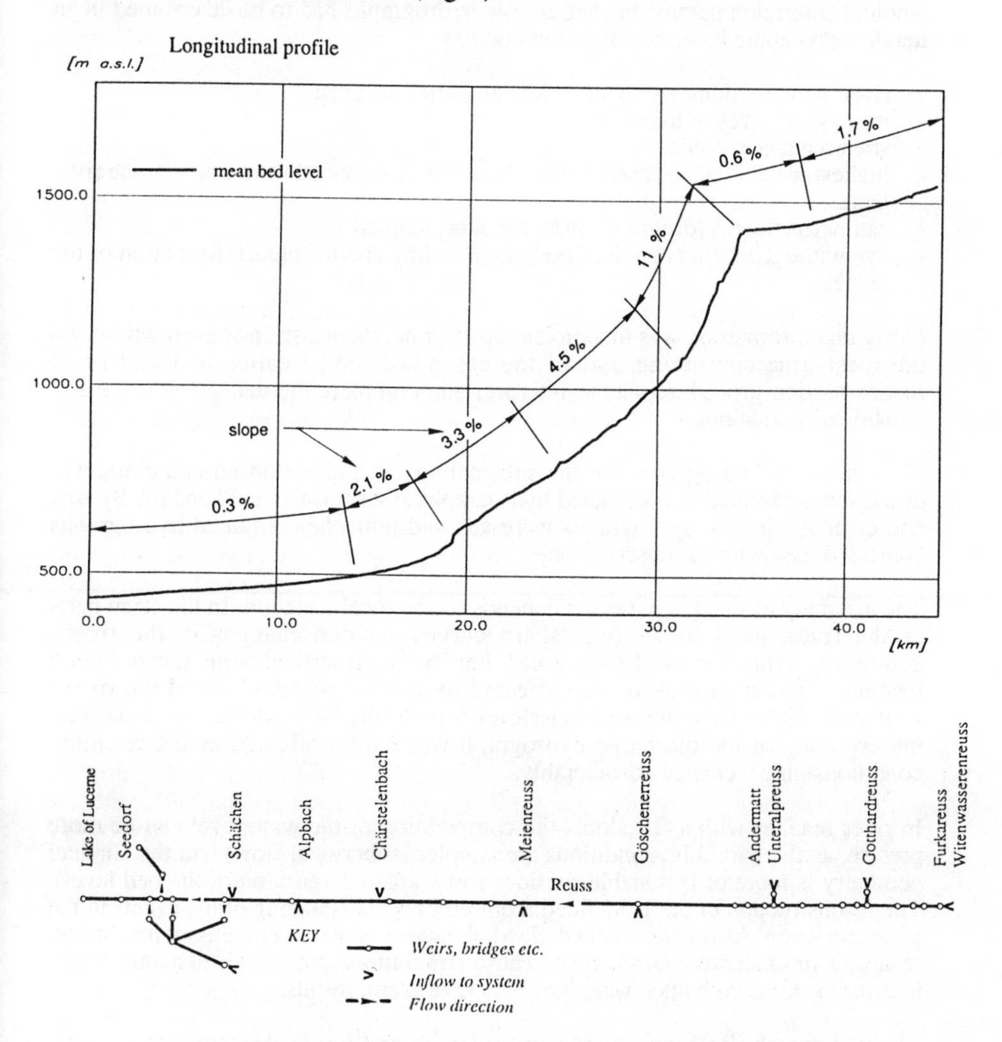

Figure 2: Model Schematisation and Longitudinal Profile of the River Reuss

2.3 Calibration and reconstruction of the flood

To simulate a flood wave with a mathematical model, the parameters which represent the energy losses, overfall coefficients etc. must be calibrated. Usually these parameters are varied as long as measured and computed waterlevels at a known discharge coincide satisfactorly. In the reconstruction of the flood in the Reuss, the unknown parameters could not be determined in this way, because there were measurements of the waterlevel only for small discharges which were not relevant for the extrem flood. For this reason, the calibration of the model and the reconstruction of the 1987 event had to be done simultaneously, using all the information about the hydrological, hydraulic and morphological processes as a whole. Calibration parameters and inflow hydrographs had to be determined in an iterative procedure based on the following data:

- river cross-sections, surveyed before and after the event;
- mean grain sizes of the river bed;
- stream gauge records;
- highest waterlevels reached during the flood as indicated form traces at the river banks;
- estimated flood hydrographs from the subcatchments
- eye witness accounts on the flood, the flooding and the breach formation of the levees.

Partly this information was incomplete, inaccurate, inconsistent or even wrong. So the most time consuming part of the combined model calibration and flood reconstruction procedure was to interpret and complete the data based on many numerical simulations.

The estimated hydrographs for the subcatchments, superimposed and computed downstreams formed the computed hydrographs at Andermatt and Seedorf. By trial and error the inflow hydrographs were adapted until the computed hydrographs coincided well with the observed ones.

The accuracy of the model results depends on the local situation. In the steep parts of the river, local losses (e.g. sharp curves, sudden changes in the river's geometry, natural overfalls etc.) can hardly be described with the common formulae. These parts were also affected by erosion which changed the river's geometry. There, the computed waterlevel may locally be rather inexact. However, the accuracy of the discharge hydrograph was hardly affected as the retention conditions didn't change considerably.

In river reaches with a flat slope, the computation of the waterlevel can be more precise, as the hydraulic conditions are simpler (subcritical flow) and the channel geometry is more or less stable (besides some gradual variation of the bed level). The reconstruction of the 1987 flood required the understanding of the events in the plain between Attinghausen and Seedorf where several embankments broke, resulting in extensive inundations. These simulations put a high demand on the accuracies of the computed water levels to give useful results.

The first breach (Br1) was formed on the left levee (Fig. 3). The outflowing water filled the adjoining plains behind the levee. Later, the levee was overtopped from behind, with the water flowing back into the river, forming two new breaches (Br2,

Br4). The increased flow in the river caused another breach (Br3) on the right levee.

In the mathematical model, the breach formation is described by a trapezoidal breach extending linearly after the waterlevel has overtopped the crest with a certain amount. Outflow is calculated using a usual weir formula which also takes into account the backwater effects from downstream. Thus, it is evident, that the stage of the waterlevel in the river is a sensitive value for the simulation of the hydraulic situation at this location.

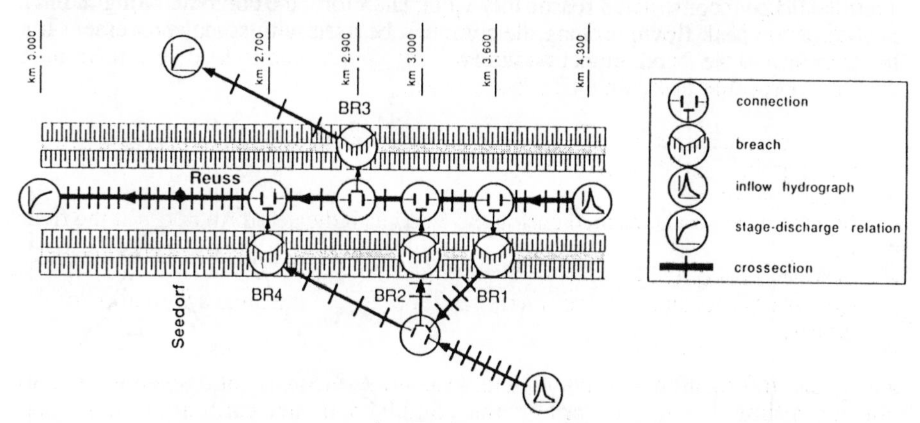

Figure 3 Model schematisation - details in the lower reach, where several embankments broke

Fig. 4 shows in- and outflow through the different breaches. The outflow through the breaches was high; at 400 m3/s it reached 50% of the peak discharge at Seedorf. With intact levees, the observed peak flow at Seedorf would have increased only by 100 m3/s because the breaches occured just before maximum discharge was reached and a considerable part of the outflown water flew back into the river, after it had filled the plains. At Seedorf, the breaches caused a sharp decrease in flow, followed by a steep rise when the water flew back again (Fig. 5).

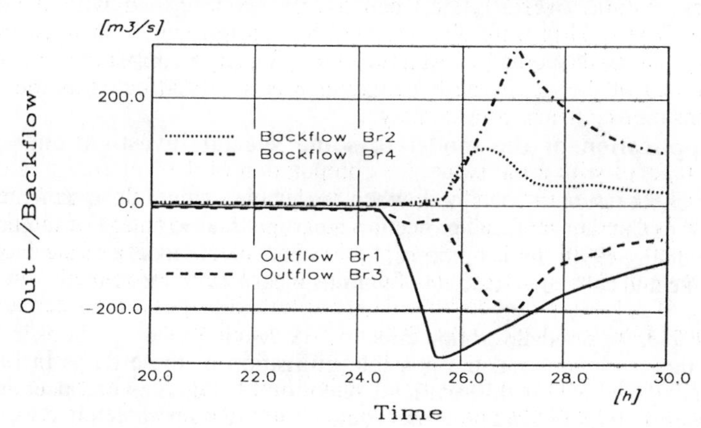

Figure 4 Out- and Backflow through the different breaches in the lower reach of the river Reuss

To test the sensitivity of the mathematical model, the choice of the input parameters and the changes in the river morphology several computations were carried out with different resistance coefficients and cross-sections surveyed before and after the flood. In general, morphological changes of the river bed and variations of the resistance coefficients have little impact on the peak discharge and its attenuation along the river.

In Fig. 5, the discharge hydrographs at Seedorf and Andermatt are plotted for the 1987 flood. The agreement between observed and computed flow indicates, that the event could be reconstructed reasonably well. Therefore, the computed longitudinal profile of the peak flowing along the river can be used with some ensurement for the planning of the flood protection works.

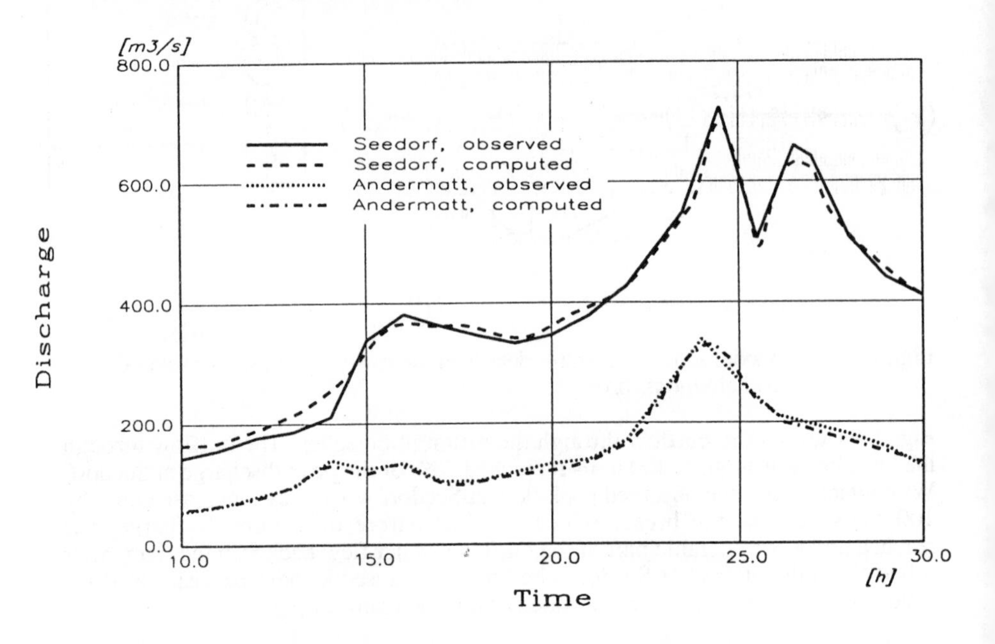

Figure 5 1987 Reuss flood at the gauging station of Andermatt and Seedorf

2.3 Application of the model to some special investigations

Soon after recession of the flood, when the whole extent of the damage became visible, the planning of flood protection measures started (Jaeggi and Zarn, 1990; Bezzola et al. , 1990). In this process, the mathematical model was used as a tool to investigate and compare the effect of various measures on the runoff.

For example, the flood absorbtion effect of the two large storage dams in the upper part of the catchment and the possible utilization of these dams in future was investigated.The use of this artificial retention of the lakes of Lucendro and of Göscheneralp requires that the reservoirs are not filled completely during normal operation.

The retention influence of the lake of Lucendro in the river reach below Andermatt is small because of the natural retention in the Urseren Valley (Fig. 6). Downstream of Andermatt, the valley of the Reuss is either steep and narrow or the river is conveyed in a channel; so there is little attenuation of the peak discharge.

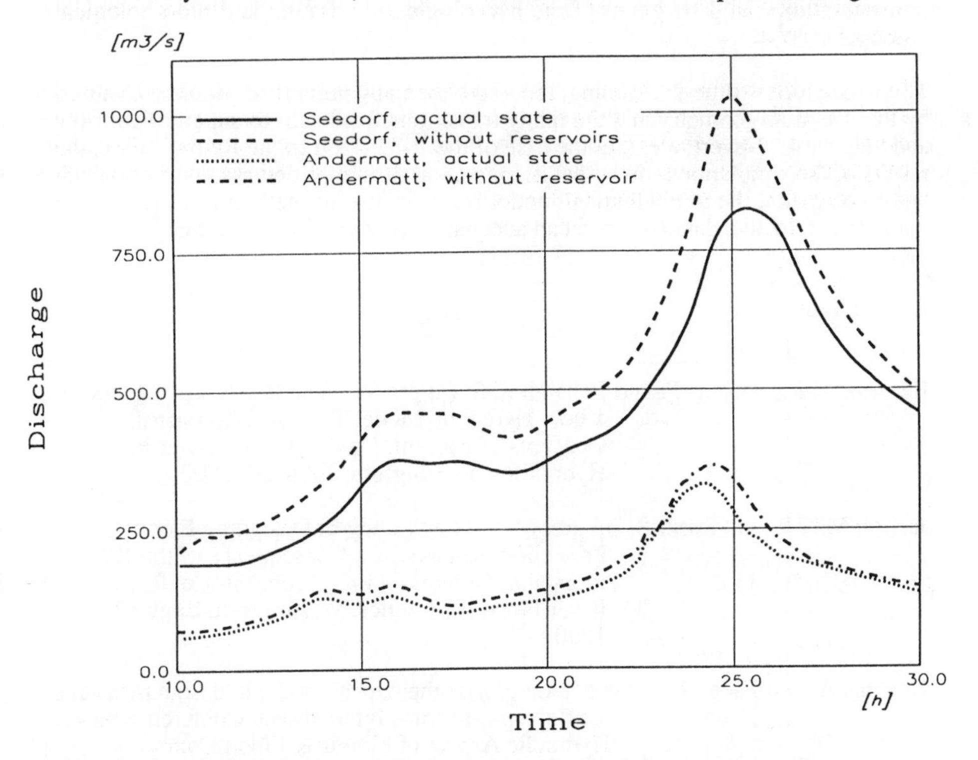

Figure 6 1987 flood at Seedorf and Andermatt; influence of storage dams

The retention effect of the lake of Goescheneralp had decreased the peak discharge by 20 % in 1987, although the catchment area of this reservoir is only 5% of the area up to Seedorf. The impact of the reservoir obviously depends very much on the temporal and spatial distribution of the rainfall.

4. Conclusions

The computer aided reconstruction of a flood in a mountainous region is faced with special difficulties caused by the steep slope and the irregular geometry of the river. The water flows at high velocities and the resulting kinetic energy developes an enourmous destructive power. Stream gauges are either destroyed or the accuracy of the measurements becomes uncertain.

Under these circumstances, the conventional procedure to simulate a flood by using a mathematical model which is first calibrated with data from other periods, had to be replaced by an iterative approach.

In a first step, the unknown input parameters of the mathematical model had to be estimated based on the defective database and experiences from similar computations. Then, numerous simulation runs had to be carried out with varied input parameters until all the fragment information fit together and a reasonably well representation could be given of the hydrological, hydraulic and morphological processes.

This procedure is time-consuming, rendered by many numerical problems, caused by the irregular geometry and the many transitions from sub- to supercritical flow and vice versa. Nevertheless, in the case of the 1987 flood in the Reuss Valley, the results of the simulations show, that despite of all the simplified assumptions which had to be made, the mathematical model is a very useful method to interpret and work up a defective database to get an adequate reconstruction of the flood event.

References

Bezzola, G.R., Kuster, P. and Pellandini, S. (in press): "The Reuss River Flood of 1987 - Hydraulic Model Tests and Reconstruction Concepts", Proc. Int. Conference on River Flood Hydraulics, Wallingford, England, 1990

Jaeggi, M.N.R. and Zarn, B. (in press): "A New Policy in Designing Flood Protection Schemes as a Consequence of the 1987 Floods in the Swiss Alps", Proc. Int. Conference on River Flood Hydraulics, Wallingford, England, 1990

Kuehne, A. and Faeh, R.: "Application of a mathematical model to design measures for flood protection", International Conference on the Hydraulic Aspect of Floods & Flood Control, London, England: September 13-15, 1983

Molinas A. and Young C.T.: "Generalized water surface profile computations", Journal of Hydraulic Engineering, Vol. 111, No. 3, March, 1985

International Conference on
RIVER FLOOD HYDRAULICS
17-20 September, 1990

A New Policy in Designing Flood Protection Schemes as a Consequence of the 1987 Floods in the Swiss Alps

Martin N.R. Jaeggi and Benno Zarn

Laboratory of Hydraulics, Hydrology and Glaciology , Swiss Federal Institute of Technology, CH-8092 Zurich; Switzerland

ABSTRACT

A flood design guideline based on the experience of the 1987 floods in the Swiss Alps is presented. It is based on the principle that more than one design discharge should be chosen. The design discharges depend on the objects to be protected and the processes involved. In contradiction to more conventional approaches the impact of extreme high discharges have to be looked at and limited appropriate measures have to be considered.

INTRODUCTION

Channel geometry, slope and roughness are defining a maximum discharge capacity. It is therefore common to select a predefined discharge as a design discharge and then to work out the corresponding flood protection scheme. Usually the so called 100-year flood is chosen as the design flood. In the most cases flood protection schemes have been resulted in active protection measures, especially in increased channel capacities. In spite of active protection measures increasing flood damage can be observed. In some countries, e.g. Canada, the U.S.A. (Lawrence 1986), Austria (Fink et al.1986), passive protection measures are worked out as flood hazard zones, either based on flow depth and flow velocity or on events with different probability of occurrence. In New Zealand additional to the flood hazard zones design discharges dependent on the object to be protected are discussed (Bewick 1988).

The design discharge is extrapolated from a series of recordings at gaging stations which are hardly longer than fifty years in industrial countries. Hence, even when using a refined extrapolation procedure, there will always be a large uncertainty about the discharge which really has a chance to occur in a hundred years. Generally a new flood protection scheme is supposed to last and be effective at least for a period of this length. Within that period there is a 63%-chance that the 100-year flood will be exceeded (e.g. Dracos 1980). Up to now, although the design engineers have been aware of this fact, the consequences of it have rarely been investigated.

International Conference on River Flood Hydraulics, edited by W.R.White

If damage during minor floods is prevented by a flood protection scheme, the period from one flooding to the next increases. It is said among Swiss river engineers that if flooding occurred more than seven years ago, people generally hardly can remember it. However, in the public opinion, protected grounds tend to be considered as 'safe'. This may lead to further investigation in these so called 'safe' areas and, hence, increase the damage potential. It must be admitted that even the specialists, although aware of calculated risk, tend to forget it . The 1987 floods in the Swiss Alps offered a lesson with respect to the consequences of the exceeding the design flood.

THE FLOOD IN THE REUSS VALLEY IN AUGUST 1987

The upper Reuss River flows from the Gotthard pass in central Switzerland in south-north direction to the Lucerne Lake. In this valley, during the early hours of August 25, 1987, after a long and heavy rainfall and the zero-degree isotherm above 4000 m.s.l., the Reuss River reached an extraordinary peak discharge (Faeh et al. in these Proceedings). Along the whole Reuss River from the source to the estuary of the Lucerne Lake severe damage could be observed.

The track of the Gotthard railway was washed away in Gurtnellen. The Wassen bridge of the Gotthard motorway nearly collapsed due to the subsidence of a pillar during severe bank erosion (figure 1). One of the main traffic connections, between the north and the south of Europe was then interrupted for several days. In Gurtnellen half of the cemetery and the presbytery disappeared in the floods (figure 2) (Bezzola et al. in these Proceedings).

In the lower part of the Reuss River Valley close to the estuary into the Lucerne Lake, as seen in figure 3, the water leaving through the breach on the right bank could not find the way back to the channel . They expanded over the plain and crossed the village of Fluelen before flowing into the Lucerne Lake. The upper breach on the left bank led to the formation of a lake near Attinghausen, since an alluvial fan forced the water back into the river, which was possible only after a certain submersion level was reached. The worst situation was observed near the lower breach of the left bank. Here, the motorway is crossing the plain on a dam. Flooding with 3 to 4 m depth in the lower parts of the village of Seedorf was the consequence of this obstacle.

As the flood marks indicate, the levees of the last canalized stretch upstream of the lake (figure 3) must have been acting as side weirs over a long distance. The channel in this lower part of the river was designed for an estimated 100-year flood of 600 m^3/s, with a freeboard of one meter. However, in 1987 the peak flow was nearly 800 m^3/s. With an overstress of 25% it is not surprising that three dam breaches were the consequence. Assuming that the flood of 600 m^3/s has really a 1:100 chance of occurring in a certain year, then the exceeding of this value was just an event which

Fig. 1: The foundation of the pillar of the Wassen bridge on the left was laid on a moraine. During the 1987 flood the bank (moraine) was eroded and the pillar subsided about 1.2 meter.

Fig. 2: The presbytery and cemetery of Gurtnellen was situated on the right hand side of the church before disappearing in the floods.

Fig. 3: In the foreground the estuary of the Reuss River into the Lucerne Lake is visible. In the top right corner, the village of Attinghausen is situated opposite the village of Altdorf in the bottom left, part of the village of Fluelen and opposite part of the village of Seedorf. The Gotthard motorway comes from the right, crosses the Reuss River and leads to the south along the river. The Gotthard railway crosses the plain from Fluelen towards Attinghausen. In the canalized section the levees broke twice on the left and once on the right river bank. (courtesy R.Meier, Baden)

conformed to the calculated and accepted risk. Indeed recent investigation indicate that the 1987 flood had an estimated return period between 150 and 300 years (Faeh et al. in these Proceedings). Can the river engineers, the population in this area and the general public opinion be satisfied with this result?

THE FLOOD IN THE POSCHIAVO VALLEY IN JULY 1987

The Poschiavino River drains a valley in the south east of Switzerland at the border to Italy. About 10% of the deposition of a massive debris flow reached the Poschiavino River (Haeberli and Naef, 1988), which was heavily overloaded and filled its bed with sediment at the lower end of the fan where the gradient decreases. A low bridge at this point, at the upper edge of the village of Poschiavo, partly caused the complete clogging of the channel, which finally diverted the river through the village (figure 4).

Fig. 4: On the top, the deposition on the lower edge of the torrent fan is visible in the front, the upper edge of the village Poschiavo. Here part of the Poschiavino River flows through the village due to aggradation of its bed.

THE CONSEQUENCES OF THE 1987 FLOOD EVENTS

The consequences of the 1987 flood events lead to a flood protection scheme with the following considerations:

(1) The level of protection depends on the importance of the object to be protected. Only part of the damage of an object can be expressed in money. Because the value of some objects may be intangible, it is necessary to divide them into categories with different levels of protection. For example, the design discharge for pasture should be definitely lower than the one for settlements.

(2) Processes have to be distinguished according to their potential threat. The threat will be different if submersion alone, dangerous submersion with high flow velocities in the flooded area, or extreme processes like heavy bank erosion and massive debris flows occur.

(3) The impact of higher flow rates than the conventional design flood has to be looked at, especially when active measures are planned for flood protection. Open channel flow hydraulics presuppose that a single value is chosen for channel capacity. Hence, by exceeding this value, flooding and certain damage have to be accepted. However , the effects of flooding can be minimized by appropriate measures. If the motorway dam in figure 3 had sufficient openings, flooding in its backwater area could have been limited to the ground floor and would not have reached the first floor of the houses. The flooding area on the right side could be limited by a dam on which the railway runs.

(4) Passive protection measures (mainly land use planning) are preferable to active protection measures against these higher discharges. If active protection measures fail, e.g. levees due to exceeding the design discharge, damage may be higher if no protection measures had been realized at all.

(5) The planned protection measures should, however, not allow a transfer of the flood risk in other zones outside the project area.

PROPOSAL FOR A GUIDELINE FOR A NEW DESIGN POLICY

Objects with similar protection levels can be gathered together in the same category. Six different categories with progressive protection levels are proposed. The allocation of the objects is shown in figure 6. In category 1, natural landscape, the processes pass according to their natural dynamics. This category is included for comparison with the others.

Objects of national infrastructure excluding large engineered structures, e.g. viaducts, are classified in category 5. If large engineered structures are destroyed it may take several years to reconstruct them, and traffic is often endangered. Hence, large engineered structures are allocated in category 6, e.g. the Wassen bridge of the Gotthard motorway. In the case of a motorway flooding in the floodplain it takes only days until the traffic can pass again. Therefore, the section of the motorway in the floodplain in the lower part of the Reuss River (figure 3) is classified in category 5.

Four dominant processes are distinguished. They can be described as follows:

Moderate / Extreme Flooding: The distinction between moderate flooding and extreme flooding, shown in figure 5, is dependent on the flow velocity and the flow depth in the flooded area. In moderately flooded areas life is not endangered, in extreme flooded areas life is endangered and severe damage to buildings can occur.

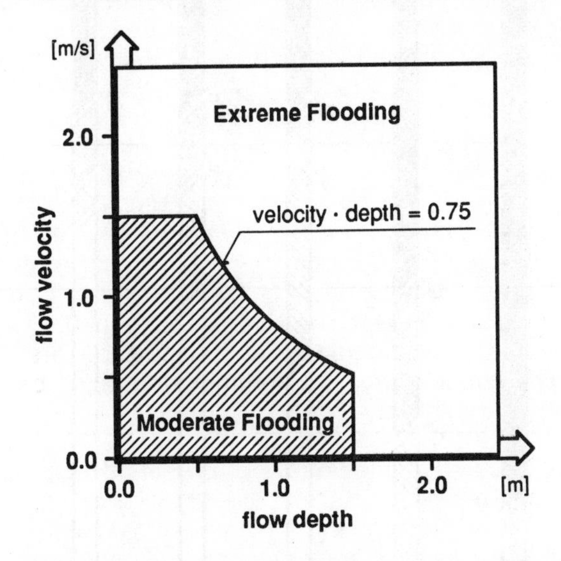

Fig. 5: Modified Definition of Moderate and Extreme Flooding according to Fink (1986) and Bewick (1988).

Erosion: In steeper rivers the bed is usually quite stable against erosion, due to the presence of coarse grains. However, if those are brought into motion during rare events, the consequences can be disastrous.

Deposition (debris flows): Debris flows threaten virtually the whole alluvial fan of a torrent. They can have a heavy impact on the main river, too.

Figure 6 shows a proposal for flood design guidelines based on the experience from the 1987 floods. A first design discharge Q_A defines the limit up to which no damage should occur. For the more valuable object categories this should approximately correspond to the common 100-year flood, Q_{100}, or a known value of an extreme event, the maximum observed flood, like the 1987-flood in the Reuss valley. For a low level of protection,

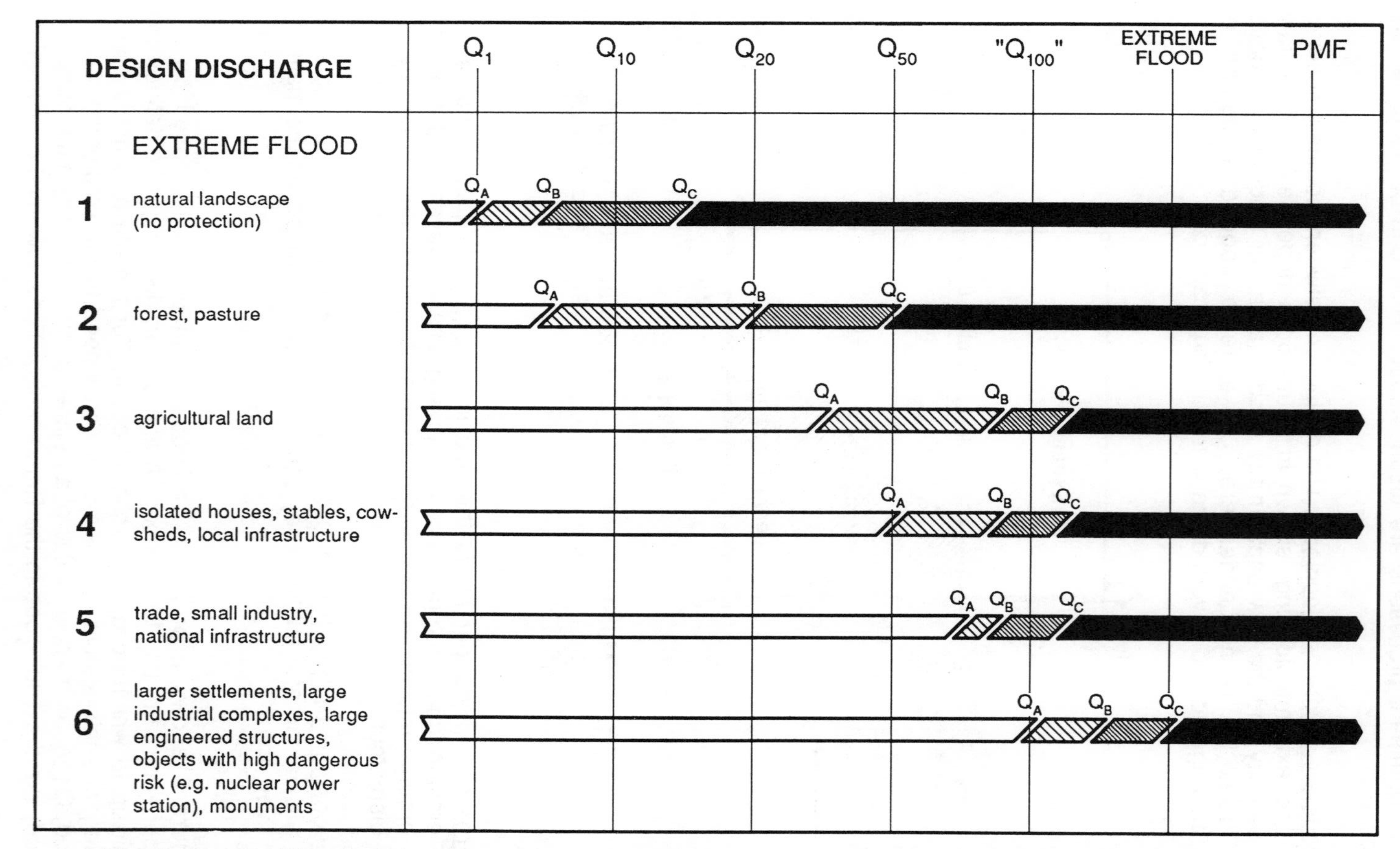

Fig. 6: Proposal for design discharges dependent on the objects to be protected and processes involved.

Q_A will correspond to higher frequency floods in the range of a 10-year to a 50-year flood ($Q_{10} < Q_A < Q_{50}$). Another value, Q_C, is supposed to define the upper limit up to which passive or active protection measures should be planned. For discharges higher than this value the processes, e.g. bank erosion or debris flow deposition, will get out of control and follow natural dynamics. For very valuable objects Q_C should have an almost zero probability. The upper limit for Q_C is called "extreme flood" (in figure 6). It may be defined by extreme hydrological scenarios.

Between Q_A and Q_C damage should be tolerated progressively with increasing discharge. However, it is important to study what will happen under these conditions and to declare what areas will be affected. Limited active measures and passive measures which can relieve the severeness of damage (e.g. limitation of the flooded zone) are as important as constructions which are designed to cope with discharges up to Q_A. Severe erosion and deposition are only allowed for discharges higher than Q_C. Protection measures have to be designed for discharges up to this value.

Another discharge Q_B may be selected to distinguish between moderate and extreme flooding. Q_A is then normally the limit between no damage and moderate flooding (tolerable). If only moderate flooding is anticipated, Q_B and Q_C are identical. The range between Q_A and Q_B or Q_C then just defines the range of accepted limited damage.

The oblique separation lines between the different ranges in figure 6 indicate that, because of the uncertainty in determining flood frequency, the design values Q_A, Q_B and Q_C may be selected in a certain discharge range. Hydraulic model testing may be necessary to determine the threshold value for bank collapsing. In case of debris flow events, the basic ideas of this proposal may be applied by analogy, although an actual frequency analysis is difficult to estimate.

It is planned to investigate the applicability of these guidelines in the realization of the flood protection scheme for the Reuss River Valley in co-oparation with the Swiss Federal Office of Water Management and the Canton Uri.

REFERENCES

Bewick, D.J. (1988) : Guidelines for Floodplain Management Planning Studies, Second draft; W&S Miscellaneous Publication No 029, Water and Soil Directorate, MWD, Wellington, New Zealand

Bezzola , G.R.; Kuster, P.; Pellandini, S. (in Press): The Reuss Flood 1987 - Hydraulic Model Tests for Reconstruction; International Conference on River Flood Hydraulics, Wallingford, England

Dracos, Th. (1980): Hydrologie, Eine Einführung für Ingenieure, Springer Verlag, New York/Wien

Faeh, R.; Koella, E.; Naef, F. (in Press): The Flood in The Reuss Valley in August 1987 - A Computer Aided Reconstruction of a Flood in a Mountaneous Region; International Conference on River Flood Hydraulics, Wallingford, England

Fink, M.H. et al. (1986): Raumordnung und Naturgefahren; Oesterreichische Raumordnungskonferenz (OeROK), Schriftenreihe Nr. 50, Wien

Haeberli, W.; Naef, F. (1988): Murgaenge im Hochgebirge; Ereignisse 1987 im Puschlav und Obergoms; "DieAlpen", Zeitschrift des Schweizer Alpen-Clubs; Jahrgang 64, 4. Quartal, p.331-343

Lawrence, J. (1986): Floodplain Management Planning in USA and Canada; Report of conference and study tour; Water and Soil Directorate, Ministry of Works and Development, Wellington, New Zealand

International Conference on
RIVER FLOOD HYDRAULICS
17-20 September, 1990

A REAL TIME SYSTEM FOR FLOOD FORECASTING OF AN ICE DAM OUTBURST

Pedro Fernández; O.Roby; J.Maza; H.Yañez; A.Vargas Aranibar
Instituto Nacional de Ciencia y Técnica Hídricas
Centro Regional Andino, Mendoza-Argentina

ABSTRACT

In the Mendoza river upper watershed, at elevations higher than 4,000 m.asl and close to the Argentine-Chilean border, a group of glaciers associated with winter snowfall give birth to runoff main sources. From this group of glaciers, the so called "Grande del Nevado del Plomo" periodically produces a glacier lake on the Plomo river valley, due to the advance of an unstable glacier tongue. Sudden outburst from the glacier-dammed lake produces flood waves. These waves and the summer snowmelt waves were studied by means of hydrologic and hydrodynamic mathematical models in order to simulate their translation along the river. This paper deals with the analysis of the translation of waves from recorded as well as simulated floods, in order to determine points for alert stations, define flood tables and inundation maps for flood forecasting, and for the operation of a real time alert system which has line of sight VHF stations and DCP GOES stations.

INTRODUCTION

The Mendoza River with a mean annual flow of 50 m^3/s is located in the province of Mendoza, at a south latitude of 33° (Figure 1). The watershed comprises a total area of 9,040 km^2, with the upper basin leaning on the highest mountains of the Andes, the Aconcagua peak (7,000 m.asl) included. At elevations higher than 4,000 m.asl highly glacierized zones exist (Corte 1981). The "Nevado del Plomo" glacier cyclically produces surges (Chow, 1964) and a big ice dam 1,200 m. long, 700 m. wide and 90 m. high closing the Plomo river valley to form a glacier-dammed lake. The elevation of the water surface in the lake produces the double effect of flotation and water pressure on the ice mass and generates the dam failure. The mode of the dam failure is critical to the size and shape of the flood wave and sequels downstream. Historical and possible conditions of outburst production by means of hydrologic and hydraulic calculations were studied (Fernández 1985). The mathematical simulation of flood routing of the outflow discharges along the river valley (Fernández 1989) is used in this paper for the design and monitoring of a real time hydrologic alert system, the determination of inundation maps and flood emergency plans. The system is an extension, with VHF stations, repeaters and DCP-GOES stations, of the telemetering hydrometeorological network for summer thunderstorms set up in the zone in 1982 (Fernández 1984).

International Conference on River Flood Hydraulics, edited by W.R.White

MATERIALS AND METHODS

As a result of the thorough data collection obtained from the outburst of the glacier-dammed lake of March 12-15, 1985 and the study of such situation (Fernández 1989), it is possible to develop a methodology, verify it for other historical events and apply it for predicting maximum possible floods. As there are no statistical analyses for historical events of this kind the term "maximum possible floods" is used instead of "maximum probable". For the 12-15 March,1985 outburst there are observations of water surface elevations vs time. With these observations and the volume-elevation curve of the lake, a generated outburst hydrograph for the ice dam is obtained (Fernández 1989).

Consistence of Peak and Shape for the Ice Dam Outflow Hydrograph It was necessary to verify the results in order to observe the consistency of the outflow hydrograph, which is the main element used in other calculations. There are two measured hydrographs along the river for the outburst of 12-15 March 1985; at Punta de Vacas (50 km downstream of the ice dam) and Guido (136 km downstream of the ice dam). Figure 2 exhibits the hydrographs for Punta de Vacas (a) and Guido (b). The hydrograph at P.de Vacas should be an image of the ice dam outflow hydrograph due to the fact that the distance is short (50km), the slope is steep (1.5%) and the river valley is narrow. To check this consistency, a Muskingum flood routing technique was used to route the calculated outflow hydrograph from the ice dam to Punta de Vacas, Fig.3a, and the translation from this point to Guido, Fig.3b. It is possible to conclude that Punta de Vacas is a good spot to measure the discharges of the ice dam and maintain one of the streamgauge stations for the alert system. A consistency of volumes for the total ice dam discharge was also obtained for this event (Fernández 1989). The maximum historical recorded flood produced by the outburst of the glacier-dammed lake was on January 10-11, 1934 (King 1934,1935; Fernández 1985).

TABLE 1 - COMPARATIVE VALUES FOR THE 1934 AND 1985 OUTBURST FLOODS

	10-11/01/34	12-16/03/85
Breach area (m^2)	225	30
Discharged Volume (Hm^3)	53	20
Breach developing time (hr)	5	4
Level difference (m)	75	33
Maximum Flow discharged (m^3/s)	2,700	184

There are other historical floods produced by the outburst of the glacier-dammed lake but with little quantitative information. In 1900 a flood with estimated peak of 2,000 m^3/s destroyed a diversion dam. In 1926 a flood with estimated peak of 1,000 m^3/s produced erosion and sedimentation along the river (Prieto 1985).

Maximum possible floods As pointed out, because of the few recorded events of this kind, a statistical analysis was discarded and a deterministic hydrologic, hydraulic and physical study of the different situations was carried out. The hydrologic characteristics of the river basin are important, since the glacier outburst floods will be superimposed on the normal streamflows. The maximum discharges for this river occur in summer. The mean monthly flow for January is 120 m^3/s. The maximum possible discharges from the ice-dammed lake, in relation with their physical conditions were determined (Fernández 1989) and a working value of 5,000 m^3/s was used. For the generation of maximum possible floods the DAMBRK model was used (Fread 1984, Fernández 1989).

Downstream routing simulation For the outbursts of February-March 1985, the downstream routing was determined by the Muskingum method with good results, but for the 1934 outburst and the hydrographs of maximum possible floods it was necessary to use the hydrodynamic flood routing method, because of the significance of inertial forces. The DAMBRK model was used (Fread 1984). Thirty-four cross sections of the river were employed and a detailed study was done for the estimation of the roughness coefficient and the determination of inactive and active flow areas. During the first run of the model a very detailed study of cross section locations was carried out, in order to characterize the flow paths, evaluate the expansion and contraction coefficients and select weighting factors to solve the Saint-Vennant equations by means of an implicit scheme. A value of 0.7 was used for θ, and a convergence criterion of 0.1 feet (Figure 4).

Mendoza River Hydraulic Characteristics It is a typical gravel and boulder-bed mountain river with large scale roughness. For most of the discharges the depth of flow is in the same order of magnitude as the size of the bed material. For these rivers the flow resistance is greatly affected by the relative submergence of the bed boulders. The flow resistance depends mainly on three factors (Bathurst 1981, 1985): grain roughness; form resistance and transport rates. The relative contribution of each of them vary with the depth and velocity of the flow. For the 1985 Guido stage-discharge curve the best fit values were: Main channel n = 0.034 ; Overbank n = 0.050 (r^2=0.95). These values were taken for the first runs of the model but later on, for its calibration, different values had to be adopted for the different reaches (Fernández 1989).

RESULTS

Real time alert system As a consequence of the previous analysis and the characteristics of the river, two points were selected for the telemetric alert stations, Punta de Vacas and Guido, 120 km and 55 km upstream from Cipolletti Diversion Dam. Punta de Vacas is the main station because of its strategic location in relation with the ice-dammed outbursts, as mentioned previously, and also due to the existence of army headquarters furnished with good comunications systems. At this place the river runs through a canyon 40 metres deep, harmless for the people and for the station. This station is a DCP-GOES-East operating under self-timed mode every 4 hours with a scan interval of 1 hour and under random reporting transmission mode for monitoring and reporting potential emergency situations according to the conditions in Table 2. The sensor is a pressure transducer. The other station, at Guido, is part of the VHF event reporting telemetering system of INCYTH (Fernández 1984) linked to the central station by means of a repeater because of distance and topographical conditions. The response of this station is instantaneous because of the event reporting mode, which in this case transmits when the water level changes 2 centimetres or every hour if there is no change. It also operates in an alert mode when the river level reaches 2.40 m. and the water level changes more than 5 cm/hour. Both stations send the reports to a Central station via radio (VHF) or via telephone modem from the GOES ground station of Mendoza. The databank and management software (IHS 1988) is arranged in a menu-driven mode.

Selection of discharges The upper limit for normal flows is 200 m^3/s, TR = 2.33 years (Fernández 1976). Flood tables, inundation maps and hazard table were determined for floods between 230 and 4.650 m^3/s, Table 3. According to previous studies (Fernández 1988) the snowmelt floods are within the limits of 230 m^3/s, TR = 8 years; 340 m^3/s, TR = 25 years; 450 m^3/s, TR = 50 years; and 990 m^3/s, TR = 500 years. For the ice dam outburst floods are between 1,000 and 5,000 m^3/s. Because this is a different kind of event there are no time of return calculations (the glacier surge cycle should be between 25 and 50 years).

Inundations maps The downstream consequences for snowmelt flood and ice-dam outburst floods were determined based on the extent of flooding areas, with the use of the HEC2 model (US Corps of Engineers 1982), Figure 6, and according to the following criteria (ASCE 1988):

-People safety limits: water depth exceeds 1 metre,or depth times velocity exceeds 0.65 m^2/s.
-Structural safety limits: water depth exceeds 3.60 metres, or depth times velocity exceeds 1.9 m^2/s.

Operation of the system Figure 5 is a diagram of the operation of the real time system for flood forecasting for the Mendoza River and the warning dissemination process. At present there is no telemetric station at the glacier, so monitoring of the glacier surge through exploration flights from October to April gives the first alert in case of valley closure (it takes more than 20 days for the lake to be filled). The rest of the system is telemetric: continuous reception of the river level at Punta de Vacas and Guido, with the help of the tables and maps, offers the oportunity of attaining a flood forecasting with a lag time of 11 to 4 hours for Cipolletti, and more time for downstream localities where there are more inundation problems.

Flood and Hazard tables (Tables 2 and 3) The Alert 1 condition is the one in which an emergency condition could occur due to some inminent increase of discharge. Slow evacuation downstream from Cipolletti diversion dam is possible - this is a normal flood situation. The Alert 2 condition is a range of discharges higher than 450 m^3/s. The time available for evacuation is less than 8 hours, so "Fast evacuation is considered for life-saving, with exclusion of property considerations". The Alert 3 is hazardous inundation, it was historically due to the ice-dam outbursts of 1900 (2,000 m^3/s), 1926 (1,000 m^3/s) and 1934 (2,490 m^3/s). High critical conditions are maximum possible floods caused by ice-dam outbursts: there are no historical events of such magnitude, and the general situation is catastrophic for all structures along the river and for flooding areas. Hazardous inundation zones are those in which water depths and depth times velocity exceed the values previously mentioned.

TABLE 2 - FLOOD TABLE ACCORDING TO PUNTA DE VACAS DATA

STAGE AT P.DE VACAS	DISCHARGE AT P. DE VACAS	ALERT CONDITION	RIVER LOCATIONS							
			GUIDO		POTRERILLOS HOTEL		CACHEUTA POWER PLANT		CIPOLLETTI DIVERSION DAM	
			MAX. STAGE	T.TIME	MAX. STAGE	T.TIME	MAX. STAGE	T.TIME	MAX. STAGE	T.TIME
m	m^3/s		m	hours	m	hours	m	hours	m	hours
5.35	230	ATTENTION	2.10	7.2	2.60	7.6	4.10	8.6	1.10	11.2
5.80	340	ALERT 1	2.40	6.6	2.90	7.0	4.60	8.0	1.50	10.2
7.60	990	ALERT 2	3.00	4.4	4.00	4.8	6.30	5.6	2.45	7.4
9.05	1700	ALERT 3	4.10	3.6	5.10	3.9	8.10	4.5	2.50	6.2
10.15	2490		5.00	3.3	5.90	3.6	9.50	4.2	3.60	5.3
12.25	3970	HIGH CRITICAL CONDITION	5.80	2.8	6.80	3.1	11.00	3.5	5.00	4.6
13.00	4650		6.40	2.4	7.00	2.6	11.50	3.0	5.40	3.9

MAX.STAGE WITH REFERENCE TO MAIN CHANNEL
TRAVEL TIME OF PEAK DISCHARGE (HOURS AND FRACTION)

TABLE 3 - HAZARD TABLE ACCORDING TO PUNTA DE VACAS DATA

STAGE AT P.DE VACAS	DISCHARGE AT P. DE VACAS	ALERT CONDITION	RIVER LOCATIONS							
			GUIDO		POTRERILLOS HOTEL		CACHEUTA POWER PLANT		CIPOLLETTI DIVERSION DAM	
			MAX. STAGE	MAX. VELOC.	MAX. STAGE	MAX. VELOC.	MAX. STAGE	MAX. VELOC.	MAX. STAGE	MAX. VELOC.
m	m^3/s		m	m/s	m	m/s	m	m/s	m	m/s
5.35	230	ATTENTION	2.10	5.60	2.60	2.50	4.10	2.90	1.10	1.00
5.80	340	ALERT 1	2.40	6.00	2.90	2.70	4.60	3.15	1.50	1.40
7.60	990	ALERT 2	3.00	7.00	4.00	3.35	6.30	4.20	2.45	2.20
9.05	1700	ALERT 3	4.10	8.10	5.10	4.00	8.10	5.20	2.50	3.00
10.15	2490		5.00	8.90	5.90	4.60	9.50	5.90	3.60	3.40
12.25	3970	HIGH CRITICAL CONDITION	5.80	9.90	6.80	5.22	11.00	6.80	5.00	2.60
13.00	4650		6.40	10.60	7.00	6.90	11.50	9.40	5.40	2.65

MAX.STAGE AND MAX.VELOCITY ARE WITH REFERENCE TO MAIN CHANNEL.
OVERBANK VELOCITIES ASSUMED TO BE 25% OF MAXIMUM VELOCITY.

DISCUSSION

In mountain rivers subject to glacier outbursts or similar events it is important to study the significance of such floods, with peaks usually well above the ones produced by precipitation or summer melting. Most of the glacier-dammed lakes are produced by a cyclic surge activity, which disappears once the glacier retreats. Monitoring the glacier surges, through satellite imagery or exploratory flights, and an analysis of river discharges in relation with historical trends are necessary. The dynamic character of these flood waves greatly enhance the risk on towns, human lives and civil works along the river as well as erosion effects and sediment transport. Real time telemetric equipment, with the help of flood tables and inundation maps, gives good support for the implementation of an effective flood forecasting system and determination of alert conditions. It is necessary to determine the occurrence of hazardous conditions in relation with flood depths, velocities, and depth times velocity according to some criteria for human and structural safeties. The use of hydrodynamic flood waves models and water surface profile models such as DAMBRK and HEC-2 and digital cartographic techniques give good support in accomplishing and preparing the studies and related flood emergency plans.

ACKNOWLEGMENTS

The authors wish to thank Luis Fornero for his permanent assistance in the implementation of the mathematical models and software installation for the real time system, as well as Daniel Tarántola for his dedication in the installation of the system.

REFERENCES

ASCE (1988). "Evaluation Procedures for Hydrologic Safety of Dams", Task Committee on Spilway Design Flood Selection.

Bathurst,J.C. Ruh-Ming Li, and Simons,D.B. (1981). "Resistance Equation for a Large Scale Roughness", Journal of the Hydraulic Division, ASCE, Vol.107 Hy 12, pp.1593-1613.

Bathurst,J.C. (1985). "Flow Resistance Estimation in Mountain Rivers". Journal of Hydraulic Engineering, ASCE, Vol.111 N 4, pp 625-643.

Corte,A.,and Espinosa,L. (1981). "Inventario de glaciares de la Cuenca del Río Mendoza". Instituto Argentino de Nivología y Glaciología. Argentina.

Chow,V.T., Editor (1964). "Handbook of Applied Hydrology", pp 16-30, 16-31 McGraw-Hill.

Fernández,P.,Segerer,C.and Caridad,R. (1976). "Estudio Hidrológico de los Ríos de Cuyo - Análisis Regional de Frecuencia y Magnitud de Crecientes". Instituto Nacional de Ciencia y Técnica Hídricas. Argentina.

Fernández,P.,Roby,O.,Fornero,L.and Maza,J. (1984). "Telemetering Hydrometeorological Network in Mendoza, Argentina. One Year of Experiments and Research". Microprocessors in Operational Hydrology, WMO, Riedel P. Co.

Fernández,P., Fornero,L., Maza,J., Rollán,R., and Yañez,H. (1985). "Hidrología del Río Mendoza. Simulación Matemática de las Hipótesis de Rotura del Dique Natural Formado por el Glaciar Grande del Nevado del Plomo y del traslado de las Crecientes desde el Glaciar hasta

200m. Aguas Abajo de Alvarez Condarco". Instituto Nacional de Ciencia y Técnica Hídricas. Argentina.
Fernández,P.,Maza,J.and Vargas Aranibar,A. (1988). "Delimitación de Líneas de Rivera y Zonas de Inundación en el Río Mendoza". Jornadas de Seguridad de Presas y Aspectos de la Defensa Civil en Mendoza. Universidad Nacional de Cuyo. Argentina.
Fernández,P.,Fornero,L.,Maza,J.and Yañez,H. (1989)."Simulation of Flood Waves From the Outburst of a Glacier Dammed Lake" submitted for publication to Journal of Hydraulic Engineering ASCE.
Fread,D.L. (1984). "DAMBRK The National Weather Service Dam-Break Flood Forecasting Model, National Weather Service, Silver Spring, Maryland.
IHS (1988). "Enhanced ALERT Users Manual", Sacramento, California.
King,W.D.V. (1934). "El aluvión del río Mendoza en enero de 1934". Conferencia ofrecida en el Centro Nacional de Ingeniería. Buenos Aires - Argentina.
King,W.D.V. (1935). "Observaciones Adicionales sobre la Obstrucción en el Valle del río Plomo, recogida en febrero de 1935". Conferencia en el Centro Nacional de Ingeniería. Buenos Aires - Argentina.
Prieto,M. (1985). "Un Fenómeno Cíclico? Hubo otros endicamientos en el río del Plomo?. Diario Los Andes, Mendoza - Argentina.
U.S.Corps of Engineers (1982). "HEC2 Water Surface Profiles Model". Davis, California.

International Conference on
RIVER FLOOD HYDRAULICS
17-20 September, 1990

AN HISTORICAL PERSPECTIVE AND ANALYSIS OF FLOODING IN THE UPPER REACHES OF THE KALI GANDAKI RIVER VALLEY, NEPAL.

MARK D. GILL. BSc, DIS, HTC, CEng, MICE, MIED, (MBTS).
PROJECT MANAGER, TATOPANI SMALL HYDEL PROJECT

ABSTRACT.

In the Himalayan Kingdom of Nepal, there run three major river courses: the Sun Kosi in the east, the Karnali in the far west and the Kali Gandaki in the near west of the country. They are fed by thousands of rivulets which channel water from the vast mountainous watershed. These vary in many respects, not the least of which are: glacial or spring sources, seasonal flows or non-flows, sediment content and gradient. In various ways these factors are both directly and indirectly related to the main rivers' discharge, performance and consequence on the development of the valley and river itself.

This paper will concentrate on the recent history of flooding in the Kali Gandaki River Valley: including a preview of its origins, observations of flood characteristics with analysis of possible control and use. Further, the analysis will especially comment on the flood of July 1987 which is unparalleled in living memory and even possibly for a few generations previous to that. Among other factors, the effects of erosion, surging, sedimentation and induced earth tremors will be mentioned showing that the river flood is truly a complex system, but nonetheless one which can be studied.

The Kali Gandaki River may be marginally the lesser of the three great rivers of Nepal in terms of volume flow; but it possesses exceptional topography, unique geology, uncommon hydrology and an interesting history which is worth record and study. The author will reflect on his observations of living in the deepest land gorge on earth, since 1986.

INTRODUCTION.

Birth. In the Pleistocene epoch, 2 million years ago, when the northern parts of the earth were undergoing massive glaciation, the sub-continent of India had just completed its amazing journey of 200 million years from its connexion with Gondwanaland, 10,000 km to the south, to collide with the main Asian plate (Blythe, de Freitas, 1984). Subsequently, this caused massive uplift of the sediments in the Tethys sea (fig 6); uplifting and overthrusting, to the south, of intermediate stratums (fig 7).

Thus the new condition promoted erosion and consequent formation of

International Conference on River Flood Hydraulics, edited by W.R.White

river valleys to drain the uplifted area. Due to metamorphosis of sediments through pressure and heat, harder rocks formed in the Mahabharat Lekh, to the south of the nappe root zones, to form the new river valleys in circuitous routes east and west until a break in the mountain chain was found. Such locations number only three in a 1000km distance across Nepal: they are from west to east, Karnali, Kali Gandaki and Sun Kosi.

Sources. Generally, river sources are found in mountainous areas. For most rivers, underground water leading to springs result in the start of a river system. In higher massifs, and Arctic areas, glaciers and ice play the lead role in river sources.

Precipitation may also be regarded as a direct source from run-off. This is the case in monsoonal areas where normally dry valleys are engulfed with the onslaught of sudden run-off.

Climate. Had it not been for the Himalayan massif, Tibet would be a much wetter region than it is. They prove a physical barrier to the southern monsoons which sweep in from the Indian Ocean. Without doubt, this is the major influence on the Himalaya rivers. With such a concentration of precipitation - up to 4000mm within 4 months - the rivers swell and undulate to present a river system seemingly out of control. However, nature underlies invisible control.

Notably in the Kali Gandaki valley, beyond the northern monsoonal boundary which runs from the Dhaulagiri massif to the Great Barrier of Annapurna, this residual monsoon precipitation affects the topography and vegetation in an unique way. Because of high solar radiation, the surrounding mountains become greatly heated and suck in air. Thus the dry wind causes an arid desert valley floor while dissolving the overhead cloud to give excellent conditions for higher altitude forests (Hagen 1980). Further, the precipitation allows run-off to swell the rivers even in these arid valleys.

When walking down the valley there is a distinct change in the surroundings: notably from the arid to the temperate zones near the village of Kalopani at 8300 feet. It is worth noting that it is at this point where the Kali Gandaki begins its steepest descent (fig 6). This may be largely due to the huge increase in run-off causing greater erosion during monsoonal periods.

Flows. As has been mentioned, there is a wide variation in climatological conditions leading to erratic yet cyclical river patterns. Annual hydrographs vary according to inherent annual climatological conditions. A typical hydrograph for the Kali Gandaki discharge at location of Fig 1 follows:

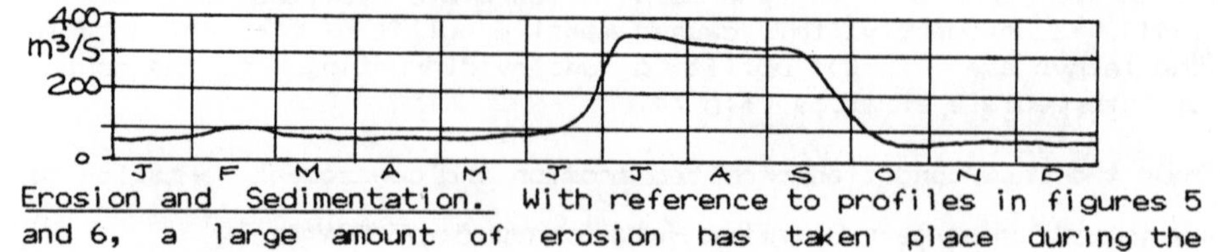

Erosion and Sedimentation. With reference to profiles in figures 5 and 6, a large amount of erosion has taken place during the formation of the Himalaya. Huge amounts of sediment were transported downstream creating unique geological structures.

The annual monsoonal cycle ensures a dry-wet condition leading to more than average erosion as compared with other typical mountain ranges not subject to monsoon. For example, in the Swiss Alps erosion is said to be 1mm per year whereas the Himalaya erosion reflects a figure 60% higher at 1.6mm per year (Hagen 1980) - for a similar area. The dry-wet effect is probably most prominent at the end of the monsoon when banks terraces and hillsides dry out; thus affecting their stability and causing slippage.

KALI GANDAKI VALLEY HISTORY.

Ancient and Modern. A reconnaisance of a contour map of Nepal will quickly give an idea of the immense variation inherent to this part of the world. Topography depicts a situation almost unprecendented elsewhere: within 100km of horizontal distance elevations rise from near sea level to well over 8 km in vertical height. This scenario creates many and varied climatic conditions from the tropical to the arctic range.

The Kali Gandaki rises from what appears to be a spring source at an elevation of about 4700m (15400') just below a saddle point on the Nepali-Tibetan border. An adjacent saddle point on the ridge line, called Simawali Pass, acts as the main trade route from Tibet. The dry arid desert of Mustang District is typical of what lies behind the Himalaya (fig 7). It is not dissimilar to other areas along the chain such as in Kashmir and Afghanistan. This is as a result of the uplift of the Tethys Sea and partly it is the sediment from that ancient sea which has been eroded and transported downstream along the 'new' valleys.

The river appears to fall in two specific series of gradients: from the source to Kalopani (fig 6); then from Kalopani to the plains. The differences in elevation drop are 7100' and 8300' respectively. Up to Kalopani the valley is wide: sometimes with deeply rutted cliffs, with consequent talus and sometimes with more stable rounded hills leading up to craggy peaks. The valley from the source downstream, is typically V-shaped, graduating quickly to a wide U-shape and terminating the first specific gradient section with a 500m wide flat bottomed section.

This large flat area, just north of Kalopani, tends to act as a de-silting basin for larger particles: thus sediment has collected here and tends to keep the level of this section fairly static. Even for large floods, the desilting capability of this basin must be quite effective. However, with such a profile, bed-load may not be insignificant.

After leaving this end point of the first gradient section, the river falls sharply through a slope of 1^{v} in 10^{h} immediately at Kalopani. This levels out to 1^{v} in 35^{h} at location of fig 1 (fig 0) ie where main central thrust crosses the Kali Gandaki in fig 6. At this latter location, the river valley becomes the deepest land gorge on earth. To the west, Dhaulagiri stands at 8167m (26795') and to the east, Annapurna stands at 8091m (26575'). With the valley floor at 1187m (3900') the sides rise 6940m (22796') at gradients over 1^v in 2^h (Map, 1987). The peaks themselves are 25.5km apart. It is worth noting that even towards the source, the gradient does not appear to exceed 1 in 20 (Map 08, 1976). The geology has changed from that of the Tibetan sediments to the Kathmandu zone (or Himalayan Gneiss Zone). Talus from the steep sides has mixed with some moraine, along with alluvium transported from the north to give a localised terracing on the valley floor. These deposits cause the river alignment to deviate within a short distance - no more than ±10m from the centre-line. This is synonymous with the steep terrain and thus any large floods are fairly well contained. It is in this Kathmandu Zone of Gneiss that the valley alignment becomes like that of an eggtimer neck. Just 1km to the north of the main central thrust the valley opens again. Thus the velocity, already increased from the steep gradient, is channelled through this conduit carrying large amounts of sediment which can be laid down as the valley widens again. It is at this point where huge river terraces are noted 1km south of the main central thrust (fig 3). Evidently the river level varied at a much higher elevation, in excess of 200m, within the last 100,000 years; the Holocene epoch. In the largest of these terraces, 50m tall, 5 bedding planes can be distinctly seen. A similar number of divisions have been noted, in many locations, as the overall thickness has decreased the further down the valley. At Beni 18km downstream a 15m high river terrace also shows 5 distinct bedding planes: the terrace continues beyond a further 25km.

At the location of fig 1 where a tunnel was being built for a hydro project the main central thrust was crossed. Just on the north side of the thrust fault, the tunnel went through alluvium at a depth of 125m below the surface (fig 2). It appears that a gully or crevasse existed in the northern gneiss formation, the Kali Gandaki flooded and filled up the gully later to be covered by a landslide of muscovite schist of the southern Nawakot zone. Particles in this underground alluvium ranged from silt to 1m boulders - identical to that found on the surface and at other terrace locations. Particles of timber were also discovered during excavation. Carbon dating of these samples would indicate an accurate date when massive floods engulfed the valley to make these huge river terrace cliffs. Further evidence of these gigantic floods appear on the eastern side of the Baskot ridge (fig 1) where sediment appears to have spilled over into the adjacent Mistri Khola valley. There is no evidence upstream that such material is indigenous to that valley. Such large flows, carrying such an amount of sediment can only be the result of the phenomenon known as glacier lake outburst floods - or as in the original Icelandic, Jokulhlaups.

1987 FLOOD.

Event. In 1954, a great flood swept down the Kali Gandaki taking out bridges and sweeping away large chunks of land. It appears from records that the flood did not significantly affect the upper reaches in the upper gradient zone. Local people remember it as the largest in living memory - until 1987.

To open the drama, here is part of the author's weekly report:

"On Thursday night our house shook from an earth tremor - not from a geological source, but from the Kali Gandaki. Overnight the river has changed its course dramatically. Cliffs have collapsed severely; half of Tatopani Bazaar has disappeared.. there has been major loss.

A hydrograph of the event shows a distinct correlation to that of a glacier moraine lake outburst flood (Ives, 1986).

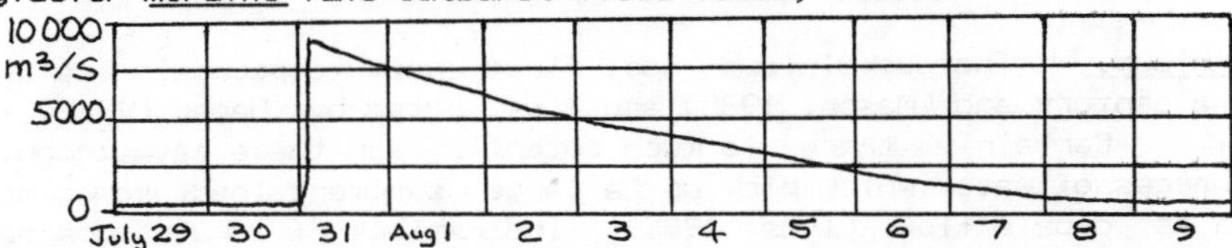

At the location of the Fig 4 cross-section, the average monsoon flow was measured to be about 350m³/s. Dry season flow was measured at 65m³/s. The 1987 monsoon flow appeared to follow the norm. There was no indication of a rise in level or anything to the contrary occuring to the river ie no surging in level.

The initial 10 to 12m flood wave surged down at 1 am. As dawn broke, the river colour appeared to be grey-brown. It almost seemed that the fluid was not far past the liquid limit as it appeared so viscous because of the sediment load - however, viscous or not - it appeared to be travelling around 12m/s. The noise was tremendous. One could hear the bed load bouncing and rolling its way along- like a squadron of helicopters - for 5 days non-stop. The power in the flood was colossal. This was immediately evident from the induced earth tremors felt up to 500m away. The author's house and separate office, 300m away, shook and rattled for 2 days after the initial wave struck. Surely this aided the devastation of the valley, literally shaking it apart. Major landslides occurred; undercutting of slopes led to slips 100m high. Within the first two days, the flow seemed to fill the cross-section; thereafter in the following 3 days, the river meandered as many times - finally settling on a course nothing remotely like what it had been 5 days previously. The peak flow was estimated to be in excess of 8500m³/s, 131 times normal dry season flow and 24 times average monsoon flow.

Analysis. Reports of damage filled conversation; who lost so much land, etc. It came to light that the local bazaar of Tatopani had been badly hit, up to 50% of it had been washed away. It was sited on the river terrace of which about 100,000m³ must have disappeared within the first few hours of the flood. Thankfully there was not much loss of life - although there was some. Six bridges were washed out, cutting off communities for months afterwards. Over 60 houses were lost with hundreds of thousands of cubic metres of tallus, alluvial fans, river terraces and hillsides devastated for over 70km downstream from the probable source.

After some research, it is felt that the flood was the result of a Jokulhlaup. The author would have liked to have gone north into Mustang to investigate, however, it is closed to foreigners.

Like the 1954 flood, little damage appears to have been done in the upper gradient section. This may be due to the lesser gradient and wider cross-section available for the discharge. But certainly more damage appears to have occurred in the 1987 flood. Hence it is obvious that the narrower the valley, the more potential there is for damage - especially where there are existing river terraces or other quickly erodable geological structures.

<u>Jokulhlaup.</u> The Jokulhlaup was first known to occur in Iceland over a century ago (Mason, 1935) and first noted by Hagen (1963) in Nepal. Certainly there is much potential for these catastrophic discharges of water which pick up a large sediment load, sometimes known as debris flow (Ives, 1986). Indications of Jokulhlaups may include all or some of the effects mentioned in Table 1.

TABLE 1.

A. Glacier environs	B. Downstream
- perched lake shorelines	- stripped bedrock
- collapsed end moraines	- giant blocks
- stranded icebergs in former lake basins	- coarse stream deposits in excess of normal flood competance
- lake sediment	- undercut toes of talus cones and alluvial fans
- alternate high lake spillways lateral and sub-lateral glacial drainage channels	- large numbers of undercut landslides and debris flow
	- extensive siltation
	- accounts of local inhabitants/folklore.

(Reproduced by permisson of J Ives, Colorado.)

Taking into account the above noted effects, it seems there is no doubt that the cause of the huge alluvial deposits in the Kali Gandaki valley are the results of Jokulhlaups in fairly recent geological history.

Some tributaries of the Kali Gandaki give greater monsoonal peak flows than that of the Kali Gandaki itself. One such river is the Mistri Khola where flows of $400 m^3/s$ have been noted; 114 times that of dry season flow. These events have happened almost annually and at times of not so heavy precipitation. The Mistri Khola also exhibits Jokulhlaup effects and it may be the case that there are almost annual Jokulhlaups from one of the glaciers that feed the river from the slopes of Nilgiri or Annapurna massifs.

<u>Control and use.</u> In the face of such phenomenal discharges, it would appear economically unviable to channel rivers or build other structures to protect inhabited areas. Rather, it may be necessary to account for such events when planning extensions to communities. When even gabion and masonary abutments, and large naturally located

boulders (up to 50m³) are destroyed, it seems a fallacy to think that replacement of such structures would offer control. Recognition of potential disaster areas with mapping of glacial sources may add to understanding and relief from such huge floods.
In Nepal there are several schemes, presently at the feasibiltiy stage, where high dams (up to 260m) for hydro power are planned. Figures quote a sedimentation consumption life of up to 40 years- but noting the possible occurrence of Jokulhlaups on most of Nepal's larger rivers, this figure may be reduced drastically - thus shortening the probable life of such schemes.

Further work. There is much further study and work which could be completed on subjects mentioned in this paper. Among them, as mentioned, is the mapping and designation of potential Jokulhlaup sources with the possibility of draining glacial lakes to prevent catastrophic outburst.

REFERENCES.

BLYTH, F.G.H. and de FRIETAS, M.H. (1984). A Geology for Engineers. Edward Arnold, London.
HAGEN, T. (1963). Mount Everest. Oxford University Press, London.
HAGEN, T. (1980). Nepal. Kummerly and Frey, Switzerland.
IVES, J. (1986). Glacial Lake Outburst Floods and Risk Engineering in the Himalaya. ICIMOD, Kathmandu.
Map 08 2033 (1976). Dhaulagiri Zone. HMG Ministry of Land Reform, Survey Dept, Topographical Section.
Map (1987). Pokhara to Jomoson, Trekking Map. Mandala Production.
MASON, K. (1935). The Study of threatening Glaciers. Geog. Journal 85(1): 24-35.

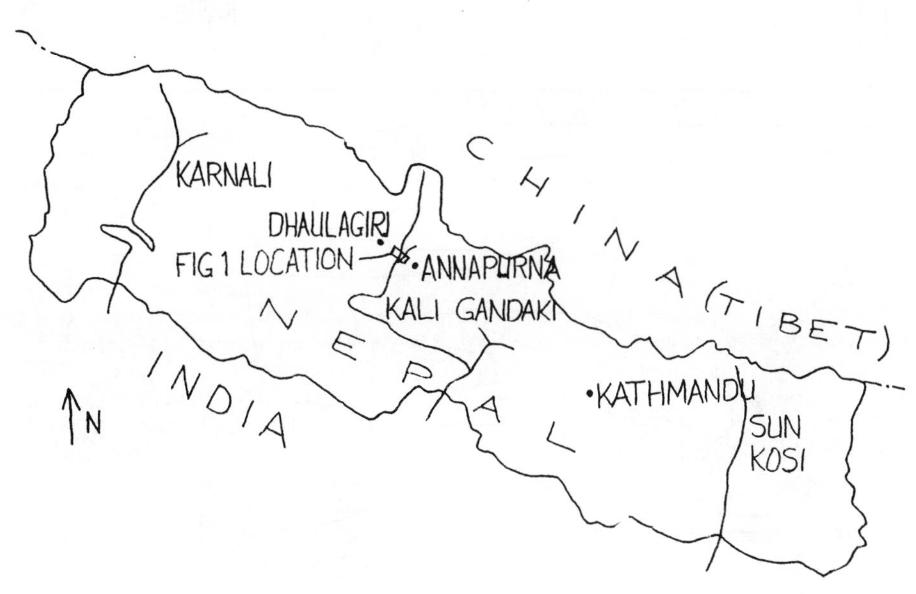

FIG 0: LOCATION MAP

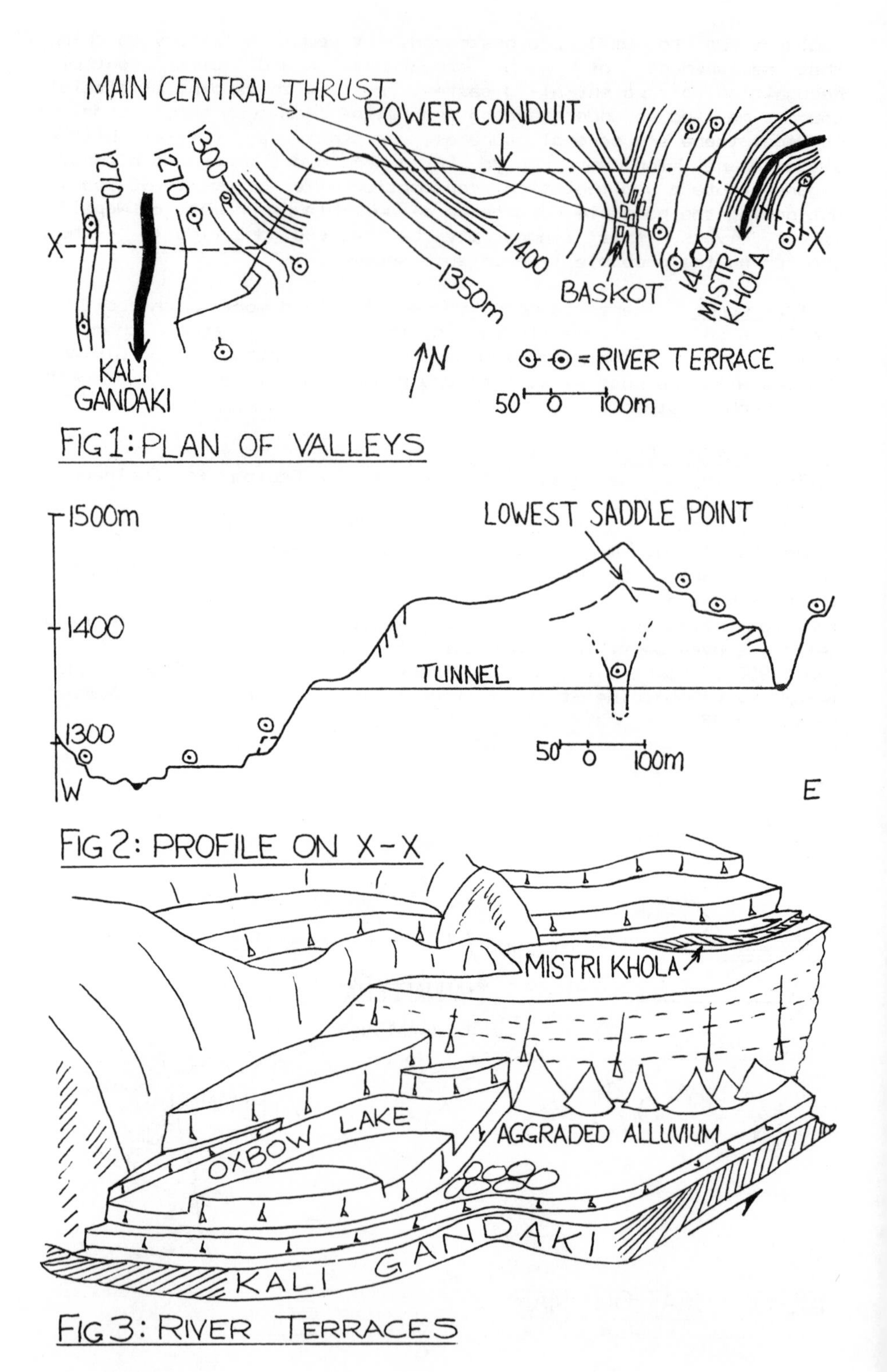

FIG 1: PLAN OF VALLEYS

FIG 2: PROFILE ON X–X

FIG 3: RIVER TERRACES

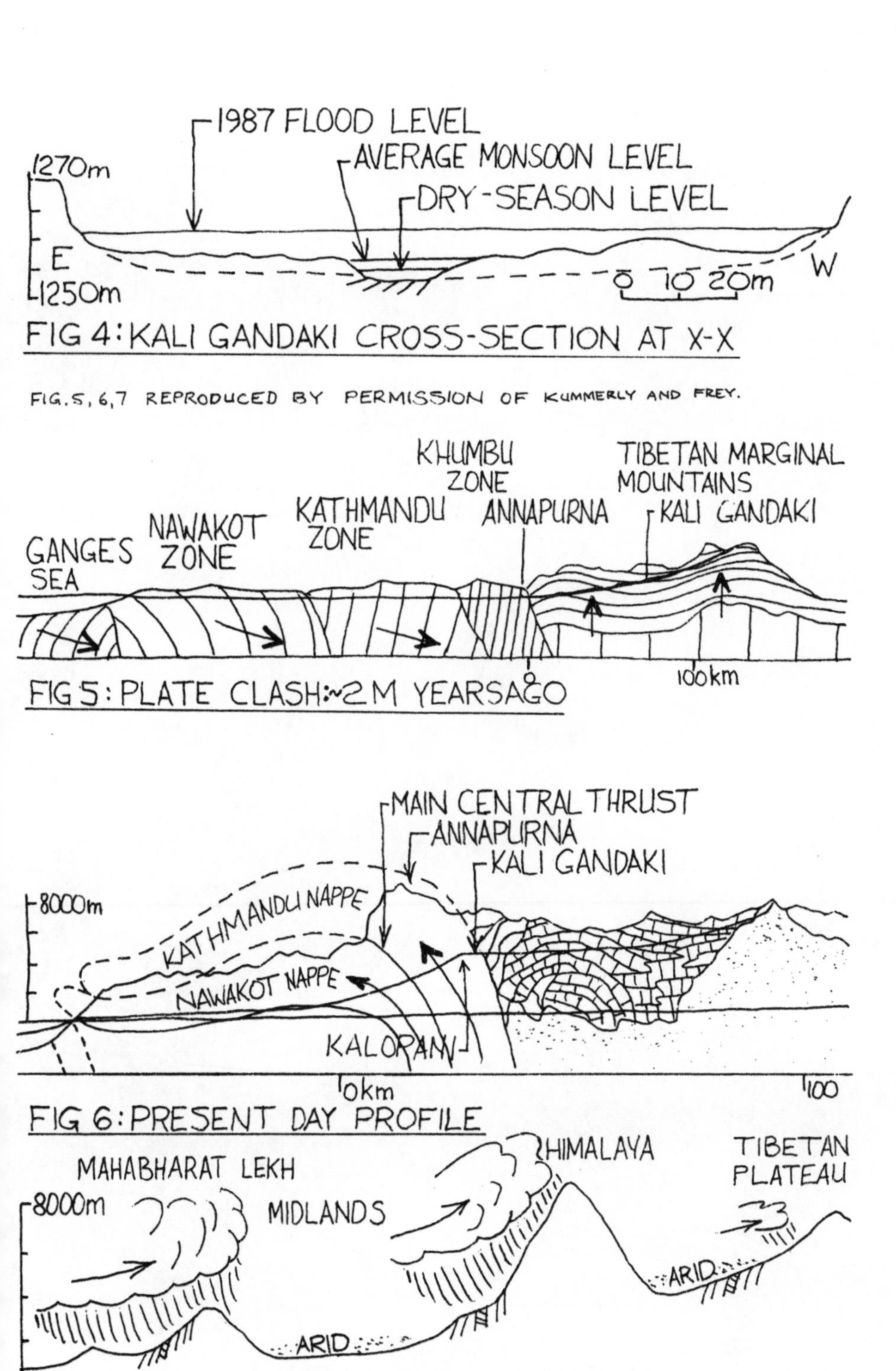

FIG 4: KALI GANDAKI CROSS-SECTION AT X-X

FIG 5: PLATE CLASH: ~2 M YEARS AGO

FIG 6: PRESENT DAY PROFILE

FIG 7: PRINCIPLE ZONES OF PRECIPITATION

PAPER D1

International Conference on
RIVER FLOOD HYDRAULICS
17-20 September, 1990

2D MATHEMATICAL MODEL FOR FLOOD SIMULATION AND DRAINAGE DESIGN

U. Maione, P. Mignosa and M.G. Tanda
Istituto di Idraulica, Politecnico di Milano
Piazza Leonardo da Vinci, 32
20133 Milano - Italy

ABSTRACT

The paper describes the mathematical simulation of the inundation occurred on July 1987 in Valtellina (Northern Italy) due to the failure of the Adda river levee. A diffusion 2D model in the flooded area, linked with a 1D model in the river, was adopted. Results of simulation showed clearly the behavior of the flood dynamics and the backwater effects of the downstream constriction on water levels and permanence. The same model and the simulated flood were then utilized after changing size and characteristics of the outlet channel, in order to reach a better design of the drainage in the valley in case of hydraulic emergency.

INTRODUCTION

During a severe flood occurred on July 1987 in Valtellina, Northern Italy, a 150 m length of the Adda river levee failed, causing the flooding of an 800 ha valley area. Water levels raised up to more than three meters. Railways and roadways were partly destroyed and many damages were also caused to the surrounding villages. In order to understood the dynamics of the flood event and the influence of the downstream boundary condition, and to investigate the possible drainage alternatives, a 2D mathematical model was applied and tested.

STUDY AREA

Selvetta plain (Fig.1) is an alluvial valley originated by the Adda river and surrounded by high mountains, situated in the middle part of Valtellina. Until the last century, the river was not constricted by levees and spread out in the surroundings during floods, frequently changing the course. Afterwards, it was decided to confine the river in the left side of the valley, between a levee and the first declivities of the mountains. In order to drive away the waters coming from the small creeks, some drainage channels were dug, among which the principal one, named Old Adda, follows an ancient thalweg of the Adda river (Fig.2).
During the sixties the area was involved in a hydroelectric power project. Consequently a weir with movable gates, a channel diversion and a left levee were built, and the right levee was made higher to hold the raised water level in the river. At the outlet of the main drainage channel a siphon was designed to allow

International Conference on River Flood Hydraulics, edited by W.R.White

the crossing of the hydroelectric channel embankment.

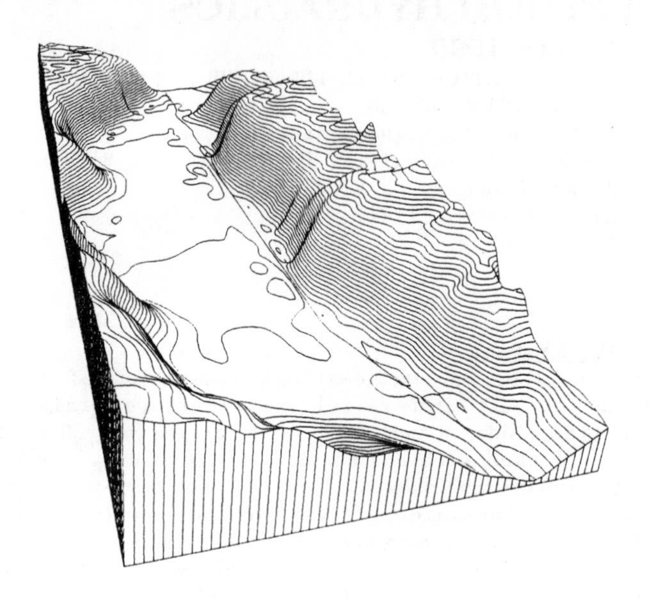

Fig.1. Perspective view of Selvetta valley.

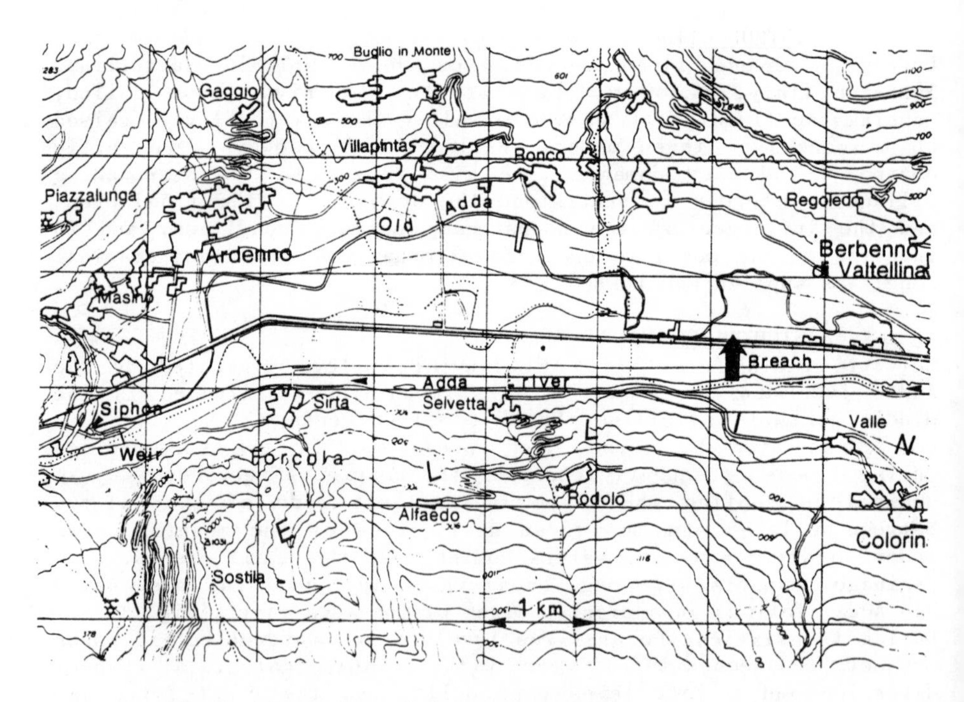

Fig.2. Plan view of Selvetta valley.

The constriction of the river, together with the increased sedimentation in the reach upstream the weir, have made in the recent decades the water levels higher than the surrounding countries and increased the damages following from a failure of the right levee of the Adda river.

THE FLOOD EVENT

Selvetta plain inundation was caused by the failure of a 150 m length of the Adda river levee during the heavy storm occurred on 18th-19th of July, 1987. About $20 \cdot 10^6$ m^3 of water spread out from the breach into the plain, flooding a wide area of 8 km^2 with water levels rising up to more than three meters. The inundation was worsened by the constricted outlet of the valley which caused strong backwater effects in the upper part of the area and a fast increase of water levels. As a consequence of this situation, some hours after the breach, downstream water levels were rather higher in the plain than in the river. To avoid long permanence of water over the surface and further increase of water levels, it was decided to open an artificial breach in the valley part of the Adda levee.

MATHEMATICAL MODEL

Several 2D mathematical models were presented in the recent literature, based on different solutions and approximation schemes of the governing equations. They can be roughly subdivided into a) models based on two-dimensional De Saint-Venant equations of shallow water motion, solved by different numerical methods: finite differences (Jovanovic and Radojkovic, 1982, Zech et al., 1983), finite elements (Lee et al, 1982), characteristics (Schmitz and Seus, 1984); b) "quasi" two-dimensional models (Zanobetti and Lorgere, 1968; Cunge, 1980; Ballofet and Scheffler, 1982) which schematize the whole area as a series of cells and channels in which the one-dimensional equations are applied.
In this paper a literature hydrodynamic model (DHM, Hromadka II and Yen, 1986) was applied to handle the 1D-2D problem of the flow in the river and plain.
The model solves the diffusive approximation of the two-dimensional De Saint-Venant equations, i.e.

$$\frac{\partial q_x}{\partial x} + \frac{\partial q_y}{\partial y} + \frac{\partial H}{\partial t} = 0 \qquad S_{fx} + \frac{\partial H}{\partial x} = 0 \qquad S_{fy} + \frac{\partial H}{\partial y} = 0 \qquad (1)$$

by means of an explicit finite differences scheme on a regular grid. In Eq.(1), q_x and q_y represent the specific discharges (m^2/s) in the two orthogonal directions x, y; H is the absolute water level; t is the time and S_{fx}, S_{fy} are the friction slopes in the same directions.
A 1D model based on the same approximations allows to simulate the river and channel network in which the motion is essentially one-dimensional. It is coupled with the 2D model by means of an interface model based on continuity equation only.
The DHM model was selected, despite its simplicity, mainly because

it can take into account the backwater effects and channel overflow.

TOPOGRAPHIC DESCRIPTION AND BOUNDARY CONDITIONS

The whole area and the river floodplains were subdivided into square cells of 150×150 m in order to describe correctly the distance between the two river levees and the breach dimension without local refinements. The elevation of each cell was obtained by a Digital Elevation Model (DEM) on the basis of the available topographical maps (1:2000 and 1:10000). Figure 1 shows a perspective view of the valley obtained with DEM.
Channel reaches of the Adda river and of the main drainage system were described with a cross-section data base. They represent the network in which the water preferably propagates.
The right levee of the Adda river was modeled as a closed boundary which inhibits water exchanges between the river and the plain. The closed boundary was then removed from the location of the breach (cell 358) after its occurrence. The erosional process of the breach development was not simulated: local inspections have shown in fact that the levee was not overtopped during the flood event. Failure was probably originated by piping with a quite fast destruction of the embankment. The breach opening was then assumed to be instantaneous.
Figure 3 shows the lay-out of the area. As the contour boundaries follow the first mountain declivities, zero flow was assumed through them, except for the cell n.488 (inflow), n.1 (outflow from the Adda river) and n.2 (outflow from the siphon), for which it was necessary to select the proper boundary conditions.

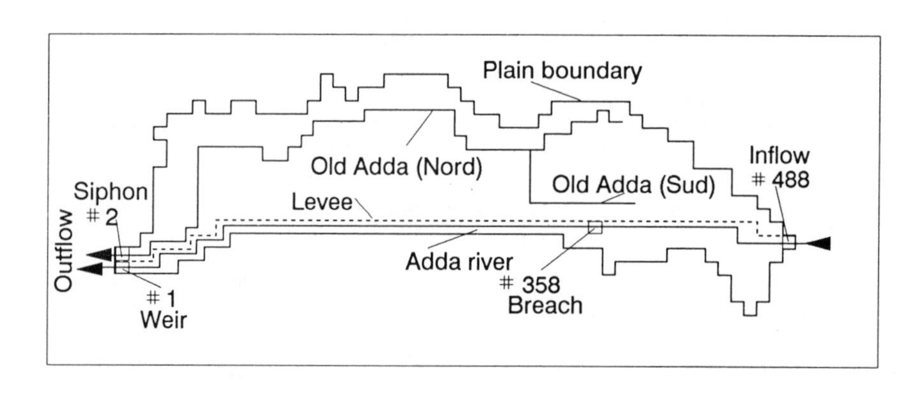

Fig.3. Lay-out of the study area.

At the cell n.1 a critical stage-discharge relationship was imposed, due to a bottom jump at the weir location and a sudden increase of bed slope downstream. Gates were assumed completely open, as occurred during the real flood.
At the cell n.2 the flow through the siphon was approximated by

means of a stage-discharge relation. As a matter of fact a refined description of the siphon conveyance is not really necessary due to the small discharge allowed to pass through the constriction.
An attempt was made to estimate the incoming discharge hydrograph at cell n.488. Unfortunately, no information was available from upstream. The only measuring station is located some kilometers away from downstream; the recorded hydrograph was heavily influenced by the inundation and by significant contribution of some tributaries. Figure 4 shows the recorded event at the station (solid line) together with the estimated hydrograph in the same location (dotted line). A volume of water equal to that flowed through the breach into the plain was added to the recorded hydrograph during the period of inundation. The same volume was then subtracted from the period of emptying of the area.
The flood wave was then reduced in order to take approximately into account the different tributary areas at the breach location and at the recording station.

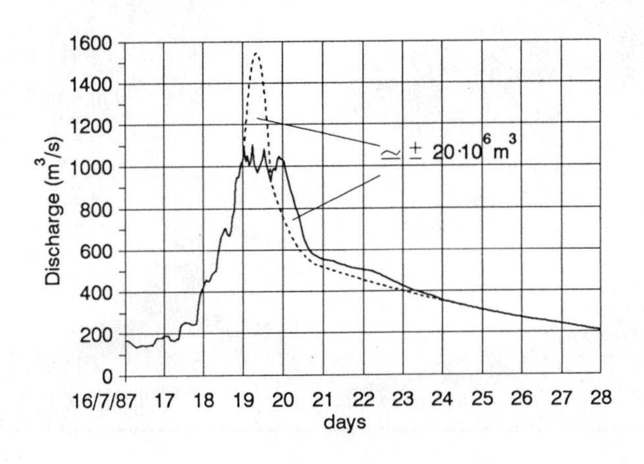

Fig.4. Recorded and estimated downstream waves.

FLOOD SIMULATION AND RESULTS

The simulation of flood was performed by two separate steps. In the first step, the propagation into the Adda river was computed, from the beginning of the flood event until the breach occurred. In this way the water profile in the river at the time of the levee failure was determined. In the second step, the inhibition of water exchange between cell n.358 (in the river) and cell n.359 (in the plain) was removed and the simulation was carried out for 11 hours, until the artificial breach in the levee downstream was opened.
Figure 5 shows water levels and flooded areas at different time after the occurrence of the breach. Ground morphology and drainage channels are not shown in the drawings. Figure 6 shows the wave propagation along the Old-Adda channel. In the first few hours the

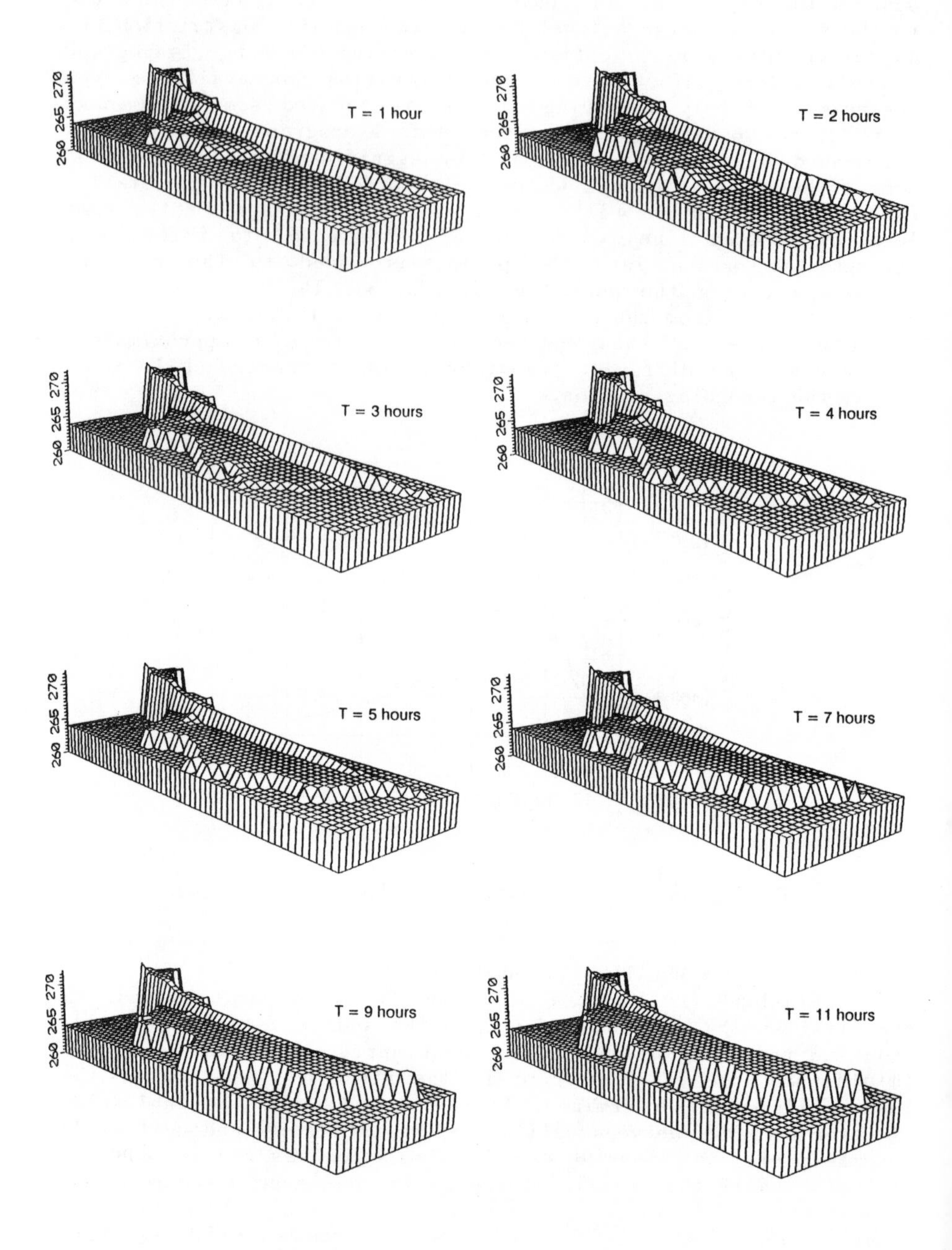

Fig.5. Water levels and flooded areas at different time after the occurrence of the breach.

flow spread out in the plain reaching the north mountains declivities which acted like a boundary. After 3 hours (Fig.6) the flow reached the downstream boundary where the siphon is placed. Levels began then to rise fast due to the constricted outlet and the water supplied from the breach. Seven hours after the failure, the water levels were almost the same in all the plain and they were already higher than the downstream levels in the river (Fig.5). During this phase some upstream areas, not flooded at the beginning of the event, were inundated due to backwater effects.

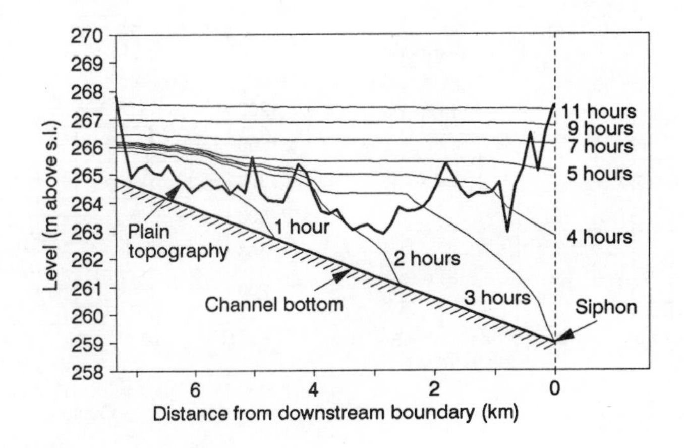

Fig.6. Computed water profiles in the Old-Adda channel at different time (siphon outlet).

Thereafter the water levels continued to rise until the artificial breach in the downstream levee was not opened, 11 hours after the failure.
Fig.7a shows the water level history in the two cells of the river (n.358) and of the plain (n.359) contiguous to the breach. At the moment of the failure (42 hours after the beginning of the simulation) the level rose rapidly in the cell n.359, due to the high waters in the river and to the absence of an hydraulic head downstream. Two hours after, the water volume contained in the river was exhausted and water levels in the two cells reached a minimum. Successively they begun to increase once again. The discharge flowing through the breach, drawn in Fig.7b together with the inflow and outflow hydrographs, shows the same trend. The behavior at the beginning of the transient is strictly dependent on the hypothesis of instantaneous failure of the levee and could not be fully realistic.
Notwithstanding this, water levels in the plain at the end of the simulation were quite well estimated comparing with the maximum levels observed, with positive differences of no more than 10-20 centimeters.

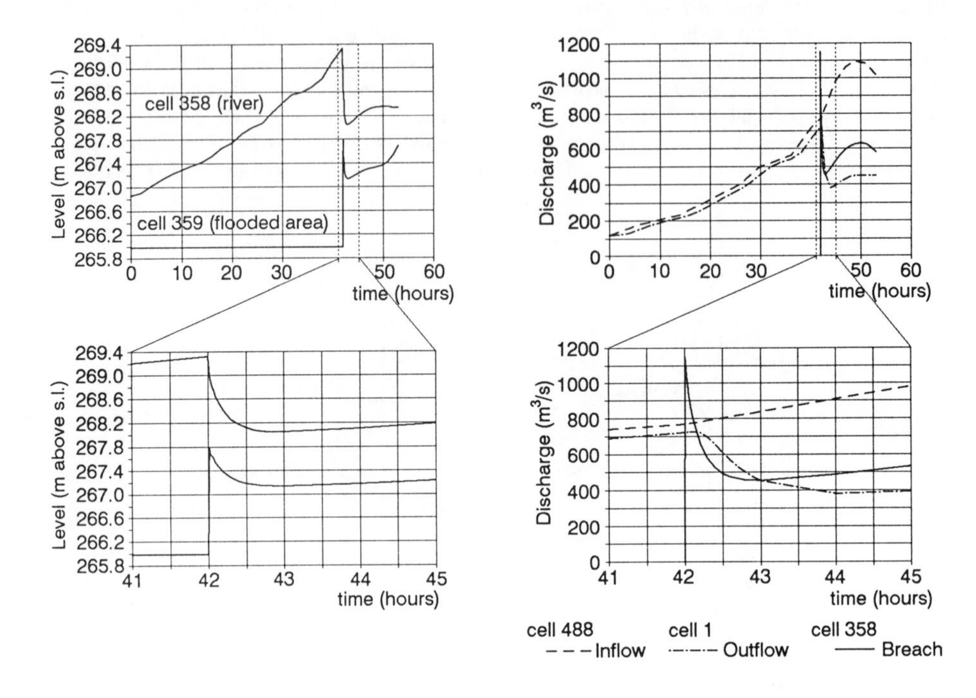

Fig.7. Water level histories (7a) and discharge hydrographs (7b).

DRAINAGE ALTERNATIVES

In order to evaluate the real influence of the downstream boundary condition and to suggest the possible alternatives for the drainage of the valley in case of emergencies, another simulation was carried out. In the cell n.1 a steady stage-discharge relationship was introduced, removing the siphon outlet.
Furthermore, the last half kilometer of the main channel was enlarged from 10 to 20 meters. Everything else was maintained as that in the first simulation. The resulting flood propagation along the Old-Adda channel is shown in Fig.8.
In the first 3 hours the levels are obviously the same as those in the previous simulation since they are not affected by the downstream boundary condition. Afterwards the influence of the enlarged channel and of the increased capacity of the outlet becomes significant. As a whole, water levels at the end of the flood are about 1 metre lower than the previous situation. At first sight the results seem to indicate that even a large and free drainage channel could not reduce very much damage of the inundation.
Nevertheless the reduction of 1 meter in the maximum water levels

means a significant reduction of the flooded area either in the upstream zone or at the border of the plain, where most of the villages are located. Moreover the permanence of high water levels would be reduced significantly.

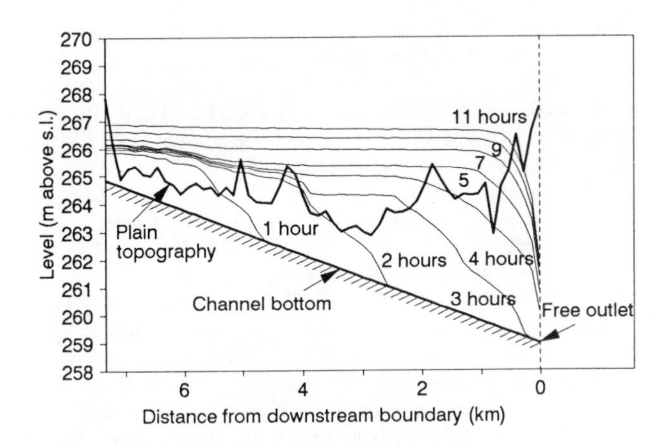

Fig.8. Computed water profiles in the Old-Adda channel at different time (free outlet).

CONCLUSIONS

A diffusion 1D-2D model (DHM, Hromadka II and Yen, 1986) has been applied in order to simulate the inundation occurred on July 1987 in the Selvetta plain (Northern Italy), caused by failure of the Adda river levee. The flooded area was described by means of a grid of square cells with a Digital Elevation Model based on the available topographical maps (1:2000 and 1:10000). The incoming flood wave was estimated on the basis of the hydrograph recorded at a station some kilometers downstream the study area.

Maximum water levels (and flooded areas) obtained by simulation are in good agreement with those observed at the end of the real event. Moreover the main behavior of the inundation dynamics seems to be well simulated, showing strong backwater effects of the constricted outlet.

Another simulation was then performed in order to evaluate the benefits coming from a new design of the outlet channel with a better hydraulic conveyance.

REFERENCES

Ballofet A. & M.L. Scheffler: Numerical Analysis of the Teton Dam Failure Flood, Journal of the Hydraulic Division, ASCE, Vol.20, N.4, pp. 317-328, 1982.

Cunge J.A.: Two-Dimensional Modelling of Flood Plains, in: Unsteady Flow in Open Channels, Vol. II, K. Mahmood and V. Yevjevich Ed., Water Resources Publications, 1975.

Cunge J.A., Holly F.M. Jr. & A. Verwey: Practical Aspects of Computational River Hydraulics, Pitman Advanced Publishing Program, Boston, London, Melbourne, 1980.

Hromadka II T.V. & C.C. Yen: A Diffusion Hydrodynamic Model (DHM), Adv. Water Resources, Vol. 9, pp.118-170, 1986.

Jovanovic M. & M. Radojkovic: Numerical and experimental study of two dimensional dam break problems, Proceedings of Symposium on Refined Modelling of Flows, Vol. 2, Paris, 1982.

Laura R.A. & J.D. Wang: Two Dimensional Flood Routing on steep slopes, Journal of the Hydraulic Division, ASCE, Vol.110, n.8, pp.1121-1135, 1984.

Lee J.K., Froelich D.C., Gilbert J.J. & G.J. Wiche: Two Dimensional Analysis of Bridge Backwater, Proceedings of the Conference on Applying Research to Hydraulic Practice, Jackson, Mississippi, 1982.

Lesleighter E.J.: Flood Plain Flow Using a Two-Dimensional Numerical Simulation, Proc. Int. Conf. on Hydraulic Aspects of Floods and Flood Control, London, 1983.

Maione U, Mignosa P. & M.G. Tanda: Influence of a Highway Embankment on a Flood Event, The Science of Total Environment, Elsevier Science Publ., n.59, pp. 425-430, 1987.

Schmitz G. & G.J. Seus: Simulating Flood Flows by coupled 1-D and 2-D Models, Proceedings of the V International Conference on Finite Elements in Water Resources, Burlington, U.S.A., 1984.

Zanobetti D. & H. Lorgere: Le modele mathematique du Delta du Mekong, La Huille Blanche, Grenoble, Vol. XXIII, n. 1, 4, 5, 1968.

Zech Y., Sorel M.C. & M. Vansnick: Mathematical Modelling of Floods in Rivers Flooding and Uncovering of Flood Plains, Proc. Int. Conf. on the Hydraulic Aspects of Floods and Flood Control, London, 1983.

PAPER D2

International Conference on
RIVER FLOOD HYDRAULICS
17-20 September, 1990

Prediction Method of Flow Resistance in Rivers with Compound Channels and Application to River Course Design

Shoji FUKUOKA Department of Civil Engineering,
Tokyo Institute of Technology, Japan
Koh-ichi FUJITA Research Planning Department, National
Institute for Research Advancement, Japan

Abstract

The composite roughness coefficient of river courses with compound channels was measured in experimental channels having various shapes close to the aspect ratio of real river courses, and the method of predicting composite roughness coefficient in river courses with compound channels was proposed by considering mutual interaction of the flow between main channel and flood channel.

1. introduction

The conventional relation between discharge Q and water depth H in the section division method (Ida 1960) can be obtained from the assumptions that the uniform flow stands good in respective cross section, the shear force at the interface shown by dotted line in Fig.1 is neglected, and the river courses have symmetrical cross sections :

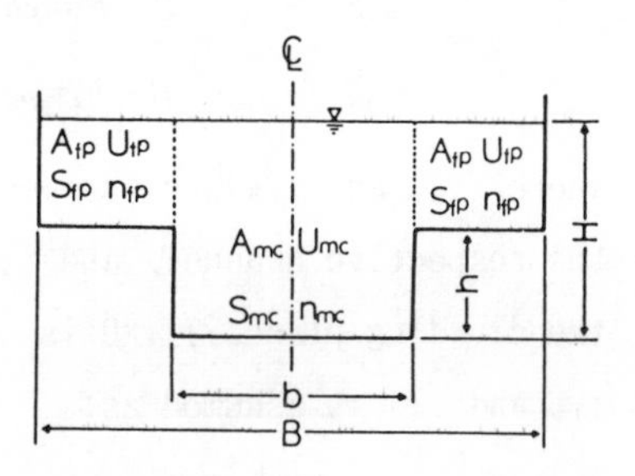

Fig. 1 Description of symbols

$$Q=2\frac{A_{fp}}{n_{fp}}\left(\frac{A_{fp}}{S_{fp}}\right)^{2/3}\cdot I_b^{1/2}+\frac{A_{mc}}{n_{mc}}\left(\frac{A_{mc}}{S_{mc}}\right)^{2/3}\cdot I_b^{1/2} \quad (1)$$

where, $R_{mc} = A_{mc}/S_{mc}$, $R_{fp} = A_{fp}/S_{fp}$, n_{fp} and n_{mc}: roughness coefficient in the respective channel, u_{mc} and u_{fp}: mean velocity in the respective channel I_b: inclination of river bed, and the subscripts fp and mc respectively indicate the correspondence with various quantities for flood channel and main channel. Then, the composite roughness coefficient Nc is calculated from the Manning formula:

$$N_c = \frac{A_{mc} + 2A_{fp}}{Q} \cdot R_c^{2/3} \cdot I_b^{1/2} \qquad (2)$$

The hydraulic radius R_c is expressed by

$$R_c = \left\{ \frac{A_{mc}(A_{mc}/S_{mc})^{2/3} + 2A_{fp}(A_{fp}/S_{fp})^{2/3}}{A_{mc} + 2A_{fp}} \right\}^{3/2} \qquad (3)$$

The value of Nc by the section division method can be calculated from equations (1) to (3).

2. Composite Roughness Coefficient Considering the Apparent Shear Force Acting to the Dividing Boundary

An apparent shear force τ_{as} acts to the dividing plane because of the lateral transfer of momentum between the main channel and flood channel.

The equations of motion can be given to the flow in the respective channel (Myers 1978) (Wormleaton et al 1982) (Knight et al) :

$$\tau_{mc} S_{mc} + \tau_{as} \cdot 2(H - h) = \rho g A_{mc} I_b \qquad (4)$$

$$\tau_{fp} S_{fp} - \tau_{as} \cdot 2(H - h) = \rho g A_{fp} I_b \qquad (5)$$

where, τ_{mc} and τ_{fp} are the mean shear force at the wetted perimeter of the respective channel, and τ_{as} is the apparent shear force acting to the dividing plane. $\tau_{as}=0$ is used in the section division method. Now, τ_{fp} and τ_{mc} is assumed as:

$$\tau_{mc} = \frac{\rho g n_{mc}^2 u_{mc}^2}{R_{mc}^{1/3}} \qquad (6)$$

$$\tau_{fp} = \frac{\rho g n_{fp}^2 u_{fp}^2}{R_{fp}^{1/3}}. \qquad (7)$$

The apparent shear force is assumed in the form (Ishikawa, et al 1984) (Ognik 1985) (Mckee, et al 1985) as:

$$\tau_{as} = \rho \cdot f \cdot (u_{mc} - u_{fp})^2 \qquad (8)$$

Where ρ : density of water, and f : boundary mixing coefficient. By turning equations (4) to (8) into simultaneous equations, the following equations are obtained:

$$\frac{\rho g n_{mc}^2 u_{mc}^2}{R_{mc}^{1/3}}\left(\frac{b}{2}+h\right)+\rho f(u_{mc}-u_{fp})^2(H-h)=\rho g H\frac{b}{2}I_b \qquad (9)$$

$$\frac{\rho g n_{fp}^2 u_{fp}^2}{R_{fp}^{1/3}}\left(\frac{B-b}{2}+H-h\right)-\rho f(u_{mc}-u_{fp})^2(H-h)=\rho g(H-h)\frac{(B-b)}{2}I_b \qquad (10)$$

Unknown quantities u_{mc} and u_{fp} can be obtained by solving the two equations simultaneously. From these results, the discharge for any water level can be obtained. The unknown value of f will be checked by experiments of river courses with compound channels.

3. Outlines of Experiments

Experiments were performed for the river courses having several kinds of b/B and b/h in order to know the influence of these parameters upon f-value. The selected value of b/B ~ b/h used as the aspect ratio of the experiment channel is shown in Fig. 2, which is in the same region as that of the natural rivers in Japan. Also two kinds of conditions were set; a case where n_{fp} is larger than n_{mc} (series A), and another case where n_{fp} is almost the same as n_{mc} (series B). Table 1 shows characteristics of channel used, and Table 2 indicates the cross sectional shape in each experimental case. Both of them are straight channels with an uniform section. From the longitudinal change in water level and the discharge obtained, Nc was determined.

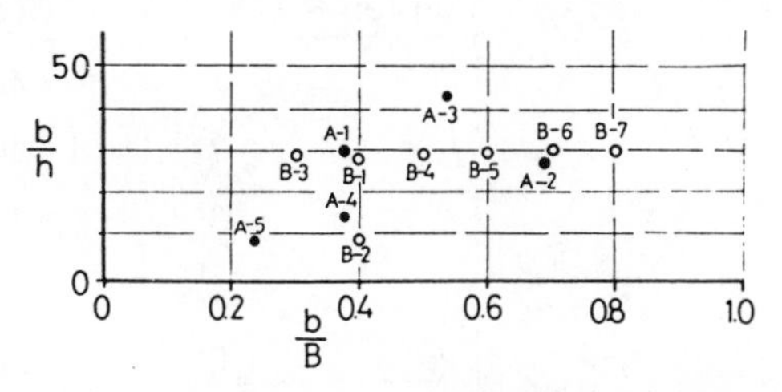

Fig.2 Shape of river course with compound channels used in the experiment

4. Results of Experiments

4.1 Series A experiment   Shown in Fig.3 is the results of plotted relations between Nc and H for each shape of compound channels. Solid line in the Figure is the predicted value of N_c by the section division method. Broken line in the Figure is the predicted value of N_c considering τ_{as}. The boundary mixing coefficient f to be used for calculating the broken line was so established that the measured value will the best agree with the calculated value.

Table. 1 Principal Items of Experimental Channel

Series	Length[m]	Gradient	Width[m]	n_{mc}	n_{fp}
A	30	1/1000	2	0.01	0.028
B	50	1/1000	3	0.01	0.01

Table. 2 Cross Sectional Shape of Each Experimental Case

Series	Case No.	B(cm)	b(cm)	h(cm)	Remarks*
A	1	200	75.5	5.0	1.
	2	200	137.8	5.0	2.
	3	200	106.8	5.0	1.
	4	200	75.8	5.0	2.
	5	200	47.0	5.0	2.
B	1	300	120	4.2	2.
	2	300	120	12.1	2.
	3	300	90	3.1	2.
	4	300	150	5.1	2.
	5	300	180	6.0	2.
	6	300	210	6.9	2.
	7	300	240	8.0	2.

* 1. Flood channel at one side only
  2. Flood channel at two sides

4.2 Series B experiment   Solid line in the Fig.4 is N_c by the section division method. Two patterns can be seen in the relation of Nc/n_{mc}~H/h. The first pattern is seen in the cases B-1,-2, and -3 where the ratio b/B is relatively small, in which Nc exceeds the calculated value by the section division method when water is on the flood channel and Nc decreases when water level rises further and approaches the calculated values by the section division method. In this case, Nc increases by about 20% maximum. The second pattern hardly has the increase in Nc and is seen in the cases B-4, -5 -6 and -7 where b/B is large. Nc increases in the first pattern probably because of mutual interaction of flows in main channel and flood channel. Shown by broken lines in Fig. 4are the calculated values considering τ_{as}. By comparing the measured values with the broken lines, f-values well explaining the measured values can be roughly known. Value of f is about 0.1 to 0.5 in the cases B-1, -2 and -3 where the significant increase of the value of Nc is seen, but f-value is less than 0.1 in the cases B-4, -5, -6 and -7 where such an increase is not recognized.

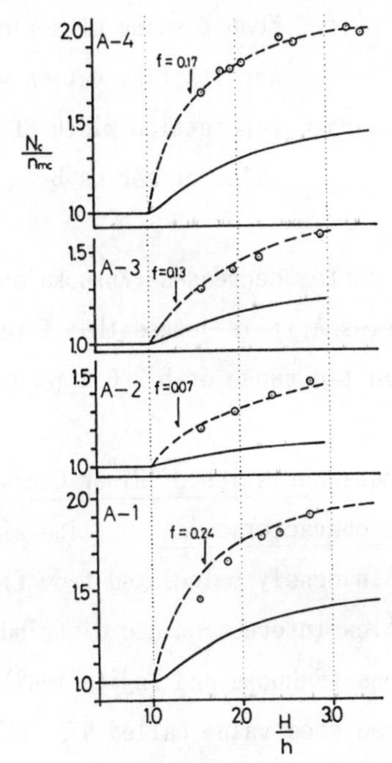

Fig. 3 Relation between composite roughness coefficient Nc and water depth H (series A)

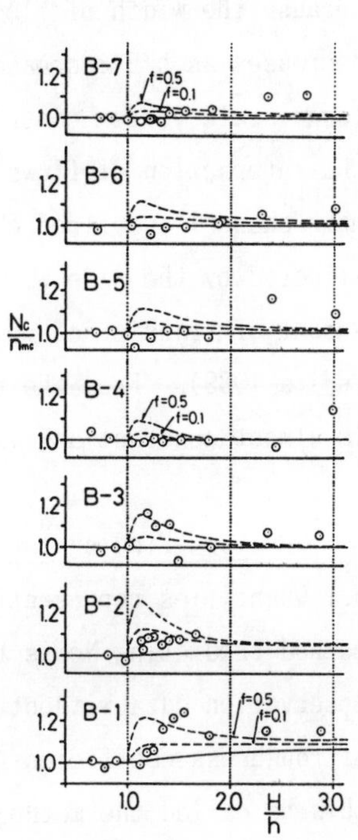

Fig. 4 Relation between composite roughness coefficient Nc and water depth H (series B)

4.3 f-value Fig. 5 shows the relation between f inversely calculated from the composite roughness coefficient obtained from experiments and b/B. The accuracy of f-value in series B is relatively low compared to series A. Thus, only the fluctuation range is indicated by dotted line in the Figure. From this Figure, if b/B exceeds 0.6, f-value tends to slightly decrease as b/B begins to increase. This seems to occur because the width of flood channel decreases as b/B increases, the large-scale vortex contributing to the interaction of flows between main channel and flood channel is affected by the side wall, and the amount of transfer of momentum by the vortex decreases (Fukuoka and Fujita 1989). From the results of series A, it is judged that f-value is almost constant and is about 0.17 in the range of b/B=0.2 to 0.6.

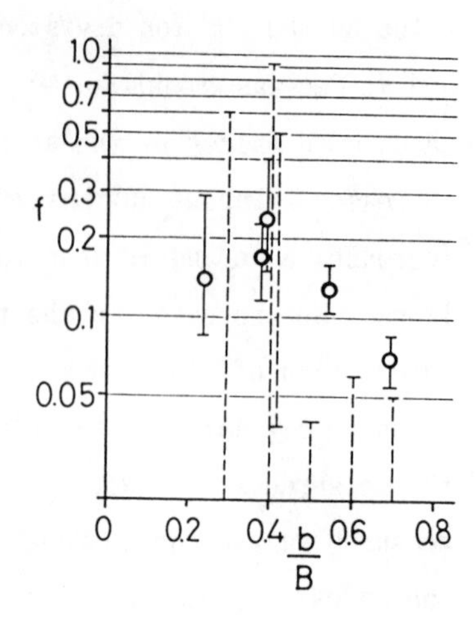

Fig. 5 Relation between f and b/B

⊢o⊣ Mean f-value of series A and its fluctuation width

⊢--⊣ Fluctuation width of f-value of series B

5. Finding the Resistance Characteristics of River Course

5.1 Quantities representing resistance characteristics The simplest method predicting Nc is the use of Nc inversely calculated from flood observation data without considering flow interaction and distribution of roughness coefficient within sections (Fukuoka and Fujita 1986). Let this be called the method1, and the predicted value called N_1. Method 2 is the section division method explained in 1. Its predicted value is N_2. Method 3 is for predicting Nc by considering the apparent shear force due to the interaction of flows and its predicted value is N_3.

Among the relations of N_3 to H and N_2 to H , the following two hydraulic quantities are specially important in the river course planning:

(1) dN_3/dH: Rate of increase of N_3 due to the increase in water depth

(2) N_3-N_2: Difference between N_3 and N_2

If the difference between the water depth of design flood and the water depth of flood used for inverse calculation is ΔH, an approximate error of $\Delta H \cdot dN_3/dH$ is created in the method 1. Therefore, depending on the magnitude of dN_3/dH, the properness of adopting the method 1 can be judged. N_3-N_2 expresses the increment in roughness coefficient due to the resistance added by the interaction. If this quantity is large, the river course easily creates added resistance due to interaction. Also, where N_3-N_2 is small, it can be judged that the method 2 which is simpler than method 3 may be used.

5.2 Relations between dN_3/dH and N_3-N_2/N_2 and river characteristics

Since the discharge and velocity on flood channel are smaller than those in the main channel, the increment in the velocity in flood channel by interaction is assumed to have little affect the value of Nc. Therefore , as the primary approximation, equation (11), which the term expressing the interaction of flow is neglected, will be used instead of equation (10) to flood channel.

$$\frac{\rho g n_{fp}^2 u_{fp}^2}{R_{fp}^{1/3}}\left(\frac{B-b}{2}+H-h\right)=\rho g(H-h)\frac{(B-b)}{2}I_b \tag{11}$$

By using equations (9) and (11) and also considering that the hydraulic radius of each divided section is equal to respective water depth, an equation for obtaining the approximate value N_3' of N_3 is determined, and dN_3'/dH (=C_1) and $(N_3'-N_2)/N_2$ (=C_2) are calculated from above results:

$$C_1=\frac{dN_3'}{dH}=\frac{n_m}{(xyz^{5/3}+A)^2}\cdot\left\{\frac{5}{3}xz^{2/3}z'(A-y)-B(1+xz^{5/3})\right\} \tag{12}$$

$$C_2=\frac{N_3'-N_2}{N_2}=\frac{(1-A)}{xyz^{5/3}+A} \tag{13}$$

Where, $x=b_f/b_m,\ y=n_m/n_f,\ z=H_f/H_m$

$$A=\frac{\theta}{(1+\theta)}\cdot yz^{2/3}+\frac{1}{(1+\theta)}\cdot\sqrt{1+\theta-\theta y^2z^{4/3}},$$

$$B=\frac{\theta'}{(1+\theta)^2}\cdot yz^{2/3}+\frac{2}{3}\frac{\theta}{(1+\theta)}yz^{-1/3}z'-\frac{\theta'}{(1+\theta)^2}\cdot\sqrt{1+\theta-\theta y^2z^{4/3}}+\frac{1}{(1+\theta)}\cdot\left(\frac{\theta'-\theta'y^2z^{4/3}-\frac{4}{3}\theta y^2z^{1/3}z'}{2\sqrt{1+\theta-\theta y^2z^{4/3}}}\right),$$

$$\theta=\frac{S_T\cdot f\cdot H_m^{1/3}}{gb_mn_m^2},\quad \theta'=\frac{2f}{gb_mn_m^2}\left\{\frac{4}{3}H_m^{1/3}-\frac{1}{3}hH_m^{-2/3}\right\},\quad z'=\frac{h}{H_m^2}$$

Also, Sr: Length of wetted perimeter to which apparent shear force due to interaction acts.

Shown in Figs. 6 and 7 are the relations between C_1 and C_2 determined from equations (12) and (13), and dN_3/dH, and $(N_3-N_2)/N_2$ obtained from the numerical calculations based on the equations (8) to (10) without performing said approximation and simplification for typical river courses with compound channels across the nation.

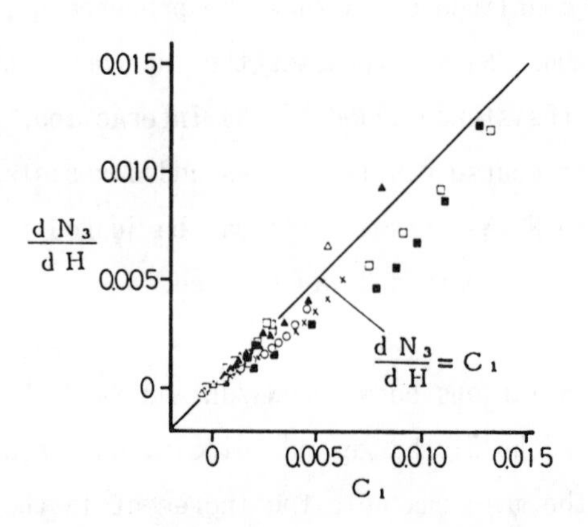

Fig. 6 Relation between C_1 and dN_3/dH

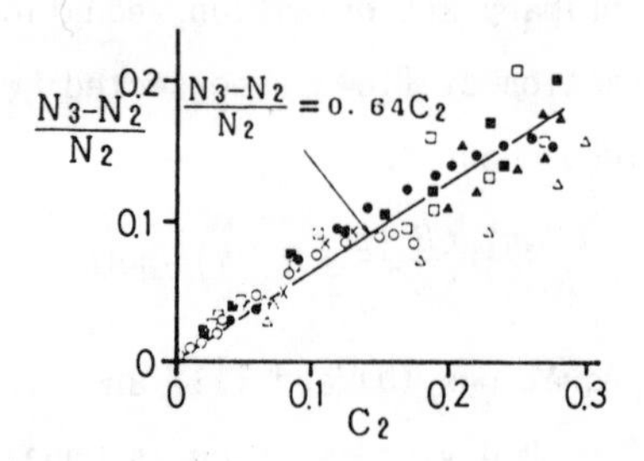

Fig. 7 Relation between C_2 and $(N_3-N_2)/N_2$

Since the approximation and simplification were performed in deriving C_1 and C_2, they do not agree with dN_3/dH, and $(N_3-N_2)/N_2$, but, it can be known that there is a universe relation as indicated below.

$$dN_3/dH \doteqdot C_1 \tag{14}$$

$$(N_3-N_2)/N_2 \doteqdot 0.64\ C_2 \tag{15}$$

5.3 Classification graph for resistance prediction In Fig. 8, the following judgment can be made: Application of the method 1 is possible for river course having a large water depth of flood channel or a wide width of main channel. On the contrary, the application of the method 1 is not appropriate to the river course having no such shapes. In this case, the method 3 has to be used where the main channel is deep or the roughness coefficient of flood channel is large. In other cases, the application of the method 2 is possible. By using classification graph, a rational judgment is made for selecting the prediction method of Nc.

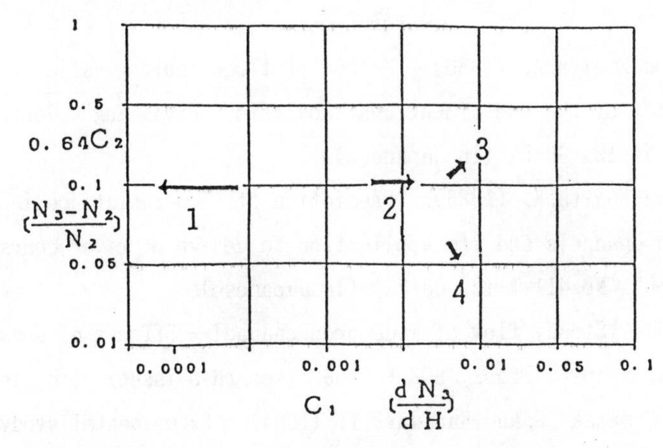

Fig 8 Resistance characteristics classification graph for river courses with compound channels, and the concept of selecting composite roughness coefficient prediction method

1. Method 1 applicable. 2. Method 1 not applicable.

3. method 3 is required. 4. method 2 is applicable.

6. Conclusions

(1) By considering the apparent shear force due to the interaction of flows in the flood channel and main channel, the accuracy of predicting the composite roughness coefficient was greately enhanced

(2) Under the conditions of $n_{fp} \fallingdotseq 3n_{mc}$ and $b/B = 0.2 \sim 0.6$, the value of f is approximately 0.17.

(3) As indexes for expressing the resistance characteristics of river

courses with compound channels, two hydraulic quantities of dN_3/dH and N_3-N_2/N_2 were selected.

(4) The resistance characteristics classification graph is proposed as functions of the said two hydraulic quantities. By using this, the selection of a method for predicting the composite roughness coefficient to be used and the finding of the change in resistance characteristics due to river improvement work can be performed easily and rationally.

References

Fukuoka, S. and Fujita, K. (1986). 'Method of flood routing-validity and limitation of the one-dimentional analysis', Civil Eng'g Journal, Vol.28, No.12, 46-51 (in Japanese).

Fukuoka, S. and Fujita, K. (1986). 'Prediction of flow resistance in compound channels and its application to design of river courses', Proc. JSCE, No.411/Ⅱ-12, 63-72, (in Japanese).

Ida, S. (1960). 'Steady flow of wide open channel— Effects of cross-sectional shape', Proc. JSCE, Vol 69, (separate issue), (in Japanese)

Ishikawa, T., Yamazaki, S. and Kanamaru, T. (1984). 'Experimental study on shallow water flow in open channels', Proc. Annual Congress of JSCE, 2, 473-474, (in Japanese).

Knight, D.W. and Demetriou, J.D. (1983) 'Flood Plain and main channel flow interaction', Jour. Hy. Eng, ASCE, Vol.109, No.8, 1412-1430.

Myers, W.R.C. (1978). 'Momentum transfer in a compound channel', Jour. Hydrauric Res., Vol.16, No2, 139-150.

Mckee, P.M., Elsawy, E.M. and Mckeogh, E.J. (1985). 'A study of the hydrauric characteristics of open channels with flood-plain,' Proc. 21st Congress, IAHR.

Ognik, H.J.M. (1985). 'The effective viscosity coefficient in 2-D depth-averaged flow models', Proc. 21st Congress, IAHR.

Wormleaton, P.R., Allen, J. and Hadjipanos, P. (1982). 'Discharge assessment in compound channel flow', Jour. Hy. Div., ASCE, Vol.108, Hy.9, 975-994

PAPER D3

International Conference on
RIVER FLOOD HYDRAULICS
17-20 September, 1990

THE GEOMORPHOLOGICALLY-EFFECTIVE FLOOD AND VERTICAL INSTABILITY IN RIVER CHANNELS - A FEEDBACK MECHANISM IN THE FLOOD SERIES FOR GRAVEL-BED RIVERS

M. D. Newson and M. G. Macklin,
Department of Geography,
University of Newcastle upon Tyne.

INTRODUCTION

It is now more than a decade since a distinction was drawn (by Wolman and Gerson, 1978) between the flood exceedence series as an energy continuum, potentially bringing about more WORK in river channels (or whole basins) as peak streamflows increase, and the quantized variant of this principle which involves a particular and distinctive role (in respect of their EFFECTIVENESS) for 'rare great floods' (Baker and Costa, 1987). Even within large floods there have been further subdivisions based upon dominant flow and sediment transport processes (Wells and Harvey, 1987). A distinction between work and effectiveness was inevitable in the wake of changes in our concepts of the sediment system in river basins (notably in the separation of supply and transport processes and thereby of slopes and channels - especially during floods - Newson, 1980) and the introduction of new equilibrium concepts in which threshold phenomena became a central focus for research (Schumm, 1977). The relative inefficiency of the sediment transport system, now quantified for the channel phase of gravel bed river systems (e.g. Hayward, 1980), makes the study of 'potential' and 'actual' rates as lively in the field of bed-load sediment transport as in the field of evaporation, with the critical question of 'availability' a further parallel between the two scientific problems. Floods may, or may not, see the conjunction of potential and actual rates; floods, therefore, may or may not represent periods of profound slope and channel changes.

This paper addresses the question of the role of the effective flood, not only as an agent of geomorphological change but as a source of new, indirect, data on potential and actual sediment transport and on the role of the threshold event brought about by an extrinsic, climatic, drive. The 'rare, great flood' may change the channel's morphology from a state of dependency on the flow to one of independence; this has obvious repercussions for the flood series as measured and as perceived in hazard terms by river managers. There are clearly potential and actual out-of-bank flood frequencies too if channels are mobile in the vertical dimension.

Hitherto, geomorphologists have been preoccupied with changes in the planform properties of alluvial channels (Gregory,

International Conference on River Flood Hydraulics, edited by W.R.White

1977). The reasons are clear: planform changes are readily recorded by historical editions of maps and aerial photographs and, because planform properties are considered the more likely to change in the shorter term (Knighton, 1984), questions of degradation and aggradation are inferred from planform change or measured over short periods in intensive field studies (e.g. arguments over the threshold transition from braided to meandering planforms based upon "primary braiding", "secondary anastamosis" etc. (Werritty and Ferguson, 1980; Thompson, 1987).

This paper, therefore, pays particular attention to vertical changes of channel profile, both in the uplands and lowlands. It uses evidence from what we might call the "active zone" of British river channels - mainly gravel-bed reaches (e.g. maps in Newson, 1986; Hooke and Redmond, 1989). Such headwater streams and gravel-bed reaches have the added advantage of making morphological change plainly visible because of their wide flow range.

Because vertical changes in channel form are critical to the longer-term evolution of whole basins in response to climatic or base-level change we are also able from this work to consider implications for post-glacial floodplain and valley floor development. This is important in view of the relevance of climatic change scenarios within present planning agendas in the field of river basin management.

THE CONTEXT OF GEOMORPHOLOGICAL FLOOD STUDIES

Many disciplines are involved in the study of floods; this conference is arranged around hydraulic studies which seek to match 'hard science' of controlled experimentation and theory with field observations. However, the empirical side of such studies, particularly in 'rare great floods' is both expensive and dangerous; delimiting the boundary conditions under which theoretically-defined processes operate is especially problematic. The geomorphological approach is, instead, inductive and uses carefully compiled and standardized post-hoc studies (Williams and Costa, 1987) to bring out regularities of flood morphology and morphological change. This geomorphological approach has recently made major strides, as evidenced by the publication of three important conferences (Mayer and Nash, 1987; Baker, Kochel and Patton, 1988; Beven and Carling, 1989). The theoretical context of a new convergence of observations and methodology in flood geomorphology was set by Schumm (1977) who first identified two important principles of river basin development:

a. <u>Sediment supply and sediment transport are disjointed in river systems (in both space and time)</u>; later Newson (1981) distinguished between "slope" and "channel" floods but recent studies in Northern England indicate that this distinction is blurred in certain events and locations.

b. Disjunction produces the potential for <u>intrinsically</u>-stimulated change in sediment transport rates and the resulting morphology (i.e. as well as the extrinsically-forced changes in flood events); catchments may be seen to differ in their response to threshold events in relation to the point they have reached in "relaxation time" (Allen, 1974) after the previous event (McEwen, 1989).

Schumm made profound progress by studying compressed time sequences: he used an experimental catchment/flume facility at Fort Collins and field data from fast-developing fluvial systems including semi-arid arroyos and streams recovering from major engineering disturbance (Schumm, Harvey and Watson, 1984). Geomorphologists working in glaciated mountain and upland river environments over more extended timescales have, however, confirmed the basic principles of Schumm's model in much larger systems. Church (1983) and Church and Ryder (1972) have suggested that the implications for large basins and longer timescales ($\geqslant 10^2$) is the development of "sedimentation zones" moving downstream by both threshold and progressive developments; such zones have been identified in the field areas reported here (Macklin and Lewin, 1989).

This paper reports mainly from the Yorkshire Dales and Northern Pennines in an area affected severely by flooding in August 1986 (Hurricane "Charley") but draw a contrast between flood effectiveness in this area of sandstone-dominated lithologies and effectiveness in catchments dominated by shale lithologies - also prominent in the British 'rare great flood' record. Lithology is important in the potential control it exerts upon not only sediment supply but also upon flood transport processes; in 'rare great' upland floods non-Newtonian transport processes have been identified as a cause of distinctive types of morphological change (Carling, 1986; Wells and Harvey, 1987). Lithology is identified by Kelson and Wells (1989) as having hydrological influences too, via the "relative magnitude and duration of high discharge events and the relative amounts of sediment and water produced within the basin". In the British uplands bedrock lithology has also controlled the nature of the drift deposits and their initial morphology which have been remodelled by fluvial action over the last 10,000 years.

The critical aspect of geomorphological effectiveness with which we deal is channel incision (and its obverse, aggradation). Schumm, Harvey and Watson (1984) refer to the special role of incision:

> "channel incision can be inherent in the erosional development of a valley and when geomorphic thresholds are exceeded incision will occur" (pp 11/12)

Clearly in relation to incision we also need to consider how (by what processes) it may occur in a threshold event and how the resulting sediments will aggrade other, downstream reaches. Put in the context of downstream morphological patterns, valley-floor development and flood records (Church, 1983; Macklin and Lewin, 1989) this apparently simple principle becomes critical to fluvial development. It is also important to consider the relative strength of the extrinsic causes of vertical channel change, i.e. between climate and land-use, and to demarcate the apparent flood frequency changes likely to be brought about by land-use or climatic changes.

FIELD STUDIES PROMPTED BY THE HURRICANE CHARLEY FLOOD

As revealed by the recent analysis by Acreman (1989) British 'rare great' floods fall into two very distinctive types (Figure 1); localised upland summer convective storms and widespread lowland frontal or snowmelt events. Hurricane Charley produced the wettest day ever recorded for England and Wales and resulted in one of the most widespread flood events recorded this century, especially in the North of England; much of the region measured 50-100mm of rainfall during the 25th and 26th of August, with > 100mm on high ground (115mm in the field areas reported here). The rainfall was of exceptional extent and duration but also locally of high intensity (Sawyer, 1987): in the field area the peak intensity was 9.4mm hr^{-1} but a significant intensity for upland flooding (6mm hr^{-1}) was exceeded for eight hours.

Three points of geomorphological detail were found to be common throughout the area affected by the Charley floods:

a. very impressive rates of <u>sediment transport</u> in terms of total loads and of the magnitude of individual clasts;

b. in many upland areas <u>channel incision</u> to bedrock and even into bedrock, with concomitant mini-fan deposition of cobble and boulder size material where gradients slackened;

c. a major <u>"run-out" of sand-sized material</u> which contributed to locally-impressive rates of floodplain aggradation for long distances downstream (Swale - up to 30 km, Tyne - up to 75 km) - almost to the coast.

Thus high rates of fluvial activity during the Hurricane Charley floods were associated mainly with VERTICAL channel change.

<u>Results from Shaw Beck, Swaledale, North Yorkshire.</u> Figure 2 maps the extent of flood effectiveness in the Shaw Beck catchment (7.5 km^2); the neighbouring Slei Gill and Faggergill catchments were also mapped but Shaw Beck is of particular interest because of its remarkable incision features and its record, in the form of both small terraces and boulder deposits, of both aggradation and incision by <u>previous effective floods</u>.

Survey of changes included morphological mapping and accurate survey of both long- and cross-sections, sediment size sampling and lichenometry. Figure 2 illustrates quite clearly an alternation between incised and depositional reaches along Shaw Beck, not as a regularly-spaced sequence but with deposition invariably downstream of incised reaches and those which experienced bedrock erosion. The sequence of channel or floodplain incision, or bluff erosion and deposition is well illustrated by a number of boulder berms indicative of heavily charged streamflow or hyperconcentrated flow (Carling, 1989). Plate 1 shows one such feature where detailed mapping + survey demonstrates that incision dominated channel change (Figure 2).

The meander bend/river cliff feature at this site has developed at a point where the narrow, confined valley broadens and is floored by fluvial deposits (including coarse flood sediments lichenometrically dated to 1851). During the Charley event, following partial blockage of the channel by coarse flood sediment, avulsion and straightening of the flow path occurred and two head-cuts developed, neither of which eroded far enough upstream to complete the straightening for post-flood flows. At other sites in the Northern Pennines head-cuts were complete. Nevertheless, the site shown in Figure 3 re-excavated its pre-flood course incising its channel, the extent of which is the more dramatic because the site also received a considerable volume of deposition from incised sites upstream. It is therefore conjectured that subsequent floods in this reach (of smaller magnitude and transporting less sediment than Charley) will contribute increased streampower to promote further incision. Had the head-cuts completed the cut off, incision would have spread more quickly to the upstream reach. (Plate 2).
It is interesting to speculate on the timing during a major flood event of the processes controlling such channel changes: major deposition, avulsion and incision. The position of the Shaw Beck reach suggests that at peak flows sediment was eroded from the reach immediately upstream, transported probably in the form of a hyperconcentrated flow and dumped in the upper part of the study reach. This resulted in the blocking of the pre-flood channel and diversion of flow across the valley floor. As the avulsed flows re-entered the pre-flood channel downstream they eroded flood sediments producing a head-cut that moved upstream rapidly. The erosion was most probably occasioned by clear water following the massive deposition.

It is necessary to speculate on the hydraulic conditions which prevailed during such developments; Wells and Harvey (1987) were able to attempt a reconstruction of flow processes based on morphology. Carling (1989) suggests high magnitude channel flows in small catchments such as Shaw Beck are Newtonian in character even with concentration of gravel and boulders up to 50%. His study of boulder berms stresses the importance of flow separation and vorticity in creating the conditions for (sudden) deposition, notably at points where constrained channels widen. Whilst berms are not a feature of Shaw Beck "fill and cut" sites they occur very definitely at sites of flow expansion. As Wells and Harvey (1987) stipulate, slope activity must be involved in some way to create high sediment concentrations that include a wide range of grain sizes (they quote 50mm hr^{-1} rain and widespread overland flow). However, McEwan and Werritty (1988) demonstrate how reactivation of old bluffs and slides (in their case created by a flood 22 years previously) can be equally important. This is the most likely case in Shaw Beck, with the additional effects of intensive erosion of old mine spoil heaps upstream.

The fill and cut sequence and head-cutting generally is important to identify as a process because it extends for the confined upland valley environment the primary braiding and secondary anastamosing processes proposed for braided and wandering gravel bed rivers in wider alluvial reaches (Werritty and Ferguson, 1980; Thompson, 1987).

It is clear from the sections measured in the reach near Shaw House that incision of Shaw Beck has been a recurring response to 'rare, great' floods (just how rare and great we discuss below). Figure 3 shows possibly three terrace levels above the low feature formed by the Charley flood incision. Boulder deposits on the two lower terraces have been dated by lichenomtric techniques (using the lichen species *Rhizocarpon geographicum*) and appear to have been formed by floods reported by local commentators in 1835 and 1866. Coarse flood deposits attributed to the latter event, which seems to have been of a similar magnitude to Charley, are evident at a number of sites in Shaw Beck (Figure 2).

In terms of flood frequency analysis, Charley was analysed in a variety of ways using both rainfall and peak discharge information. Estimates settle around a 50-year return period (Institute of Hydrology, 1988), though many stations recorded their highest flows, albeit in short records. The work of relating the dated sequence of channel incision in Shaw Beck to documented floods and statistical frequencies continues but, purely from observation, it can be concluded that threshold effects dominate. Clearly the stability of side-slopes is involved in creating thresholds (a major rotational slip was initiated by Charley) as is the position of the channel bed in relation to the alternating sandstones and shales. The effect of mining activity last century must also be evaluated.

Overbank fine-grained flood sediments and floodplain stratigraphy in the Tyne Basin. Hurricane Charley produced very widespread flooding resulting in a considerable "runout" of suspended material from the Northern Pennines and the deposition of extensive sheets of fine grained sediment (mostly sand) across the floodplain of the Lower Tyne.

Bank erosion at Low Prudhoe (NZ 088637) in the Lower Tyne valley, 15 km west of Newcastle upon Tyne, revealed extensive sections in the floodplain of the River Tyne. Floodplain sediments were found to be composed of 2 to 3m of finely laminated sands and silts overlying 2m of sandy gravels. Granulometric and chemical analysis of prominent sand layers in the upper fine grained alluvial unit showed them to have similar physical and chemical properties to sands deposited overbank on the Tyne floodplain during Hurricane Charley (Macklin and Dowsett, 1989). This suggested that floodplain sediments at this site could provide a valuable record of recent major overbank floods in the Lower Tyne valley. Brakenridge (1988) confirms floodplain stratigraphy as "a complex but decipherable record of present and past river flood regimes, of other aspects of river history and of the internal and external geomorphic variables that control such histories" (page 139). The Low Prudhoe section confirms his optimism.

The Tyne is very well served by documented flood records, stretching back well over 200 years (Archer, personal communication). It is also fortunate that in the headwaters of the South Tyne metals have been mined since the Roman occupation, with the later stages of mining (up to early 20th Century) exceptionally well documented (Dunham 1944). There is thus a natural tracer and, with care, the metal concentrations can be used to date vertically accreted fine grained flood sediments with some precision (cf. Knox, 1987; Lewin and Macklin, 1987). Macklin (1985) has described the methodology involved and the study of the metal content of fine grained sediments deposited overbank in Charley (Macklin and Dowsett, 1989) show that the floodplain record is without substantial lag time between sediment release and sediment deposition. This also appears to have been the case during the period of mining when fine metal waste was usually discharged directly into the nearest stream. Just under 2.5m of stratified deposits were sampled from the banks of a laterally stable reach at Low Prudhoe (basin contributing 2198 km^2). Conventional sedimentological analyses were performed on each significant depositional unit and metals contents analysed by digestion in HNO^3 followed by atomic absorption spectrophotometry with an air-acetylene flame. Twenty-six flood events(dating from between 1890 and 1947) were detected in the stratigraphy, culminating with the Charley flood. Sediment metal contents (Fig. 4) allow four phases of floodplain development to be identified that can be directly related to that provided by historical documents recording widespread avulsion in the Tyne. These are:

a. 1890-1900 Floodplain sediment record includes more events than documentary record; flood lenses thinner at end of period,

b. 1900-1926 Both records closely matched; flood events from North Tyne marked by metal-dilute layers,

c. 1927-1937 Floodplain sedimentation by only four floods - banks by now high above active channel by incision.

d. Post 1937 Identifiable artificial cause of incision - gravel working - and formation of current channel bed, undercutting old bridge nearby.

Brakenridge (1988) is of the opinion that "periods of enhanced fluvial activity are capable of producing river terraces" and the current banks at Low Prudhoe would appear to be "false" in that the river is really abutting its own (most recent) low terrace, reachable only by a flood as large as Charley.

THE RELATIVE EFFECTS OF CLIMATE AND LAND-USE ON LONGER-TERM VERTICAL CHANNEL INSTABILITY

The prospects of imminent climatic change have encouraged geomorphologists to take a long-term (10,000 years) approach to the relative roles of sediment supply (considered to be changed most by headwater influences such as vegetation cover and land-use) and sediment transfer controlled by changes in flood magnitude and frequency related to climate. Church and Slaymaker (1989) use the sediment yield measurements made routinely in British Columbia to suggest that fluvial adjustment to post-glacial conditions is incomplete; since sediment yields increase downstream they must be supplied by a continuing reworking of floodplain sediments. Their implicit view, therefore, is that climatic history dominates the boundary conditions experienced by river transport processes in the present day.

The situation in British rivers is hard to decipher with the same clarity. Newson's (1986) review of UK sediment yield figures cannot be interpreted in the same way; whilst the exponent of the yield v area graph shows the importance of upland sources this may reflect the fact that yields in upland Britain have been measured mainly in environments which are considered to be disturbed by land-use or land management practice. From other British evidence it is clear that, as in British Columbia, channel change and therefore sediment transfer dominate the piedmont zone; Hooke and Redmond (1989) conclude that 35% of rivers draining the uplands of Britain are experiencing planform instability. It is Hooke and Redmond's impression that artificial influences are more important than natural ones with channelization and land-use the main candidates for causes, but they also mention intrinsic river system changes such as meander cut-offs.

In comparing results from North America with those from Britain it is important to remember the different history and intensity of cultural impacts on ecosystems; nevertheless whilst drawing different conclusions, these reviews mention only river channel planform changes whereas the focus of work here has been on vertical instabilities. In this context the review by Macklin and Lewin (in press) of Holocene river alluviation in Britain is critical. Eight phases of alluviation are identified in the last 10,000 years with 8000-5200 yr B.P. a time of channel incision, slow alluviation or stability. The timing of the river instability coincides with the global climatic discontinuities identified by Wendland and Bryson (1974). The implication is that although prehistoric and historic forest clearance and agriculture were important for initiating soil erosion, significant redistribution of eroded sediment may have occurred only during relatively short periods of abrupt climatic change characterised by major changes in flood frequency and magnitude.

CONCLUSIONS

The field studies reported here fortuitously initiated by widespread regional flooding, have focused the flood effectiveness argument on two issues of major importance to fluvial geomorphology and indirectly to flood hydrology and engineering response to flooding and the extrinsic changes affecting river basins. These issues are:

a. The role of threshold behaviour during rare, great floods in promoting incision and aggradation of channels, both in the uplands and downstream in floodplain reaches. Threshold phenomena were critical throughout the system and that the thresholds are mainly geomorphological (not vegetational as in semi-arid climates - Graf, 1979).

b. The importance of quaternary climatic history and lithology of river basins in controlling (vertically) processes which set up the relevant thresholds; feedbacks from effective floods bring about long-lasting shifts in control on morphological development (e.g. incised channels develop more stream power at bank-full).

The great spatial variability in geomorphological response to floods has always stimulated debate; lithology has much to offer as an explanation, especially under climatic conditions in which vegetation does not control the force-resistance relationship (Graf, 1979). In the shale lithologies of British uplands valley sides are gentler, drift mantles more cohesive. Fluvial erosion produces both a pebble-size and a silt/clay load, but not the boulder, cobble and sand loads characteristic of the Carboniferous uplands. The Ordovician and Silurian shale gravel of both upland and piedmont reaches shows a marked tendency to armoured beds, or to imbrication, introducing a channel supply factor in addition to slope supply (Arkell et. al. 1983). Interestingly, Werritty (pers comm) records the Caldwell Burn in Dumfrieshire, which is developed on Lower Palaeozoic shales, as having passed a 1,000-year flood without substantial channel change. By contrast, the coarser blocky bed material produced by Carboniferous sandstone lithologies (and also by igneous ones) allows little armouring, and since protrusion compensates for weight (Fenton and Abbott, 1977) the very large clasts can be moved. There is thus much less tendency to incise on shale lithologies and therefore a weaker relationship between upland flood episodes and downstream valley floor history. Shaw Beck, which has alternating bands of coarse sandstone and weak shales, shows the "ideal" combination in terms of a balance between mechanical strength/weakness and transportability by flood flows. In Shaw Beck the thresholds for incision may coincide with lithological boundaries in the channel bed, or slopes of the catchment.

More minor regional effects are linked with tributary junctions (Pennine streams being relatively less branched) and vegetation's role in promoting bank stability (metal contaminated alluvium curtailing vegetative recolonisation of river systems after formative flood events in the Pennines, Macklin and Smith (in press)).

Corollaries of wider hydrological significance include:

a. Indirect estimation of flood flows in the uplands is error-prone on the basis of both cross-sectional and energy ("trash") line data as alternating periods of differing flow processes, controlled by the character and content of sediment entrained in flow, may occur. (Acreman, 1989, reveals just how important flow reconstruction techniques are to our knowledge of 'rare, great floods' in Britain)

b. Cross-sectional data is also unreliable in floodplain sections when estimating peak discharges for past floods recorded by monumental or other "permanent" markers. In channels where alternating periods of incision and aggradation are the long-term mode of the channel transport system there are also problems of changing human perception of the relative frequency of flooding - documentary flood evidence needs to be inspected carefully. McEwen (1989) points to the benefits of using a long rainfall record as a check in conjunction with documentary histories of floods.

c. It is little wonder that the "bank-full discharge" varies in frequency within river systems (Lewin, 1989); the relative position at which afflux occurs will vary according to the recent vertical tendency of the reach in question.

d. The extent to which the channel network adjusts during flood events will control the extent to which network properties are useful in predicting flood peaks (Patton, 1988).

In view of these problems of historical interpretation it is crucial that research continues into the relative influence of climate and of land-use forcing functions and intrinsic change in river systems. The Hurricane Charley flood was not a 'rare, great flood' in the longer term and in hydrological terms; the record of floods compiled by Acreman (1989) suggests that the Probable Maximum Flood is twice as large as those we have recorded in the last two hundred years; it is intriguing to think that, as far as the climatic signal is concerned, our record is moderate. Notwithstanding the weakness of the documented flood forcing function, it appears that climate changes are likely to control threshold responses by river systems; cultural influences working directly on the thresholds blur the spacing and timing of the results.

REFERENCES

1. Acreman, M. C., 1989. Extreme historical U.K. floods and maximum flood estimation. J. Inst. Wat. and Env. Mgmt., 3, 404-412.

2. Allen, J. R. L., 1974. Reaction, relaxation and lag in natural sedimentary systems; general principles, examples and lessons. Earth Science Reviews, 10, 263-342.

3. Arkell, B., Leeks, G., Newson, M. and Oldfield, F., 1983. Trapping and tracking: some recent observations of supply and transport of coarse sediment from upland Wales. Spec. Publs, Int. Ass. Sediment, 6, 107-119.

4. Baker, V. R., Kochel, R. C., and Patton, P. C., 1988. Flood geomorphology. John Wiley and Sons, 503 pp.

5. Baker, V. R. and Costa, J. E., 1987. Flood power. In L. Mayer and D. Nash (eds), Catastrophic flooding. Allen & Unwin, London, 1-24.

6. Beven, K. and Carling, P., 1989. Floods. Hydrological, sedimentological and geomorphological implications. John Wiley & Sons, Chichester, 290 pp.

7. Brakenridge, G. R., 1988. River flood regime and floodplain stratigraphy. In Baker, V. R., Kochel, R. C. and Patton, P. C. (eds), Flood Geomorphology. John Wiley & Sons, 139-156.

8. Carling, P. A., 1986. Peat slides in Teesdale and Weardale, Northern Pennines, July 1983: description and failure mechanisms. Earth Surface Processes and Landforms, 11, 193-206.

9. Carling, P. A., 1989. Hydrodynamic models of boulder berm deposition. Geomorphology, 2, 319-340.

10. Church, M., 1983. Patterns of instability in a wandering gravel bed channel. Spec. Publs. Int. Ass. Sediment, 6, 169-180.

11. Church, M. and Ryder, J. M., 1972. Paraglacial sedimentation: a consideration of fluvial processes conditioned by glaciation. Bull. Geol. Soc. Amer., 83, 3059-3072.

12. Church, M. and Slaymaker, O., 1989. Disequilibrium of Holocene sediment yield in glaciated British Columbia. Nature, 337 (6206), 452-454.

13. Costa, J. E., 1988. Rheologic, geomorphic and sedimentologic differentiation of water floods, hyperconcentrated flows and debris flows. In V. R. Baker, R. C. Kochel and P. C. Patton (eds). Flood Geomorphology. John Wiley & Sons, 113-137.

14. Dunham, K. C., 1944. The production of galena and associated minerals in the Northern Pennines; with comparative statistics for Gt. Britain. Trans. Instn. Min. Metall., 53, 181-252.

15. Fenton, J. D. and Abbott, J. E., 1977. Initial movement of grains on a stream bed: the effect of relative protrusion. Proc. R. Soc. Lond., A., 352, 523-537.

16. Graf, W. L., 1979. The development of montane arroyos and gullies. Earth Surface Processes, 4, (1), 1-14.

17. Gregory, K. J. (ed), 1977. River channel changes. John Wiley & Sons, Chichester.

18. Hayward, J. A., 1980. Hydrology and stream sediment from the Torlesse stream catchment. Lincoln College, Canterbury, New Zealand. Spec. Publ. 17.

19. Hooke, J. M. and Redmond, C. E., 1989. River-channel changes in England and Wales. J. Inst. Wat. and Env. Mgmt., 3, 328-335.

20. Institute of Hydrology/British Geological Survey, 1988. Hydrological Data United Kingdom, 1986 Yearbook. N.E.R.C., Wallingford.

21. Kelson, K. I. and Wells, S. G., 1989. Geologic influences on fluvial hydrology and bedload transport in small mountainous watersheds, northern New Mexico, U.S.A. Earth Surface Processes and Landforms, 14 (8), 671-690.

22. Knighton, A. D., 1984. Fluvial forms and processes. Edward Arnold.

23. Knox, J. C., 1987. Historical valley floor sedimentation in the Upper Mississippi Valley. Annals. Assoc. Amer. Geogrs., 77, 224-244.

24. Knox, J. C., 1988. Climatic influence on Upper Mississippi Valley floods. In Baker, V. R., Kochel, R. C. and Patton, P. C. (eds). Flood Geomorphology. John Wiley & Sons, 279-300.

25. Kochel, R. C., 1988. Geomorphic impact of large floods: review and new perspectives on magnitudes and frequency. In Baker, V. R., Kochel, R. C. and Patton, P. C. (eds). Flood Geomorphology. John Wiley & Sons, 169-187.

26. Lewin, J., 1989. Floods in fluvial geomorphology. In K. Beven and P. Carling (eds). Floods: hydrological sedimentological and geomorphological implications. John Wiley & Sons, Chichester, 265-284.

27. Lewin, J. and Macklin, M. G., 1987. Metal mining and floodplain sedimentation in Britain. In Gardiner, V. (ed). International Geomorphology, 1986. John Wiley & Sons, Chichester, Part I, 1009-1027.

28. Macklin, M. G., 1985. Floodplain sedimentation in the Upper Axe Valley, Mendip, England. Trans. Inst. Br. Geogrs., 10, 235-244.

29. Macklin, M. G. and Dowsett, R. B., 1989. The chemical and physical speciation of trace metals in fine grained overbank flood sediments in the Tyne basin, north-east England. Catena, 16 (2), 135-151.

30. Macklin, M. G., and Lewin, J., 1989. Sediment transfer and transformation of an alluvial floor: the River South Tyne, Northumbria, U.K. Earth Surface Processes and Landforms, 14 (3), 233-246.

31. Macklin, M. G. and Lewin, J. (in press). Holocene river alluviation in Britain. Proceedings 2nd Int. Geomorph. Conf., Stuttgart.

32. Macklin, M. G. and Smith, R. S. (in press). Historic riparian vegetation development and alluvial metallophyte plant communities in the Tyne basin, north-east England, U.K. In J. B. Thornes (ed), Vegetation and Erosion, John Wiley & Sons, Chichester.

33. Macklin, M. G., Rumsby, B. T. and Newson, M. D. (in submission). Historic overbank floods and floodplain sedimentation in the Lower Tyne Valley; north-east England.

34. Mayer, L. and Nash, D. (eds), 1987. Catastrophic flooding. Allen & Unwin, London.

35. McEwen, L. J., 1989. Extreme rainfall and its implications for flood frequency: a case study of the middle River Tweed basin, Scotland. Trans. Inst. Br. Geogr., 14, 287-298.

36. McEwen, L. J., 1989. River channel changes in response to flooding in the Upper River Dee catchment, Aberdeenshire, over the last 200 years. In K. Beven and P. Carling (eds). Floods: hydrological sedimentological and geomorphological implications. John Wiley & Sons, Chichester, 219-238.

37. McEwen, L. J. and Werritty, A., 1988. The hydrology and long-term geomorphic significance of a flash flood in the Cairngorm Mountains, Scotland. Catena, 15 (3/4), 361-377.

38. Newson, M. D., 1980. The geomorphological effectiveness of floods - a contribution stimulated by two recent events in mid-Wales. Earth Surface Processes, 5, 1-16.

39. Newson, M. D., 1986. River basin engineering - fluvial geomorphology. J.I.W.E.S., 40 (4), 307-324.

40. Newson, M. D., 1989. Flood effectiveness in river basins: progress in Britain in a decade of drought. In K. Beven and P. Carling (eds). Floods: Hydrological, sedimentological and geomorphological implications. John Wiley, Chichester, 151-183.

41. Patton, P. C., 1988. Drainage basin morphometry and floods. In Baker, V. R., Kochel, R. C. and Patton, P. C. (eds). Flood Geomorphology. John Wiley & Sons, 56-64.

42. Sawyer, M. S., 1987. The rainfall of 25-26 August, 1986. Weather, 42 (4), 114-117.

43. Schumm, S. A., 1977. The fluvial system. John Wiley & Sons.

44. Schumm, S. A., Harvey, M. D. and Watson, C. C., 1984. Incised channels, morphology, dynamics and control. Water Resources Publications, Littleton, Colorado, 200 pp.

45. Thompson, A., 1987. Channel response to flood events in a divided upland stream. In V. Gardiner (ed). International Geomorphology, John Wiley & Sons, Chichester. 691-709.

46. Wells, S. G. and Harvey, A. M., 1987. Sedimentologic and geomorphic variations in storm-generated alluvial fans, Howgill Fells, northwest England. Geol. Soc. Amer. Bull., 98, 182-198.

47. Wendland, W. M. and Bryson, R. A., 1974. Dating climatic episodes of the Holocene. Quaternary Research, 4, 9-24.

48. Werritty, A. (undated personal communication). A tale of two floods: a controlled comparison of flood response in Southern Scotland. 7 pp.

49. Werritty, A., 1984. Stream response to flash floods in upland Scotland. In T. P. Burt and D. E. Walling (eds). Catchment experiments in fluvial geomorphology. Geo Books, Norwich, 537-560.

50. Werritty, A. and Ferguson, R., 1980. Pattern changes in a Scottish braided river over 1, 30 and 200 years. In R. A. Callingford, D. A. Davidson and J. Lewin (eds). Timescales in geomorphology. John Wiley & Sons, Chichester, 53-68.

51. Williams, G. P. and Costa, J. E., 1988. Geomorphic measurement after a flood. In V. R. Baker, R. C. Kochel and P. C. Patton (eds). Flood Geomorphology. John Wiley & Sons, 65-77.

52. Wolman, M. G., Gerson, R., 1978. Relative scales of time and effectiveness of climate in watershed geomorphology. Earth Surface Processes, 3, 189-208.

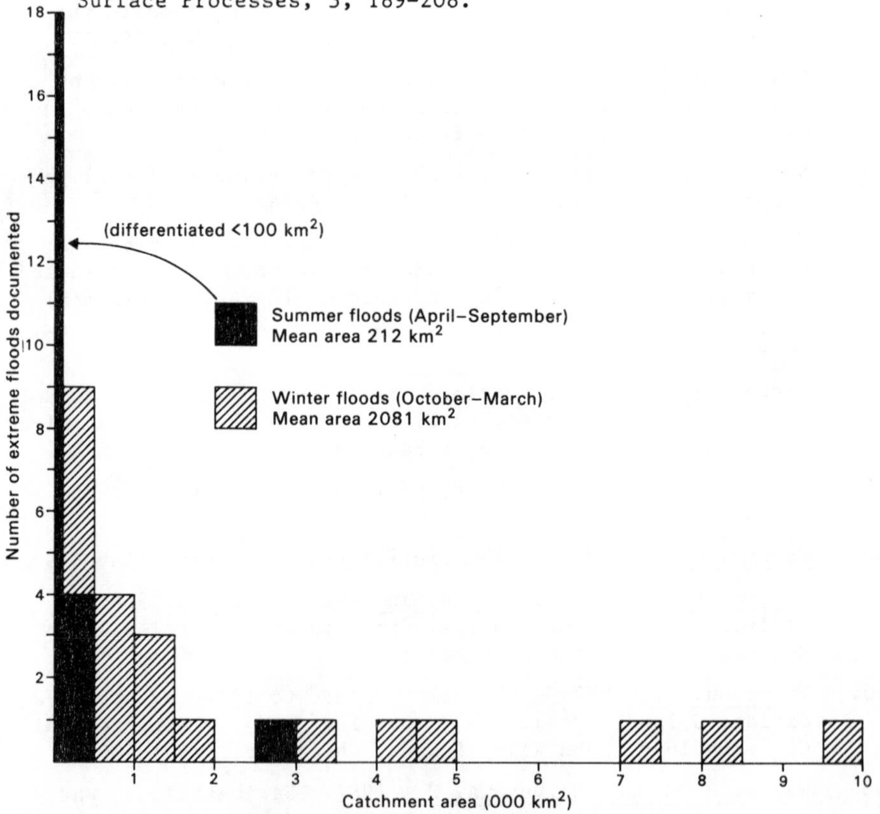

Figure 1 The duality of British rare floods (from Acreman, 1989)

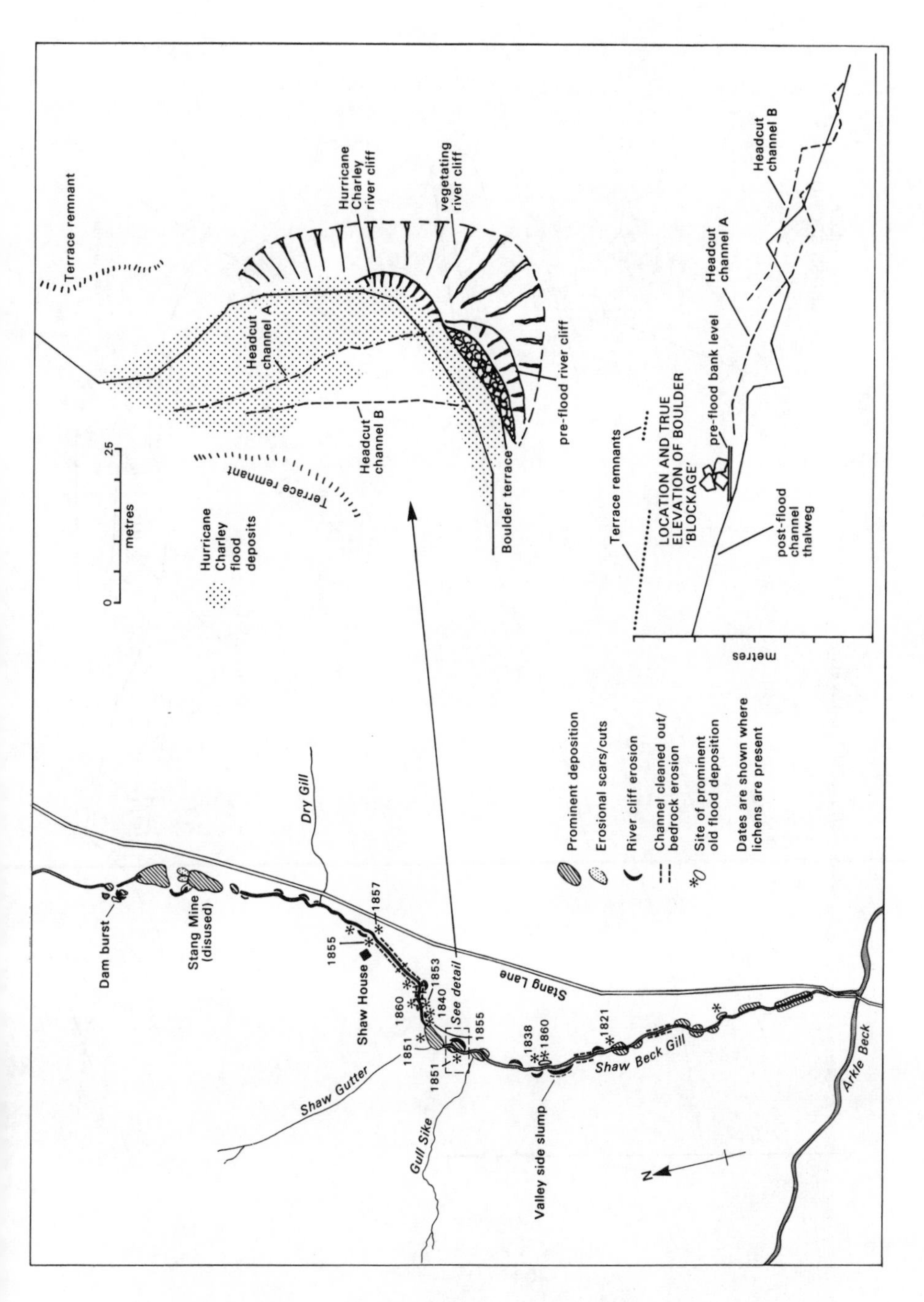

Figure 2 Flood effectiveness in Shaw Beck, Swaledale, Yorkshire, UK, after Hurricane Charley. Detail is of fill and cut site, plan and section.

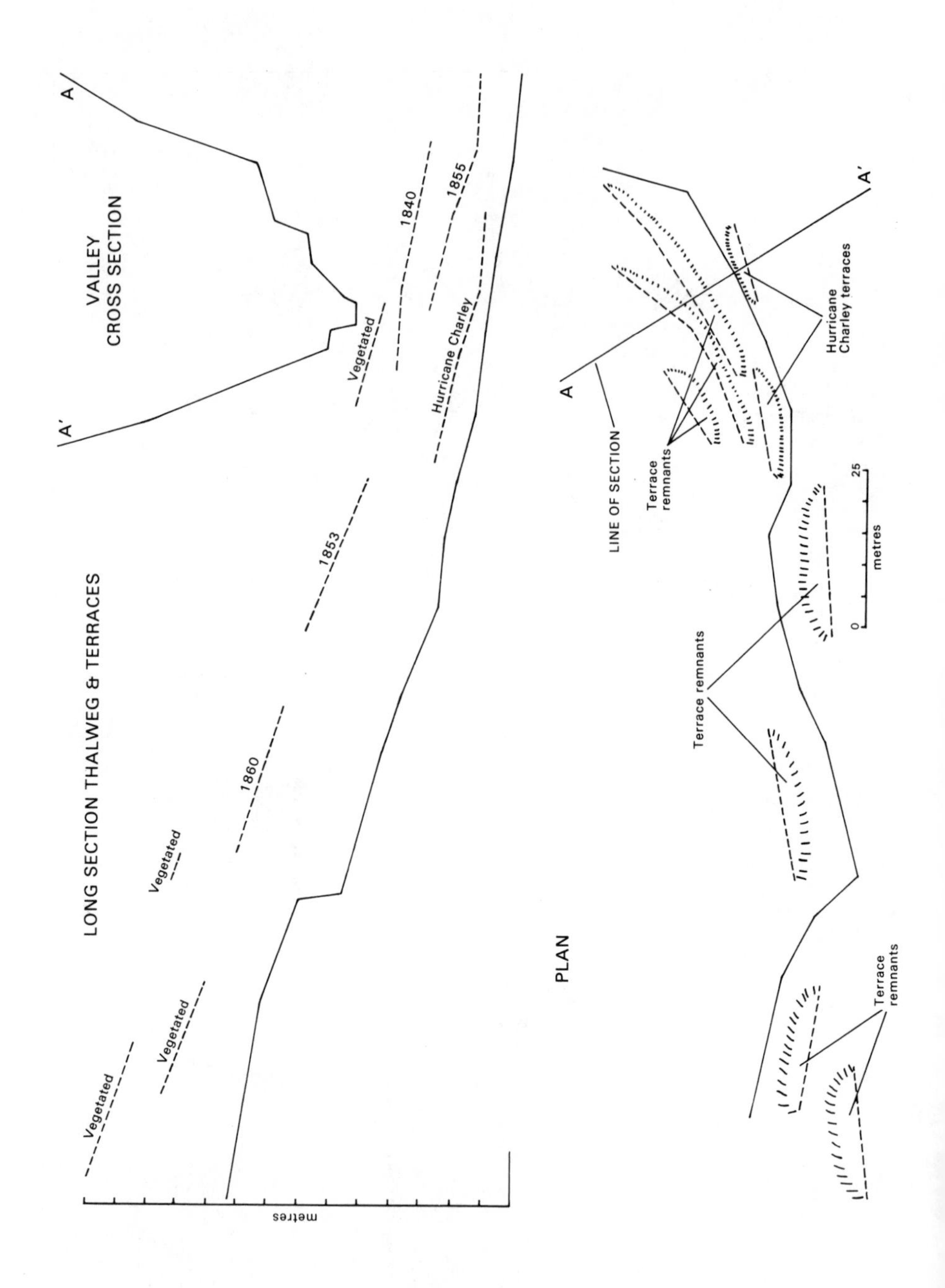

Figure 3 Plan and sections of terraced section of Shaw Beck (dates from lichenometry of boulder deposits on the appropriate terrace).

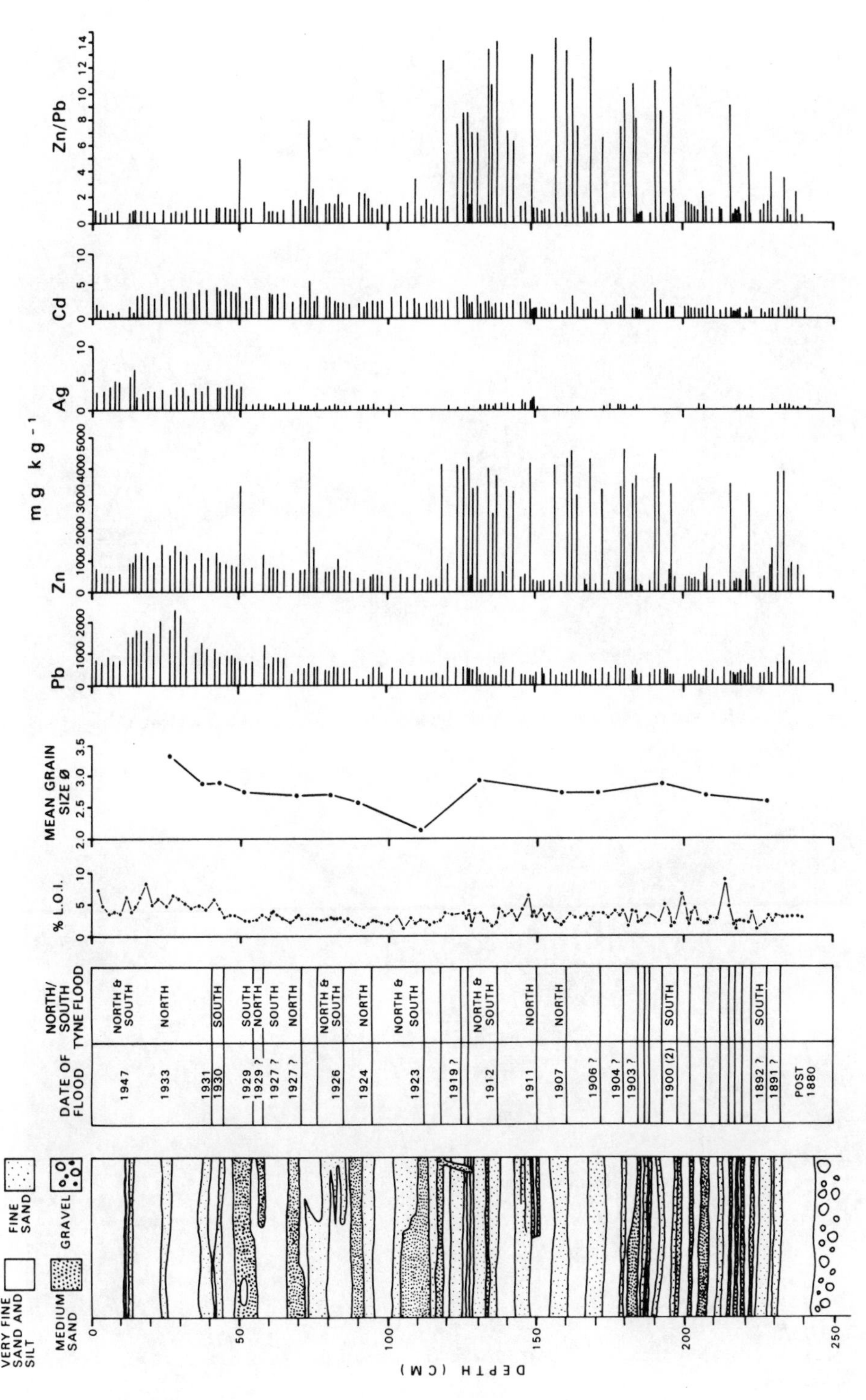

Figure 4 Stratigraphic analysis of Tyne floodplain sediments.

PLATE 1
Major site of channel blockage and headcutting, Shaw Beck, Swaledale.

PLATE 2
Terraces resulting from successive incision of Shaw Beck during the last 150 years.

Hydraulics of Flood Flows

International Conference on
RIVER FLOOD HYDRAULICS
17-20 September, 1990

CONVEYANCE DISTRIBUTION IN MULTI–SECTION STREAMS

S.P. Chee, Ph.D., C.Eng., P.Eng.
Professor of Civil and
Environmental Engineering
University of Windsor, Canada

S. Ray, M.A.Sc.
Formerly Research Graduate
University of Windsor, Canada

ABSTRACT

The distribution of flow in multi–section stream channels was investigated analytically and with the aid of experimental observations. The analysis is based on the development of the velocity distribution of wide channels and integrating the results into compound channels based on the geometry of the cross–section and roughness pattern. The developed theory can be applied to any cross–sectional configuration.

INTRODUCTION

Flow computation in compound channels has frequently been carried out by dividing the cross–section into simple left and right side channels with a central main section together with a common energy gradient, such as the dominant channel bed slope, to determine the individual flows, which on summation will provide the total streamflow (Knight et al. 1983, 1984; Morris 1963; Myers 1982, 1984; Wormleaton et al. 1982). The Manning equation or the Chezy flow resistance relation is widely employed in conjunction with this method. In some occasions, departure from straight vertical line division has been utilized to subdivide the compound cross–section.

Even in single cell river cross–sections, channel configuration has been found to influence the resistance of streamflow (Chow 1959; Hey 1979; Keulegan 1939). When the channel is multi–sectional and the boundary has more than one roughness, the system becomes more complicated. A method to solve this problem is described in this paper.

The proposed methodology of computing streamflow takes into account the shape of the multi–sectional channel as well as the roughness distribution. In order to adequately define the channel geometry and roughness pattern, as many vertical strips as are necessary would be used to properly delineate and define these hydraulic properties of the section.

A grid system is set up to encompass the vertical strips within the channel cross–section. Point velocities at nodal points within each strip are calculated. These strip velocity profiles are then integrated with developed formulae to obtain the actual point velocities of the entire cross–section.

International Conference on River Flood Hydraulics, edited by W.R.White

From these final velocity profiles, the flow for any part or the entire channel is determined by numerically integrating these point velocities with the corresponding flow areas.

NAVIER–STOKES EQUATION

The Reynolds form of the Navier–Stokes equation in two–dimensional flow is

$$\rho \left(\frac{\partial \bar{u}}{\partial t} + \bar{v} \frac{\partial \bar{u}}{\partial y} + \bar{u} \frac{\partial \bar{u}}{\partial x} \right) = - \frac{\partial \bar{P}}{\partial x} + \frac{\partial}{\partial y} \left(\mu \frac{\partial \bar{u}}{\partial y} \right) + \frac{\partial}{\partial y} \left(- \rho \, \overline{u'v'} \right) + F_x \qquad (1)$$

in which $\bar{u}$, $\bar{v}$, are the average velocities in the x and y directions; u', v' denote the local velocity variations; ρ, μ represent fluid density and viscosity; $\bar{P}$ is the average pressure; F_x is the body force. For the case of steady, uniform flow in the x–direction, with gravity as the only body force, and integrating the resulting equation with retention only of the turbulent shear

$$\frac{\partial}{\partial y} \left(\mu \frac{\partial \bar{u}}{\partial y} - \rho \, \overline{u'v'}\right) = \rho \, g \, S \qquad (2)$$

$$\tau_t = \rho \, g \, S \, (Y - y) \qquad (3)$$

in which S = bed slope, g = gravity acceleration, τ_t = turbulent shear, Y = distance of bed to surface, y = distance from bed (Fig. 1).

VELOCITY RELATION

The velocity distribution of a stream can be obtained using Prandtl's mixing length theory as

$$\tau_t = \rho \kappa^2 y^2 \left(\frac{du}{dy} \right)^2 \qquad (4)$$

where κ denotes von Karman's constant; u is the velocity at a distance y from the bed.

VERTICAL STRIP ANALYSIS

The cross–section of the channel is divided into vertical finite strips as illustrated in Fig. 2. Combining Eqs. (3) and (4) and applying it to a vertical strip

$$\frac{du_s}{dy_s} = \frac{1}{\kappa y_s} [gS_s (Y_s - y_s)] \tag{5}$$

where the subscript "s" has been added to the same variables to indicate that they apply to the strip.

Denoting $\epsilon_s = y_s/Y_s$ and substituting in Eq. (5)

$$\frac{du_s}{d\epsilon_s} = \frac{V_{*s}}{\kappa} \frac{(1 - \epsilon_s)^{1/2}}{\epsilon_s} \tag{6}$$

in which V_{*s} is given by

$$V_{*s} = (gY_sS_s)^{1/2} \tag{7}$$

Integrating Eq. (6) gives

$$u_s = \frac{V_{*s}}{\kappa} F_1 (\epsilon_s) + C_s \tag{8}$$

$$\text{where } F_1(\epsilon_s) = 2(1-\epsilon_s)^{1/2} - \ln \frac{[1 + (1-\epsilon_s)^{1/2}]}{[1 - (1-\epsilon_s)^{1/2}]} \tag{9}$$

The constant of integration C_s can be obtained from the strip continuity equation

$$\int_0^{Y_s} u_s \, dA_s = A_s V_s \tag{10}$$

in which dA_s represents a narrow horizontal area of the vertical strip of thickness dy_s and at a distance y_s from the bed; A_s and V_s denote the area and mean velocity of the vertical strip, respectively. Equation (10) can be transformed to

$$V_s = \int_0^1 u_s \, d\epsilon_s \tag{11}$$

Solution of Eq. (11) results in

$$C_s = V_s + \frac{2}{3}\frac{V_{*s}}{\kappa} \tag{12}$$

Substituting Eq. (12) into Eq. (8) gives

$$u_s = V_s - \frac{V_{*s}}{\kappa} F_2 (\epsilon_s) \tag{13}$$

$$\text{where } F_2 (\epsilon_s) = -F_1 (\epsilon_s) - \frac{2}{3} \tag{14}$$

Equation (13) is the general equation for the velocity profile for the vertical strip.

CHANNEL–STRIP INTER–RELATIONSHIPS

Theoretical equations of point velocity and flow relating to the overall channel cross–section (u) and strips (u_s) are introduced to generate total solution of the problem. In order to relate the point strip velocities (u_s) to the channel mean velocity, V, a normalizing dimensionless equation is used in the form of

$$\frac{u}{V} = E1 \left(\frac{u_s}{V_s} \right)^{E2} \tag{15}$$

in which u_s/V_s is the dimensionless velocity profile of the strip which can be expressed using Eqs. (13) and (14) as

$$\frac{u_s}{V_s} = 1 - \frac{g^{1/2} n_s^{1/2}}{Y_s^{1/6} \kappa} F_2 (\epsilon_s) \tag{16}$$

In deriving Eq. (16), the Manning flow resistance equation is used in the form of

$$V_s = \frac{1}{n_s} Y_s S_s^{1/2} \tag{17}$$

A continuity relation is required for the solution of Eq. (15) as

$$\Sigma\Sigma \left(E1 \left(\frac{u_s}{V_s} \right)^{E2} V \Delta A\right) = AV \tag{18}$$

where ΔA denotes the nodal point velocity area and applies to both the whole cross–section as well as to the strip.

EXPERIMENTAL PROGRAMME

Multi–sectional and single cell polygonal channels were used in the laboratory to verify the theory. Observations were made in flumes with widths of 475 mm and 1524 mm. Channels with diverse cross–sectional shapes were fabricated in wood and installed inside these flumes. In order to achieve a wide range of roughnesses, steel meshes were employed of different thicknesses and patterns which were fastened to the bed and sides.

Measurements of velocity through the depth and across the channel width were made using miniature current meters and magnetic velocity probes. A centrifugal pump–motor unit capable of delivering up to 300 ℓ/s was used to circulate the water in an open sump channel system. Discharges were measured using a recording magnetic flow meter and further verified by numerically integrating the measured velocity profiles.

RESULTS AND DISCUSSION

Central to the solution of the problem is the ability to compute the velocity distribution of the channel. The velocity profile of the cross–section can be derived using Eq. (15) in conjunction with Eq. (16). Assuming that the mean channel velocity, V, is given, numerical point velocities can be calculated provided the coefficient E1 and the exponent E2 are known. With the aid of laboratory observations, these parameters E1 and E2 were studied.

Tests were made in the laboratory over a wide range of discharges and roughnesses on compound sections as well as single cell polygonal channels to investigate the behaviour of the quantities E1 and E2. Some of the results are shown in Figs. 3 and 4. As can be observed from Fig. 3, the value of the coefficient E1 tends very closely to unity and is not sensitive to channel configuration, roughness and flow. However, the exponent E2 is influenced by the geometry of the cross–section as illustrated in Fig. 4.

With the knowledge that the velocity coefficient E1 can be taken as unity and is independent of the shape of the cross–section, the value of the velocity exponent E2 can be calculated for any channel configuration using Eqs. (18) and (16). With the value of E1 and E2 known, the velocity distribution of the channel can be computed using Eqs. (15) and (16) for any given value of the mean channel velocity. The conveyance in any part of the multi–section channel can be obtained by numerically integrating the developed velocity profile for the desired section.

CONCLUSIONS

The method of calculating the conveyance distribution of multi–section stream channels described in this paper showed good agreement between theoretical and measured laboratory values. However, it is desirable that the range of cross–sectional shapes, roughnesses, and discharges should be extended in laboratory channels and confirmed in rivers in nature.

NOMENCLATURE

A – Total channel cross–sectional area
A_s – Area of vertical strip
dA_s – Narrow strip area
C_s – Integration constant (Eq. 12)
dy_s – Strip thickness
E1 – Velocity coefficient (Eq. 15)
E2 – Shape factor (velocity exponent – Eq. (15))
F_x – Body force
g – Gravity acceleration
n – Manning's coefficient of channel
n_s – Manning's coefficient of vertical strip
$\overline{P}$ – Body force
S – Overall channel energy gradient
S_s – Vertical strip energy gradient
u – channel point velocity
u_s – Vertical strip point velocity
$\overline{u}$ – Average velocity in x–direction
u' – Local velocity variation
V – Mean channel velocity
V_s – Mean strip velocity
$\overline{v}$ – Average velocity in y–direction
v' – Local velocity variation
y – Distance from bed
Y_s – Distance of bed to surface of strip
ϵ_s – y_s/Y_s
κ – Von Karman's constant
ρ – Fluid density
μ – Fluid viscosity

ACKNOWLEDGEMENT

The research grant provided by the Natural Sciences and Engineering Research Council Canada is gratefully acknowledged.

REFERENCES

Chow, V.T., 1959. Open channel hydraulics. 1st Edition, McGraw Hill, New York.

Hey, R.D., 1979. Flow resistance in gravel bed rivers. Journal of the Hydraulics Division, ASCE, Vol. 105, HY4, April.

Keulegan, G.H., 1938. Law of turbulent flow in open channels. Paper RP 1151, Journal of Research, U.S. National Bureau of Standards, Vol. 21, December, pp. 707–741.

Knight, D.W. and Demetriou, J.D., 1983. Flood plain and main channel interaction. Journal of Hydraulic Engineering, ASCE, August, 109, No. 8, pp. 1073–1092.

Knight, D.W., Demetriou, J.D. and Hamed, M.E., 1984. Stage and discharge relationships for compound channels. Proc. 1st International Conference, Channels and Channel Control Structures, Southampton, pp. 4–21 to 4–35.

Morris, H.M., 1963. Applied hydraulics in engineering. The Ronald Press, New York.

Myers, W.R.C., 1982. Flow resistance in wide rectangular channels. Journal of Hydraulic Engineering, ASCE, April, Vol. 108, HY4, pp. 471–482.

Myers, W.R.C., 1984. Frictional resistance in channels with flood plains. Proc. 1st International Conference, Channels and Channel Control Structures, Southampton, pp. 4–73 to 4–87.

Wormleaton, P.R., Allen, J. and Hadjipanos, P., 1982. Discharge assessment in compound channel flow. Journal of Hydraulic Engineering, ASCE, Sept., Vol. 108, HY9, pp. 975–994.

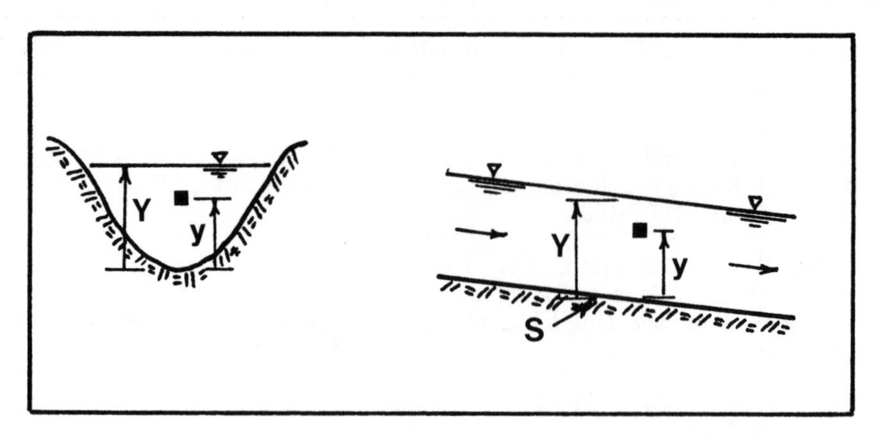

Fig. 1. Definition sketch

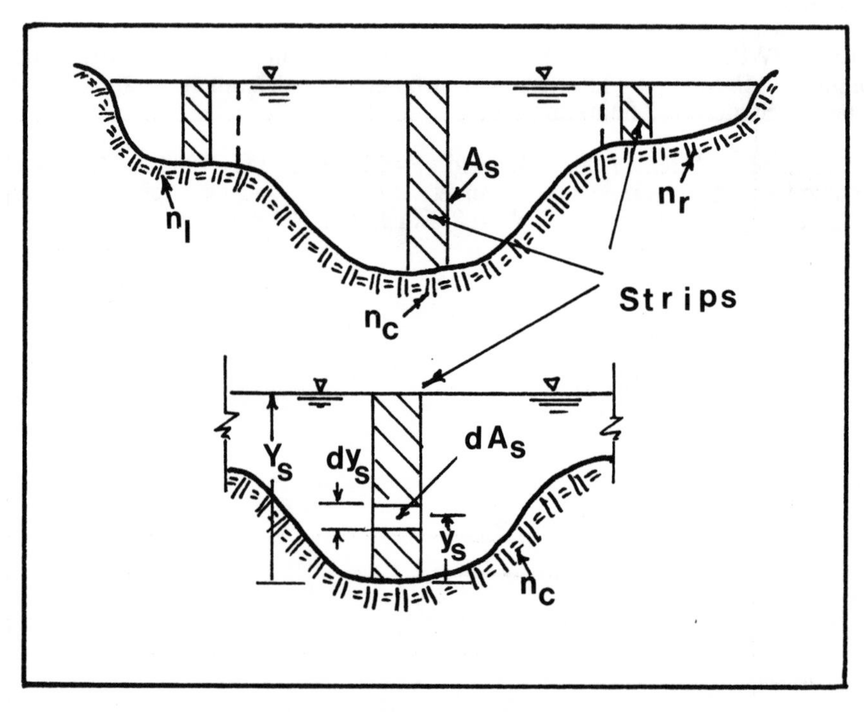

Fig. 2. Vertical strip division

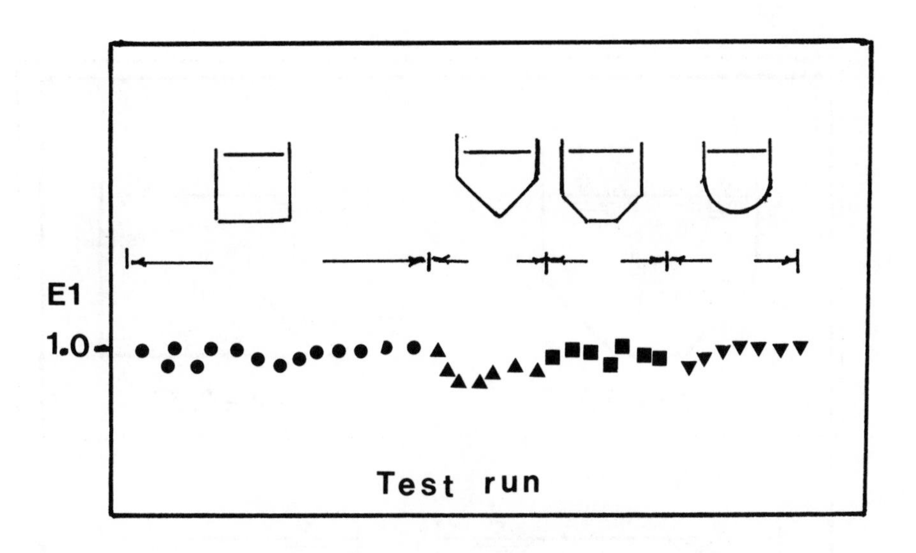

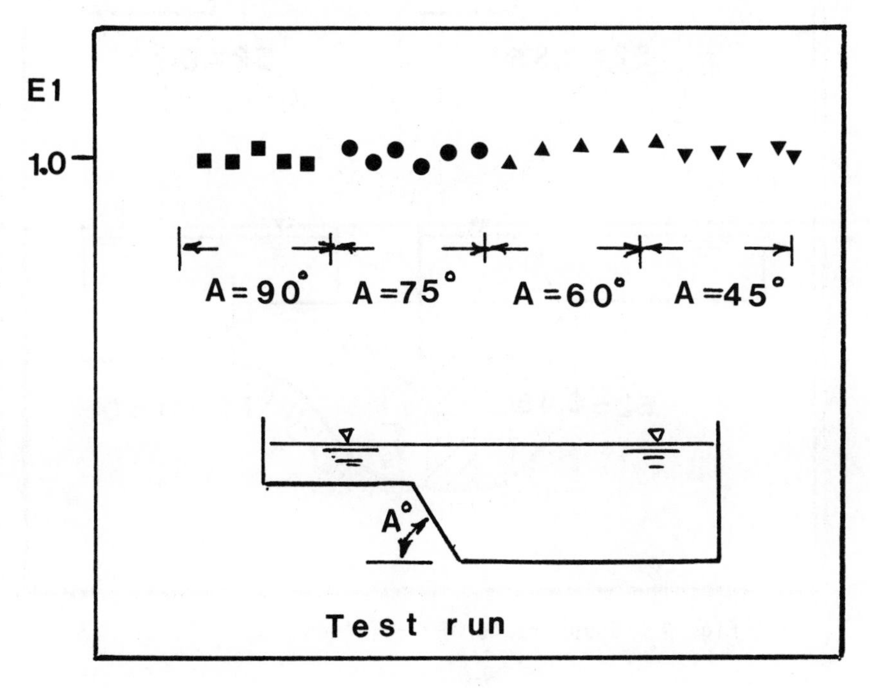

Fig. 3. Coefficient E1

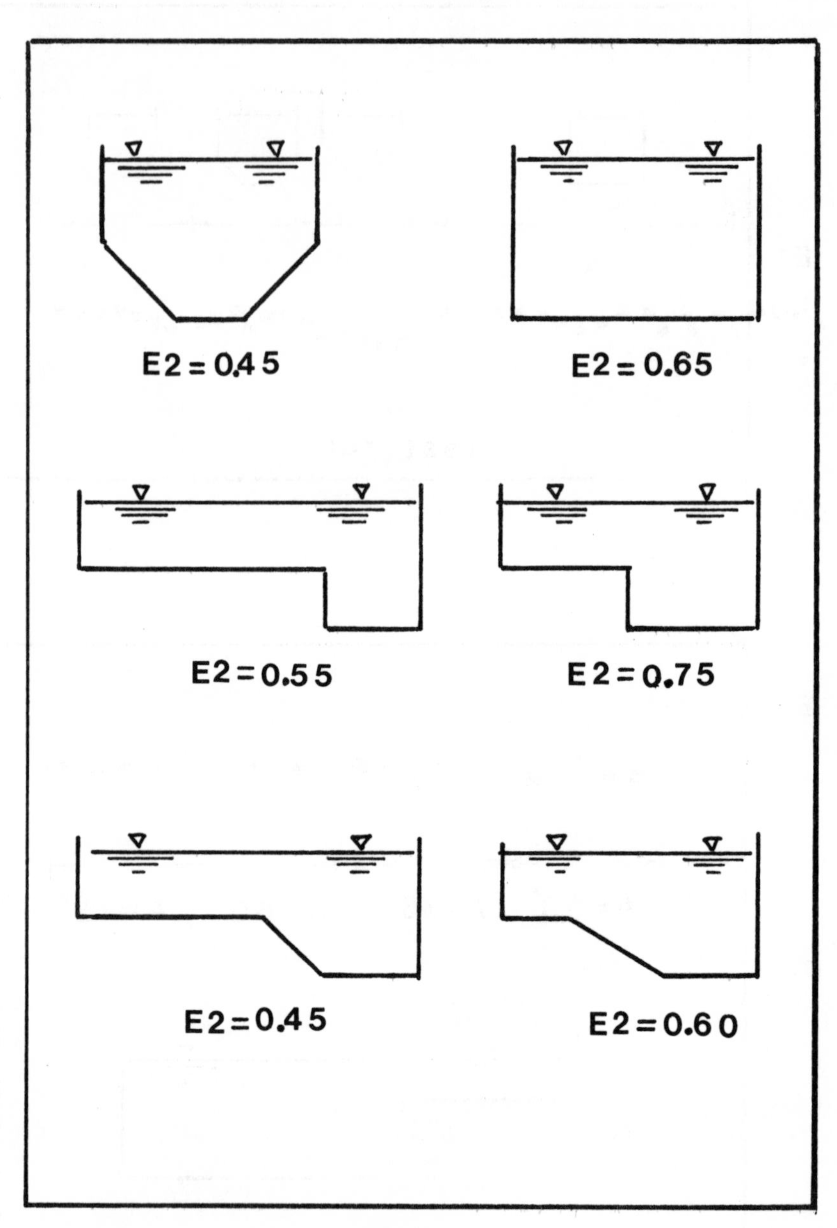

Fig. 4. Shape factor E2

PAPER E2

International Conference on
RIVER FLOOD HYDRAULICS
17-20 September, 1990

DISCHARGE ASSESSMENT IN COMPOUND CHANNEL WITH FLOODPLAIN ROUGHNESS

TERUYUKI FUKUHARA

Associate Professor
Department of Civil Engineering
Fukui University
Bunkyo 3-9-1, Fukui-Shi , 910
Japan

AKIRA MUROTA

Professor
Department of Civil Engineering
Osaka University
Yamadaoka 2-1, Suita-shi, 565
Japan

ABSTRACT

A new model for discharge assessment in compound channel flows is proposed based on a set of experimental results. It is assumed that there is no shear acting on an imaginary interface plane, therefore an imaginary main channel and floodplain are introduced. This means that Manning's resistance law cannot simply be applied to the subsection flows divided by the commonly used interface planes such as : vertical, horizontal and inclined planes. A ratio of the boundary shear force in the main channel to the total shear force is necessary to calculate the stage-discharge curves. It is possible to express this ratio as a function of the floodplain width, main channel width, floodplain height, water depth, and the roughness coefficient.

It was confirmed that the proposed model can reproduce not only the authors' stage-discharge curves but also other researchers' experimental results.

INTRODUCTION

Generally research on compound channel flows may be classified into two categories: One is research pertaining to hydraulic properties such as velocity, turbulent intensity and boundary shear stress. The other includes explanation of characterisics of flow capacity and the development of discharge-calculation methods. Since the final goal of this kind of study is to calculate the relationship between water level and discharge, the results, obtained from the two groups of research, should be effectively combined towards the common goal.

In previous studies Manning or Chezy formulas were mainly used to calculate discharge through a main channel and floodplains, which were split by imaginary interface planes. This approach, however, includes a basic hydraulic question. That is, if the mean wall shear stress in each subsection, calculated by the Manning or the Chezy formulas, is actually equal to the real wall shear stress. Murota et al. (1990) investigated the influence of channel geometry and floodplain roughness on the flow structure in compound channels. They indicated that the roughness elements on floodplains and water depth have a very strong influence on velocity, turbulent intensity and wall shear stress. As Yen and Overton (1973) indicated, there

International Conference on River Flood Hydraulics, edited by W.R.White

are two kinds of methods for predicting discharge through compound channels. If the interface planes are to be included in the wetted perimeter, the internal shear stress, which acts on the interface planes, i.e. the apparent shear stress, should be measured precisely. If the interface planes are not included in the wetted perimeter, we should deduce the characteristics of the division lines decided as the lines of zero shear stress in the experimental results. Whether it is a good model or an unfavorable model depends on which of the apparent shear stresses or the flow sectional areas, subdivided by the division lines, can be systematically and easily expressed as a function of the hydraulic parameters such as the depth of the main channel, the width of the main channel, the width of the floodplain, and the roughness coefficient.

This paper presents a new method for calculating the discharge and then compares it with other methods. Furthermore, the present method is applied to the stage-discharge curves obtained by other researchers and its validity is discussed.

EXPERIMENTAL METHOD AND CONDITIONS

Experiments were conducted in a rectangular channel *20m* long, *0.7m* wide and *0.3m* deep with a smooth wall, which was made of acrylic resin. The compound cross section, as in Fig.1, was composed of acrylic resin 10*m* in length. *5mm* square acrylic resin strips were used as roughness elements, and was placed on the floodplains, at intervals of *20mm*, in the transversewise direction. In this case, an imaginary bed rises *4mm* from the actual bed because of a separation of flow due to the large number of roughness elements. As shown in Fig.2, The Manning roughness coefficient can be seen as a function of the water depth, H. This relation was used to calculate the stage-discharge curve. The main channel was hydraulically smooth and its Manning roughness coefficient, n_m, was *0.01*.

Experimental conditions are presented in Table.1. The compound sections were set up by three different variables : the depth of the main channel, D, the width of the main channel, B_m, and

TABLE 1. Experimental Conditions

CASE	B_f (m)	B_m (m)	D (m)	H_{max} (m)	H_{min} (m)	Q_{max} (cc/s)	Q_{min} (cc/s)	n_f	n_m
								($m^{-1/3}s$)	
R-15-40-3	0.146	0.4	0.029	0.0745	0.0348	10700	2930	0.023	0.01
R-20-30-3	0.196	0.3	0.029	0.0898	0.0341	9230	1850	0.023	0.01
R-25-20-3	0.246	0.2	0.029	0.0718	0.0380	5600	1550	0.023	0.01
R-15-40-5	0.146	0.4	0.049	0.0995	0.0588	15700	5990	0.023	0.01
R-20-30-5	0.196	0.3	0.049	0.0989	0.0584	12500	4180	0.023	0.01
R-25-20-5	0.246	0.2	0.049	0.0923	0.0590	7170	2510	0.023	0.01
R-15-40-7	0.146	0.4	0.070	0.1316	0.0839	21190	9440	0.023	0.01
R-20-30-7	0.196	0.3	0.070	0.1283	0.0840	12070	4060	0.023	0.01
R-25-20-7	0.246	0.2	0.070	0.1278	0.0847	16220	7170	0.023	0.01
S-15-40-5	0.150	0.4	0.047	0.0937	0.0572	18000	6900	0.010	0.01
S-20-30-5	0.200	0.3	0.047	0.0947	0.0571	15550	4880	0.010	0.01
S-25-20-5	0.250	0.2	0.047	0.0937	0.0568	12030	3280	0.010	0.01

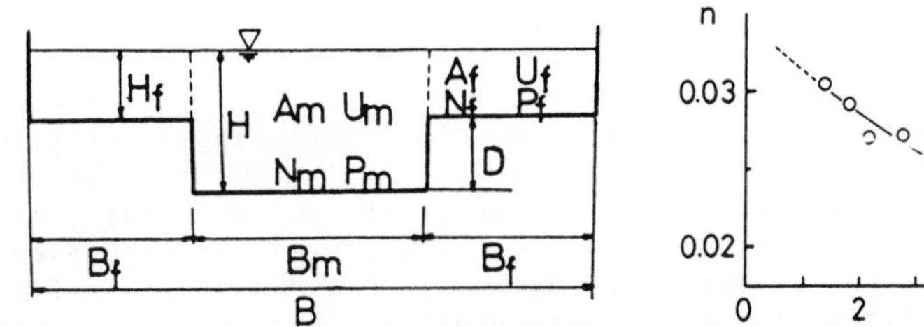

Figure 1. Illustration of Compound Channel Section

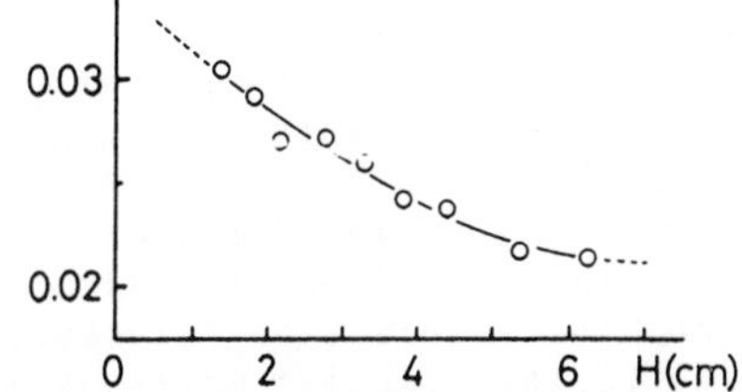

Figure 2. Variation of Manning's n with Water Depth

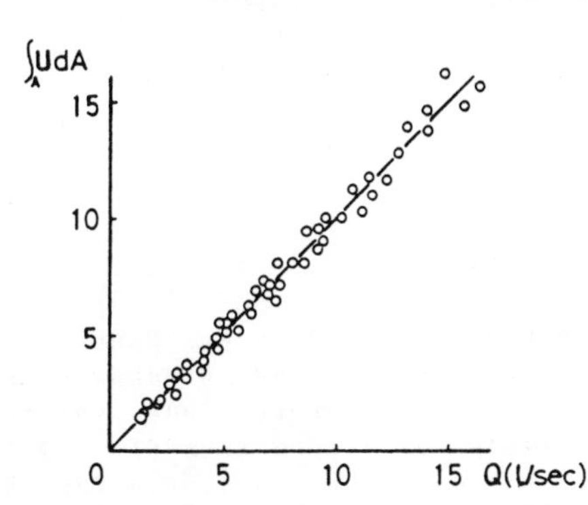

Figure 3. Accuracy of Velocity

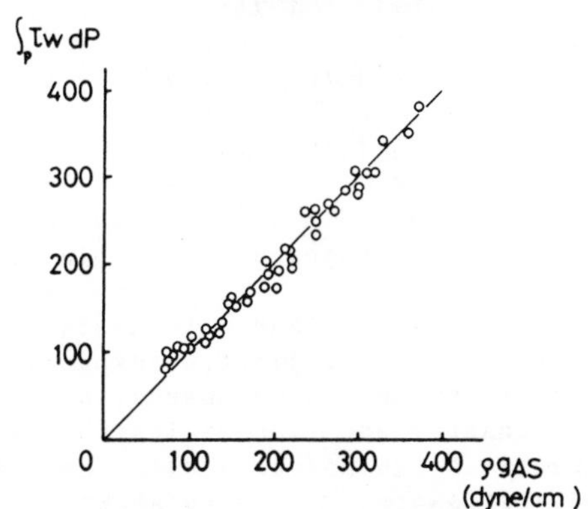

Figure 4. Accuracy of Wall Shear Stress

the width of the floodplain, B_f, respectively. In order to recognize the hydraulic effect of the floodplain roughness on flow resistance, two kinds of compound sections were used for the same geometry and size, that is, the same B_m, B_f and D. One of the two is called Type-S and Manning's n of the floodplains, n_f and n_m are the same value. The other is called Type-R and the compound channel was comprised of a smooth main channel and floodplains with roughness elements, i.e. $n_f > n_m$. In Table.1, Q_{max} and Q_{min} denote a maximum discharge and minimum discharge, respectively. H_{max} and H_{min} correspond to the flow depth in the main channel for Q_{max} and Q_{min}, respectively. In Table.1, n_f for Type-R implies the value of Manning's n when H is large as shown in Fig.2. The relation in Fig.2 referes to floodplains only.

Streamwise velocity, U was measured by *3mm* diam. propera current meter and a hot-film anemometer simultaneously. The latter is especially convenient to measure U near a wall. The wall shear stress, τ_w was calculated by the logarithmic law of the velocity profile. An accuracy of U was confirmed by the continuty equation, $Q=\int_A UdA$, where A is the total flow sectional area of the compound channel. The discharge, Q was measured using a triangular weir. An accuracy of τ_w can be checked by making a comparison of the total boundary shear force with the component of weight in the direction of flow. It is apparent from Figs.3 and 4 that errors in measurement of U and τ_w were less than $\pm 5\%$ in all experimental cases. A uniform flow was set by adjustment of a tail gate at the downstream end.

MEAN WALL SHEAR STRESS BY MANNING FORMULA

The most commonly used method of dividing the main channel and floodplains is to postulate vertical interface planes at the junctions of the main channel and floodplains. In this part of the paper, whether the Manning formula can actually reproduce the mean wall shear stress in the main channel and floodplains is discussed. Since the interaction between main channel flow and floodplain flow works as the positive force in the main channel flow (the floodplain flow retards the main channel flow) and works as the negative force in the floodplain flow, the interface may only be included in the wetted perimeter of the main channel. Thus :

$$\tau_{mcal}=(\rho g U_m{}^2 n_m{}^2)/R_m{}^{1/3}, \quad (R_m=A_m/(2H+B_m)),$$

$$\tau_{fcal}=(\rho g U_f{}^2 n_f{}^2)/R_f{}^{1/3}, \quad (R_f=A_f/(H_f+B_f)) \tag{1}$$

where τ_{mcal} and τ_{fcal} are the calculated mean wall shear stresses in the main channel and floodplains, respectively. In this paper the suffix m and f imply the main channel and the floodplain, respectively. R and n denote the hydraulic radius and Manning's roughness coefficient, respectively. Figs. 5 and 6 show the calculated mean wall shear stresses and the measured ones in the main channel and floodplains, respectively. In Type-S most of τ_{mcal} agree with the measured value of τ_m, τ_{mobs}, but τ_{mcal} in Type-R underestimates τ_{mobs} by about 20~40%. In Type-S τ_{fcal} is about 20% smaller than the measured value of τ_f, τ_{fobs}, when H/D is small. As H/D increases, however, τ_{fcal} gets close to τ_{fobs}. In Type-R τ_{fcal} is 10~40% larger than τ_{fobs} and Eq.(1) becomes inaccurate. Therefore, if the interface is not assumed to be a part of the wetted perimeter, τ_{mcal} becomes smaller than that in Eq.(1).

DISCHARGE ASSESSMENT MODEL

It is supposed that the compound channel may be subdivided into the main channel and floodplains, and transversewise slope of the water surface is ignored. If the vertical interface planes are

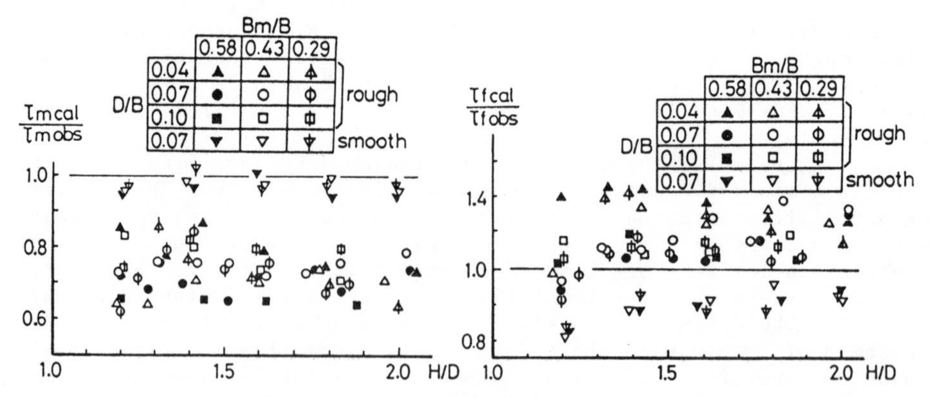

Figure 5. Ratio of τ_{mcal} to τ_{mobs} Figure 6. Ratio of τ_{fcal} to τ_{fobs}

used to subdivide the main channel and floodplains, the hydraulic radius for each subsection, R_m and R_f, are in general expressed as:

$$R_m = A_m/(2D+B_m) \quad , \quad R_f = A_f/(H_f+B_f) \tag{2}$$

The Manning Roughness coefficient n_m and n_f are given by

$$n_m = (R_m{}^{2/3}S^{1/2})/U_m \quad , \quad n_f = (R_f{}^{2/3}S^{1/2})/U_f \tag{3}$$

Furthemore, Manning's n, n_m' and n_f' are also determined by using the cross sectional mean velocity U_m and U_f as follows,

$$n_m' = (\tau_m/\rho g)^{1/2}(R_m{}^{1/6}/U_m) \ , \ n_f' = (\tau_f/\rho g)^{1/2}(R_f{}^{1/6}/U_f) \tag{4}$$

The differences between n_m and n_m' are presented in Fig.7. These differences are relatively large in Type-R. However, n_m must be equal to n_m' in usual rectangular channels. Therefore, the hydraulic radius given by Eq.(2) cannot relate the mean velocity and mean wall shear stress. If Manning's formula is used to calculate the discharge, we should use the hydraulic radius, R_{mo} and R_{fo} to satisfy the following relation, Eq.(3) = Eq.(4). Using the actual wetted perimeters, P_m and P_f, as written by Eq.(2), R_{mo} and R_{fo} are described as follows,

$$R_{mo} = \tau_m/\rho gS = A_{mo}/P_m \quad , \quad R_{fo} = \tau_f/\rho gS = A_{fo}/P_f \tag{5}$$

A_{mo} and A_{fo} denote the imaginary flow sectional area of the main channel and floodplains, respectively. Eq.(6) implies that the main channel and floodplains are split by the planes of zero shear stress. Thus the proposed discharge equation is written by

$$Q = Q_{mo} + 2Q_{fo} \ , \ Q_{mo} = A_{mo}\cdot R_{mo}{}^{2/3}\cdot S^{1/2}/n_m \ , \ Q_{fo} = A_{fo}\cdot R_{fo}{}^{2/3}\cdot S^{1/2}/n_f \tag{6}$$

$$A_{mo}/A = S_m/S_{all} \quad , \quad A = A_{mo} + 2A_{fo} \ ,$$

$$R_{mo} = A_{mo}/P_m(= \tau_m/\rho gS) \ , \quad R_{fo} = A_{fo}/P_f(= \tau_f/\rho gS) \tag{7}$$

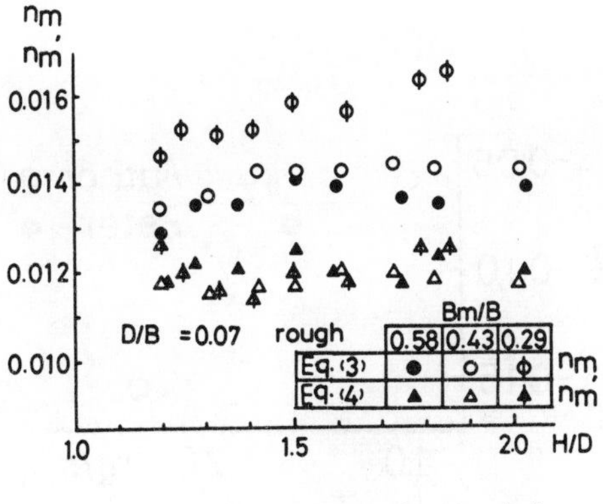

Figure 7. Comparison of n_m with n_m'

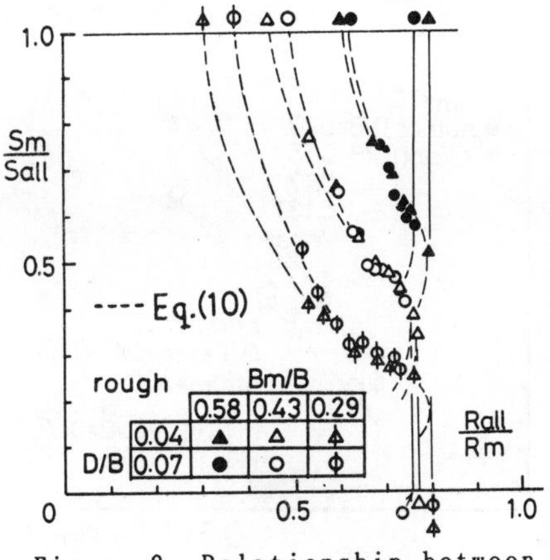

Figure 8. Relationship between S_m/S_{all} and R_{all}/R_m

where S_m is the wall shear force in the main channel and S_{all} is the total wall shear force. S_m/S_{all} is only one unknown parameter in Eq.(7) and is the most important factor, because it reflects the interaction between main-channel flow and floodplain flow. Fig.8 shows the relation between S_m/S_{all} and R_{all}/R_m, where R_{all} is the overall hydraulic radius and is given by $A/P(P=P_m+2P_f)$. As R_{all}/R_m decreases S_m/S_{all} increases and finally S_m/S_{all} reaches levels near 1.0. It may occur at $H/D=1.0$. When S_m/S_{all} is 1.0, R_{all}/R_m becomes α, given by Eq.(8).

$$\alpha=(B^*+2D^*)/(1+2D^*) \quad , \quad \beta=(H^*-D^*+B^*D^*)(B^*+2D^*)/(1+2H^*)H^*B^* \qquad (8)$$

where

$$B^*=B_m/B \quad , \quad D^*=D/B \quad , \quad H^*=(1-B^*)D^*+[\{D^*(1-B^*)\}^2+D^*(1-B^*)/2]^{1/2} \qquad (9)$$

The value of β in Eq.(8) denotes the maximum value of R_{all}/R_m, but R_{all}/R_m generally does not reach β unless $H/D>3.0$. The relationship between S_m/S_{all} and R_{all}/R_m may be described as:

$$S_m/S_{all}=[-a+\{a^2+2b(R_{all}/R_m)-\Delta\}^{1/2}]/\{(R_{all}/R_m)-\Delta\} \qquad (10)$$

where

$$a=2\gamma(\Delta-\beta) \ , \ b=2\gamma^2(\Delta-\beta) \ , \ \Delta=(\alpha-2\beta\gamma+\beta\gamma^2)/(\gamma^2-2\gamma+1) \qquad (11)$$

In Fig.8 the broken lines represent the relationship between S_m/S_{all} and R_{all}/R_m, given by Eq.(10), and reproduce the experimental results. The value of γ can only be decided from experiments. It can be seen from Fig.9 that γ mainly depends on B_m/B and n_f/n_m. Two parallel lines represent the relationship between γ and B_m/B for $n_f/n_m=1.0$ and $n_f/n_m=2.3$, respectively, and may be expressed as follows:

$$\gamma=1.23(B_m/B)-0.066 \qquad (n_f/n_m=1.0) \ ,$$

$$\gamma=1.23(B_m/B)-0.16 \qquad (n_f/n_m=2.3) \qquad (12)$$

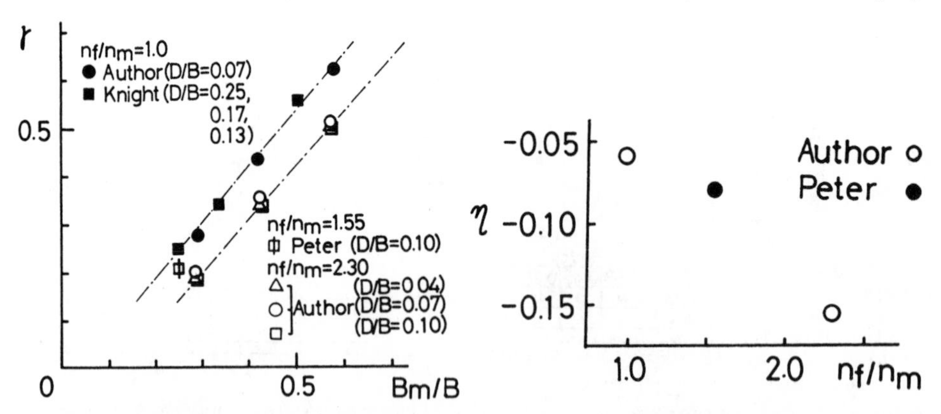

Figure 9. Characteristics of γ Figure 10. Characteristics of η

In Fig.9 the experimental data after collected Knight and Demetriiou (1983) and Peter et al. (1983) are also plotted in addition to authors' data. Especially the datum, obtained by Peter et al. (n_f/n_m= 1.55), is located between the two regression lines. From this result, it seems that the value of y axis-intercept, γ , in Fig.9, may be described as a function of n_f/n_m. Fig.10 shows the change of γ with n_f/n_m, and γ is approximately described in the form of the following equation.

$$\gamma = -0.72(n_f/n_m)+0.006 \tag{13}$$

However, it is supposed that γ is affected by not only B_m/B and n_f/n_m but also by D/B as D/B becomes larger.

After all Eq.(10) can be applied to the range of n_f/n_m= $1.0 \sim 2.3$, $B_m/B=0.29 \sim 1.58$ and $D/B=0.04 \sim 0.18$.

If B_m/B, D/B, n_f/n_m and H/D are given as input data, the discharge is calculated according to the flow chart as shown in Fig.11.

RESULTS AND DISCUSSION

Fig.12 shows the accuracy of the calculated discharge, Q_{cal} and the x axis represents the measured discharge, Q_{obs}. The broken lines and solid lines show deviations of $\pm 5\%$ and $\pm 10\%$ from the proposed relationship, respectively. The errors included in Q_{cal} were within $\pm 10\%$. Figs.13 and 14 show the applications of the proposed model to the stage-discharge curves obtained by Imamoto et al. (1976), Tamai and Kawahara (1981), and authors. All data belong to Type-S. Furthermore, these data are compared with other methods, i.e. Methods 1, 2 and 3. Method 1 is a uniform-flow formula, which

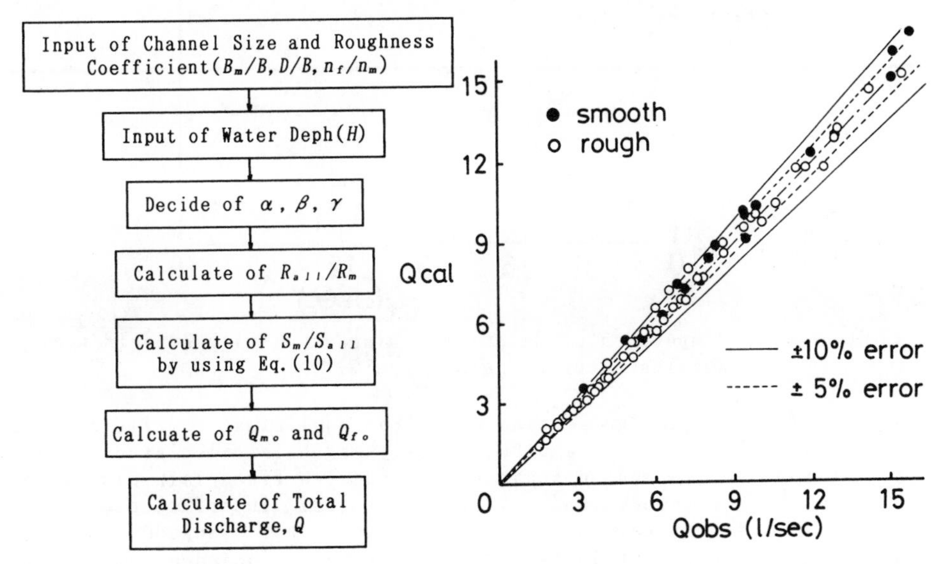

Figure 11. Flow Chart for Calculation of Stage-Discharge Curve

Figure 12. Accuracy of Present Method

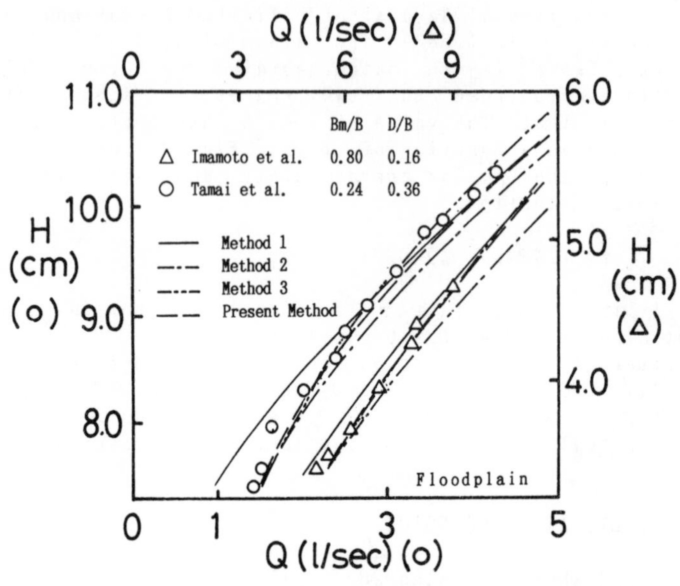

Figure 13. Comparison of Calculated Discharges with Experimental Results after Imamoto et al. and Tamai et al.(Type-S)

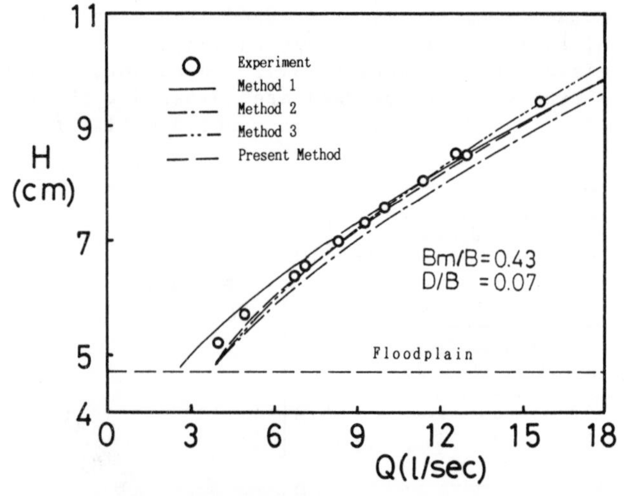

Figure 14. Comparison of Calculated Discharges with Experimental Results after Authors (Type-S)

does not subdivide the section using the equivalent coefficient of roughness. In Methods 2 and 3, the discharge is calculated as the sum of the main channel discharge, Q_m, and the floodplain discharge, Q_f, which are subdivided by the vertical interface planes. In Method 2, the vertical interface planes are not included in the wetted perimeter, but in Method 3, they are included only in the wetted perimeter of the main channel. Figs.15 and 16 represent the calculated and experimental discharges obtained by authors and

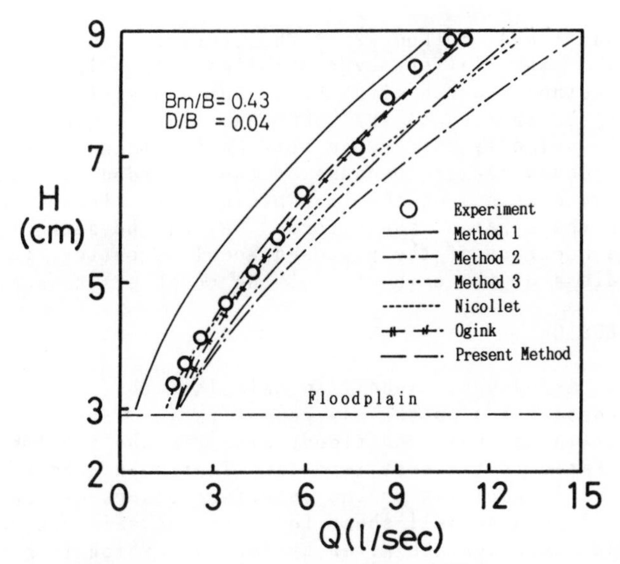

Figure 15. Comparison of Calculated Discharges with Experimental Results after Authors (Type-R)

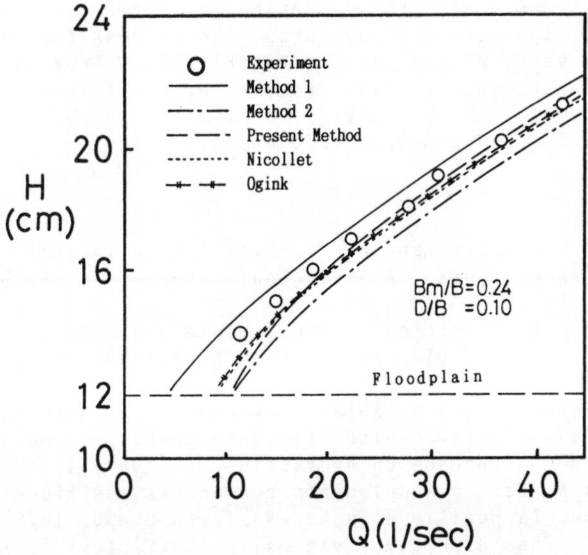

Figure 16. Comparison of Calculated Discharges with Experimental Results after Peter et al. (Type-R)

Pater et al. (1983) for Type-R. The authors' model is compared with other methods proposed by Nicollet and Uan (1979) , and Ogink(1985) in addition to Methods 1, 2 and 3. The apparent shear stress using Ogink's method(1985) was calculated according to the regression curve, suggested by Knight and Demetriiou(1983). Because the apparent shear stresses, obtained from authors' experiments, almost fitted their regression curves. The experimental data are plotted between Method 1 and Method 2. The former underestimates the discharge, and the latter overestimates it. The discharges calculated by Method 3 agree with the measured ones for Type-S, but Method 3 cannot be applied to the compound channel flows of Type-R. In Type-R , the velocity difference between the main channel and the floodplains becomes larger because of the retarded floodplain flow due to roughness elements on the floodplains, and therefore brings an increase in the apparent shear force. As can be seen from Fig.13 to Fig.16, the accuracy of the proposed model is better than other methods regardless of the existence of the roughness elements.

CONCLUSION

A new assessment model to calculate the stage-discharge curve was proposed based on the assignment ratio of the wall shear force in the main channel and floodplains to the total wall shear force. This ratio is the most important factor in subdividing the main channel and floodplains by the interface planes of zero shear stress. The ratio of the wall shear force in the main channel to the total wall shear force can be given by Eq.(10), which is governed by the size of the compound channel such as B_m, B_f, D and H, and the Manning roughness coefficient in the main channel and floodplains. Since in the present model it is not necessary to calculate the apparent shear stress, nor to determine the lines of zero shear stress from the iso-velocity contours, the process for discharge calculations is very simple and easy. Finally, from many stage-discharge curves obtained by many researchers, it was confirmed that the present model can be applied to the range of $n_f/n_m=1.0 \sim 2.3$, $B_m/B=0.29-1.58$, and $D/B=0.04-0.18$ and $H/D<2.6$.

REFERENCES

Imamoto, T., T. Hisashita, and K. Yoshino : Experimental study on compound channel flows, Annual Conference of Kansai Branch of JSCE, II-35, 1976

Knight, D.W. and J.D. Demetriou : Flood plain and main channel flow interaction, J.Hydr. Div. Proc. of ASCE, Vol.109, HY8, pp.1073-1092, 1983

Murota, A., T. Fukuhara and M. Seta : Hydraulic characteristics of compound channel flows with flood roughness, Proc. of the 34st Japanese conference on hydraulics, pp.409-414, 1990

Nicollet, G. and M. Uan : Ecoulements permanents a surface libe et lits compose, La Houille Blanche, No.1, pp.21-30, 1979

Ogink, H.J.M. : The effective viscosity coefficient in 2-D depth averaged flow model, 21st. IAHR, PP.475-479, 1985

Peter, R.W., A. John and H. Panos : Discharge assessment in compound channel flow, J.Hydr. Div. Proc. of ASCE, Vol.108, HY9, pp.975-994, 1982

Tamai, N. and Y. Kawahara : On the large scale eddies and the resistance law with large depth-gradient, Proc. of the 25st Japanese conference on hydraulics, pp.113-118, 1981

Yen, C. and D.E. Overton : Shape effects on resistance in flood-plain channels, J.Hydr. Div. Proc. of ASCE, Vol.99, HY1, pp.219-238, 1973

International Conference on
RIVER FLOOD HYDRAULICS
17-20 September, 1990

A PRACTICAL METHOD OF ESTIMATING VELOCITY AND DISCHARGE IN COMPOUND CHANNELS

J.B. Wark Dept. of Civil Engineering, University of Glasgow.
P.G. Samuels Hydraulics Research Ltd., Wallingford.
D.A. Ervine Dept. of Civil Engineering, University of Glasgow.

ABSTRACT

A method of estimating velocity and discharge in compound channels is presented. This is based on solving the equation for the lateral distribution of flow in a channel. Results are given for laboratory and natural river channels.

1. INTRODUCTION

Two-stage or compound channels are of interest to the river engineer for several reasons. Many rivers have compound channels, possessing a main channel, which always carries flow, and one or two floodplains, which only carry flow at above bankfull stages, fig. 1. The use of artificial compound channels in flood relief schemes is achieved by cutting berms on either side of the existing channel. This increases the capacity of the channel and reduces downstream water levels, during extreme flood events. Sellin, 1989, describes an example of this type of scheme.

It is important that the engineer be able to estimate the stage-discharge relationship of compound channels. First to predict the effect of possible floods in natural channels and second to enable design of economic flood relief schemes using two-stage channel sections.

2. ESTIMATING FLOW IN COMPOUND CHANNELS

Traditionally flow in two-stage channels has been calculated using simple 1-D theory. The two most commonly applied approaches are:

Single Channel Method in which the complete channel is treated as a single unit. Usually no account is taken of roughness variation across the channel. In terms of Manning's equation this may be expressed :

$$Q_t = \frac{1}{n_t} A_t R_t^{2/3} S_{xf}^{1/2} \qquad (1)$$

$$R_t = A_t / P_t \qquad (2)$$

Where
A_t - Total area of channel
n_t - Manning's coefficient for whole channel
P_t - Wetted perimeter of whole channel

International Conference on River Flood Hydraulics, edited by W.R.White

Q_t - Total flow
R_t - Hydraulic radius of whole channel
S_{xf}- A longitudinal slope, taken as the bed slope in uniform flow and as the slope of the energy line in non-uniform flow.

This method underpredicts flows by up to 30% at low overbank stages.

Divided Channel Methods are based on splitting the main channel from the floodplains, fig. 2, and calculating the flow in each sub-area seperately, using equations 3 and 4. Variations in roughness can be included and the total flow is obtained by summation.

$$Q_i = \frac{1}{n_t} A_i \; R_i^{2/3} \; S_{xf}^{1/2} \tag{3}$$

$$R_t = A_i \,/\, P_i \tag{4}$$

(Where Q_i is the flow in sub-area i, etc.)

There are many divided channel methods which differ in the position and direction of the dividing lines and whether or not these lines are included when calculating the wetted perimeters of the sub-areas. In general they all tend to overpredict the total flow by significant margins, Ramsbottom, 1989.

Other methods for calculating flow in compound channels have appeared in the literature, (eg. the effective stress method or the correction factor method). These procedures are largely empirical and require calibration, this is usually provided based on small scale laboratory tests. See Ervine and Baird, 1982, and James and Brown, 1977. Because of scale effects such methods are unlikely to be accurate in application to prototype channels.

The main reason that the above methods all fail to give accurate results, when applied to compound channels, is that the flow distribution is nonuniform. The simple 1-D theory is based on the underlying assumption of uniform flow and bed shear stress, which is untrue in two-stage channels. The above empirical approaches to taking this non-uniformity into account are based on simplistic analysis and inadequate understanding of the basic flow mechanisms occuring in compound channels. In recent years work has concentrated on gaining an accurate picture of the processes taking place and has stimulated interest in methods of discharge estimation based on 2-D, depth averaged, flow theory.

3. LATERAL DISTRIBUTION METHOD OF DISCHARGE ESTIMATION

This is based on calculating the distribution of flow within the channel. The governing equation, (either 5 or 6), is derived from the general 2-D, shallow water equations. There are many assumptions and approximations involved in the derivation of these equations including : Flow is steady and uniform (in the longitudinal direction) and the water surface is horizontal across the channel. Further discussion of these aspects is outwith the scope of this paper, see Samuels, 1985 or Wark, 1988. Most authors have solved for the depth averaged velocity, U, using equation 5. Samuels, 1988, shows that in certain cases the use of unit flow, q, and equation 6 may be theoretically more sound. It is unclear, as yet, which form of the equation is to be preferred in practice.

$$gDS_{xf} \quad - \quad \frac{Bf|U|U}{8} \quad + \quad \frac{\partial}{\partial y}\left[\nu_t D \frac{\partial U}{\partial y} \right] \quad = \quad 0 \qquad (5)$$

$$gDS_{xf} \quad - \quad \frac{Bf|q|q}{8\ D^2} \quad + \quad \frac{\partial}{\partial y}\left[\nu_t \frac{\partial q}{\partial y} \right] \quad = \quad 0 \qquad (6)$$

Gravity Bed shear Lateral shear

Where

$B = (1 + S_x^2 + S_y^2)^{1/2}$: A factor relating stress on an inclined surface to stress in the horizontal plane, see Wark, 1988.

D - Flow depth

f - Darcy friction factor

g - Gravitational acceleration

S_x - Longitudinal slope of channel bed

S_y - Lateral slope of channel bed

x - Longitudinal coordinate direction

y - Lateral coordinate direction

q - Longitudinal unit flow (=UD)

U - Longitudinal depth averaged velocity

ν_t - Lateral eddy viscosity

Given estimates of the bed shear and lateral shear terms it is possible to solve equation 5 or 6 for the distribution of flow within the channel. This in turn may be integrated to provide the discharge or used to calculate the distribution of bed shear stress across the channel.

The bed shear term is calculated by local application of 1–D theory. For example Manning's equation :

$$f \quad = \quad 8gn^2 \ / \ D^{1/3} \qquad (7)$$

n - Manning's n

The lateral shear term is more difficult to evaluate and various models for the lateral eddy viscosity have been proposed. An early example, Vreugdenhil and Wijbenga, 1982, used a constant value of ν_t but did not compare the solution with measured data. More physically realistic models may be obtained by dimensional analysis. The lateral eddy viscosity relating to bed roughness generated turbulence is given by equation 8.

$$\nu_t \quad = \quad \lambda \ U_* \ D \qquad (8)$$

Where

U_* - The shear velocity = $(\tau_b/\rho)^{1/2}$

λ - The nondimensional eddy viscosity (NEV)

ρ - Fluid density

τ_b - Bed shear stress

Values of λ are usually quoted as being approximately 0.16 ± 50% in straight laboratory flumes increasing to between 0.6 and 2.0 in river channels, see Okoye, 1970. Some authors, eg. Wormleaton, 1988, suggest that shear layer driven turbulence may be an important source of lateral shear in compound channels. In this case it can be shown that the lateral eddy viscosity is given by an expression of the form :

$$\nu_t = C\, l_s\, \Delta U \qquad (9)$$

Where
C - A constant
l_s - A length scale related to the width of shear layer
ΔU - Velocity difference across the shear layer

More sophisticated attempts have been made using a depth averaged form of the k– ϵ turbulence model, Keller and Rodi, 1989. However the cost of the additional computation is large and k– ϵ models are unlikely to form the basis of practical design aids. Analytic solutions to equation 5 are available only for certain simplified cases, Samuels, 1988 and Shiono and Knight, 1988. In general a numerical solution must be sought and the following section describes the method developed by the authors.

4. NUMERICAL SOLUTION METHOD

The authors have found that an appropriate finite difference scheme to use, when solving equation 6, is one in which the lateral shear term is computed at the mid– node positions, (Staggered grid). Equation 6 is nonlinear and the solution is obtained by iteration using Newton's method. The initial 'seed' solution is obtained from equation 6 by setting $\nu_t = 0$. The required boundary conditions are that q = 0 at the solid channel boundaries. The numerical model has been developed to require the minimum amount of information : the channel geometry; the bed roughness and eddy viscosity parameters in each sub– area of the channel. Convergence is usually obtained within five or six iterations and the method is computationaly efficient. It is simple to incorporate variations in roughness and eddy viscosity in the method.

5. COMPARISONS BETWEEN THE COMPUTATIONAL MODEL AND PHYSICAL MEASUREMENTS

The above model has been applied to a wide range of data, varying from small scale laboratory flumes to large scale laboratory channels to real rivers. In all of the examples quoted below equation 8 was used to estimate the lateral eddy viscosity.

Small Scale Model Kiely, 1989, presents velocity distributions and stage– discharge data for a small flume. The cross– sectional geometry is shown in figure 3, with the main channel being 0.2 m wide and the bankfull depth 0.05 m. The Floodplains were each 0.5 m wide and the bed slope set to 0.001. Calculations were carried out with the Manning's n in the main channel, for bankfull stage and above, set to 0.0095. On the floodplains n was varied between 0.02 and 0.005, depending on stage. The nondimensional eddy viscosity (NEV), λ, was taken as zero on the floodplains. The calculations were carried out for a range of λ values in the main channel. Figure 4 shows measured and computed velocity distributions for a stage of approximately 100 mm and figure 5 is a comparison between measured and computed stage–discharge relationships. As can be seen the computed velocity and discharge distributions follow the measured values closely, the best agreement being obtained with λ in the range 0.16 to 0.24.

Large Scale Model The SERC Flood Channel Facility, Wallingford is a large experimental flume, approximately 50 m long by 10 m wide. A long term research programme into the behaviour of two stage channels is being carried out using this facility. Series A of the the programme, now complete, dealt with straight channels. A number of different cross sectional shapes were investigated with stage–discharge, velocity and bed shear distributions all being measured.

Figure 8 shows one of the geometries, the main channel was 1.5 m wide and bankfull depth 0.15 m. The main channel and floodplains had laterally sloping sides of gradient 1.0 and the longitudinal slope was 1.027×10^{-3}. Several different floodplain widths were tested and comparisons between measured and computed stage–discharges are shown in figures 6 and 7, for narrow and wide floodplains respectively.

The friction factors were obtained from equation 10, as recommended by Ackers, 1989, and the λ factor was taken as constant across the channel.

$$\frac{1}{\sqrt{f}} = 2.02 \log_{10} (R_e \sqrt{f}) - 1.38 \qquad (10)$$

Again best agreement between computed and measured values was obtained with the λ factor between 0.16 and 0.24. In this case the computed stage–discharges are closer to the measurements than the computed velocity distributions.

River Measurements Stage–discharge and velocity data are available for the River Severn at Montford, Ramsbottom, 1989. The irregular cross–sectional geometry was approximated with straight lines, as shown in figure 9. The main channel is 34 m wide with Bankfull depth about 5.5 m. The floodplains extend 65 m to the left and about 25 m to the right. The longitudinal bed slope is 1.94×10^{-4}.

Calculations were carried out, see figure 10, with the bankfull Manning's n 0.033. On the floodplain n was taken as 0.045, which is consistent with the vegetation being mainly short, cropped grass. The λ value appears to lie in the range 0.08 to 0.24. This is considerably lower than typical values normally associated with natural channels.

6. CONCLUSIONS

(1) A 1–D numerical model of the lateral distribution of flow has been developed which requires the minimum of input information. This model has been shown to predict reliable stage–discharge and velocity distributions for compound channels. Although based on uniform, (in the longitudinal direction), flow theory the method can be applied to the non–uniform case.

(2) The numerical model has been applied satisfactorily to small scale model data, large scale model results and field measurements in seven British rivers.

(3) In applying the model values of roughness and lateral eddy viscosity are

required. The computed stage-discharges were found to be more sensitive to variations in roughness than to changes in the lateral eddy viscosity. Given an accurate value of bankfull roughness the method can produce discharge estimates to within ± 5% of measured values.

(4) The authors have found that the lateral eddy viscosity can be modelled with adequate precision using only the bed generated shear model, (equation 8). The λ factor was found to lie within the range 0.16 ± 0.08. In View of the uncertainity relating to lateral eddy viscosity the use of constant values of λ in each sub-area of the channel is recommended.

(5) The method is numerically efficient and is suitable for inclusion in general river modelling packages.

(6) The experimental channels and river gauging sites which have been simulated with the above 1-D model are not typical. They are straight and exhibt a greater degree of uniformity than is common. Care will be required when extending application of the model to more typical, sinuous, river channels.

7. ACKNOWLEDGEMENTS

The first author is grateful to The Science and Engineering Research Council and Hydraulics Research Ltd. for finacial support, in the form of a CASE Studentship.

8. REFERENCES

Ackers P., (1989), Private Communication

Ervine D.A. and Baird J.I., (1982), Rating curves for rivers with overbank flow, Proc. Instn. Civ. Engrs., Part 2, 73.

James M. and Brown B.J., (1977), Geometric parameters which influence floodway flow, United States Waterways Experimental Station, Research Report H-77-1.

Keller R.J. and Rodi W., (1989), Prediction of flow characteristics in main channel/floodplain flows, Jrnl. of Hydr. Resch., Vol. 26, no. 4.

Kiely G.K., (1989), An experimental study of overbank flow in straight and meandering compound channels, Ph.D. Thesis, Dept. of Civil Engineering, University College, Cork.

Okoye J.K., (1970), Characteristics of transverse mixing in open channel flows, California Institute of Technology, Pasedena, California, Report No. KH-R-23.

Ramsbottom D.R., (1989), Flood discharge assessment, Interim Report, Hydraulics Research Ltd., Report SR195.

Samuels P.G., (1985), Modelling of river and floodplain flow using the finite element method, Hydraulics Research Ltd., Report SR61.

Samuels P.G., (1988), Lateral shear layers in compound channels, Proc. Intl. Confr. on fluvial hydraulics, Vitaki, Budapest.

Sellin R.H.J., (1989), Two stage channel flow, University of Bristol, Dept. of Civil Engineering, Final Report prepared for Thames Water Authority.

Shiono K. and Knight D.W., (1988), Two dimensional analytic solution for a compound channel, Third Intl. Symp. on refined flow modelling and turbulence measurements, Tokyo, Japan.

Wark J.B., (1988), The equations of river and floodplain flow, Research Report submitted to the Dept. of Civil Engineering, University of Glasgow.

Wormleaton D.R., (1988), Determination of discharge in compound channels using the dynamic equation for lateral velocity distribution., Proc. Intl. Confr. on fluvial hydraulics, Vitaki, Budapest.

9. FIGURES

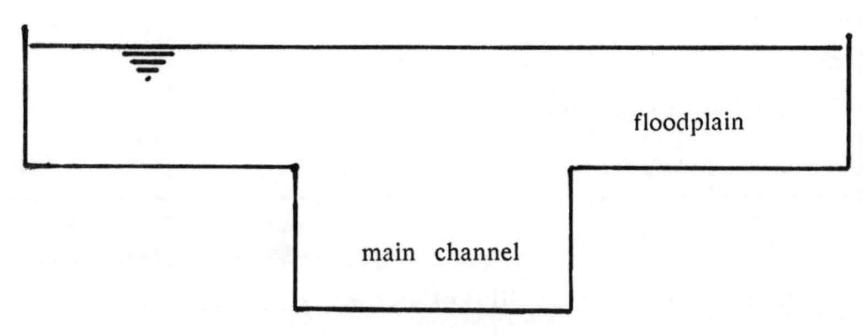

Figure 1. Compound Channel

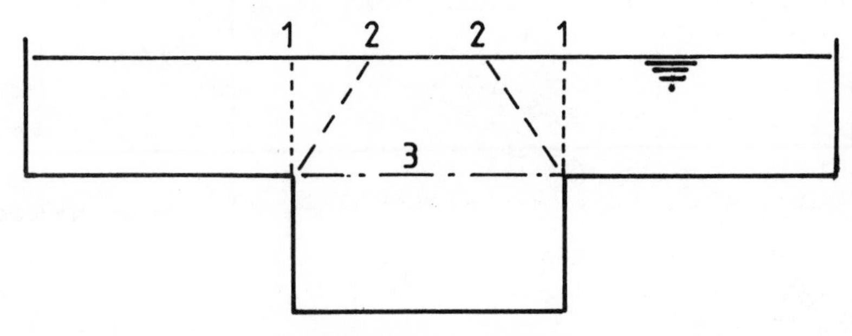

Figure 2. Divided Channel Methods

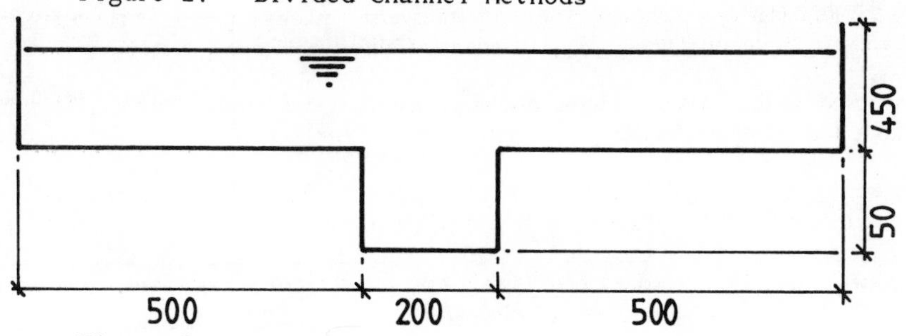

Figure 3. Cross-Section of Kiely's Channel

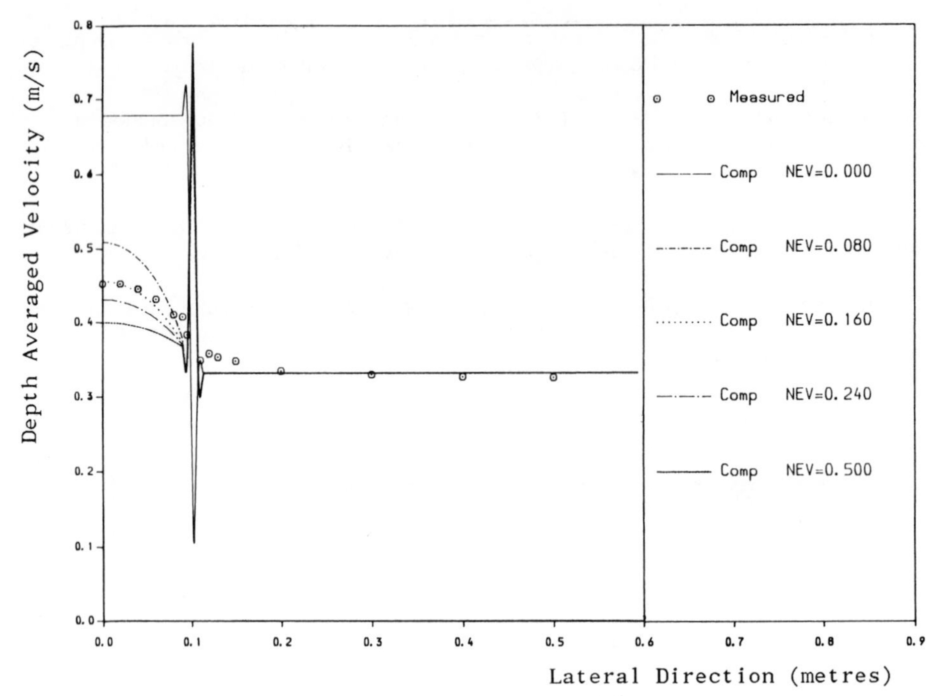

Figure 4. Velocity Distribution, Stage 100 mm, Kiely

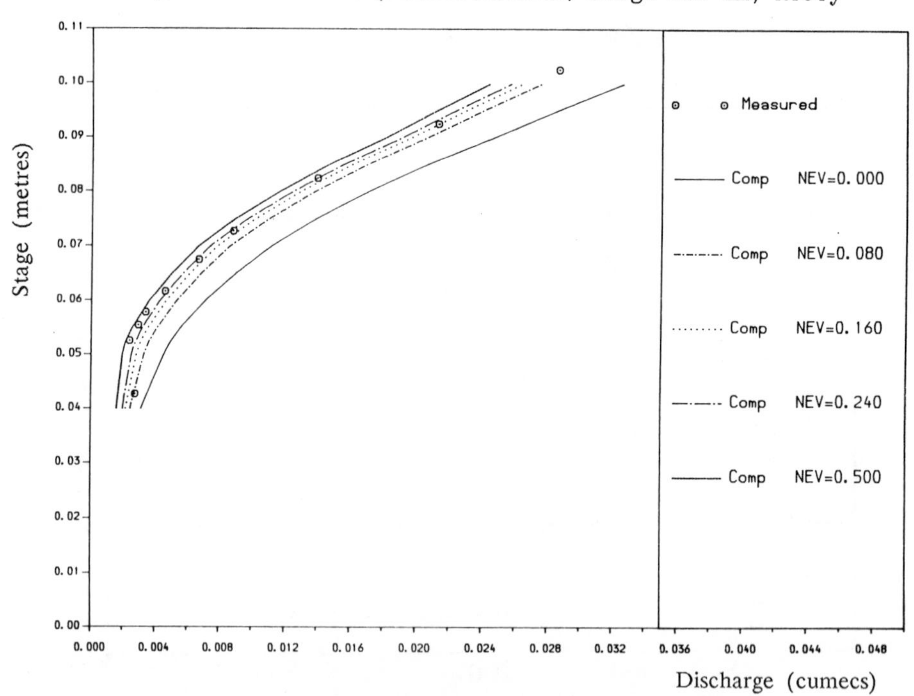

Figure 5. Stage-Discharge Relationship, Kiely

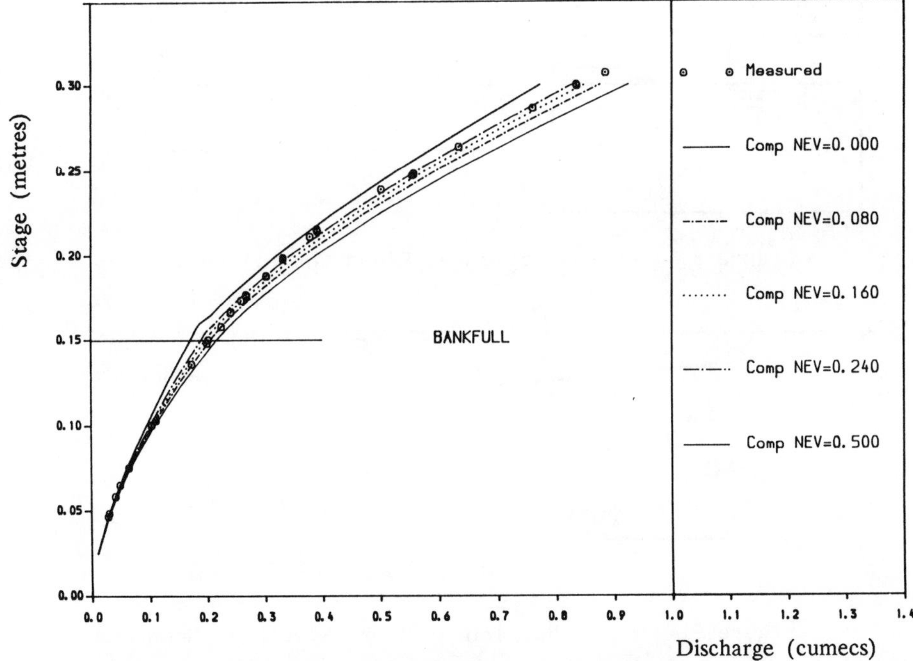

Figure 6. Stage-Discharge Relationship, FCF
Narrow Floodplain, B/b = 2.2

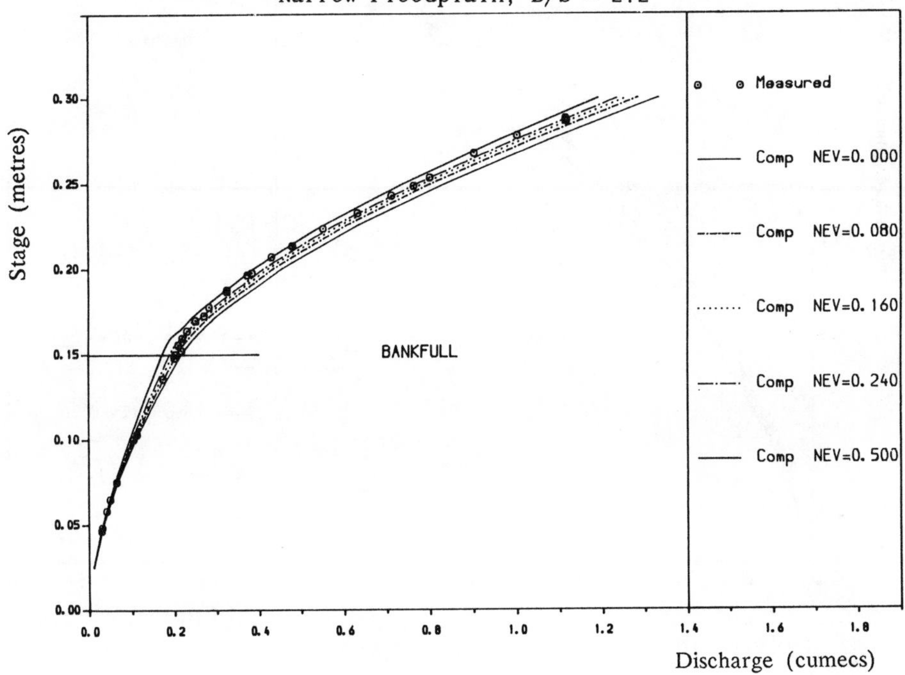

Figure 7. Stage-Discharge Relationship, FCF
Wide Floodplain, B/b = 4.2

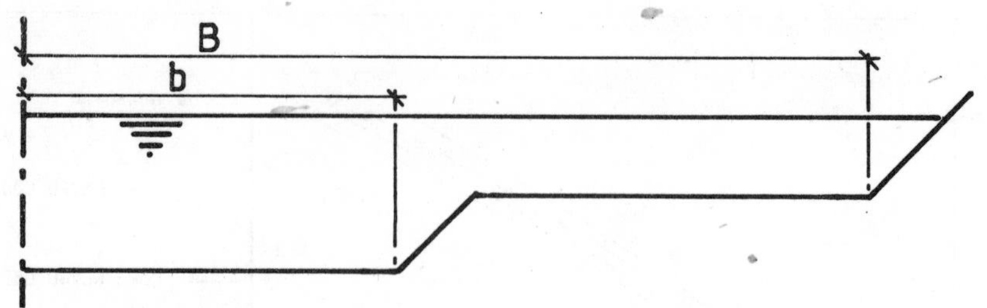

Figure 8. Cross-Section of Flood Channel Facility

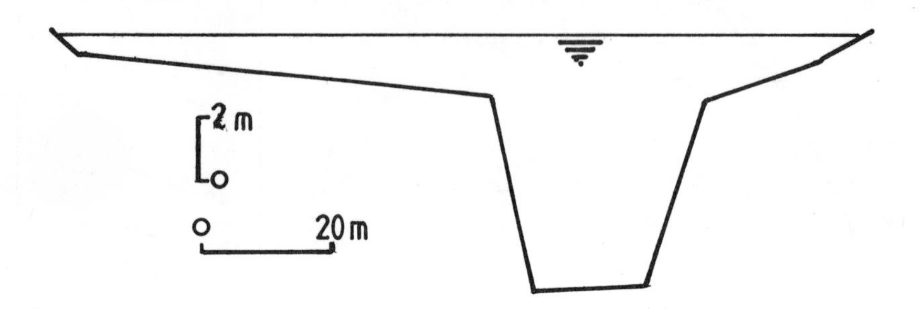

Figure 9. Cross-Section of River Severn at Montford

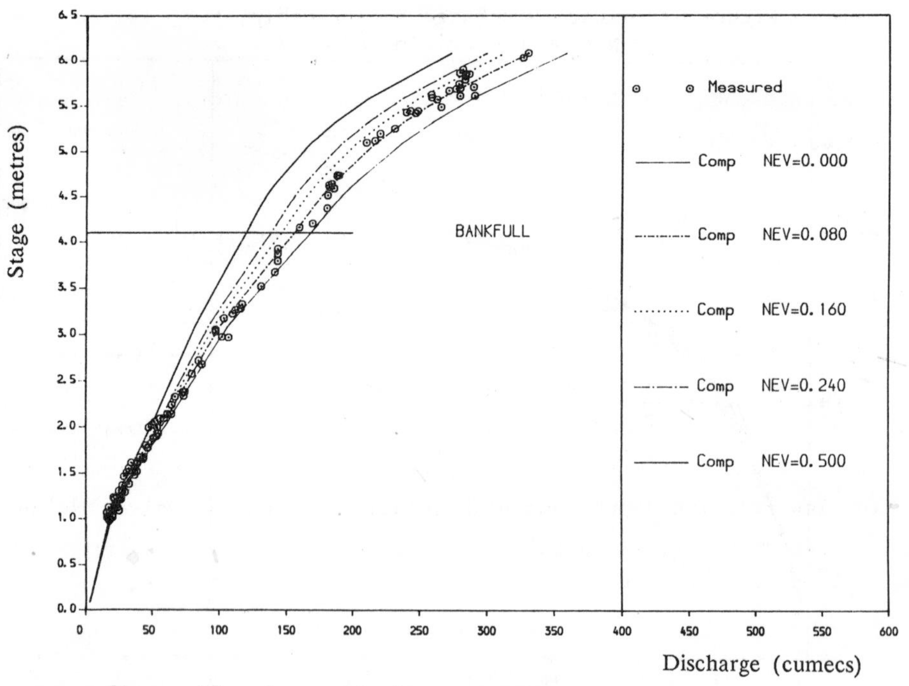

figure 10. Stage-Discharge Relationship River Severn at Montford

PAPER E4

International Conference on
RIVER FLOOD HYDRAULICS
17-20 September, 1990

TURBULENCE MODELLING OF MAIN CHANNEL-FLOOD PLAIN FLOWS WITH AN ALGEBRAIC STRESS MODEL.

P.Prinos

Lab. of Fluid Mechanics, Dept of Mechanical Eng.,
University of Thessaloniki, Greece.

ABSTRACT

Characteristics of flow in compound open channels have been computed using the three-dimensional Navier-Stokes equations in conjuction with an algebraic stress model of turbulence. The latter is used for the calculation of the Reynolds stress components responsible for the generation of the secondary currents. Calculations are presented for strong interacting conditions between main channel and fluid plain flows, and compared with experimental results. It is shown that the model performs well and indicates properly the complex phenomena observed in the junction regions of compound open channels.

INTRODUCTION

Experimental work in compound open channels has been undertaken by many investigators (5, 10, 13, 17, 18) and the flow characteristics in such channels have been determined in detail.
The effects of the strong shear layer, developed in the junction region of the compound cross section, on mean velocity, boundary shear stress and overall capacity have been defined experimentally for low relative depths and high relative roughness. Also, recently the use of Hot Film and Laser Doppler Anemometry has permitted measurements of turbulence characteristics (1, 17) and the structure of secondary currents in the junction region.

In contrast to the experimental work, computational studies of flow characteristics in compound open channels are rather limited (3, 4, 6, 14) and applied for conditions in which the effects of the shear

International Conference on River Flood Hydraulics, edited by W.R.White

layer are not significant (high relative depths low relative roughness). For such conditions prediction of mean flow characteristics was satisfactory.
Also, Keller and Rodi (4) and Prinos (14) have attempted to use the depth-averaged version of the k-ε model with limited success for low relative depth conditions in which the shear layer in the junction region affects significantly the flow characteristics in both subsections.

Three-Dimensional modelling has been also attempted (3, 6, 14) using the k-ε (14) and algebraic stress models of turbulence (3, 6). Results are satisfactory for high relative depths and low relative roughness (weak momentum exchange, velocity differential, e.t.c) but for strong interaction predictions of the mechanism's effects on flow characteristics are less satisfactory.

Apart of problems of mesh refinement in conditions of low flood plain depths the previously used models of turbulence either do not produce secondary motion at all (i.e. k-ε model) or the algebraic stress model of Launder-Ying (9), which has been used by all investigators (3, 6) contains empirical constants, tuned appropriately for the correct prediction of the secondary currents.

In the present study the algebraic model of Demuren and Rodi (2) has been used in conjuction with the 3-D parabolic Navier-Stokes equ. The above model of turbulence is thought to be more general.

The stress components $\overline{v^2}$ and $\overline{w^2}$ and $\overline{vw}$ driving the secondary motion (v and w are in the vertical y and transverse z-directions respectively) are calculated from algebraic expressions, derived from full stress equations of transport, while the main shear stresses $-\overline{uv}$ and $-\overline{uw}$ are calculated from the k-ε model, based on the eddy viscosity concept. The use of a refined turbulence model (algebraic) for the calculation of $-\overline{uv}$ and $-\overline{uw}$ is not so essential and also an iterative procedure would be required for their calculation at each step of the solution procedure.

The model is applied in different experimental conditions with experimental results taken from Knight and Demetriou (5).
Comparisons are made in terms of percentage of flow carried by the main channel and the shear force applied in the various parts of the compound boundary.

Also, computational results of Lau and Drishnappan (6) are included and finally computational isovel patterns and secondary circulation produced in the model are presented for the various conditions examined.

MEAN FLOW EQUATIONS: The three-dimensional equations, parabolic in the lingitudinal direction, are used for predicting the mean velocity components U, V and W in the longitudinal, vertical and transverse directions respectively.

Continuity equation: $$\frac{\partial U}{\partial x} + \frac{\partial V}{\partial y} + \frac{\partial W}{\partial z} = 0 \tag{1}$$

U-Momentum: $$U\frac{\partial U}{\partial x} + V\frac{\partial U}{\partial y} + W\frac{\partial U}{\partial z} = -g\frac{\partial y_f}{\partial x} + gS_o - \frac{\partial(\overline{uv})}{\partial y} - \frac{\partial(\overline{uw})}{\partial z} \tag{2}$$

V-Momentum: $$U\frac{\partial V}{\partial x} + V\frac{\partial V}{\partial y} + W\frac{\partial V}{\partial z} = -\frac{1}{\rho}\frac{\partial p}{\partial y} - \frac{\partial(\overline{vw})}{\partial z} - \frac{\partial(v^2)}{\partial y} \tag{3}$$

W-Momentum: $$U\frac{\partial W}{\partial x} + V\frac{\partial W}{\partial y} + W\frac{\partial W}{\partial z} = -\frac{1}{\rho}\frac{\partial p}{\partial z} - \frac{\partial(\overline{vw})}{\partial y} - \frac{\partial(w^2)}{\partial z} \tag{4}$$

Using the above equations, the solution can not be influenced by downstream events and hence an efficient and economic marching forward procedure can be applied.
In the above equations y_f is the flow depth (y_c) is flow depth in the main channel and y_{fp} is the flood plain flow depth) and S_o is the channel slope, while $\bar{v}^2$, $\bar{w}^2$, $\overline{uv}$ and $\overline{vw}$ are components of the Reynolds stresses. A turbulence model has to be included in the solution of the above equations for determining the above components and hence closing the system of equations. Special attention is given to $\bar{v}^2$, $\bar{w}^2$ and $\overline{vw}$ appearing in the momentum equations (3) and (4) since they cause the secondary motion, while the other two stresses $-\overline{uv}$ and $-\overline{uw}$ are modelled based on an eddy viscosity model. Modelling of the stresses $-\overline{uv}$ and $-\overline{uw}$ with an algebraic stress model

is not essential and also causes coupling of the Reynolds-stress components which in turn requires an iterative procedure for their solution. The equations for the algebraic stress model are presented in the following section.

ALGEBRAIC STRESS MODEL: The algebraic stress model is based on the transport equation for the Reynolds-stress component $\overline{u_i u_j}$ developed by Launder et al (7). Convection and diffusion of the Reynolds stresses are neglected and hence the original differential equation reduces to an algebraic equation of the form:

$$0 = \underbrace{-\overline{u_i u_l}\frac{\partial U_j}{\partial x_l} - \overline{u_j u_l}\frac{\partial U_i}{\partial x_l}}_{P_{ij} = \text{production}} - \underbrace{\frac{2}{3}\delta_{ij}\varepsilon}_{\text{dissipation}} - \underbrace{c_1\frac{\varepsilon}{k}(\overline{u_i u_j} - \frac{2}{3}\delta_{ij}k)}_{\text{pressure - strain}} -$$

$$\underbrace{-a(P_{ij} - \frac{2}{3}\delta_{ij}P)}_{\text{pressure-strain}} - \underbrace{\beta(D_{ij} - \frac{2}{3}\delta_{ij}P) - \gamma(\frac{\partial U_i}{\partial x_j} + \frac{\partial U_j}{\partial x_i})k}_{\text{pressure - strain}} \qquad (5)$$

where P is the production of turbulent kinetic energy and is equal to $-\overline{u_i u_k}(\partial U_i/\partial x_k)$. According to the above equation the production of the Reynolds stresses by the interaction of stresses and mean-velocity gradients is balanced by viscous dissipation and also by an interaction between fluctuating pressure and fluctuating strain rate which tends to make turbulence more isotropic.

The surface-proximity effect on the turbulent stresses is accounted for in this model by making the empirical constants α,β,γ functions of a dimensionless distance from the wall.
c_1=1.5-5f, α=0.7636-0.06f, β=0.1091+0.06f, α=0.7636-0.06f
where f is calculated from the relationship: f=L/y
where L = the lengthscale of the turbulent motion at a point, which is equal to $(c_\mu^{3/4}k^{1.5})\kappa\varepsilon$ and y is the distance from the wall normal to the stress considered. With the latter definition of y it is assumed that the normal stress in the x_i direction is only damped by the wall normal to x_i and is not influenced by the wall parallel to x_i.

Assuming that the production P is equal to dissipation ε equ (5) is simplified and when it is solved for the stress components $\overline{u^2}$, $\overline{v^2}$, $\overline{w^2}$ and $\overline{vw}$ it gives the following relationships for the individual stresses.

$$\overline{u^2} = \frac{2K}{c_1\varepsilon}\left[\frac{\varepsilon}{3}(\alpha+\beta+c_1-1)-(1-\alpha)\left(\overline{uw}\frac{\partial U}{\partial z}+\overline{uv}\frac{\partial U}{\partial y}\right)\right] \quad (6)$$

$$\overline{v^2} = \frac{\frac{2K}{c_1\varepsilon}\left[\frac{\varepsilon}{3}(\alpha+\beta+c_1-1)+\beta\overline{uv}\frac{\partial U}{\partial y} - \overline{vw}\left\{(1-\alpha)\frac{\partial V}{\partial z}-\beta\frac{\partial W}{\partial y}\right\}-\gamma K\frac{\partial V}{\partial y}\right]}{1+\frac{2K}{c_1\varepsilon}(1-\alpha-\beta)\frac{\partial V}{\partial y}} \quad (7)$$

$$\overline{w^2} = \frac{\frac{2K}{c_1\varepsilon}\left[\frac{\varepsilon}{3}(\alpha+\beta+c_1-1)+\beta\overline{uw}\left\{(1-\alpha)\frac{\partial W}{\partial y}-\beta\frac{\partial V}{\partial z}\right\}-\gamma K\frac{\partial W}{\partial z}\right]}{1+\frac{2K}{c_1\varepsilon}(1-\alpha-\beta)\frac{\partial w}{\partial z}} \quad (8)$$

$$\overline{vw} = \frac{K}{c_1\varepsilon}\left[\beta\left(\overline{uw}\frac{\partial U}{\partial y}+\overline{uv}\frac{\partial U}{\partial z}\right)-\left\{(1-\alpha)\overline{v^2}-\beta\overline{w^2}+\gamma K\right\}\frac{\partial W}{\partial y} - \left\{(1-\alpha)\overline{w^2}-\beta\overline{v^2}+\gamma K\right\}\frac{\partial V}{\partial z}\right] \quad (9)$$

The calculation of the primary shear stresses $-\overline{uv}$ and $-\overline{uw}$ is based on the isotropic eddy-viscosity hypothesis since a refined turbulence model for these stresses is not essential. The calculation of the $\overline{v^2}-\overline{w^2}$ and $-\overline{vw}$ is essential for the calculation of the secondary currents.

$$-\overline{uv} = \nu_t\frac{\partial U}{\partial y} \quad (10)$$

$$-\overline{uw} = \nu_t\frac{\partial U}{\partial z} \quad (11)$$

where the longitudinal velocity gradients have been neglected.

The isotropic eddy viscosity in equs (10) and (11) is calculated through the k-ε model since ν_t is related to the turbulent kinetic energy k and the dissipation rate ε through the equation $\nu_t=0.09\frac{k^2}{\varepsilon}$.

The quantities k and ε which also appear in the algebraic stress model are calculated from the usual transport equation, for k and ε which are not repeated here (Rodi (16)).

Hence, the mean flow equations (1) to (4) together with the algebraic expressions for the Reynolds stresses and the k-ε model form a set of equations which is solved simultaneously using appropriate boundary conditions. The solution procedure and the boundary conditions employed in this study are discussed in the following section.

SOLUTION PROCEDURE: All the differential equations introduced previously are parabolic in the longitudinal direction can be expressed in a common form as follows:

$$U\frac{\partial \phi}{\partial x} + \nu \frac{\partial \phi}{\partial y} + W \frac{\partial \phi}{\partial z} = \frac{\partial}{\partial y} (\Gamma\phi \frac{\partial \phi}{\partial y}) + \frac{\partial}{\partial z} (\Gamma\phi \frac{\partial \phi}{\partial z}) + S\phi \qquad (12)$$

and an efficient forward-marching solution procedure can be employed. With this procedure the calculation domain is covered only once without iteration, starting from given initial conclusions and two-dimensional storage of the variables is required at the grid-points located in one cross-section. In the presesnt study the numerical scheme proposed by Patankar and Spalding (12) was employed. At the inlet compound cross-section a uniform distribution of all variables was prescribed. The secondary velocities V and W were set equal to zero and k and ε had such small values that the eddy viscosity was approximately 10-15 times the kinematic viscosity ν. The step-by-step integration was carried out until the flow became fully developed (no change in velocity distribution in the longitudinal direction). At each step the momentum equations were solved with a guessed pressure field (the longitudinal momentum equation had a known pressure gradient equal to gS_o) with the upstream values taken as guesses. Pressure and velocity fields were corrected subsequently to satisfy the continuity equation and the Reynolds stresses were determined from the algebraic expressions and from the eddy-viscosity relations with known upstream values of ν_t. Finally the equations of k and ε were solved.

The solutions were obtained with a grid 40x20 (40 in the horizontal and 20 in the vertical direction) distributed non-uniformly over the compound cross-section.

A finer grid was also used in the vertical direction (up to 35 grid lines) but the results were almost identical with the coarser grid . Hence the coarser grid was used in the subsequent calculations. The longitudinal step was taken approximately 1/40 of the total flow depth for most of the test cases considered.

BOUNDARY CONDITIONS: Boundary conditions should be specified at solid walls, free surface and symmetry planes for all variables U, V, W, k, ε.

At symmetry plane the velocity component normal to plane was set equal to zero, while for all other variables the gradients normal to the plane were set to zero.

At solid walls, the wall function technique proposed by Launder and Spalding (8) was used, by which the boundary conditions are specified at a grid point which lies outside the laminar sublayer. At this point with distance y from the wall the velocity follow the "law of the wall" given by:

$$\frac{U_r}{U_*} = \frac{1}{\varkappa} \ln \left(E \frac{U_* y}{\nu}\right) \tag{13}$$

where U_r=the resultant velocity, U_*=the resultant friction velocity, $\varkappa$=von Karman constant (=0.4187) and E=wall roughness parameter (=90 for smooth walls).

The boundary conditions for k and ε are also specified at the same point, assuming local equilibrium from the following relationships:

$$k = U_*/\sqrt{c_\mu} \qquad \varepsilon = U_*^3/\varkappa y \tag{14}$$

The boundary conditions at the free surface are specified following the approach of Rastogi and Rodi (15) which considers the free surface as a symmetry plane. Hence normal gradients of U, W, k were set to zero. For the condition of ε at the free surface the approach of Lau and Krishnappan (6) was employed, calculating ε from the following relationship:

$$\varepsilon_f = \frac{c_f \left(\frac{k_f}{\sqrt{c_\mu}}\right)^{1.5}}{\varkappa y_f} \tag{15}$$

where c_f=constant (=0.164), k_f=kinetic energy at free surface and y_f=distance between nearest grid point and the free surface.

COMPUTATIONAL RESULTS: Computational results are presented for the experimental conditions taken from Knight and Demetriou (5). The compound cross section, examined experimentally by the above researchers (fig.1), had a main channel width to depth ratio equal to 2 (and hence 3-dimensional effects are present), the slope of the channel was set equal to 0.000966, the flood plain width and the total flow depth were varied. Hence, the relative width of the channel ($Wr=W/W_c$) was varied from 2 to 4 and the relative depth $y_r= y_{fp}/y_f$ was varied from 0.24 to 0.5. For the above experimental conditions the interaction between main channel and flood plain flows is significant only for the lower values of the relative depth and hence the model should perform satisfactorly for higher relative depths while its performance should be tested for strong interacting conditions.

Therefore it was decided to apply the model for relative depths up to 0.250 (strong interacting conditions) and compare the computational results with experimental curves derived by Knight and Demetriou (5) from their experimental results. The lowest value of y_r was set to 0.1 for having adequate grid points in the shallow flood plain region and hence resolving the interacting zone satisfactorily.

Figure 2 shows the percentage of total flow carried by the main channel as a function of the relative depths y_r and relative width W_r. The curves have been produced by the experimental results taken from (5) while predicted values by Lau and Krishnappan (6) are included but for higher relative depths (y_r>0.28). The values predicted by the model for y_r between 0.1 and 0.25 are shown to be in close agreement with the experimental curves even for such strong interacting conditions.

Figure 3 shows the percentage of the shear force applied in the various parts of the compound cross section boundary in relation with y_r and for W_r=2 and 3. Some differences between computed and experimental results exist but the model performs better than the one used by Lau and Krishnappan (6) especially for W_r=2 and in the flood plain bed where their model shows poor performance even for high relative depths.

Figure 4 shows the computed isovel patterns for y_r=0.24 and W_r=2. The maximum velocity filament is predicted below the free surface, as it has been observed and predicted for 3-dimensional flows in channels of simple cross-sections (11). Also, the bulging of contours in the interacting region shows the imaginary iterface of zero apparent shear stress which has an inclination with regard to the vertical interface. Hence methods of calculating the discharge in compound channels have to account for the inclined zero shear interface. Usually the methods applied consider the vertical interface as the one with zero shear and hence their prediction of discharge is not satisfactory.

Figure 5 shows the secondary motion produced by the model for the same conditions, indicating the strong secondary currents in the interacting region and their effects on the primary velocity field. Unfortunately no measurements of secondary motion has been reported and hence comparison of the model prediction with experimental measurement is not possible.

<u>CONCLUSIONS:</u> An algebraic stress model was applied for the prediction of the flow characteristics in compound open channels. Predictions of the model were compared with experimental measurements taken from (5) and show satisfactory agreement.

Computed isovel patterns indicate interfaces of zero shear stress which are inclined and not vertical, as supposed in methods for calculating the discharge in compound open channels.

Finally, the secondary currents produced by the algebraic stress model, indicate the complexity of the flow in the interacting region for low relative depth and width and their effects on the primary velocity field.

REFERENCES:

1. Arnold U, Hottges J and Rovve G. "Turbulence and mixing mechasisms in compound open channel Flow" Proc of XXIII Congress of IAHR, pp. A15-A22, 1989.
2. Demuren A.O. and Rodi W., "Calculation of turbulence-driven secondary motion in non-circular ducts", J.F.M., vol. 140, pp. 189-222, 1984.
3. Kawahara Y and Tamai N., "Mechanism of lateral momentum transfer in compound channel flows", Proc of XXIII Congress of IAHR, pp B463-B470, 1989.
4. Keller R.J. and Rodi W., "Prediction of Flow characteristics in Main Channel/Flood plain Flows" J.of Hydraulic Research, vol 26, pp 425-441, 1988.
5. Knight D.W and Demetriou J.D., "Flood Plain and Main Channel Flow Interaction", J of Hydraulic Eng, vol 109(8), pp.1073-1092, 1983
6. Law U.L. and Krishnappan B.G. "Turbulence Modelling of Flood Plain Flows", J of Hydraulic Eng, vol. 112(4), pp.251-267, 1986.
7. Launder B.E., Reece G.J. and Rodi W., "Progress in the development of a Reynolds stress turbulence closure" J.F.M., vol.68, pp. 537-566, 1975.
8. Launder B.E. and Spalding D.B., "The Numerical computation of Turbulent Flow" Computer methods in Applied Mechanics and Eng, vol. 3, pp. 269-289.
9. Launder B.E. and Ying W.M., "Predictions of flow and heat transfer in ducts of square cross-section, Proc. Inst. Mech.Engineers vol. 187, pp. 4550461, 1973.
10. McKeogh E.J. and Kiely G.K., "Experimental study of the mechanisms of flood flow in meandering channels" Proc of XXIII Congress of IAHR, pp. B491-B498, 1989.

11. Nezu F., Nakagawa H. and Rodi W., "Significant Difference between secondary Currents in closed channels and Narrow Open Channels", Proc of XXIII Congress of IAHR, pp. A125-A132.
12. Patankar S.V. and Spalding B.D., "A Calculation procedure for Heat, Mass and Momentum transfer in the Three-Dimensional Parabolic Flows", Int. Journal at Heat and Mass transfer, vol. 15, pp. 1787-1806, 1972.
13. Prinos P, Townsend R.D. and Tavoularis S., "Structure of Turbulence in Compound channel Flows" Journal of Hydraulic Eng., vol. 111(9), pp. 1246-1261, 1985.
14. Prinos P. "Experiments and Numerical Modelling in Compound Open Channels and Duct Flows" Proc. of "HYDROCOMP 89", pp.215-225.
15. Rastogi A.K. and Rodi W., "Predictions of Heat and Mass Transfer" J of Hydraulics Dir, ASCE, vol. 104(3), pp.397-420, 1978.
16. Rodi W., "Turbulence models and their Application in Hydraulics", IAHR Publication, 1982.
17. Tominaga A., Nezu I. and Ezaki K., "Experimental study on secondary currents in compound open-channel Flows" Proc. of XXIII Congress of IAHR, pp. A15-A22, 1989.
18. Wormleaton P.R., Allen J. and Hadjipanos P., "Discharge Assesment in Compound Channel Flow", J. of Hydraulic, ASCE, vol 108, pp. 975-994, 1982.

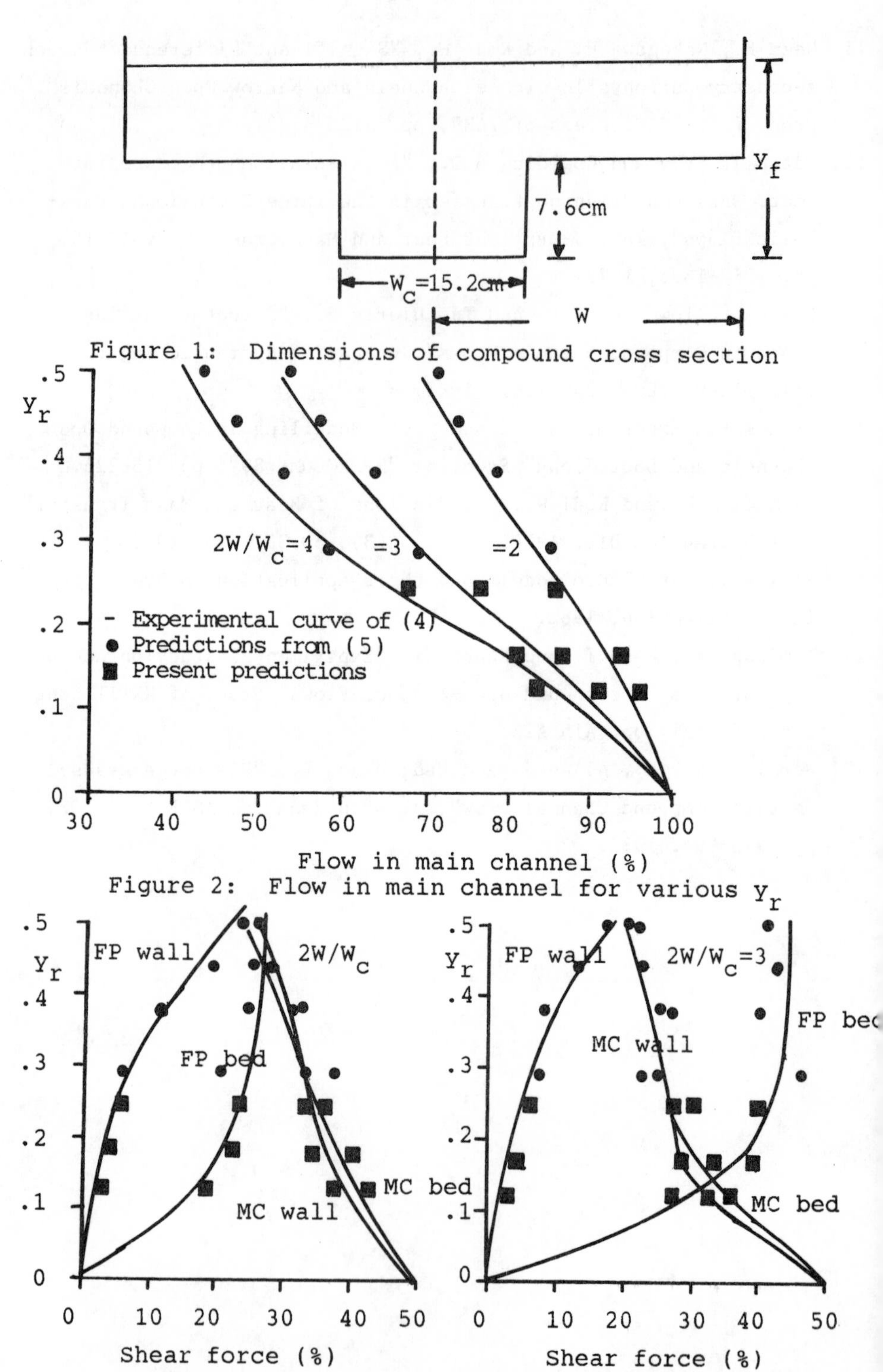

Figure 1: Dimensions of compound cross section

Figure 2: Flow in main channel for various Y_r

Figure 3: Experimental and Predicted Shear Force

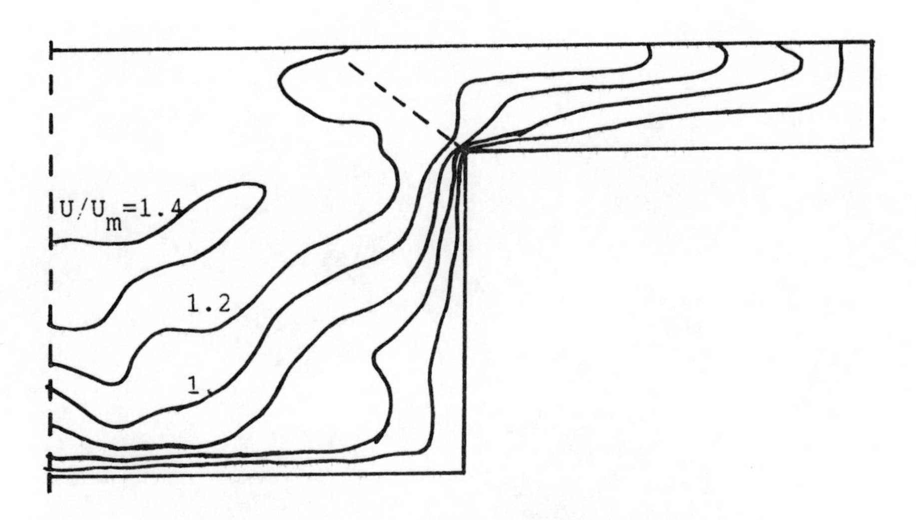

Figure 4: Isovel contours for y_r=0.24 and W_r=2

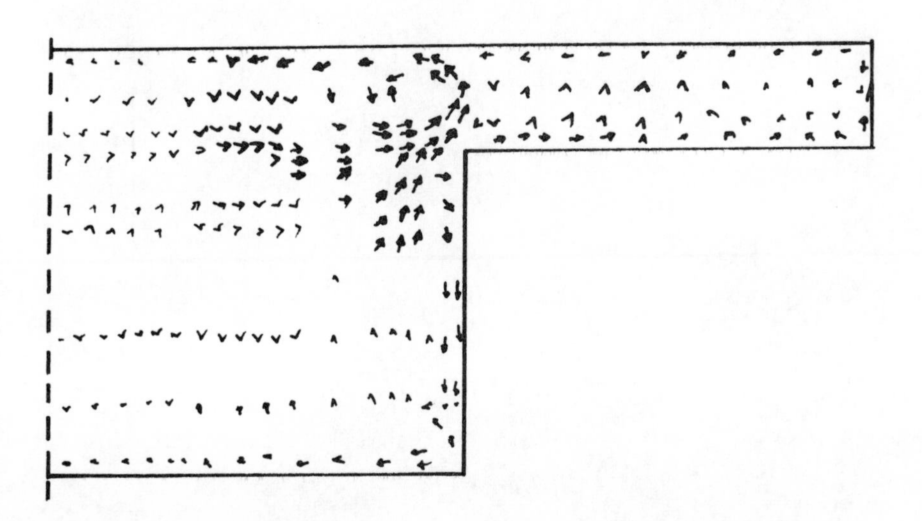

Figure 5: Secondary currents for y_r=0.24 and W_r=2

PAPER F1

International Conference on
RIVER FLOOD HYDRAULICS
17-20 September, 1990

Discharge/Stage Relations in vegetated Danish Streams

Torben Larsen
Jens-Ole Frier
Kristian Vestergaard

University of Aalborg, Department of Civil Engineering,
Sohngårdholmsvej 57, DK-9000 Aalborg, Denmark

Abstract

This paper describes how the friction in Danish streams varies as function of the vegetation. The major species of vegetation are presented. A series of laboratory and field experiments are described, and a hypothesis for the influence of the vegetation on the Manning's n is discussed.

Introduction

Danish streams are all typical lowland streams, since the country are totally devoid of rocks or mountains. The streams are meandering through glacial deposits of moraine clay in the eastern part of the country and more sandy soils in the western part. Although the streams are comparatively small most of them have a stable waterflow through the year. The surroundings are almost entirely agricultural land, mostly pastures for cattle.

Fifty or more different species of macrophytes make up the flora of these streams, but only few are quantitatively important. Among these the sibling species of *Batrachium* or the two monocotyledonts *Glyceria maxima* or *Sparganium simplex* are dominant. *Helodea canadense* or species of *Callitriche* are subdominant with either of the dominant vegetation types.

Due to intensivation of farming methods during this century macrophyte growth in streams has become a severe problem. The heavy growth of plants raises water levels and causes draining systems to stop working and yields from farming to fall drastically. This effect has been accentuated by channelisation of streams making the water systems even more susceptible to macrophytes than before.

Public authorities are responsible for removal of macrophyte vegetation in almost all the streams. Until now this has been done by cutting the weeds 1-4 times a year. The removal has always been done by clear cutting, and due care was taken not to leave any vegetation.

International Conference on River Flood Hydraulics, edited by W.R.White

The consequences of clear cutting were dramatic alterations of water levels from situations with a dense vegetation to situations without any plants.

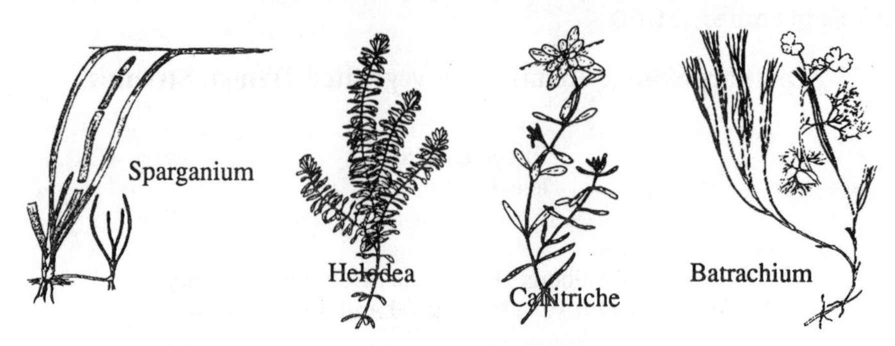

Fig. 1. Dominant species of vegetation in Danish streams

Most danish steams are polluted to some extent either from sewage plants or from trout farms. The big variation in vegetation density during the summer caused organic matters to degrade over either a very short (dense growth) or a much longer (no growth) length of water. This made oxygen levels fluctuate between intolerable and tolerable levels .

Through interaction with the carbonate system of the water macrophyte growth makes the streams more alkaline. The old management practice for vegetation caused bigger fluctuations in pH than necessary, sometimes making the environment dangerous to stream animals.

Most invertebrates in the streams, especially stoneflies (Plecopthera), mayflies (Emphemerida), and dragonflies (Trichopthera) are delimited in their distribution by the unfavourable oxygen levels and unfavourable pH levels of danish streams caused partly by the above mentioned clear cutting practice for the vegetation management. In addition the method in most cases causes the animals to live in suboptimal densities, because they found themselves in surroundings fluctuating between lots of food and practically no food, between no shelter and ample hideaways.

The commercially most important non salmonid fish in danish streams are eels. Like other fishes they have been moving around in the streams due to the fluctuating oxygen levels in the environment. The exact effect of this phenomenon is not well known.

The salmonid fishes (mostly trout) are teritorial during their stream life, and their moving around due to oxygen fluctuations and cover removal causes suboptimal population sizes of these fishes.

New methods for weed removal have been developed during the last decade. The vegetation are cut during the whole summer to avoid fluctuations in water levels and in biological important water parameters. Clear cutting is also avoided, by regular thinning or channel cutting through the vegetation. The ultimate goal for the management practice is a constant water level and constant and favourable biological conditions in the stream in conjunction with a permanent function af the agricultural draining systems.

Optimal strategies for weed management calls for rigid hydraulic tools for estimation of the effect on water level and water flow from various stands of underwater vegetation.

The objective of this paper is to provide some of the basis for such tools by means of a combination of mathematical models, experiments in artificial channels and measurements and experiments in nature.

Materials and methods

The field experiments was caried out in Herredsbækken, a smaller stream near the city Aars in the nothern part of Jutland. The chosen reach is approximately 150 m long, 2-2.5 m wide. The cross section is almost rectangular. The bottom slope is 0.1-0.2 percent and during the period of measurement in September 1989 the discharge was approximately 100 l/sec. The average depth was between 0.2 and 0.4 m (see figure 3).

The reach in Herredsbækken was densily covered with weed totally dominated by *Sparganium simplex*. The biomass of the weed was measured as wet weight and was found to 2.38 kg/m^2 for the upper reach and 1.55 kg/m^2 for the lower reach. The percentage dry matter was found to 7.4 %.

	Dry weight g/m^2	Dry matter %
Flume tank experiment, density I	390	4
Flume tank experiment, density II	190	4
Flume tank experiment, density III	80	4
Sparganium simplex - Herredsbæk - September, Area 3	120	7.4
Sparganium simplex - Herredsbæk - September, Area 6	180	7.4
Batrachium sp. - Gryde Å - July, August	200	
Batrachium sp. - Gryde Å - Winter	40	
Batrachium sp - Simested Å - May, Average of 6 areas	48	5.0
Batrachium sp. - Fjederholt Å - July, Average for 2 summers	350	

Fig. 2. Biomass density of plants in our experiment and in typical situations in Danish streams. Result from Gryde Å are from Jeppesen and Thyssen (1985). Result from Fjerderholt Å are from Kern-Hansen et al (1980). The rest are own measurements.

The water level was measured at 7 stations, and the flow was found by "velocity area integration", where the velocity was measured at a number of points at the cross section near station no. 3. Approximately 600 m upstream the brook widens into a lake with a 20000 m^2 large surface. By controlling the outlet from the lake by a weir, the discharge at the reach could be varied in the range from 80 to 450 l/sec.

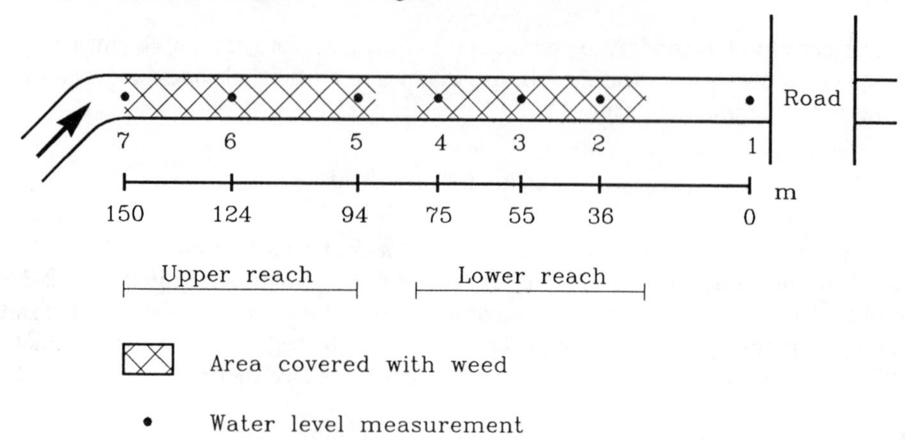

Fig. 3. The reach in Herredsbækken

The results was discharge-depth series for each station. Using a backwater calculation it was possible to obtain the Manning coefficients for each flow-series.

The flume tank experiments in the laboratory at the University of Aalborg was carried out in a 15 m long rectangular flume tank with a width of 30.5 cm.

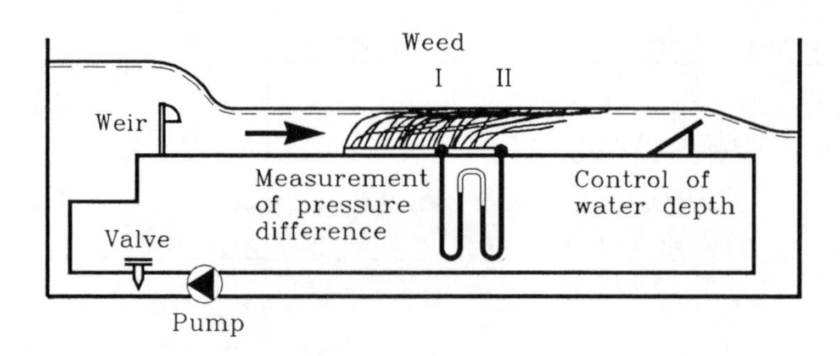

Fig. 4 Flume tank experiment

In this flume tank a 1.5 m long reach with weeds of *Sparganium simplex* was built. Each stem was fixed in a net of metalwire, which afterwards was founded in plaster. The average length of the weed was 81 cm, the specific gravity 802 kg/m^3, and the percentage dry matter 4.0 %. The biomass densities of *Sparganium* covered the ranges normally found in Danish streams (see figure 2).

The discharge could be controlled by a valve and was measured by use of a sharp crested weir. The discharge could be varied in a range from 1 to 18 l/sec. The slope of the water surface was measured as a difference in pressure between point I and II (see figure 4). The distance between point I and II was 61.3 cm. The water depth was measured in point I and could be varied in the range from 6 to 22 cm.

The slope of the water surface was measured for a large number of combinations of discharge and depth, then the density of weed was decreased by removing approximately half of the straws, before the measurements were repeated. Measurements were performed for four different densities of weed, and from a backwater calculation the Manning coefficients was found for each combination of discharge, depth and density of weed.

Hydraulic considerations and results

The main objective of this work was to establish and discuss methods for the determination of discharge/stage relations for vegetated streams. Especially it is relevant to evaluate the flooding risk for streams in the summer period in connection with uncommon high discharges. A typical discharge/stage relation is shown in figure 5.

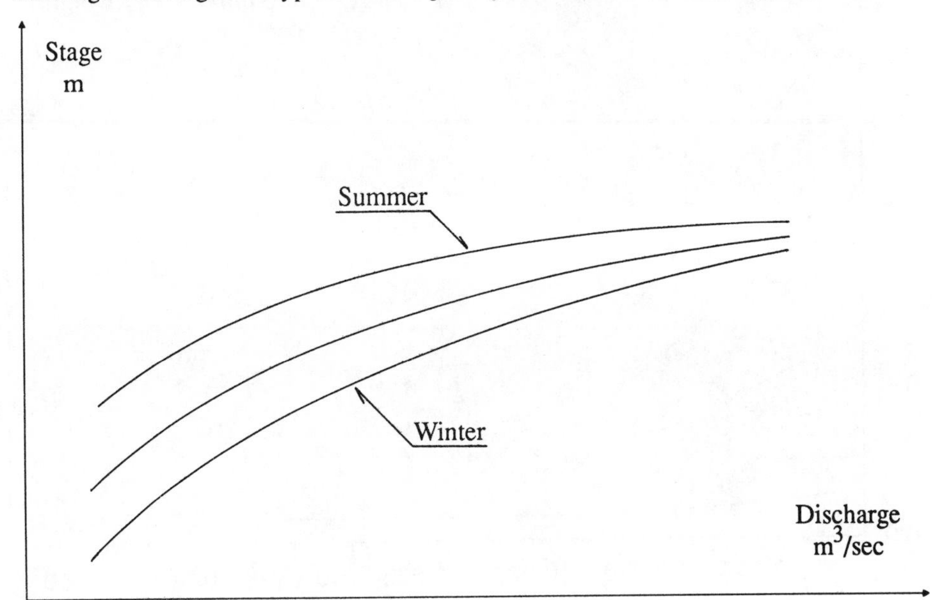

Fig. 5. Discharge/stage relations for a stream with vegetation

It is a generally accepted fact that the friction in vegetated streams and rivers depends on the discharge rate, see e.g. (Chow 1959). Many words could have been spent on discussing which friction equation to use under such circumstances. But this seems to be irrelevant because the physics of the phenomena indicates that a varying friction coefficent would anyhow be necessary. The friction will here be described as the variation of the Manning's n from the well-known Manning equation:

$$V = \frac{1}{n} R^{2/3} S^{1/2} \qquad \text{or} \qquad Q = A \frac{1}{n} R^{2/3} S^{1/2}$$

where

V is cross-section average velocity [m/s]
Q is discharge [m^3/s]
A is cross-section area [m^2]
n is Manning's n
R is hydraulic radius [m]
S is the slope of the energy line [dimensionless]

Chow(1959) refers to a number of investigations on grassed channels, which show how the Manning's n depends on the product of V• R (average cross-section velocity times hydraulic radius).

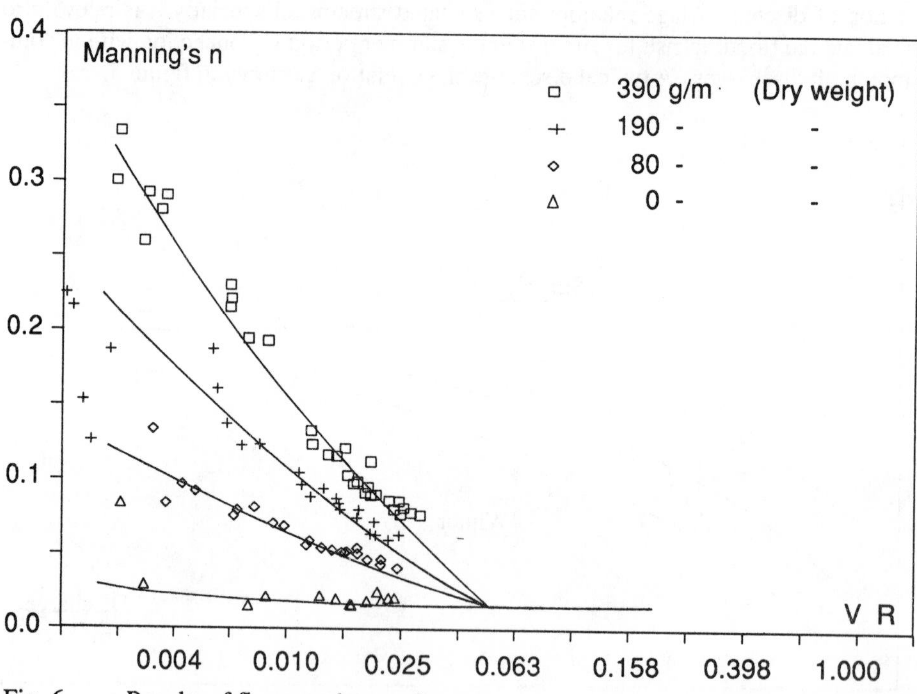

Fig. 6. Results of flume tank experiment.

In this investigation different ways of plotting the results was tried, e.g. n was plotted against discharge, velocity, bottom shear etc. But the conclusion was that plotting n against V• R gave the most consistent results (figure 6).

Figure 6 shows the results the laboratory experiments described . This gives a clear picture how the friction increases with vegetation density and decreases with the product of V• R. It should here be repeated that in the laboratory experiments a large number of independent combinations of V and R were tested. The laboratory results confirm that the product V• R is a reasonable variable in the description of the varying n. Furthermore the results make it probable that the curves converge against one point of intersection. For similarity reasons it cannot be expected that the laboratory results can be directly compared with the field experiment.

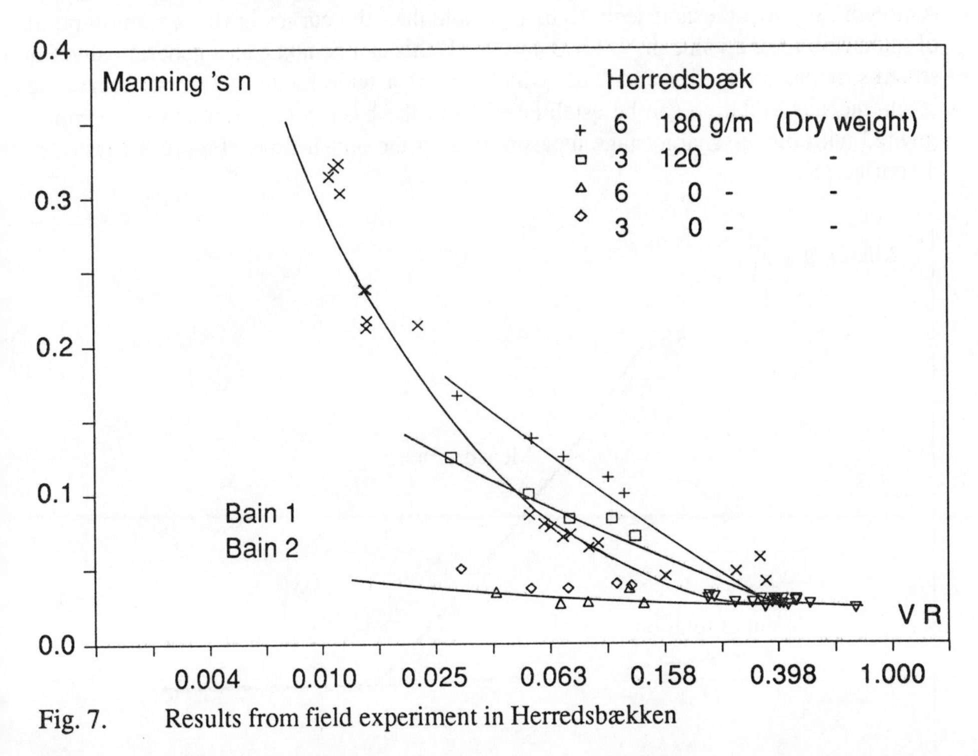

Fig. 7. Results from field experiment in Herredsbækken

Details will not be given here, but it should be mentioned, that the head loss for the small discharge part of the laboratory experiments, where the weed covered all the cross section, was almost proportional to the velocity. This indicates that the flexible and slightly moving plants absorb the turbulence to give an almost laminar friction relation.

The results of the field experiments are plotted on figure 7 together with results published by Powell(1979).

The results of Powell were measurements from River Bain in U.K. for a short rain period in July 1973, where discharge varied over a range from 0.1 to 6 m^3/sec. The vegetation was dense and dominated by pondweed *(Potamogeton pectinatus* and *Helodea canadense)*. It was reported that approx. 70 %of the river surface was covered by weed. The dry weight of the vegetation was not measured

The field results from U.K. and Denmark show the general dependence of the Manning's n in respect to the product of V• R. In this case V and R were almost 100 % correlated because of the unique discharge/stage relationship during the measurements. This means that the field measurements do not confirm that V• R can be used in general, but fortunately the laboratory results were quite clear on that point.

As a working hypothesis it seem to be probable that the curves have a common point of intersection for a value of V• R= 0.4 m^2/s. If this can be taken as a general value for streams of the actual size and type, which covers a wide range of Danish streams, a discharge/stage relation can be established from the basic winter relation and supplemented with one discharge/stage measurement at the actual time. Figure 8 illustrates this principle.

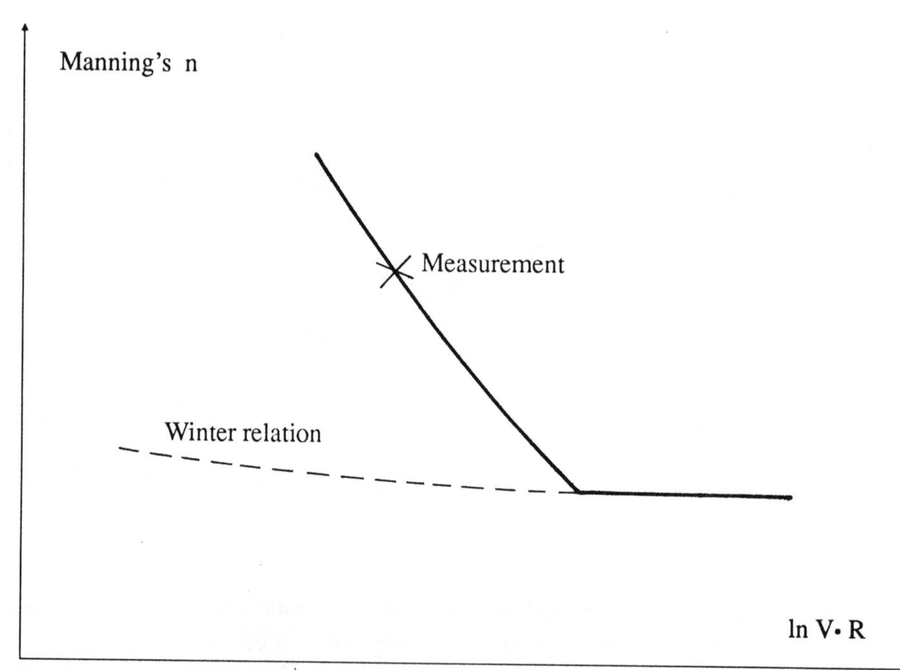

Fig. 8. Actual Manning's n.

In this investigation it was tried, but without succes, to characterize the friction also on the basis of typical plant characteristics with parameters like the dry weight per unit stream bed area (or volume), the plant surface area per stream bed area or the like. A temporary conclusion on this point is, that the actual Manning's n up till now, is the best parameter to characterize the vegetation in this respect. On the other hand the empirical approach taken here can without doubt be improved based on further similarity considerations combined with more data.

Conclusion

This investigation confirms that vegetation has a significant and often dominating influence on the hydraulic friction in streams. But the effect decreases and even vanishes under high discharge conditions. There seems to be a clear relation between the Manning'n and the actual product V• R of average velocity and hydraulic radius. For discharge conditions, where V• R is greater than 0.4 m^2/sec, the friction is no longer influenced by the vegetation. From these general observations, it is possible to establish an actual discharge/stage relation in the vegetated period, based on only a single set of measured discharge/stage values.

Because the functional description of the variation of Manning's n use V• R as the independent variable, the relation is valid not only for uniform flow, but also for backwater and unsteady calculations.

Acknowledgements

We wish to thank our former students S. A. B. Jensen, N. Olsen, and J. Pedersen for help in the laboratory and measurements of important parameters in Herredsbækken.

References

Chow, V. T. (1959)
Open-Channel Hydraulics
Mc.Graw-Hill, New York.

Jeppesen, E. and N. Thyssen (1985)
Biologiske strukturmodeller for vandløb
Vand og miljø 2(2)

Kern-Hansen, U. ; T. F. Holm; B. L. Madsen; N. Thyssen; J. Mikkelsen. (1980)
Rapport over undersøgelse vedrørende vedligeholdelse af vandløb.
Miljøministeriet, Copenhagen.

Powell, K.E.C. (1979)
Weed growth - A factor of Channel Rougness
From : Hydrometry (ed. R.W. Herschy)
John Wiley & Sons, London.

PAPER F2

International Conference on
RIVER FLOOD HYDRAULICS
17-20 September, 1990

MODEL STUDIES OF OVERBANK FLOW FROM A MEANDERING CHANNEL

B.B. Willetts and R.I. Hardwick, University of Aberdeen and A.G. MacLean, Grampian Regional Council

Summary Laboratory observations are reported of flow in a system comprising a sequence of uniform meanders cut in a flat flood-plain with straight parallel boundaries. In most of the reported experiments the channel sinuosity is 1.41. Flows are compared for a uniform trapezoidal channel cross-section and for a channel produced naturally by bed erosion and deposition.

Stage/discharge curves are plotted for each of the channels and are compared with those obtained for trapezoidal channels of sinuosity 1 and 2.06. In all cases the increase of stage with discharge suffers a check when flow first goes over-bank. Differences are noted in the prominence of this effect when the channels are compared.

Tentative interpretations of the velocity data collected suggest that an important influence on flow resistance is the substitution of flood-plain flow for channel flow in the inter-bend reaches, and that this is stimulated by concentrated vorticity created near the inner bank immediately downstream of the bend. The effect is diminished when the bed of the channel shoals naturally at this location.

Attention is drawn to the need for observations in larger channels than the ones used here, in order to confirm and elaborate the findings reported, which have considerable potential importance in flood prediction.

INTRODUCTION

The hydraulics of overbank flow is important in two circumstances. When rivers flood, the extent of the damage and danger to life depends on the stage reached for a given flow rate. This can only be predicted for a variety of rivers and floods if the flow behaviour which governs the stage-discharge relationship is properly understood. Similar understanding is needed in the design of compound channels in which most flows are contained within an inner channel but quite modest floods occupy a flood plain provided and managed for that purpose.

International Conference on River Flood Hydraulics, edited by W.R.White

The economic and social importance of the topic has been recognised recently in a substantial programme of research (Knight, 1989). This has mainly concerned straight channels in straight flood plains. It has clarified the interaction between the generally sluggish flood-plain flow and the faster channel flow via a zone of high vorticity(with axis nearly vertical) in the vicinity of each bank of the inner channel. However, most field problems involve inner channels which are neither straight nor of uniform cross-section. It is, therefore, important that river flood research is not confined to straight channels, but also attacks the much more difficult problems associated with a meandering inner channel. In very crude terms the situation may be considered as a sinuous channel flow having an interface with a sheet flow which is physically superimposed on it and also covers the flood plains. Clearly the channel and flood-plain flows must interact, as they do in the case of straight channels, but the resemblance between the two cases will not be close because the meandering channel has a different gradient from that of the flood plain, and the flow direction conforms with the flood plain axis only at the bend apices. It seems inevitable, therefore, that the mechanisims of momentum exchange will differ in the cases of straight and meandering channels and that this fundamental difference will limit the application of the output of research on straight channels to the more complex case.

In-bank meander flow has been much studied. The nature of the secondary currents in the bend flow is well known, and the resulting channel geometry has been documented several times (de Vriend, 1981). Quite successful numerical models of bend flow have been published (Crosato,1987). The flows revealed by these studies are not directly relevant to overbank meander flows, because the lateral surface profiles and pressure distributions associated with flow in the inner channel meander are distorted by the superimposed flood-plain flows. However, the geometry of the channel bed is moulded by the in-bank flows. To the extent that inner channel geometry influences the flood flow structures, therefore, the in-bank bend flows are indirectly influential.

This paper outlines a laboratory study undertaken with the objectives of identifying the principal flow structures associated with the channel/floodplain interaction, of exploring their dependency on the channel cross section-geometry, and of detecting whether inner channel sinuosity and cross-section shape have significant influence on stage-discharge relationships.

Experimental Procedure

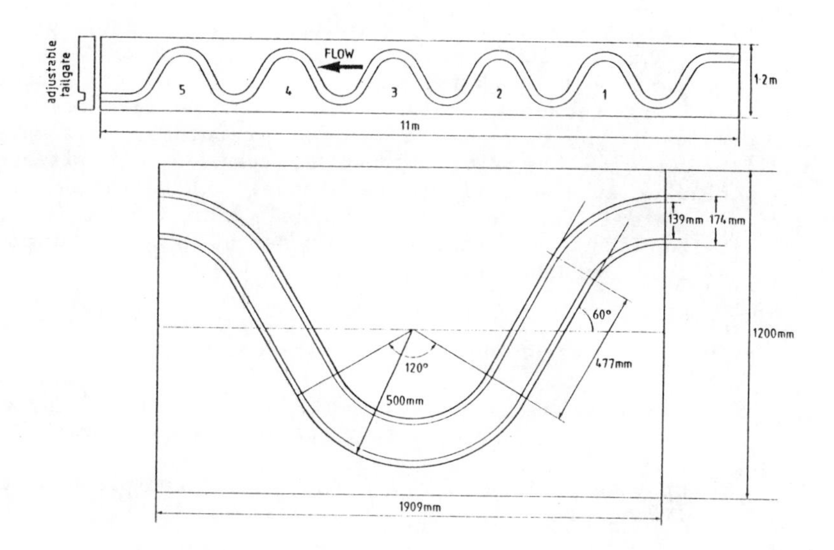

Fig 1 Plan view of the whole channel (above) and an enlarged view of one bend, with dimensions.

The plan geometry of the experimental channel is detailed in fig. 1. The trapezoidal channel with which the series began is 50mm deep and has a top width of 174mm - unnaturally narrow with respect to its depth - and side slopes of 71°. The exaggerated depth of the channel was adopted so that measurements of velocity could be made at several distinct depths within the channel.

The flood-plain longitudinal gradient is adjustable. It was set in all these experiments at 1:1000. The sinuosity of the channel was 1.41, so the average channel gradient was 1:1410. Channel and flood-plain are formed in expanded polystyrene foam and painted at the exposed surface which, therefore, was of reasonably uniform texture.

Water was supplied at a metered rate to the tank at the head of the flood-plain. A weir at the downstream end was adjusted so as to give the greatest possible length of flow at uniform depth for each flow in the channel/floodplain system. For this purpose depth measurements were taken at each intersection of the channel and flood-plain centre-lines.

Two channel geometries were investigated, both having the same form in plan. In the first case, the inner channel was uniformly trapezoidal as detailed above and in fig 1. The second geometry was formed by placing granular bakelite to a depth of 20mm in the trapezodial section, and exposing the bakelite surface to bank-full flow for a period of 2 hours. The resulting geometry exhibits many of the features of a natural meandering channel but is not, of course, in complete equilibrium with the flow because of the sediment transport discontinuity at the head of the channel. Nevertheless this will be termed the "natural" channel, for brevity. the bakelite surface was stabilised with cement powder and paint for the natural channel experiments.

For each of the trapezoidal and the natural channels the following programme of observations was completed.

1. Stage/discharge measurements for inbank flows and overbank flows up to a flood-plain depth of 40mm.

2. For each of three flood flows, with flood-plain depths of 8mm, 20mm and 40mm respectively:-

    i) plan view photographs of surface floats, and of dye released at preselected points in the flow;
    ii) measurements of velocity component (magnitude and direction) in each of six horizontal planes over one wavelength . In the natural channel, there are apparent gaps in the velocity record because the shoals formed in the bed buried parts of the lower planes of measurement.
    iii) Water surface levels over a wavelength of the meander pattern.

Because unexpected velocity vectors were observed near the bend apices, shear stress vector directions were investigated in and near the channel over a quarter wavelength. This was done for the natural channel only using the following method. The bed, bank and floodplain were excavated to a depth of approximately 10mm and the original flow boundary was re-moulded in plaster of paris. Its surface was indented at regular intervals with a 2mm drill. After exposure to the flow, each originally circular indentation is fluted in the local boundary stress direction, so that collectively they indicate the shear stress field. The results so obtained at flood depth 20mm were consistent with the observed velocity vectors; shear stress observations were not made at the other two depths.

RESULTS

Stage discharge graphs are shown in fig 2 for the trapezoidal and natural channels. For comparison, the graphs for a straight trapezoidal channel and for trapezoidal and natural channels of sinuosity 2.06 are also included. All the graphs show normalised flow, the denominator in all cases being the bank-full flow for sinuosity 1.41 and the trapezoidal cross-section.

Fig 3 shows the path of floats released over the flood-plain width and fig 4(a) the escape onto the flood-plain of dye released deep in the channel. Fig 4(b) identifies, by means of dye, a strong vortex filament originating near the bend apex and diffusing in the inter-bend reach.

Velocity measurements were used to produce local values of velocity gradient, averaged between each pair of measurement planes. Fig 5 is an example of the contour pattern of velocity gradient obtained from a set of such data near the plane of the flood-plain for flow with a flood-plain depth 20mm.

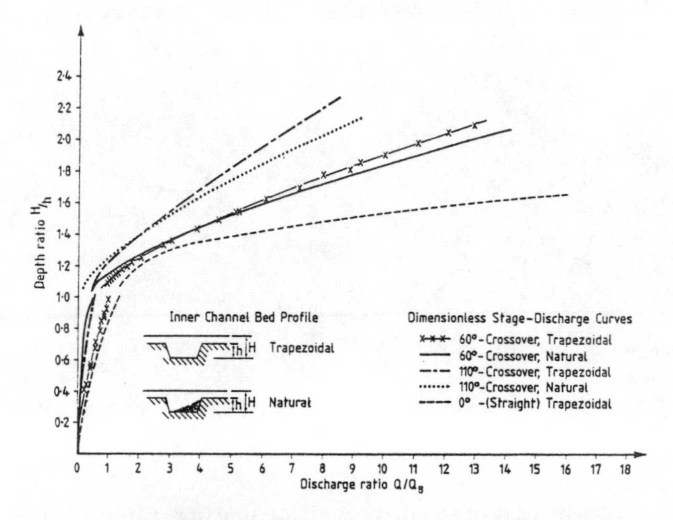

Fig 2 Stage discharge curves for channels of three sinuosities (1, 1.41 and 2.06) and two types of cross-section: the trapezoidal and natural cross-sections described in the text. Note that all discharges are normalised with respect to one particular flow: the bank-full flow in the trapezoidal channel of sinuosity 1.41. For sinuosity 2.06 the valley slope was 1:1618, whereas for the other sinuosities it was 1:1000.

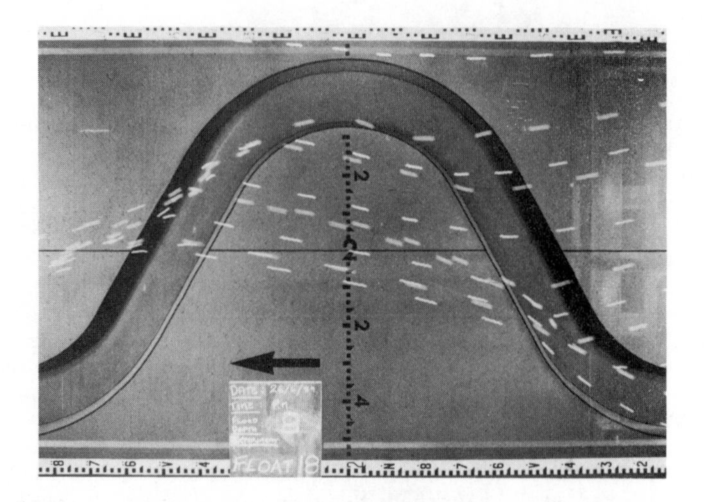

Fig 3 Stroboscopic photograph of floats taken with depth on the flood-plain 8mm (relative depth 8/58). The flow is deflected laterally in each half wave-length of the meander.

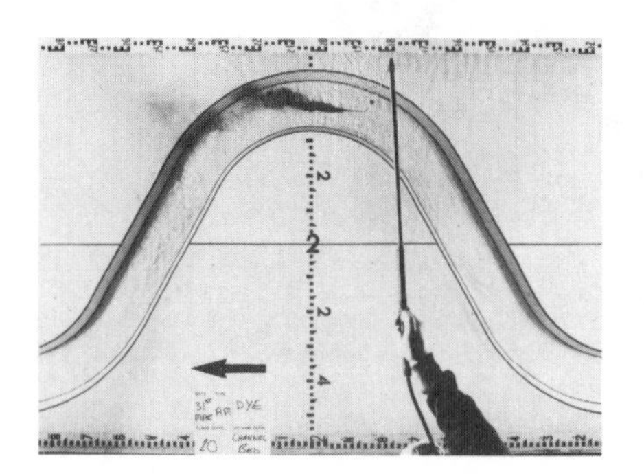

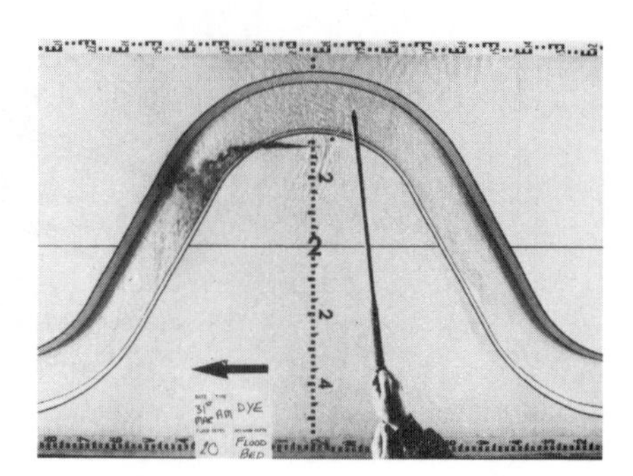

Fig 4 Dye injected into a flow having flood-plain depth 20mm.
4a) Dye released near the bed, within the meandering inner channel, first mixes and then escapes onto the flood-plain.
4b) Dye released on the flood-plain near the bed is entrained in a vigorous vortex near the inner bank and diffuses as it convects along the channel.

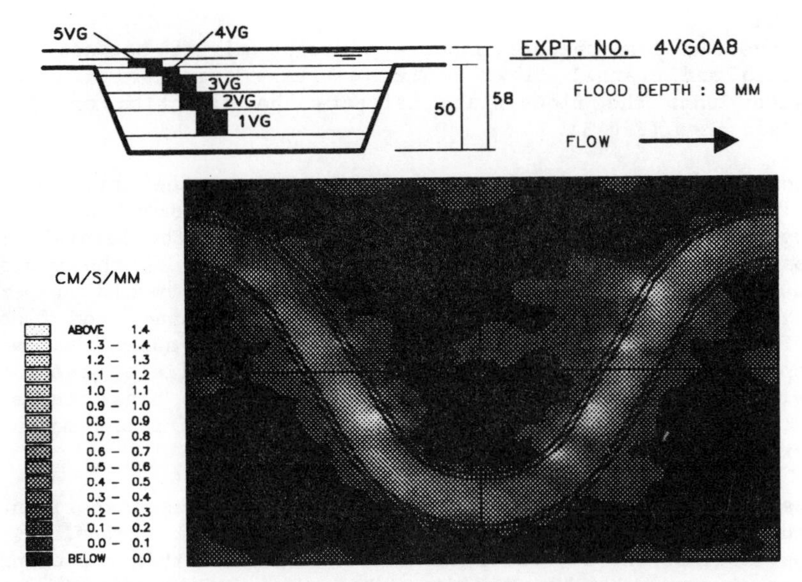

Fig 5 Contours of resultant velocity gradient in the vertical averaged over the depth interval indicated as 4VG in the inset cross-section. Note the high intensity zones strung downstream from the inner bank of each bend.

DISCUSSION

The predominant mechanism of interaction between the channel and flood-plain flows is no longer the vertical plane vorticity, as it is for straight channels. In the circumstances of these preliminary experiments, the mixing into the channel flow of water off the flood-plain (and consequent spilling onto the flood-plain of water delivered by the channel) seems a much more vigorous momentum exchange. The mixing is concentrated in the inter-bend reaches, but is strongly influenced by flow structures originating at the bend upstream of each reach. It is significant that the flow structures and the mixing process are inhibited by the geometric features of the natural channel. Not only is the principal vortex weaker in the natural channel than in the trapezoidal one, but also its convection along the channel is different, and therefore the pattern of vigorous mixing also differs.

The bend flow plays a key role in structuring the flow in the subsequent inter-bend reach. The linkage can be outlined as follows in the trapezoidal channel. The radial pressure gradient at the bend induces flood-plain flow with a lateral component at the bend apex. This flow, together with upward flow on the inner bank at the bend, creates a compact vortex filament near the crest of the bank (Fig 4b). This vorticity, convected down-channel induces vigorous mixing between flood plain and channel flows. The resulting transfer of channel water onto the flood-plain deflects the direction of flood-plain flow (Fig 3).

Some tentative deductions can be made about the influence of sinousity and bend radius on the basis of the foregoing account of the flow. A tighter bend would accentuate the lateral flow on the flood-plain and increase the strength of the vortex. Consequently mixing in the inter-bend reach would be more vigorous and exchange of momentum between channel and flood-plain more effective. Greater sinuosity is associated with more sluggish channel flows. The pressure field associated with the bend is therefore less severe, and high sinuosity might be expected to reduce the vigour of mixing and momentum exchange.

Because of the low width to depth ratio in these experiments, there are uncertainties in scaling up to real channels. In particular, the lateral distribution of flow within the channel may be considerably modified when the width to depth ratio becomes more natural.

CONCLUSIONS

1. Inner channel meanders influence the stage at which a flood discharges as compared with flood behaviour involving a straight channel.

2. The difference is associated with different mechanisims of interaction between channel and flood-plain flows.

3. Transverse (secondary) flows in channel bends are quite different when accompanied by overbank flow from those frequently recognised for in-bank flow. It follows that persistent overbank flow will produce channel geometry unlike that associated with in-bank meander flows. Thus, two-stage channels which are designed to flood quite frequently may not share the classical meander morphology of natural channels.

4. Channel bed features produced in response to secondary currents influence the flow structure at overbank stages. Therefore laboratory studies conducted in trapezodial (or rectangular) channels require careful interpretation before results are applied to natural channels.

5. The experiments reported here utilised a channel of unnaturally small width to depth ratio. Consequently detailed conclusions of direct relevance to natural rivers are not available.

References

Crosato, A., 1987: "Development of a computer program to simulate the meandering processes of rivers." Rep. Q422.06, Delft Hyd. Lab.

Knight, D.W., 1989: "Hydraulics of flood channels." In: Floods: hydrological sedimentology and geomorphological implications, Ed by K. Beven and P. Carling. Wiley & Sons, London.

Vriend, H.J. de 1981: "Steady flow in shallow channel bends. Rep. 81-3 Dept. of Civil Engineering, Delft Uni. of Tech.

Acknowledgements

The project is financed by a grant from the Science and Engineering Research Council. We have benefited from discussions with A. Ervine, D.W. Knight and R.H.J. Sellin who are also involved in a co-ordinated programme funded by SERC.

PAPER F3

International Conference on
RIVER FLOOD HYDRAULICS
17-20 September, 1990

OVERBANK FLOW IN MEANDERING COMPOUND CHANNELS THE IMPORTANT MECHANISMS

Gerard Kiely
Civil Engineering Department
University College, Cork, Ireland

ABSTRACT

Detailed velocity and turbulence measurements were taken in three different Flood flow geometries, to examine the flow mechanisms. The measurements were taken using a Laser Doppler Anemometer oriented to measure the resultant velocity component. The results clearly show the important flow mechanisms, as identified in velocity and directional distributions throughout the flow.

INTRODUCTION

For the management of rivers and floodplains it is important to understand the behaviour of overbank flow. As most river reaches tend to be meandering, rather than straight, the topic of overbank meandering flow must be addressed. The river engineer needs to be able to predict stage/discharge curves. He also needs to understand the flow characteristics and mechanisms as the river overtops its banks. Ultimately, he needs to be able to predict the profile of velocities across the river and floodplains. This is possible in an approximate way for straight compound channels, *Kiely* and *Thomas* (1990). However, such 1-Dimensional numerical models are into the future, for meandering channels.

Much research in recent years on overbank flow has concentrated on straight compound channels. While the physics of straight compound channels is reasonably well understood (except that pertaining to secondary currents), the physics of overbank flow in meandering channels is in its infancy. Early work by *Toebes* and *Sooky* (1967) identified some of the flow characteristics in a multiple meandering channel. More recently *Ahmadi* (1979) examined the velocity characteristics in a multiple meandering channel. *Sellin* and *Giles* (1989) examined the flow over a specific reach of the river Roding, in the U.K. *Stein* and *Rouvé* (1988) examined the flow in a single meander compound channel. *Kiely* (1989) in an experimental program at University College, Cork, examined the flow characteristics in straight, single meander and multiple meander compound channels. This study identified the extremely complex nature of the

International Conference on River Flood Hydraulics, edited by W.R.White

flow and specifically identified the important flow mechanisms, reported in this paper. This study is currently being extended to incorporate varying floodplain roughnesses over the multiple meander geometry.

EXPERIMENTAL ARRANGEMENT

The experimental work was carried out in a 14.4m long by 1.2m wide recirculating flume. The height of the flume walls was 0.5m, and the discharge capacity was 50 l/sec. A test section, 2.4m long was located 7.2m from the inlet to the flume as shown in figure 1. A glass floor in the test section allowed uninterrupted access to an area 2.4m long by 1.2m wide for Laser Doppler Anemometry (LDA). Within the main flume a multiple meander compound channel with dimensions shown in figure 1 was constructed. Both main channel and floodplain floor were constructed of smooth glass. Data for three depth ratios (H-h/H) of 0.12, 0.25 and 0.38 were collected.

For the meandering geometry, velocities and RMS velocities were recorded at seven(7) different cross sections. These sections went from one apex of a bend to the next downstream apex of a bend, distant a half wavelength away. Again, data were collected for several different overbank water levels. Repeat experiments with rough floodplains is underway.

Initially, at each data point, the orientation of the resultant velocity was first recorded using a direction fin attached to a potentiometer with voltage output, which was regularly calibrated to read orientation in degrees. The laser beams were then rotated into the direction of the resultant vector and its magnitude recorded.

RESULTS

Resultant Velocity Vector for Multiple Meandering Channel Figures 2a and 2b show the direction and magnitude of the resultant velocity vector at 5 and 20mms above the floodplain for the single water depth of 30mms on the floodplain. It is clear that the direction of flow over the floodplain is essentially longitudinal (parallel with the outer floodplain walls). The direction of flow at low overbank depths over the main channel is almost parallel with the main channel walls. At highest depths, this flow has changed direction to being almost parallel with floodplain flow. This indicates the existence of horizontal shearing at the junction of floodplain flow with main channel flow.

Depth Averaged Velocity for the Multiple Meandering Geometry The depth averaged velocity for the sections S1, S4 and S7 are shown in figures 3a, 3b and 3c. These correspond to the locations shown in figure 1, as the upstream bend, the crossover section and the downstream bend. Figure 3d shows the plot of the seven cross sections, all fitted on the one graph.

In figures 3a, 3b and 3c, two lines are plotted, one for the depth averaged velocity above bank level and the second for below bank level. In figure 3a, it is seen that the above bank and below bank lines, across the main channel show similar trends with maximum velocity at the inner bend. The maximum velocities over the full section are noted at the outer floodplain, on that part of the floodplain outside the meander belt. There is a low value on the wider floodplain, about midway between the main channel wall and the outer floodplain wall. There is a secondary peak on the floodplain close to the inner wall of the main channel. This is the profile for the smooth floodplain and obviously with rough floodplains the floodplain values would be reduced. Similar trends are shown in figures 3b and 3c. It is seen in figure 3c that the trends are similar to 3a, but the behaviour over the width of the main channel is different. There is a large difference in the values below bank, across the main channel, while the above bank velocity is almost constant. This suggests that this geometry with sinuosity of 1.25, is not fully developed flow, i.e. there is not an exact mirror image at the bends. This could be achieved by a longer, straight tangent length between the bends.

Figure 3d shows the seven sections superimposed. It is seen that the maximum velocities at all cross sections are on the floodplain outside the meander belt. There are two low value areas, on the floodplain, typically midway between main channel and floodplain wall. There is then a secondary peak, which appears to line up about midway on the floodway width.

Magnitude and Direction of Secondary Currents Figures 4a, 4b and 4c, show the magnitude and direction of secondary velocities at sections S1, S4 and S7. These figures show the trends over the width of the main channel only and up to water level, which is 30mms overbank. In figure 4a, it is seen that the direction of the secondary cell is anti- clockwise, with some magnitude as high as 30% of the primary velocities. It is noted that this direction is opposite to that for inbank flow. At the cross-over section, figure 4b shows the secondary cell, clockwise in direction, occupying the left two-thirds of the main channel. The magnitude of these velocities (at right angles to the wall of the main channel) are almost as high as the resultant velocity. This secondary current is not a secondary current of the first kind as defined by *Prandtl*, which would be due to the plan curvature of the main channel. Instead, the secondary currents here are known as those of the *Prandtl* second kind, which is primarily due to the shearing nature of the flow. This latter is caused by the longitudinal floodplain flow impinging on the main channel flow of a different direction. Figure 4c, shows the trends at section S7. Here again, the secondary current direction is clockwise, which is opposite to that for inbank flow in curved channels.

MECHANISMS OF FLOW

Straight Compound Channels The typical open channel flow energy loss mechanisms are bed and wall friction. The straight compound channel, because of the step at the interface, is much more complex. As seen in figure 5, there is a distinct velocity discontinuity at the step. The faster main channel flow is retarded by interaction with the slower moving floodplain flow, which at its interface region speeds up. Momentum is transferred from the deeper main channel to the shallower floodplain flow. This transfer is partly the result of the velocity gradient. The transfer is brought about by faster filaments of fluid flow moving across the interface on to the floodplain. These filaments are documented as vortices with vertical axes, *Sellin* (1964). More recently, *Kawahara et al* (1989) suggest that momentum transfer is made up of two components; advection by secondary flow and turbulent diffusion due to the velocity gradient. *Kawahara et al* (1989) measured secondary currents of the order of 2%–4%, and suggested that they were the dominant contributor to momentum transfer. This idea is as yet unproven and this paper suggests that the diffusion due to the velocity gradient must be substantial, particularly at low floodplain depths, and also with rough floodplains, where the velocity gradient is significant.

Kiely (1989) measured high turbulence values on both sides of the interface for the straight compound channel. He showed that the flow close to the floodplain bed was highly turbulent (about 15% T.I.) irrespective of whether interaction of main channel and floodplain is permitted to occur or not. In the non-interacting case, turbulence values in the main channel at bank height (adjacent the wall) are much lower than 15%. For the interacting case, it was seen that the turbulence values in the main channel at bank height are similar to those at the floodplain bed. This suggests that the high turbulence values of the floodplain bed spread out into the main channel. This contributes to retarding the velocity in the main channel in the interaction region of the main channel.

Meandering Compound Channels — Mechanisms The following additional mechanisms are identified for the multiple meandering compound channel:

1 Secondary Currents
2 Horizontal Shearing
3 Flow expansion and contraction
4 Downstream effects of cross over flow.

These primary mechanisms render overbank meandering flow as highly complex and much more difficult to analyse than straight compound channel flow.

1. Secondary Currents For inbank meandering flow, it is well established that the direction of secondary currents at bends is that the surface water follows the direction of the superelevation and the deeper water the reverse direction. For the geometry of figure 1, at section S1, the in-bank secondary flow direction was clockwise, while that of section S7 was anti-clockwise.

For overbank flow, the secondary flow directions are opposite to those of in-bank flow. They are shown schematically in figures 6a, 6b and 6c for a depth ratio of 0.38. The secondary current magnitudes are much reduced for lower depth ratios. This means then that the secondary cell identified at the bends, is not due to the curvature of the main channel, as is the case for in-bank flow, which is known to have secondary currents of the *Prandtl* first kind. It is postulated that the overbank secondary currents are those of the *Prandtl* second kind, which are caused by the intense shear layer across the interface of the outer bend. It is seen from figure 3a that a very steep velocity gradient spreads across the outer bend interface, with high values on the floodplain and low values at the outer bend side of the main channel. This vertical shear layer is postulated as causative of the strong anti-clockwise secondary currents at section S1. It is somewhat similar to the secondary current directions of straight compound channel secondary currents as shown by *Tominaga* (1989).

In the straight tangent length between the two bends, the mechanism causing the resulting direction in the cross-over locations is the superposition of left floodplain flow on the main channel flow. The residue of what occurs at the cross-over is still present at the downstream bend (section S7), as the tangent length is too short. This residue, allied with the intense shear layers across the outer wall interface produces a clockwise secondary cell at section S7. Examining the secondary currents at S1 and S7, it is seen that the mechanism of secondary currents in overbank flow is much stronger than the secondary flow mechanism of in-bank flow. This is suggested, based on the premise that the flow must first overcome and nullify the natural secondary currents due to curvature, before imposing new opposing secondary currents over the full depth of flow. It is suggested then that the energy loss due to overbank secondary currents must exceed those due to in bank secondary currents.

2. Horizontal Shearing It is seen from figures 2a and 2b that the essential direction of floodplain flow is longitudinal and parallel to the outer floodplain walls. The main channel flow, below bank level, is parallel to the main channel walls. Above bank level, over the main channel, the direction of flow changes from being parallel to the main channel walls below bank level, to being almost parallel with the floodplain flow, close to the water surface. Therefore, as the floodplain flow impinges onto the main channel, a horizontal shear layer occurs between the upper and lower parts of the main channel.

Verification of this horizontal shear layer (as distinct from a vertical shear layer at the main channel/floodplain interface) is seen in figure 7. The horizontal shear layer is strongest towards the left side and tapering to zero around the centre, followed by a strong layer again at the right side of the main channel. It is seen from figure 7 that the velocity at bank level is almost zero for the left third of the main channel. Current analyses, considering width averaged (as distinct from depth averaged) velocities over the main channel width, indicate a horizontal shear layer, of magnitude less than that for the corresponding vertical shear layer at the main channel/floodplain interface.

3. Flow Expansion and Contraction Examining the flow behavior along the straight tangent length between bends, it is observed that the longitudinal (left) floodplain flow impinges onto the deeper main channel flow, leading to flow expansion. Continuing on, the flow over the main channel encounters an abrupt rise on re-entering the floodplain, causing flow contraction. Figure 8 shows the transverse profiles of longitudinal velocity at the cross- over section S4. On the right floodplain, close to the main channel wall, there is evidence of low velocity close to the floodplain bed with high velocity close to the water surface. This is shown schematically in figure 9. This is evidence of flow contraction. Figure 4b shows evidence of flow expansion at section S4. This figure shows the magnitude (and direction) of the secondary currents. Additionally, it is seen that the broken line, beginning close to bank level at the left main channel wall, and joining the locus of zero secondary current, identifies the flow as expanding from left floodplain into the deeper main channel.

4. Downstream Effects of Cross-over Flow Figures 3a, 3b and 3c show the depth averaged velocities at sections S1, S4 and S7. It is seen that for the wider floodplain midway between the main channel wall and the outer floodplain wall, there is a sag in the velocity profile. It is seen that the highly turbulent flow, leaving the downstream side of the cross-over section, is slowed down so much as to generate a low velocity filament, in between the fast flowing outer floodplain flow and the fast filament adjacent the inner bend. Because of the short tangent length, between bends, this sag (reduced velocity) is evident over the full length of the meander. This may not be the case for longer tangent lengths.

CONCLUSIONS

1. The directions of the resultant floodplain flow is longitudinal (or parallel with the outer floodplain walls).
2. The directions of the resultant velocity in the main channel below bank level is close to being parallel to the main channel walls. Above bank level, the direction is influenced by the floodplain flow and tends to be more longitudinal in direction.
3. By comparison with straight channel flow for the same depth, the velocities in the main channel of the meander are as much as 50% lower.
4. The mean floodplain velocities in the meander are about equal to the straight channel floodplain. The straight floodplain has almost uniform velocities, while the meander floodplain velocities varied significantly.
5. At all meander sections, the highest velocities are in the floodplain outside the meander belt.
6. The maximum velocities in the main channel, above and below bank level, are close to the inner bend.
7. For the meander geometry, additional flow mechanisms were identified as:
   (i) Secondary currents
   (ii) Horizontal shearing
   (iii) Flow expansion and contraction
   (iv) Downstream effects of cross-over flow.

REFERENCES

Ahmadi R. *An Experimental Study of the Interaction Between Main Channel and Floodplain Flows.* PhD University of Alberta, Edmonton, Canada. **1980**

Kawahara Y., and Tamai N. *Mechanism of lateral momentum transfer in compound channel flows.* 23rd I.A.H.R. Congress, Ottawa. **Aug. 1989**

Kiely, G.K. and Thomas, G. *Depth Averaged Velocities in Straight Compound Channels.* J. of Hy. Res. IAHR **1990, (for publication)**

Kiely, G.K *An Experimental Study of Overbank Flow in Straight and Meandering Compound Channels.* PhD Thesis, University College, Cork, Ireland **1989**

Sellin R. and Giles A. *Flow mechanisms in spilling meander channels.* 23rd I.A.H.R. Congress, Ottawa. **Aug. 1989**

Stein C.J. and Rouvé G. *2D Depth averaged numerical predictions of the flow in a meandering channel with compound cross sections.* Hydrosoft, Southhampton. **1989**

Toebes,G.H. and Sooky,A.A. *Hydraulics of Meandering Rivers with Floodplains.* J. of Waterways and Harbors Div., Proc. A.S.C.E. **May 1967**

Tominaga A., Nezu I., Ezaki K. *Experimental study on secondary currents in compound open channel flows.* 23rd I.A.H.R. Congress, Ottawa. **Aug. 1989**

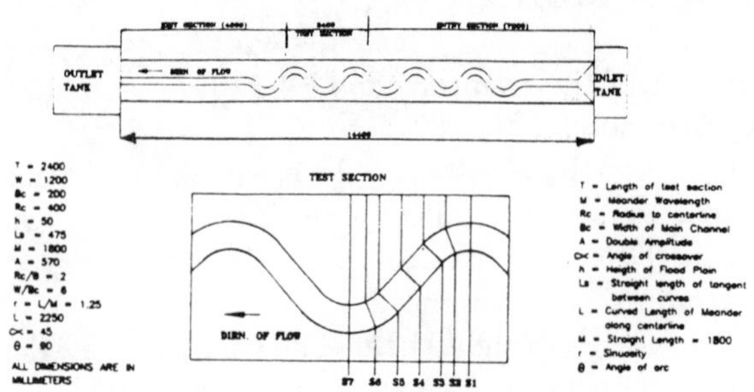

FIG. 1.

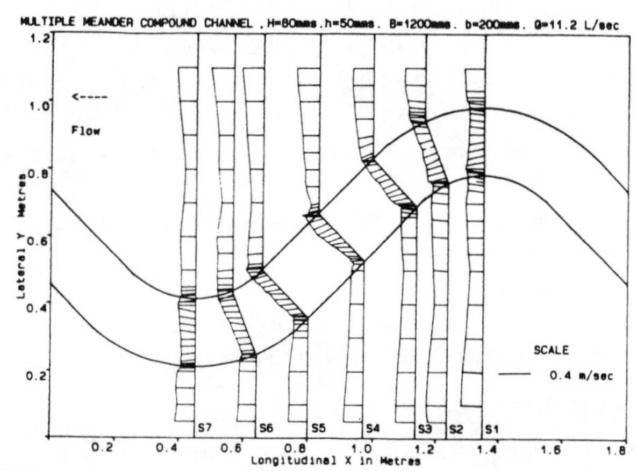

FIG. 2a. RESULTANT VELOCITY VECTOR PLOT at 5 mms ABOVE THE F/P BED

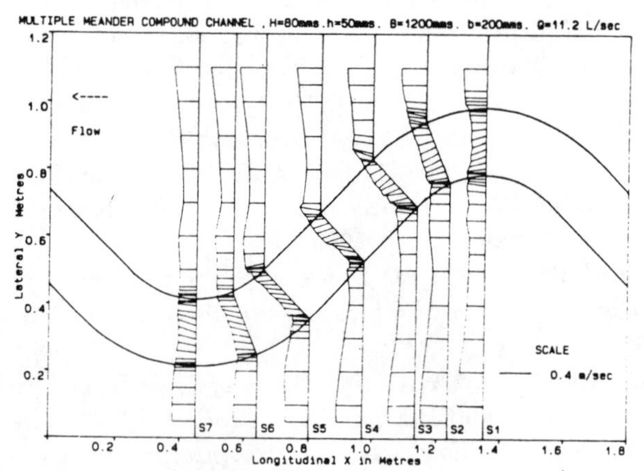

FIG. 2b. RESULTANT VELOCITY VECTOR PLOT at 20 mms ABOVE THE F/P BED

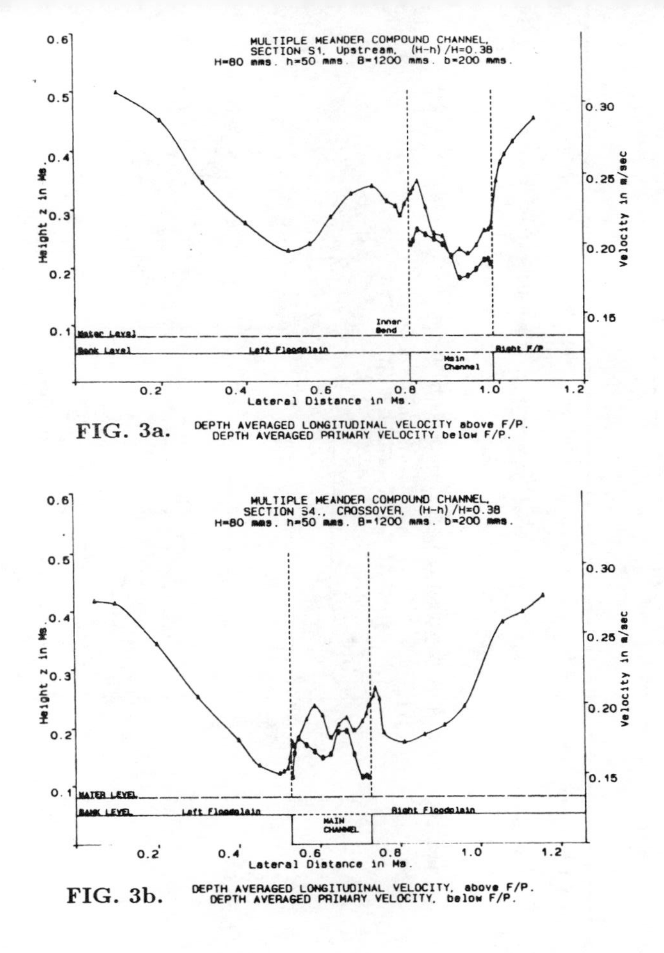

FIG. 3a. DEPTH AVERAGED LONGITUDINAL VELOCITY above F/P. DEPTH AVERAGED PRIMARY VELOCITY below F/P.

FIG. 3b. DEPTH AVERAGED LONGITUDINAL VELOCITY, above F/P. DEPTH AVERAGED PRIMARY VELOCITY, below F/P.

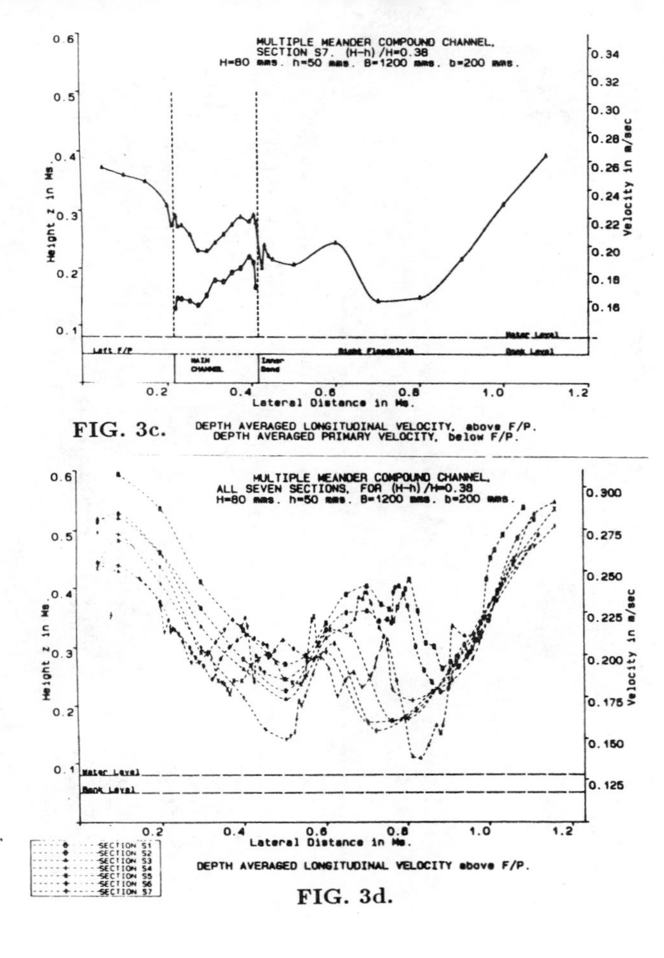

FIG. 3c. DEPTH AVERAGED LONGITUDINAL VELOCITY, above F/P. DEPTH AVERAGED PRIMARY VELOCITY, below F/P.

FIG. 3d. DEPTH AVERAGED LONGITUDINAL VELOCITY above F/P.

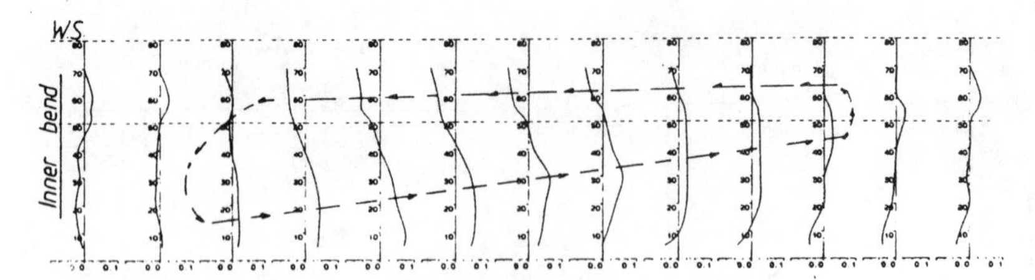

VERTICAL PROFILES of SECONDARY VELOCITY, m/sec, SECTION S1, for 200mm WIDTH of MAIN CHANNEL only

FIG. 4a.

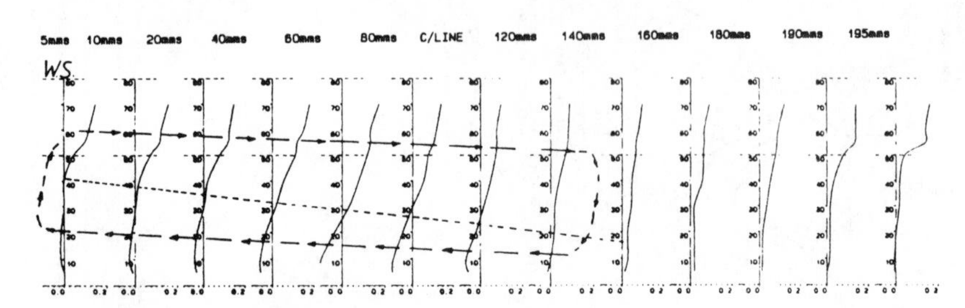

VERTICAL PROFILES of SECONDARY VELOCITY, m/sec, SECTION S4, for 200mm WIDTH of MAIN CHANNEL only
SECONDARY here is defined as 90 Degrees to the Walls of the Main Channel

FIG. 4b.

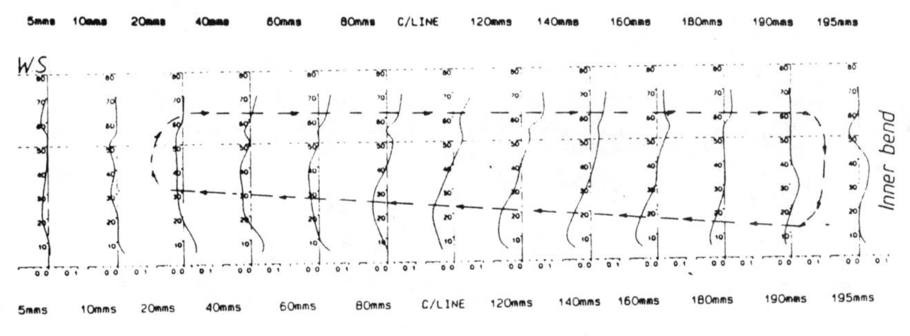

VERTICAL PROFILES of SECONDARY VELOCITY, m/sec, SECTION S7, for 200mm WIDTH of MAIN CHANNEL only

MULTIPLE MEANDERING COMPOUND CHANNEL, H=80mms. h=50 mms. B=1200 mms. b=200 mms.

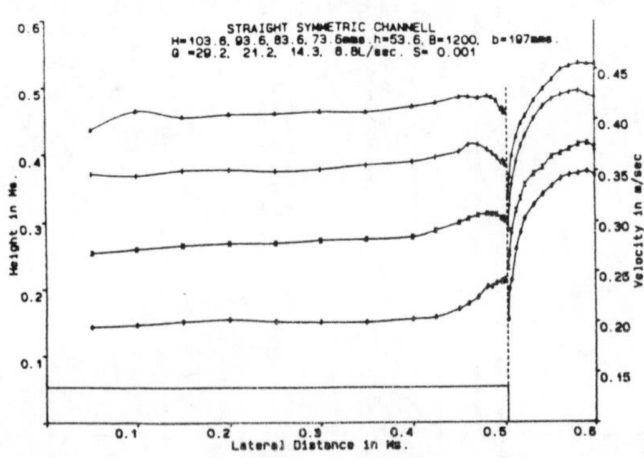

FIG. 5. LATERAL DISTRIBUTION of DEPTH AVERAGED VELOCITY

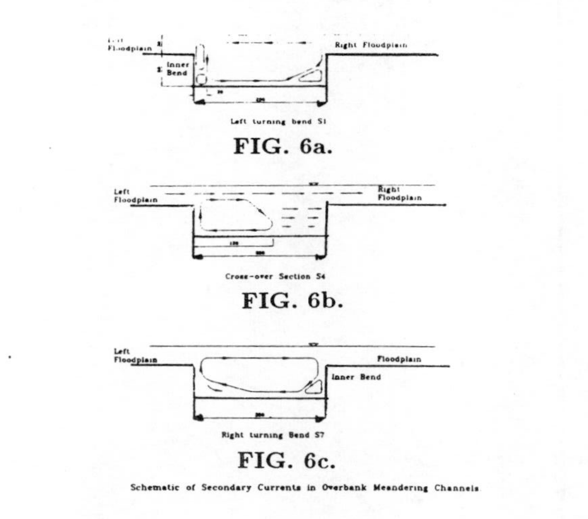

FIG. 6a.

FIG. 6b.

FIG. 6c.

Schematic of Secondary Currents in Overbank Meandering Channels

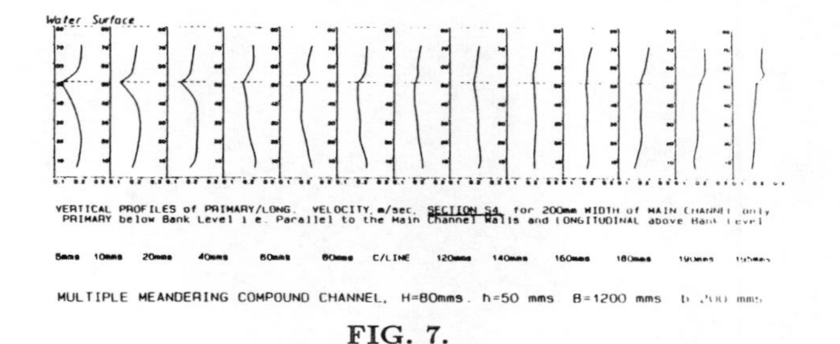

VERTICAL PROFILES of PRIMARY/LONG. VELOCITY m/sec, SECTION S4 for 200mm WIDTH of MAIN CHANNEL only
PRIMARY below Bank Level i.e. Parallel to the Main Channel Walls and LONGITUDINAL above Bank Level

MULTIPLE MEANDERING COMPOUND CHANNEL, H=80mms. h=50 mms B=1200 mms

FIG. 7.

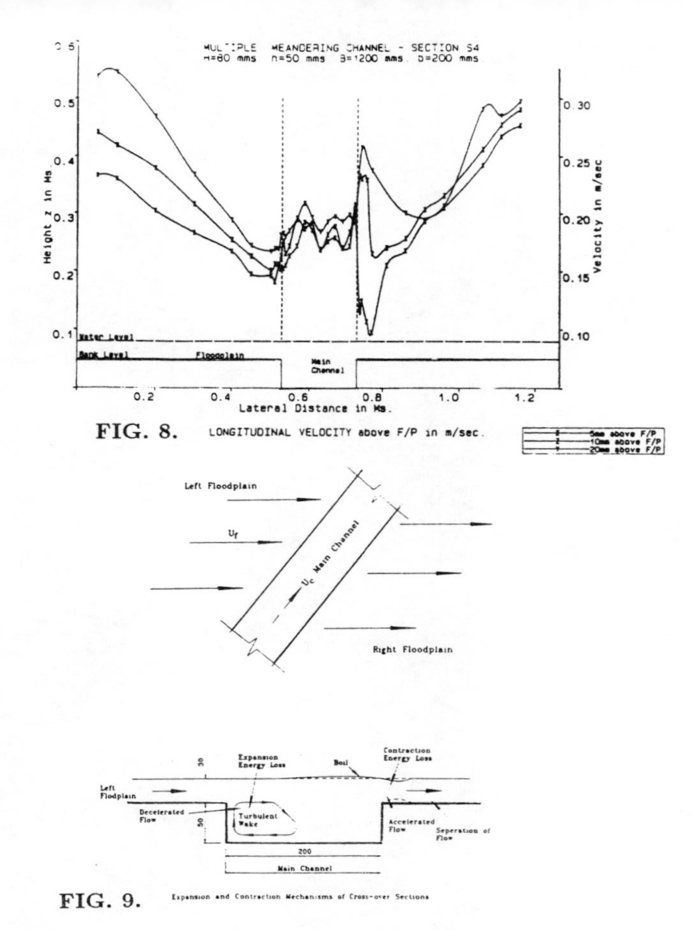

FIG. 8. LONGITUDINAL VELOCITY above F/P in m/sec.

FIG. 9. Expansion and Contraction Mechanisms of Cross-over Sections

PAPER F4

International Conference on
RIVER FLOOD HYDRAULICS
17-20 September, 1990

HYDRAULIC PHENOMENA ASSOCIATED WITH RECENT DISASTROUS FLOODS IN SOUTH AFRICA

(CATEGORY "FIELD DATA AND HYDRAULICS OF FLOOD FLOWS")

J.M. Jordaan* and D. Van Bladeren**
* Directorate of Design Services, Department of Water Affairs, South Africa
** Directorate of Hydrology, Department of Water Affairs, South Africa

ABSTRACT

Disastrous floods occurred several times in the 1980's in South Africa. Damage to hydraulic structures such as dams, bridge waterways and water conveyances is reviewed and discussed. Apparent recurrence interval and effect on the choice of design flood to be adopted in future is analysed and discussed. Consequences of failure and effects on development policy are considered. Lessons learnt are concluded with.

INTRODUCTION

A number of flood disasters occurred during the past decade in South Africa starting with the Laingsburg flash flood in January 1981 and concluding with the Orange Free State and Northern Cape regional floods of February and March 1988. Also in these abnormal events were the cyclonic floods of Domoina and Imboa in 1984 and the stationary front catastrophic flood of September 1987, and lesser floods in February 1985 and December 1989, all of these occurring in Natal.

Post event examination of damage to structures such as bridges, dams, water conveyances, railways and roads led to general revision of design standards and a changing policy toward flood plain development.

Some of the major findings were that events of the cataclysmic scale of large floods are characterised by the uniqueness of their hydrologic properties, and the vulnerability of structures in their way, practically regardless of design standards adopted. Nevertheless valuable criteria were obtained from comparing structures that withstood the onslaught of storm water and heavy downpours to those that did not. The fallibility of designing to a given return period storm and resting in confidence of structural survival was clear from the unpredictable recurrence of major storm events in various areas in one decade.

RECURRENCE INTERVAL CONSIDERATIONS

Kovacs and Alexander (1990) deal with flood frequency determination in detail. It needs to be pointed out that a great deal of misguidance exists among the public about the expectancy and recurrence interval of a given level rainstorm or flood. A 1 in 50 year flood is comfortably considered 50 years away for a structure designed for coping with that recurrence interval flood!

The occurrence of two or more such floods in succeeding years is "unheard of", nevertheless it occurred twice in Ladysmith, Natal in 1985 and in 1987, and two successive large floods also occurred in the Orange Free State in February and March 1988.

A statistical experiment is given in the Appendix to illustrate the true expectancy by means of the probability theory of rare events, Ref. 7 (Poisson distribution law of small numbers.) The real situation is thus complicated by two circumstances. Firstly, the period of record of floods is too short to establish the true long term stationary frequency distribution curve for the region in question so that the extrapolation of the mean data set from the past to the future may already be in error. Secondly, the future event's behaviour is also merely another short term sample of the true long term stationary distribution (as yet unknown). The events in the next 50 years may therefore significantly differ from those in the previous 50 years (as exemplified in the appendix).

DESIGN CRITERIA

In spite of the above dilemma the recurrence interval of given flood intensities plays an important role in the engineering design of a structure i.e. bridge waterway, spillway of a dam, or inundation levels in an urban complex. It makes a good deal of difference in a bridge design if designed to pass the 1 in 50 or the 1 in 100 years' flood. The assurance of safety of the structure designed for the latter standard may however still be false, in that the short term catastrophic flood may occur at any time. The shorter recurrence interval is therefore often conveniently adopted for reasons of economy. No structure will, after all, be completely safe from the loss of life or damage point of view. It is normal to expect most structures to be prone to failure anyhow. This was certainly the case in the five flood events here considered. No conceivable precaution could have prevented bridges in Laingsburg or in northern Natal to fail under the concerted attack of waves higher than the top girder level of through bridges, or scour well down the piled foundations under the piers. Courses of rivers changed during the four-day flood in 1987 and embankments were removed, leaving bridges standing clear. Cascade breaching of farm dams, where they occurred, could not have been cost-effectively prevented by designing for dam-break flood waves on top of the hydrologic flood.

FAILURE CONSEQUENCES

The consequences of eventual failure should thus also be anticipated beforehand in the design exercise. Alternative routing past vulnerable bridging points, consequential damage and reparability are engineering concerns of vital importance in the economics of design.

MODES OF FAILURES AND AFTER EFFECTS

The mode of failure should be anticipated for various flood scenario's as the events of the decade have shown that no two floods are alike and failure modes of any structure can be quite variable. The consequences of failure of some bridges, dams and water conveyance structures on other sectors of the economy was clearly seen when contingency plans were worked out.

The after effects could be alleviated by suitable design measures i.e. overtoppable bridges versus vulnerable approaches; partial breaching of dams in selected areas, permitting rapid rebuilding; water conveyance crossings depressed below river bed level rather than carried above. The complicating effects of debris, sediment and erosion in altering the conveyance of the stream warrant due consideration; as well as the geotechnical effects of direct saturation by rain of embankments, slopes and fills. All of these aspects were evident in these individual events.

EFFECTS ON DEVELOPMENT

Perhaps the biggest concern was the crowding of development, urbanization and industry on river banks and flood plains. Danger to some of the regions in towns situated close to rivers were aggravated by the proximity of storage dams, which, should they be broken by a catastrophic flood, would result in an even more disastrous dam-break flood to occur. Fortunately no direct loss of life occurred in the few major and many minor dam breaks that did occur. Rather, the presence of one or more dams on some of the principal rivers served admirably to attenuate the floods in most cases. Major dams are generally designed to pass safely an estimated 1 in 200 to 500 year flood and to withstand more extreme floods without failure or serious damage; whereas farm dams could possibly rarely cope with a 1 in 50 year flood.

EFFECTS ON WATER CONVEYANCE STRUCTURES

Failures occurred at canalized rivers discharging into the sea, and involved also damage to intake and outfall canals skirting river banks, flooding of pumping stations and breaching of river crossings consisting of elevated pipelines. Extensive silt and debris deposits occurred in reservoirs and incidentally also on recreational beaches downstream of river mouths. Repair to these facilities involved with water supply was generally carried out within weeks. Valuable lessons were learnt regarding the vulnerability of pumping station intakes, types of pipeline crossings and spillway structures in dams.

EFFECTS ON ROAD AND RAIL COMMUNICATIONS, BRIDGES.

The failures were generally of two classes - embankment failures (corrected within days and weeks at the most) and river crossing (bridge) failures. Railway bridges were repaired or replaced in weeks or months and road bridges in closer to a year. The transportive power of water on steel girder bridge trusses was phenomenal. Due to debris buoyancy effect some trusses over the Umfolozi River in Natal were carried several kilometres downstream. Even concrete deck bridges were buoyed and overturned, ending up scores of metres downstream. The design of bridges since experienced a healthy revival, with present replacements exhibiting either greater freeboard or overtopping ability, with less resistance to flow or proneness to buoyancy and lift-off. The piers are now founded on much deeper caissons or large diameter piles of greater depth. Approach embankments remain vulnerable but are readily replacable, although in repair work not generally with the best quality materials.

EFFECTS ON URBAN DEVELOPMENT

Building in flood prone areas is a contentious point. The present code calls for indication of 1 in 20 year floodlines and hopefully their observance in authorizing new developments by Municipal Councils. Unfortunately this does not apply to existing developments where repeated inundations do occur as at Ladysmith, Natal. In Laingsburg, Cape and Wepener, Orange Free State, to name examples, new developments away from the flood plain of the adjoining rivers took place or is encouraged.
Many towns, such as Bloemhof, Christiana in Transvaal, and Douglas, Prieska and Upington in Northern Cape, have areas vulnerable to flooding but can be readily evacuated in time, due to adequate flood-warning time. Factory complexes situated in river bends and protected by levees were in some cases inundated and in other cases they barely escaped being wiped out.

EFFECTS ON DAMS

An in-depth study of the behaviour and structural performance of dams, large medium and small, has been going on as a result of these floods. Damage ranged from minor superstructural damage to substantial erosion of spillway channels and major breaches of two embankment dams. A large number of farm dams, some without any spillway, breached. Most of these were readily repaired; the water loss being of little consequence where the climate is humid. In the intermediate range two irrigation dams narrowly escaped failure in 1987, one of which later failed, while being repaired, in a flood in 1989.

CONCLUSION: LESSONS LEARNT

The saga of the 1980's floods, their onslaught and damage, coupled with loss of life amounting to close to 700, is not uncharacteristic of the country, which is alternately plagued by persistent droughts followed by unprecedented storms and floods in epochs of about a decade in periodicity. There were major floods in the Fifties and Seventies and droughts in the Sixties and early Eighties.

One lesson learnt was that, as unexpected as these floods were each and every one, so unexpected was the havoc created among human endeavours and the engineering structures, associated with rivers, created by man. Development in the past seemed to have been going on unchecked until checked by nature. Agriculture is perhaps the most resilient sector of the economy, although the damage sustained therein probably exceeded that of commercial enterprises and fixed structures. Other lessons in design and economy have been learnt and have been well expounded in the reference literature following these events.

Better preparation is now generally being made in the form of advanced design standards, revised flood policy, provision of flood absorption dams, and improvement in hydrological techniques of data analysis, flood forecasting and warning systems. Much of these follow-up actions are still underway, but concerted efforts are being made so as not to be caught unawares and less than adequately prepared a second time.

ACKNOWLEDGEMENT

The permission of the Director General of Water Affairs to publish a paper on this subject is gratefully acknowledged. The collaboration of colleagues in the collection and presentation of data is appreciated.

REFERENCES

1. "Floods in Perspective" Conference (1989).

   SAICE and CSIR, Pretoria, R.S.A. ISBN 0-620-13076-8.

2. The Civil Engineer in South Africa (1988).

   Special Issue on Natal Floods, Vol 30, No 1, January 1988, Johannesburg, South Africa.

3. Van Bladeren, D. and Burger, C.E. (1989).

   Documentation of the September 1987. Natal Floods, TR 139, Department of Water Affairs, Pretoria, R.S.A.

4. Kovacs, Z.P., Du Plessis, D.B. et al (1985).

   Documentation of the 1984 Domoina Floods, T.R. 122, Department of Water Affairs, Pretoria, R.S.A.

5. Roberts, C.P.R. and Alexander, W.J.R. (1982).

   Lessons learnt from the 1981 Laingsburg flood. The Civil Engineer in South Africa, Vol. 24, No. 1, January 1982, Johannesburg, South Africa.

6. Kovacs, Z.P., and Alexander, W.J.R. (1990).

   Flood peak-frequency characteristics and Regional Maximum floods in South Africa, Int. Conference on River Flood Hydraulics, 17 - 20 September 1990, Wallingford, England.

7. Sokolnikoff, I.S. and E.S. (1941).

   Higher Mathematics for Engineers and Physicists, McGraw Hill Book Company, Inc, New York and London, (pp 512-4).

INDEX

Floods, damage, disasters, hydraulics, hydrology, dambreak, failures, South Africa, inundation, flood control.

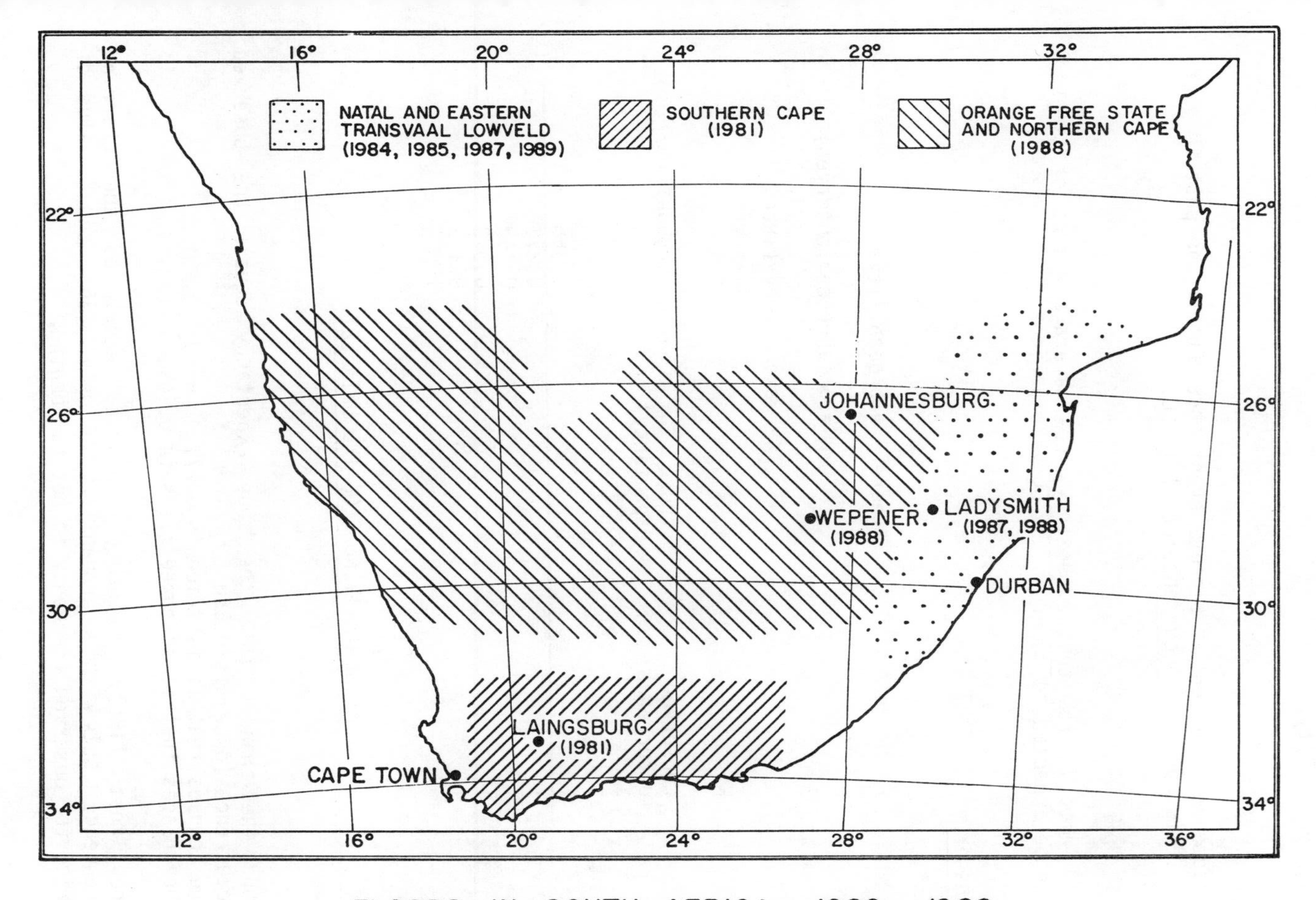

FLOODS IN SOUTH AFRICA, 1980 - 1989

APPENDIX - Representativeness of data of record and its future reproducibility.

Assume we observed an extreme event once during the past 50 years, i.e. its apparent occurrence was 1 in 50.

Q 1 What is its true expectancy, i.e. average number of times it can be expected to occur in any 50 year period?

Answer.

$$P = \frac{X^R}{R!} e^{-X}$$

Where P = probability

R = occurrence (observed)

X = expectancy (true)

R (Observed occurrence)	X (true expectancy)	P (probability)
1	0	0
1	1	0.368
1	2	0.271
1	3	0.149
1	4	0.073
1	>4	0.139
		1.000

Conclusion: REPRESENTATIVENESS OF THE DATA SET.

Thus the chances that the true expectancy equals the observed occurrence (once) is 0.368
the chances that it is twice is 0.271
the chances that it is three times is 0.149.

The "most likely frequency" thus is equal to the observed frequency, but with a probability of only 0.368, and a value of twice the observed frequency is not far behind.

Q 2 If the apparent occurrence (once) was indeed the true expectancy (once) how likely is an occurrence (in the next future period) of 0, 1, 2, 3 times?

$$P = \frac{X^R e^{-X}}{R!}$$

Where P = probability
X = expectancy (true)
R = occurrence (future)

Answer

X (true expectancy)	R (future occurrence)	P (probability)
1	0	0.368
1	1	0.368
1	2	0.184
1	3	0.061
1	4	0.019
		1.000

Conclusion

OCCURRENCE IF DATA SET IS REPRESENTATIVE

Thus the chances that in the future period the occurrence will again happen once (or not at all) is 0.368 in both cases, and that it will happen twice is 0.184.

The "most likely" value is either 0 or equal to the observed value of 1. It is more likely to happen not at all than twice!

Q 3 If however the true expectancy is not necessarily once, but is as given in Q 1, i.e. say 0,1, 2, 3, or 4 times what are the likelihood of occurrences of 0, 1, 2, 3 times in the future period?

Answer: Note: The cross multiplication of probabilities* of Q1 and Q2 and its summation yields the last column, $\sum P_R$

R times of occurrence (future)	X expectancy	P_X with probability	$\sum P_R$ (likelihood)
0	0	0	.179
1	1	.368	.235
2	2	.271	.185
3	3	.149	.118
>3	>3	.212	.283
		1.000	1.000

*

X	P_X	P_R				$P_X \cdot P_R$				
		R = 0	1	2	3	R=0	1	2	3	>3 ← R
0	0	1	0	0	0	0	0	0	0	
1	.368	.368	.368	.184	.061	.135	.135	.068	.022	
2	.271	.135	.271	.271	.180	.036	.073	.073	.049	
3	.149	.050	.146	.224	.224	.007	.022	.033	.033	
4	.073	.018	.073	.147	.195	.001	.005	.011	.014	
						.179	.235	.185	.118	.283 ← $\sum P_R$

Conclusion: OCCURRENCE IF DATA SET IS NOT REPRESENTATIVE.

Although in the real case therefore "the most likely value" of the times of occurrence is still equal to the observed value "once" its probability is only 0.235; occurrences of 0 and 2 times are now almost equally probable, and 3 times is not far behind.

Hence the apparent 1 in 50 year maximum flood of a 50 year record could be in fact a 1 in 25 or a 1 in 17 year flood (Q1) and if it is a true 1 in 50 year flood it could be expected to occur 0, 1 or 2 times in the next 50 year period (Q2), but if it is in fact a 1 in 25 year or 1 in 17 year flood, it can be expected to occur 0, 1, 2, 3 or even more than 3 times in the next 50 years. (Q3).

International Conference on
RIVER FLOOD HYDRAULICS
17-20 September, 1990

MATHEMATICAL MODELS OF FLOW IN TWO OR MULTI STAGE STRAIGHT CHANNELS

K. Shiono, Department of Civil Engineering, University of Bradford, BD7 1DP
D.W. Knight, School of Civil Engineering, University of Birmingham, B15 2TT

SUMMARY: The influence of lateral shear and secondary flows on depth averaged eddy viscosities are considered. Experimental data from the SERC Flood Channel Facility are used to determine dimensionless eddy viscosities for a two stage channel. The influence of secondary flows on analytical and numerical predictions for the lateral distributions of depth averaged velocity, boundary shear stress and friction factor are considered.

1. INTRODUCTION

Urban and rural flood alleviation schemes often require the use of mathematical and physical models to determine stage discharge relationships. Various methods have been proposed for solving the one-dimensional or two-dimensional hydrodynamic equations, with due allowance being made in the physical constants for three-dimensional effects. One dimensional methods for two or multi stage channels generally rely on the ϕ index approach **(Radojkovic & Djordjevic, 1985; Wormleaton & Merrrett, 1990)** or the apparent shear force approach **(Knight & Demetriou, 1983; Knight & Hamed, 1984; Wormleaton, Allen & Hadjipanos, 1982).** Two dimensional methods may rely on an analytical approach **(Shiono & Knight, 1989)** or a numerical approach **(Wormleaton & Hadjipanos, 1984).** The application of the two-dimensional analytical solution to gauging sites in the Severn-Trent catchment has been shown to give promising results **(Knight, Shiono & Pirt, 1989; Knight, Samuels & Shiono, 1990).** Various three dimensional effects of overbank flow, have recently been studied on the Science and Engineering Research Council Flood Channel Facility (SERC-FCF), and progress made on understanding the influence of these effects on one or two-dimensional hydraulic parameters **(Knight & Sellin, 1987; Shiono & Knight, 1989; Knight & Shiono,1990; Shiono & Knight, 1990).** The experimental data from the SERC-FCF indicate that the secondary flows can have a significant effect upon the primary main channel and flood plain flows. In particular on a wide flood plain, the boundary shear stress value, ρgHS_0, based on local equilibrium of gravitational and resisting forces, is found to be inconsistent with the data, despite their being a logarathmic velocity distribution over a vertical. It therefore follows that in laterally segmented models, the application of the simple uniform steady state one-dimensional momentum equation has to include a secondary flow term in suitably depth averaged form.

2. THEORETICAL ASPECTS OF THE SECONDARY FLOW TERM

2.1 Basic equations

The depth averaged streamwise momentum equation for steady uniform flow in a channel of depth, H, may be expressed for an arbitrary point in the cross section by

International Conference on River Flood Hydraulics, edited by W.R.White

$$\frac{\partial H(\rho\bar{U}\bar{V})_d}{\partial y} = \rho g H S_o + \frac{\partial H\bar{\tau}_{yx}}{\partial y} - \tau_b \tag{1}$$

where
$$(\rho\bar{U}\bar{V})_d = \frac{1}{H}\int_o^H \rho\bar{U}\bar{V}dz = \text{secondary flow term} \tag{2}$$

$$\bar{\tau}_{yx} = \frac{1}{H}\int_o^H (-\rho\overline{uv})\,dz = \text{turbulent Reynolds stress term} \tag{3}$$

and H = depth of flow, g = gravitational acceleration, ρ = density of water, S_o = channel bed slope and τ_b = local boundary shear stress. Introducing a depth averaged eddy viscosity and local friction factor based on the Darcy-Weisbach law

$$\bar{\tau}_{yx} = \rho\,\bar{\varepsilon}_{yx}\frac{\partial U_d}{\partial y} \tag{4}$$

$$f = \frac{8\tau_b}{\rho U_d^2} \tag{5}$$

gives

$$\frac{\partial H(\rho\bar{U}\bar{V})_d}{\partial y} = \rho g H S_o + \frac{\partial}{\partial y}\left\{\rho H\bar{\varepsilon}_{yx}\frac{\partial U_d}{\partial y}\right\} - \frac{\rho f U_d^2}{8} \tag{6}$$

If it is assumed that the depth averaged eddy viscosity is non-dimensionalised by the local shear velocity to give

$$\bar{\varepsilon}_{yx} = \lambda U_* H = \lambda H\left(\frac{f}{8}\right)^{\frac{1}{2}} U_d \tag{7}$$

then the secondary flow term becomes

$$\Gamma = \rho g H S_o + \frac{\partial}{\partial y}\left\{\rho\lambda H^2\left(\frac{f}{8}\right)^{\frac{1}{2}} U_d\frac{\partial U_d}{\partial y}\right\} - \rho\frac{f U_d^2}{8} \tag{8}$$

where $\Gamma = \partial[H(\rho\bar{U}\bar{V})_d]/\partial y$ and the parameters λ and f are assumed to be constant over the domain. Equation **(8)** has been solved analytically **(Shiono & Knight, 1989 & 1990)** to give lateral distributions of U_d and τ_b and the results compare favourably with data from the SERC-FCF. However the restriction of constant λ and f within each domain, and the use of only 8 sub areas to model the whole channel section meant that there was a discontinuity in τ_b and eddy viscosity at every joint. In order to eliminate this effect equation **(8)** has now been solved numerically using the Gauss-Seidel iterative procedure and the number of sub areas increased by an order of magnitude.

2.2 Experimental data concerning secondary flows

The data acquisition system on the SERC-FCF is described elsewhere **(Knight & Shiono, 1990)**. **Figs. 1-5** illustrate some results from 3 series of experiments in a symmetric two stage channel for which B/b = 4.2, b/h = 5 and the side slope of the main channel (1 : s, vertical : horizontal) was varied between s = 0, 1 and 2 (Series 08, 02 and 10 respectively). The depth of flow in the main channel, H, was varied from 169mm to 200mm to give overbank relative depths, Dr (=(H-h)/H) of 0.1, 0.15, 0.20 and 0.25. The symbols are defined in **Fig.1**.

Fig.1 shows lateral distributions of the depth averaged Reynolds stress measured by LDA and integrated according to equation **(3)**. For a given side slope and depth the values of $\bar{\tau}_{yx}$ generally reach a maximum at the edge of the flood plain adjacent to the main channel (y = 0.75, 0.90 and 1.05m for s = 0, 1 and 2 respectively). Values of $\bar{\varepsilon}_{yx}$ were determined from equation **(4)** using velocity data, and values of λ were then calculated from equation **(7)**, using boundary shear stress data to obtain U_*. **Fig.2** shows the lateral distributions of λ for the same three series of experiments shown in **Fig.1.** It should be noted in **Fig.2** that values of λ become indeterminate outside the zone of high lateral shear as the term $\partial U_d/dy$ becomes vanishingly small. **Fig.3** shows the corresponding values of the apparent shear stress due to secondary flows, i.e. $(\rho \bar{U}\bar{V})_d$, based on lateral integration of the right hand side of equation **(1)** using measured $\bar{\tau}_{yx}$ and τ_b data. It is clear that the secondary flow term defined by equation **(2)** is of a comparable magnitude to the turbulent Reynolds stress term based on equation **(3)**.

Figs. 4(a) & (b) show a comparison between the numerical model results and the SERC-FCF data for a relative depth Dr = 0.25 in Series 02. The numerical results are based on the half channel width being divided into 63 elements and the dimensionless eddy viscosity being held constant across the section at $\lambda = 0.16$. Lateral distributions of U_d/U_o and τ_b/τ_o are shown with and without the secondary flow term, i.e. $\Gamma \neq 0$ and $\Gamma = 0$. Different Γ values were chosen for the main channel ($\Gamma_m = 0.15$) and the flood plain ($\Gamma_f = -0.25$). It is clear that the omission of the secondary flow term makes the flood plain U_d and τ_b values lower than they should be and the main channel values correspondingly higher.

Figs. 4(c) & (d) show a comparison between the analytical model results and the SERC-FCF data. In this case a 4 sub area model was chosen for the half section, with λ and f being held constant in each domain. **Fig.5** shows a comparison between the numerical model results, including the secondary flow term, and the SERC-FCF data for relative depths of 0.15 and 0.25 in Series 02.

3. DISCUSSION OF RESULTS

3.1 The dimensionless eddy viscosity

It is recognised that the use of U_* and H in equation **(7)** to non dimensionalise the lateral depth averaged eddy viscosity is not wholly consistent with physical reasoning. However λ values are often used in this way by modellers and it is therefore appropriate to seek to understand the implications of this approach.

Figs. 4(a) & (b) show that the lateral distributions of U_d and τ_b are surprisingly good even when a constant value of dimensionless eddy viscosity ($\lambda = 0.16$) is adopted for the whole cross section. The inclusion of the secondary flow term is however essential if this approach is to give realistic values outside the zones of strong lateral shear.

Figs. 4(c) & (d) show how varying λ between sub areas can improve the simulation even when only 4 sub areas are used. For these simulations, based on the analytical model, the values of λ were taken as $\lambda_1 = 0.07$, $\lambda_2 = \lambda_4 = 0.16$, $\lambda_3 = 0.07\ (Dr)^{-4}$ and the values of Γ as $\Gamma_1/(\rho gHS_o) = 0.15$, $\Gamma_2 = \Gamma_4 = 0.2$ and $\Gamma_3/(\rho gHS_o) = -0.25$. The corresponding friction factors were varied accordingly to a general relationship given elsewhere by **Shiono & Knight (1990).** The results are generally quite good although the discontinuity in τ_b is noticeable.

Figs. 5(a)-(d) show the improvement that can ensue if λ is allowed to vary within the transverse shear layer. These simulations were based on the numerical model with $\Delta y = 0.05$m and with λ varying exponentially in the side slope domains but held constant elsewhere at the same values used in **Figs.4(a) & (b).** The f values were varied linearly along the side slope, from a constant main channel value to a constant flood plain value. The simulation is improved in the shear layer region and the discontinuity in τ_b reduced.

3.2 The significance for river simulation models

Whenever two-dimensional river simulation models are constructed and parameters allowed to vary laterally between domains within one cross section then there is a calibration problem that requires careful consideration. If the eddy viscosity concept is used then the choice appears to be either adopting a single constant value, such as $\lambda = 0.16$ for the entire section **(Wormleaton,1988)** or varying λ across the section according to some simple depth relationship based on laboratory or field data **(Shiono & Knight, 1990; Knight, Shiono & Pirt, 1989; Knight, Samuels & Shiono, 1990).** Whichever methodology is adopted, λ should be regarded as a 'catch all' parameter and the values chosen to include both turbulence and secondary flow effects. If the secondary flow and turbulence terms in equations **(2) & (3)** are represented by secondary flow and turbulence eddy viscosities $\bar{\varepsilon}_s$ and $\bar{\varepsilon}_t$, then equation **(6)** can be written in the form

$$\rho gHS_o + \frac{\partial}{\partial y}\left\{\rho H(\bar{\varepsilon}_s + \bar{\varepsilon}_t)\frac{\partial U_d}{\partial y}\right\} - \tau_b = 0 \qquad \textbf{(9)}$$

and λ calibrated accordingly. Alternatively the secondary flow term can be compounded into the friction term to give

$$\rho gHS_o + \frac{\partial}{\partial y}\left\{\rho H\bar{\varepsilon}_t\frac{\partial U_d}{\partial y}\right\} - \left\{\tau_b + \frac{\partial}{\partial y}H(\rho\overline{UV})_d\right\} = 0 \qquad \textbf{(10)}$$

In this case the local friction factors, f, will need modifying from their one dimensional flow values. **Equations (9) & (10)** thus represent the form in which strong laterally sheared flows are often represented by river engineers without perhaps recognising the significance of the individual terms and their consequent effect on calibration λ or f values.

The various components arising from bed generated turbulence, lateral shear and secondary flows are now well understood by experimentalists **(McKeogh, Kiely & Javan,1989; Shiono & Knight, 1990)** but their incorporation into calibration methodologies for river simulation models does not yet seem to have occurred. From the practical point of view, however, it must be said that since no secondary flow data are likely to be available for natural channels, then the problem may be solved by practising engineers using lumped parameters for λ and f **(Knight, Shiono & Pirt, 1989).** However modellers must then be made aware of these individual effects, particularly when they attempt to calibrate their model against laboratory data in which the boundary roughnesses are known. The data presented here from the SERC-FCF illustrate how errors can be introduced into analytical and numerical models aimed at giving the lateral distributions of U_d and τ_b in rivers.

4. CONCLUSIONS

The influence of secondary flows on λ and f values in strong laterally sheared flows has been demonstrated. Care needs to be taken when calibrating river simulation models in which the cross section is divided laterally into segments. In the absence of any secondary flow data either λ or f values will need some adjustment from their customary values used in one-dimensional models. This could have considerable implications for geomorphological models in which the boundary shear stresses are required (via f) or in pollutant transport models in which the lateral dispersion characteristics are required (via λ).

5. REFERENCES

Knight D W Demetriou J D, 1983 , Flood plain and main channel flow interaction, ASCE, J.Hyd Eng, 109, HY8, pp 1073-1092.

Knight D W and Hamed M E, 1984, Boundary shear in symmetrical compound channels, ASCE, J.Hyd Eng, 110 , HY10, pp 1412-1430.

Knight D W and Sellin R H J, 1987, The SERC Flood Channel Facility, J.Institution of Water and Environmental Management, IWEM, 1 , No.2, October, pp 198-204.

Knight D W, Shiono K and Pirt J, 1989, Prediction of depth mean velocity and discharge in natural rivers with overbank flow, in Hydraulic and Environmental Modelling of Coastal, Estuarine and River Waters, ed. Falconer, Goodwin & Matthew, Gower Technical Press, pp 419-428.

Knight D W, Samuels P G and Shiono K, 1990, River flow simulation : research and developments J.Inst.Water and Environmental Management, 4, No.2.

Knight D W and Shiono K, 1990, Turbulence measurements in a shear layer region of a compound channel, J. IAHR, 28, No.2.

McKeogh E J, Keily G.K and Javan M, 1989, Velocity and turbulence measurements in a straight channel with interacting flood plains using laser-doppler anemometry, in Hydraulic and Environmental Modelling of Coastal, Estuarine and River Waters, ed. Falconer Goodwin & Matthew, Gower Technical Press, pp 429-440 .

Radojkovic M and Djordjevic S, 1985, Computation of discharge distribution in compound channels, Proc. 21st IAHR Congress, Melbourne, Australia, Vol.3, pp 367-371.

Shiono K and Knight D W, 1989, Two-dimensional analytical solution for a compound channel, Proc. 3rd Int.Symp. on Refined Flow Modelling and Turbulence Measurements, ed. Iwasa Y and Tamai N, Universal Academy Press Inc.,Tokyo.

Shiono K and Knight D W, 1989, Vertical and transverse measurements of Reynolds stress in a shear region of a compound channel, 7th Int.Symp. on Turbulent Shear Flows, Stanford, USA, August, Vol.2, Paper 28-1.

Shiono K and Knight D W, 1990, Turbulent open channel flows with variable depth across the channel - a general model and new data, J. Fluid Mechanics (submitted for publication).

Wormleaton P R, 1988, Determination of discharge in compound channels using the dynamic equation for lateral velocity distribution, Proc. IAHR Conf. on Fluvial Hydraulics, Vituki, Budapest.

Wormleaton P R and Hadjipanos P, 1984, Modelling of discharge in compound channels, Proc.Int.Conf. on Hyd.Eng. Software, HYROSOFT 84, Portoroz, Yugoslavia, pp 2/99 - 2/110.

Wormleaton P R and Merrett D, 1990, An improved method of calculation for steady uniform flow in prismatic main channel/flood plain sections, IAHR, J.Hyd.Res. 28 No.2.

Wormleaton P R, Allen J and Hadjipanos P, 1982, Discharge assessment in compound channel flow,ASCE, J.Hyd.Eng., 108, HY9, pp 975-993.

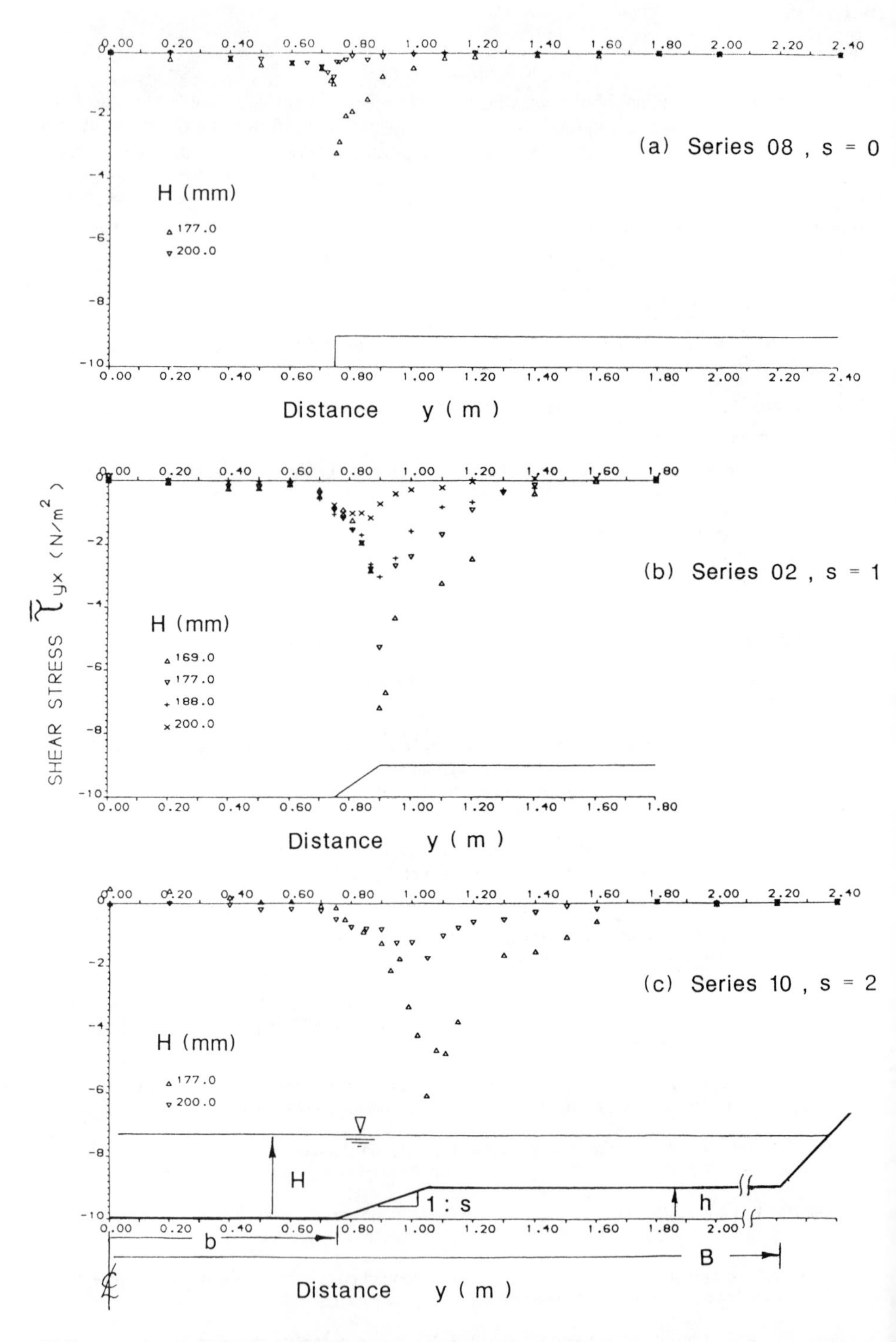

FIG. 1 Lateral distributions of depth averaged Reynolds stress

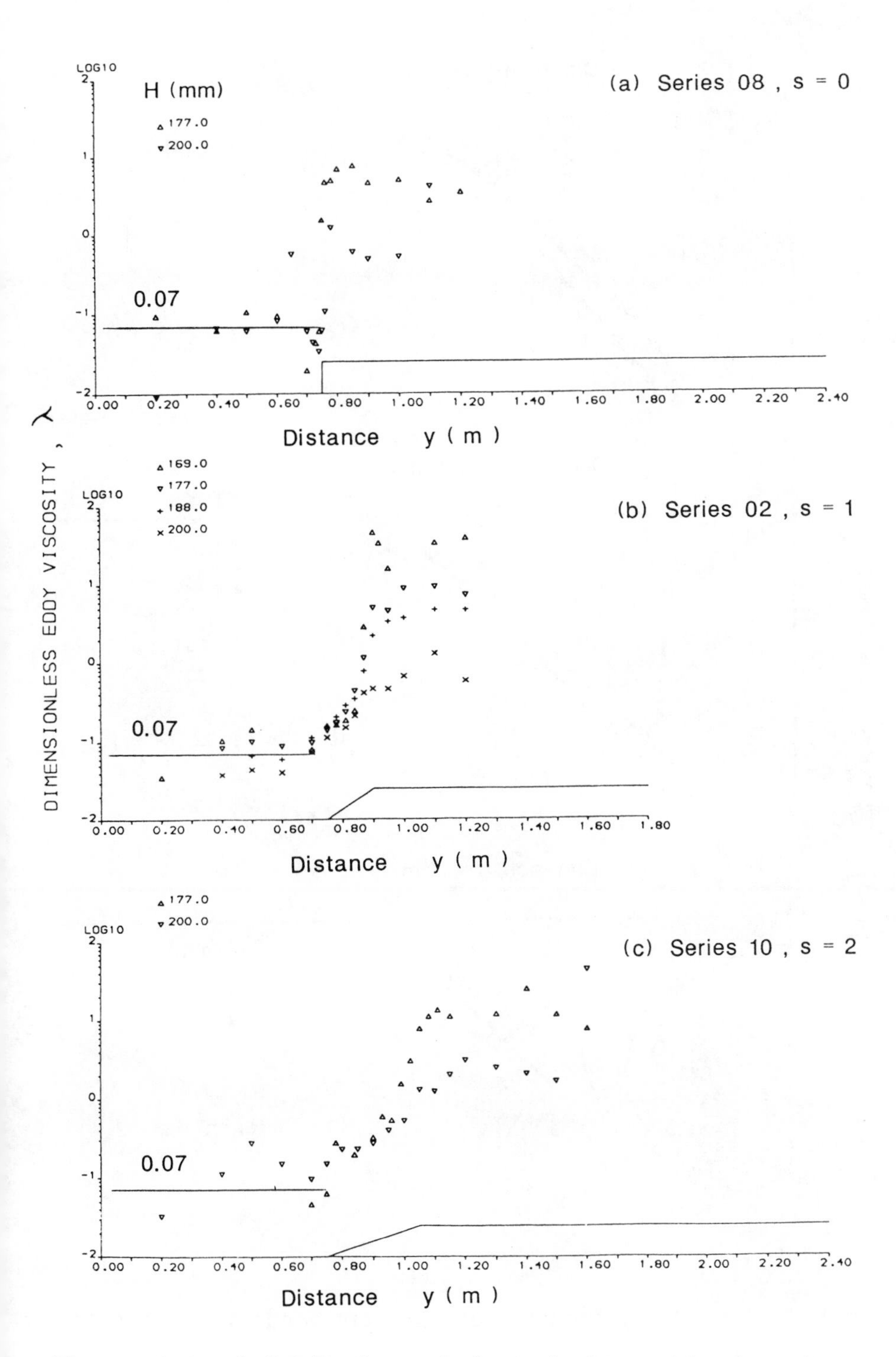

Fig. 2 Lateral distributions of dimensionless eddy viscosity

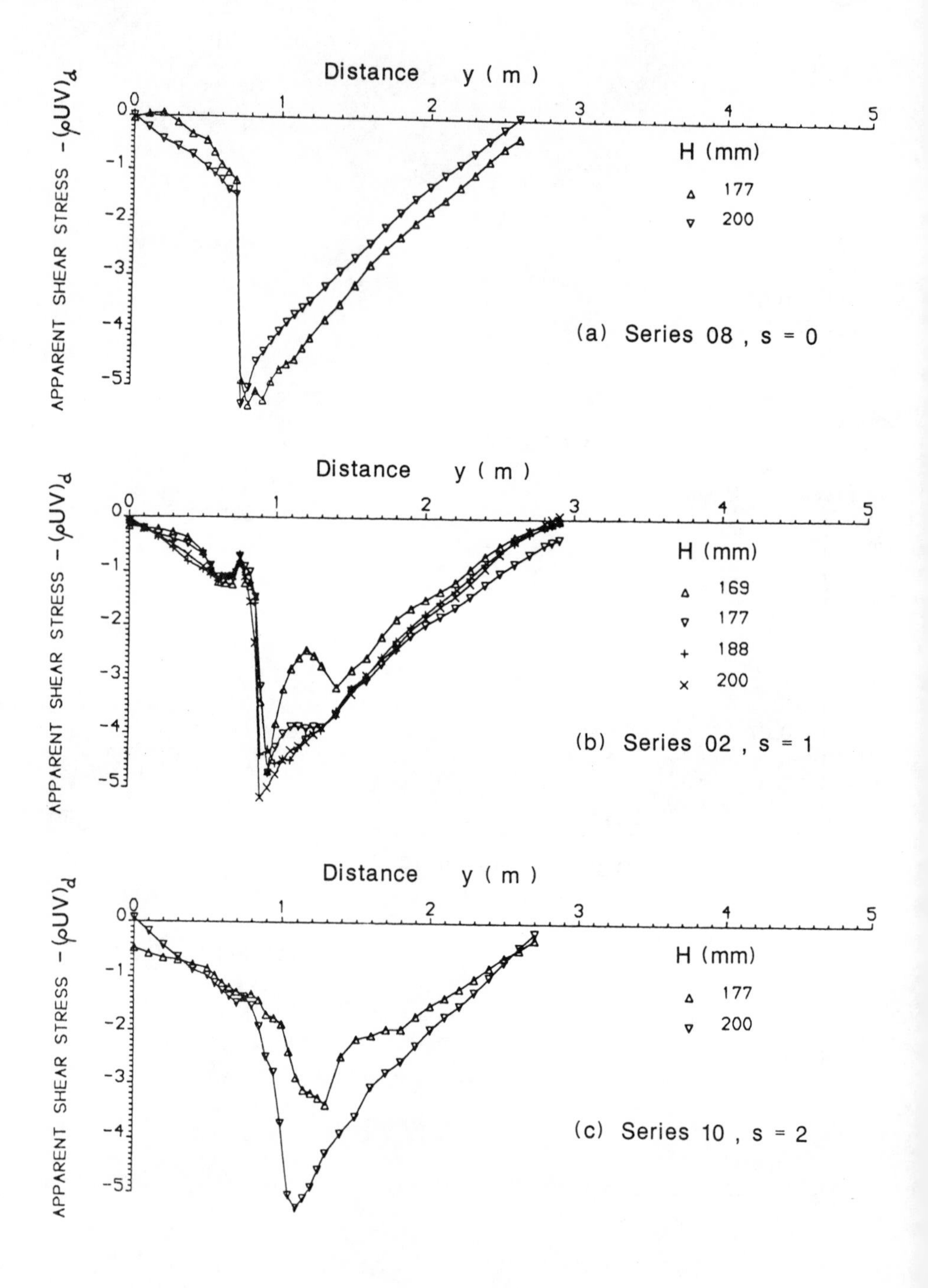

Fig. 3 Lateral distributions of apparent shear stress due to secondary flows

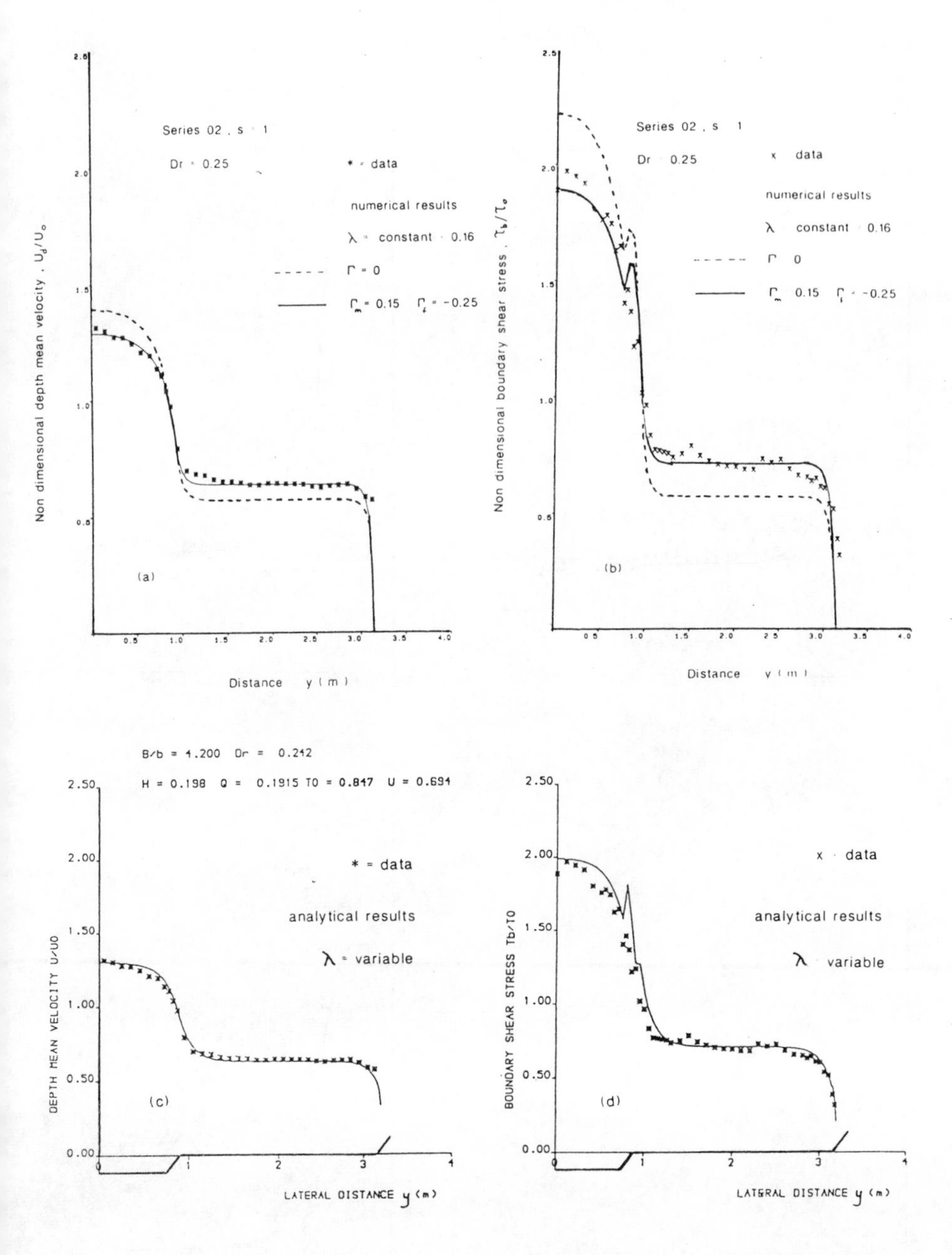

Fig. 4 Comparison between numerical and analytical simulations of the SERC-FCF data (Series 02)

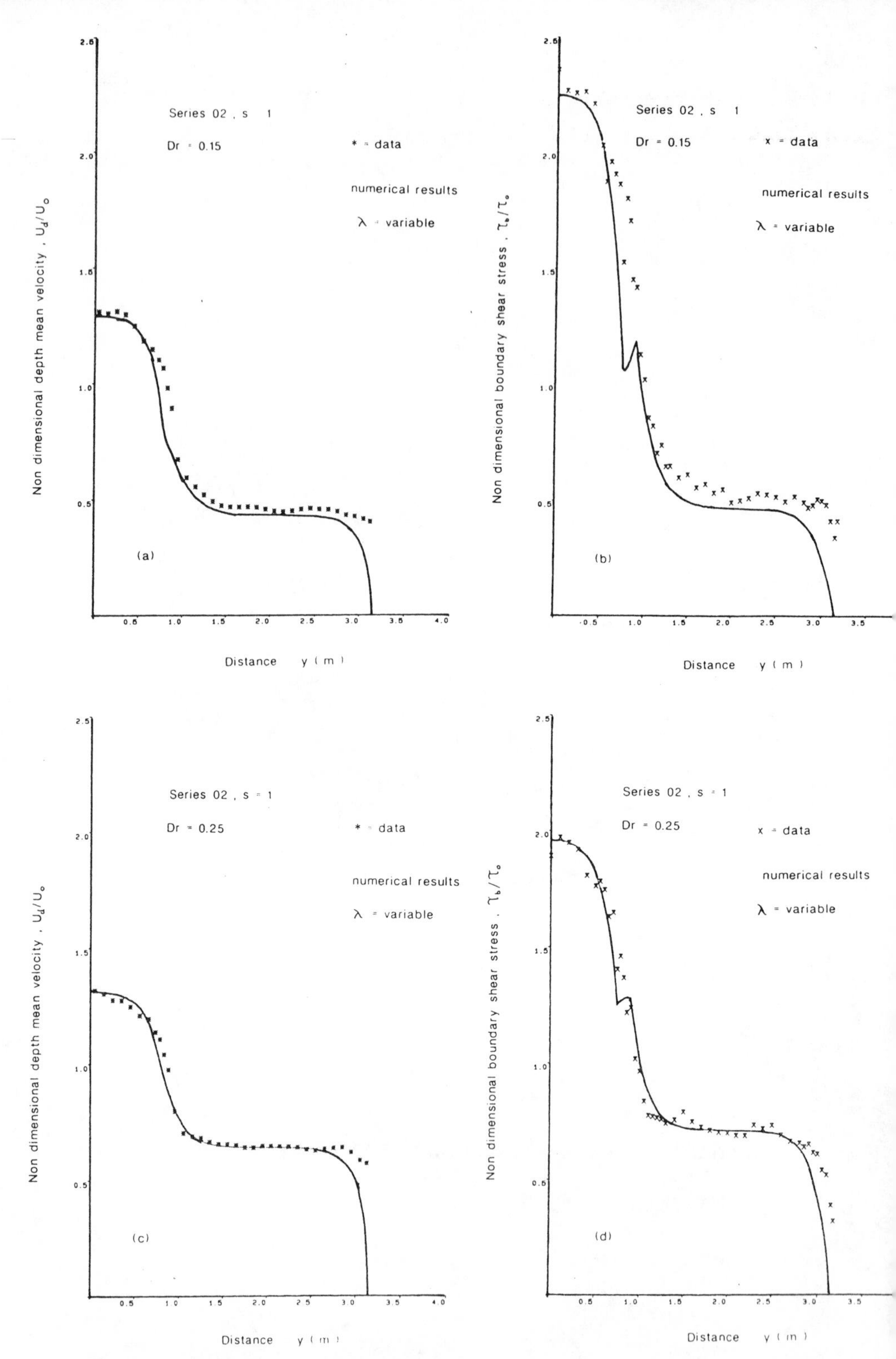

Fig. 5 Comparison between numerical and experimental data for Dr = 0.15 & 0.25 (Series 02)

PAPER G2

International Conference on
RIVER FLOOD HYDRAULICS
17-20 September, 1990

SIMULATION OF DAMBREAK WAVE ALONG ERODIBLE CHANNELS

by

Peter Y. Ko, Ph.D., P.E.[1]
Shawinigan Lavalin Inc.
1100 René Lévesque Blvd., West
Montréal, Québec H3B 4P3
CANADA

SUMMARY

Public utility companies, operating hydroelectric power plants are responsible for the security of dams. For the safety of the people living downstream of sites, studies on the effects and consequences of dambreaks are often required by civil protection agencies. However, most existing mathematical models applicable to dambreak analysis assume the river channel to be rigid. In reality, during the passage of dambreak waves, the banks and the bed of the valley will be eroded by the flood waves, which affects flood levels. The Canadian Electrical Association have sponsored an one-year project to produce a numerical model suitable for use on a personal computer for the simulation of the dambreak wave along erodible channels.

This paper presents the strategy for development and the formulation of the numerical model for modelling the breaching of dams, the routing of the dambreak flood waves and sediment by size fractions and the morphological changes to the river channel. Some preliminary simulation results are also presented.

[1] Adjunt Professor, Department of Civil Engineering, Concordia University, 1455 de Maisonneuve Blvd., West, Montréal, Québec H3G 1M8, CANADA.

International Conference on River Flood Hydraulics, edited by W.R.White

1.0 INTRODUCTION

In December, 1988, the Canadian Electrical Association (CEA) retained the services of Shawinigan Consultants Inc., a division of Lavalin Inc., to produce a numerical model for use on a personal computer for the simulation of the dambreak wave along erodible channels. The duration of the project was originally for a period of one year. (The duration has been extended by two months.) Due to the budgetary and time constraints, it was decided that the development of the numerical model would be one-dimensional and be based on existing models. Furthermore, by incorporating only proven algorithms, the testing and verification of the resulting model could be reduced drastically. A review of the readily available numerical models, within a reasonable price range, for the simulation of dambreak wave and sediment transport, proved that one of the two approaches has to be taken, namely whether to build on a "muddy water" model to simulate dam failure or to build the muddy water component onto a clear water model.

For the "muddy water" components, the following features were determined to be essential:

--- nonuniform and non-equilibrium transport of graded sediment should be considered,
--- the user should be able to use the sediment transport function of his choice,
--- the channel roughness should reflect the change of the river channel,
--- armouring of channel bed should be included,
--- bank erosion, which is a difficult phenomenon to simulate in an one-dimensional model, should be considered.

It was also necessary to verify that the sediment concentration associated with the breaching of dams (mainly hydroelectric dams in this case) will fall within the water flood classification (O'Brien and Julien 1985), therefore the hyperconcentrated sediment transport need not be considered (at least at this stage).

For the modelling of the outflow from the breach, it was considered essential that the adopted algorithm be capable of modelling the breaching of embankments as well as concrete dams. The hydrodynamic component of the model should be capable of routing the highly transient dambreak flood along natural river channels with flood plains.

Both clear water and muddy water models were identified. Since DAMBRK-88 (Fread 1988) is the most commonly used model (at least in North America) and has included many more options applicable to dambreak analysis, it was selected to be the potential base clear water model for further development. Among the muddy water models, FLUVIAL-12 (Chang 1987), MOBED (Krishnappan 1981, 1986), SEDIMENT-4H (Ariathurai 1980) and MIKE-11 (DHI 1983, 1987) were identified. MIKE-11 was dropped from the list because of its high purchase cost, however, evaluation and testing of MIKE-11 were conducted (KO 1989a). FLUVIAL-12 was selected to be the potential base muddy water model for the project because of its superior sediment transport modelling capabilities and the inclusion of a workable dynamic routing procedure.

The coupling of DAMBRK-88 and FLUVIAL-12 would provide a good product for the project. This would require studying and understanding approximately 10 000 lines of FORTRAN code (most of them are not "commented"). Furthermore, before the coupling is completed, any intermediate version would not provide a functional package for the project. Therefore, it was decided that an incremental approach using FLUVIAL-12 as the base model was adopted.

2.0 DAM FAILURE ANALYSIS

Both the parametric and erosion models from the National Weather Service (NWS) of the United States and the Danish Hydraulic Institute (DHI) were examined and compared. The parametric model requires the user to provide the breach descriptions, such as the time to maximum failure, the final elevation of the breach bottom, the side slope of the breach. A schematic diagram showing the breach parameters is given in Figure 1. The NWS models are the parametric procedures given in DAMBRK-88 (Fread 1988) and the BREACH program (Fread 1987), an erosion based procedure. Both NWS models can simulate overtopping and piping failures. A comparison of the DAMBRK-88 and the BREACH models using the Teton Dam failure is shown in Figure 2. The DHI models are the parametric and erosion procedures implemented in MIKE-11 (Havnø et al 1989). However, the DHI models can only simulate the overtopping failure. Using again the Teton Dam failure, the DHI models produced similar outflow hydrographs to the NWS DAMBRK-84 (Figure 3). Based on the previous comparisons, the parametric method is capable of providing a good approximation of the outflow hydrograph from the breach and can be applied to dams of different construction materials. Hence, it was adopted for the project, but only overtopping failure mode is implemented at this stage. The breach opening is assumed to develop according to the following relationships:

$$h_b = h_d - (h_d - h_{bm})\left[\frac{t_b}{T_b}\right] \qquad \text{for} \quad 0 < t_b \leq T_b \qquad (2.1)$$

$$b_t = b\,(t_b/T_b) \qquad (2.2)$$

where h_{bm} = lowest elevation limit of the breach bottom,
h_d = height of the dam,
h_b = elevation of the breach bottom at time t_b,
t_b = time since the beginning of breach formulation,
T_b = total failure time for the breach,
b = final bottom width, and
b_t = bottom width at time t_b.

This procedure is essentially the linear mode of breaching as implemented in DAMBRK-88. The condition at which the breaching commences will be specified by the user. The breaching may also be caused by overtopping of the dam during the passage of a flood prescribed as input. In that case the amount of overtopping before the breaching occurs will be specified. Storage routing will be used to route the incoming flood through the reservoir.

The breach outflow, Q_b, is computed by the broad-crested weir formula as implemented in DAMBRK-88 which is reproduced below (in English units):

$$Q_b = c_v k_s \left[3.1 b_t \left[h - h_b\right]^{1.5} + 2.45 z \left[h - h_b\right]^{2.5} \right] \tag{2.3}$$

$$c_v = 1.0 + \frac{0.023 Q_b^2}{B_d^2 (h - h_{bm})^2 (h - h_b)} \tag{2.4}$$

$$k_s = \begin{cases} 1.0 - 27.8 \left[\dfrac{h_t - h_b}{h - h_b} - 0.67 \right]^3 & \text{if } \dfrac{h_t - h_b}{h - h_b} > 0.67 \\ 1.0 & \text{otherwise.} \end{cases} \tag{2.5}$$

where c_v = correction coefficient for approach velocity,
k_s = submergence correction coefficient for tailwater elevation,
B_d = reservoir width at the dam,
h_{bm} = lowest elevation limit of the breach bottom,
h = water surface elevation just upstream of the dam,
h_d = height of the dam,
h_b = elevation of the breach bottom at time t_b,
h_t = tailwater elevation downstream of the dam,
t_b = time since the beginning of breach formulation,
b_t = bottom width at time t_b, and
z = side slope of the breach.

The eroded materials, from the shell and the core, are treated as sediment influx to the river reach downstream of the breach. In order to estimate the amount of eroded graded materials for each time step, the breach bottom along the direction of the river channel is assumed to be horizontal. As reported by Simmler & Samet (1982) from their physical experiments, the longitudinal slope of the breach bottom varies between dams of different construction and with time. For example, the erosion of a homogeneous dam progressed along and parallel to the downstream face then flattened gradually. For a rockfill dam with a core, the bottom remained relatively horizontal for the upstream side from the core. For the downstream side from the core, the erosion was found to follow the downstream face to start but flattened within a shorter duration than that of a homogeneous case.

The definition of the breach parameters is shown in Figure 1.

The typical sediment concentration of the flood from a dam breach was examined using seven hydroelectric dams across Canada and three dams from Fread(1988). The breaching procedure as previously described was used. The breaching parameters, in each case, were estimated (KO 1989b) such that:

$$Q_p = 1.121\ \forall_m^{0.379}\ h^{0.699} \tag{2.6}$$

where $\forall_m$ is the total outflow volume, m^3, and h is the difference in elevations as defined by MacDonald et al. (1984). The breach formation was calculated at time increments equal to 5% of the estimated time to maximum failure. For each time increment, the volume of breached material was calculated from the cross-sectional geometry of the dam and the total outflow through the breached section was estimated from reservoir routing. The ratio of the breached material to the total outflow was calculated and was considered to be a conservative estimate of the sediment concentration at the breach since all size fractions of the material were included. The estimated maximum sediment concentration, by volume, ranged from 0.39% to 4.10% with most of the others between 1.0 to 2.0%. With the absence of excessive influx of fine sediments, which will probably be the case for Canadian rivers, the sediment concentration associated with the dam break flood will be well within the range of values for water floods, less than 20% by volume, as defined by O'Brien and Julien (1985).

In order to gain insight into the variability of the computed peak outflows with the selected parameters, namely the maximum breach width, the time to maximum failure and the side slope of the breach, a sensitivity analysis of the breaching parameters, in particular the maximum breach width and the time to maximum failure, was conducted.

The maximum breach width and the time to maximum failure were then varied independently by ±50%, ±20%, and ±10%. For each case, the peak outflow from the breach was computed. The change in the computed peak outflows versus the prescribed change in the maximum breach width and the time to maximum failure are presented graphically in Figures 4 and 5 respectively.

The relationships between the percent change in the computed peak outflow and the percent change in the two selected parameters do not appear to be a function of the reservoir volume $\forall_m$ (equal to the maximum outflow volume in this study), the dam height H (taken to be the final depth of the breach), nor the parameter, $\forall_m H$, defined by Hagen (1982) as the dam factor or by MacDonald et al. (1984) as the breach formation factor. However, the percent change in the computed peak outflow versus the change in the breach width appears to be directly proportional to the parameter, $\forall_m/H$, such that the percent change in the computed peak outflow will be larger for sites with large values of $\forall_m/H$. On the contrary, the percent change in the peak outflow versus the percent change in the time to maximum failure appears to be negatively and inversely proportional to V_m/H, such that a reduction in the time to maximum failure will cause a larger increase in the peak outflow for sites with small values of V_m/H.

3.0 DYNAMIC FLOOD ROUTING

The dynamic flood routing is based on the one-dimensional St. Venant equations:

$$\frac{\partial Q}{\partial x} + \frac{\partial (A + A_o)}{\partial t} - q = 0 \tag{3.1}$$

$$\frac{\partial Q}{\partial t} + \frac{\partial (Q^2/A)}{\partial x} + gA\left[\frac{\partial h}{\partial x} + S\right] = 0 \tag{3.2}$$

where
- h = water surface elevation,
- A = cross-sectional area,
- A_o = inactive (channel storage) cross-sectional area,
- t = time,
- q = lateral inflow (or outflow) per unit length along channel,
- g = acceleration due to gravity, and
- S = total energy gradient.

The term A_o is introduced to separate the flood plain storage from the main flow section to ease the convergence problem due to abrupt increase in channel width. The weighted four-point Preissmann implicit finite difference scheme was used for the numerical solution of Equations 3.1 and 3.2. The Manning's roughness coefficients along the river channel, if specified by the user, will remain unchanged. Otherwise, the roughness coefficients will be estimated using Brownlie's (1983) approach.

The approach taken by Fread (1984, 1988) in his DAMBRK-84, -88 programs was adopted for the modelling of supercritical flows. The numerical solution for the supercritical sub-reaches requires both necessary boundary conditions to be prescribed at the upstream end of the reach, while for the subcritical sub-reaches, one is specified at either end of the reach. The flow continuity provides the necessary condition for the coupling at the transition. For the current version, the delineation of the super- and subcritical reaches has to be pre-specified by the user.

During the low flow periods or before the arrival of the flood wave, the calculated elevation along some sections of the river channel can have the tendency to fall below the river bottom between iterations. These problems will produce numerical difficulties which, if no special measures are taken prohibit the computation from continuing. Therefore, it is assumed that the water elevation along the entire river channel being modelled can not fall below the initial values. This assumption can not be generalized to all unsteady flow routing.

4.0 SEDIMENT ROUTING

Sediment routing is based on the continuity equation for non-cohesive sediment in the longitudinal direction as:

$$(1 - \eta) \frac{\partial A_b}{\partial t} + \frac{\partial Q_s}{\partial x} - q_{sl} = 0 \qquad (4.1)$$

where A_b = cross-sectional area of channel bottom within an arbitrary boundary,
Q_s = sediment discharge, equals $\sum q_{si}$,
q_{si} = sediment discharge of size fraction i,
q_{sl} = lateral sediment inflow rate per unit length, and
η = porosity of bed material.

Equation 4.1 is solved using the upstream difference in x and centred difference in time.

The following six sediment transport formulae can be selected by the user:

- -- Graf's equation,
- -- Yang's unit stream power equation for sediment sizes between 0.063 and 10 mm,
- -- Engelund-Hansen equation,
- -- Parker gravel equation,
- -- Ackers-While equation, and
- -- Meyers-Peter Muller bed load equation.

The sediment transport formula providea the estimate of the potential transport capacity of sediment of different size fractions. Then the actual sediment discharges, q_{si}, for various size fractions are adjusted, first using the residual transport capacity approach of Borah et al. (1982), then for diffusion using Zhang et al. (1983), and for sediment availability due to physical constraints. Then the ΔA_b's at all cross-sections are computed for updating the channel cross-sections.

The updating of the channel cross-section is adjusted with width corrections, then for aggradation and degradation. The direction of width adjustment is determined following the stream power approach (see e.g. Chang 1988) such that the spatial variation in energy gradient and the total power expenditure is adjusted towards uniformity in power expenditure. The rate of width adjustment is based upon the bank erodibility factor, which equals zero for non-erodible bank and unity for easily erodible banks with noncohesive materials. The slope of the erodible bank is also limited by the angle of repose of the material.

The remaining ΔA_b at each cross-section is distributed across the river channel as scour/fill. The allocation of scour/fill cross a section is assumed to be proportional to the effective tractive force, such that:

$$\Delta z_i = \frac{(\tau_o - \tau_c)^n}{\sum(\tau_o - \tau_c)^n \Delta y_i} \Delta A_b \tag{4.2}$$

where Δz_i = local correction in channel bottom elevation,
Δy_i = width of the ith panel across the channel,
τ_o = local tractive force, γDS,
γ = specific weight of water-sediment mixture,
D = local water depth,
S = energy gradient,
ΔA_b = correction to the cross-sectional area of channel, and
n = power with value between 0 and 1.

The value of n is determined such that the correction in the channel bottom profile will result in the most rapid rate towards uniformity in power expenditure.

For each time step, the dynamic flood routing using Equations 3.1 and 3.2 are performed to provide flow distributions along the channel together with the associated water elevations. The sediment routings are executed in serial to provide the sediment discharges along the channels. Then composition of the active layer is updated. The morphological modelling is performed next, including the adjustments of channel bottom elevations and the channel widths, and the updating of the cross-sections. The sequence is repeated through the duration of the simulation.

5.0 APPLICATIONS AND CONCLUSIONS

Testing of the model is being conducted. Some preliminary results using data extracted from the Buffalo Creek example of Fread (1984) have been obtained. Figure 6 shows the comparison of the results on the dynamic routing with a rigid boundary. Figure 7 shows the changes in the cross-sections along the river using some typical bed compositions. The test run indicated that scouring would occur along the upstream reaches while deposition along the downstream reaches.

Preliminary testing showed that the model as formulated is usable to perform routing of a dambreak wave along an erodible river channel. Additional options can be added which may include various hydraulic structures, the description of debris flow (Chen 1985) etc. With the inclusion of the width adjustment algorithm, it is also able to estimate the vulnerability of river banks, which will be important for civil protection agencies in the preparation of the Emergency Preparedness Plans (EPP) as they are called in Canada.

All algorithms incorporated in the model have been verified rather extensively with historic data. However, the performance of these algorithms under the dambreak flood conditions can only be verified by accurate field data. Historic dambreak data were usually estimated after the fact, therefore would not provide data for a "pure" verification particularly on the morphological changes in the river channel. Perhaps a well monitored field experiment, supported by multi-governmental agencies, would provide valuable corroborating information.

6.0 ACKNOWLEDGEMENT

This project is supported by a contract from the Canadian Electrical Association for a duration of approximately one year. Suggestions from Mr. R.B. Barnes of Newfoundland and Labrador Hydro and Dr. T.T. Quach of Hydro Québec who acted as the CEA technical advisors, are acknowledged. The support received from the Danish Hydraulic Institute for the evaluation and testing of MIKE-11 is very much appreciated. Finally, the time, the suggestions and discussions provided by the project expert advisors, Dr. Dale Bray, Dr. H.H. Chang and Dr. D.L. Fread are invaluable to the project.

7.0 REFERENCES

Ariathurai, R., "Erosion and Sedimentation Downstream from Harry S. Truman Dam as a Result of Hydropower Operations", prepared for the U.S. Army Corps of Engineers, Kansas City, Missouri, 1980.

Borah, D.K., Alonso, C.V., and Prasad, S.N., "Routing Graded Sediments in Streams: Formulations", Journal of Hydraulics Division, ASCE, Vol. 108, No. HY12, December 1982, pp. 1486-1503.

Brownlie, W.R., "Flow Depth in Sand-Bed Channels", Journal of Hydraulic Engineering, ASCE, Vol. 109, No. 7, July 1983, pp. 959-990.

Chang, H.H., "FLUVIAL-12 Mathematical Model for Erodible Channels Users Manual", San Diego, California, June 1987.

Chang, H.H., Fluvial Processes in River Engineering, John Wiley & Sons, New York, 1988, 432 pages.

Chen, Cheng-Lung, "Hydraulic Concepts in Debris Flow Simulation", Proceedings of the Specialty Conference on the Delineation of Land-slide, Flash Flood, and Debris Flow Hazards in Utah, Utah State University, Logan, Utah, August 1985, pp. 236-259.

Danish Hydraulic Institute, "System-11 Model Documentation and System-11 User's Guide", Denmark, 1983.

Danish Hydraulic Institute, "MIKE-11 A Short Description", Denmark, July 1987.

Fread, D.L., "DAMBRK: The NWS Dam-break Flood Forecasting Model", Office of Hydrology, National Weather Service, NOAA, Silver Spring, Maryland, 1982 and 1984.

Fread, D.L., "The NWS DAMBRK Model: Theoretical Background/User Documentation", Office of Hydrology, National Weather Service, NOAA, Silver Spring, Maryland, 1988.

Fread, D.L., "BREACH: An Erosion Model for Earth Dam Failures", Office of Hydrology, National Weather Service, NOAA, Silver Spring, Maryland, June 1987.

Hagen, V.K., "Re-Evaluation of Design Floods and Dam Safety", Paper presented at the 14th ICOLD Congress, Rio de Janiero, Brazil, 1982, pp. 475-491.

Havnø, K., M. Brorsen and J.C. Refsgaard, "Generalized mathematical modelling system for flood analysis and flood control design", Proceedings, 2nd International Conference on the Hydraulics of Floods and Flood Control, Cambridge, UK, September 1985, pp. 387-397.

Ko, P.Y., "Summary Descriptions of MIKE-11 Package", Technical Memorandum No. 2 submitted to the Canadian Electrical Association, Shawinigan Consultants Inc., Montreal, November 25, 1989a (revised).

Ko, P.Y., "Selection of Breaching Algorithm and Characteristics of Sediment Mixture", Technical Memorandum No. 3 submitted to the Canadian Electrical Association, Shawinigan Consultants, Inc. Montreal, October 16, 1989b.

Krishnappan, B.G., "Users Manual: Unsteady, Nonuniform, Mobile Boundary Flow Model - MOBED", National Water Research Institute, Environment Canada, Burlington, Ontario, February 1981.

Krishnappan, B.G., "MOBED Users Manual Update II", National Water Research Institute, Environment Canada, Burlington, Ontario, 1986.

MacDonald, T.C. and Langridge-Monopolis, J., "Breaching Characteristics of Dam Failures", Journal of Hydraulic Engineering, ASCE, Vol. 110, No. 5, May 1984, pp. 567-586.

O'Brien, J.S., and Julien, P.Y., "Laboratory Analysis of Mudflow Properties", Journal of Hydraulics Engineering, ASCE, Vol. 114, No. 8, August 1988, pp. 260-279.

Simmler, H. and Samet, L., "Dam Failure from Overtopping studied on a Hydraulic Model", Paper presented at the meeting of ICOLD, Rio de Janeiro, Brazil, 1982, pp. 427-445.

Zhang, Q., Zhang, Z., Yue, J., Duan, Z., and Dai, M., "A Mathematical Model for the Prediction of the Sedimentation Process in Rivers", Proceedings of the 2nd International Symposium on River Sedimentation, Nanjing, China, 1983, pp. 95-106.

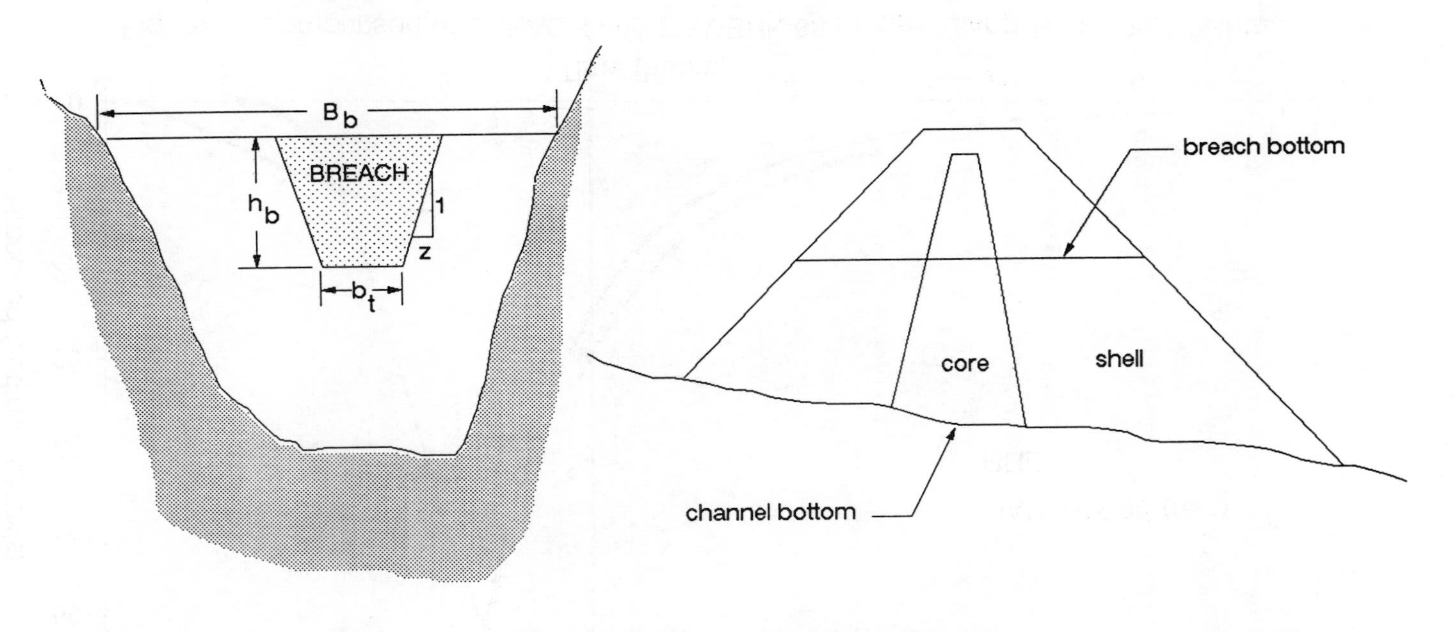

Figure 1. Definition of breach parameters

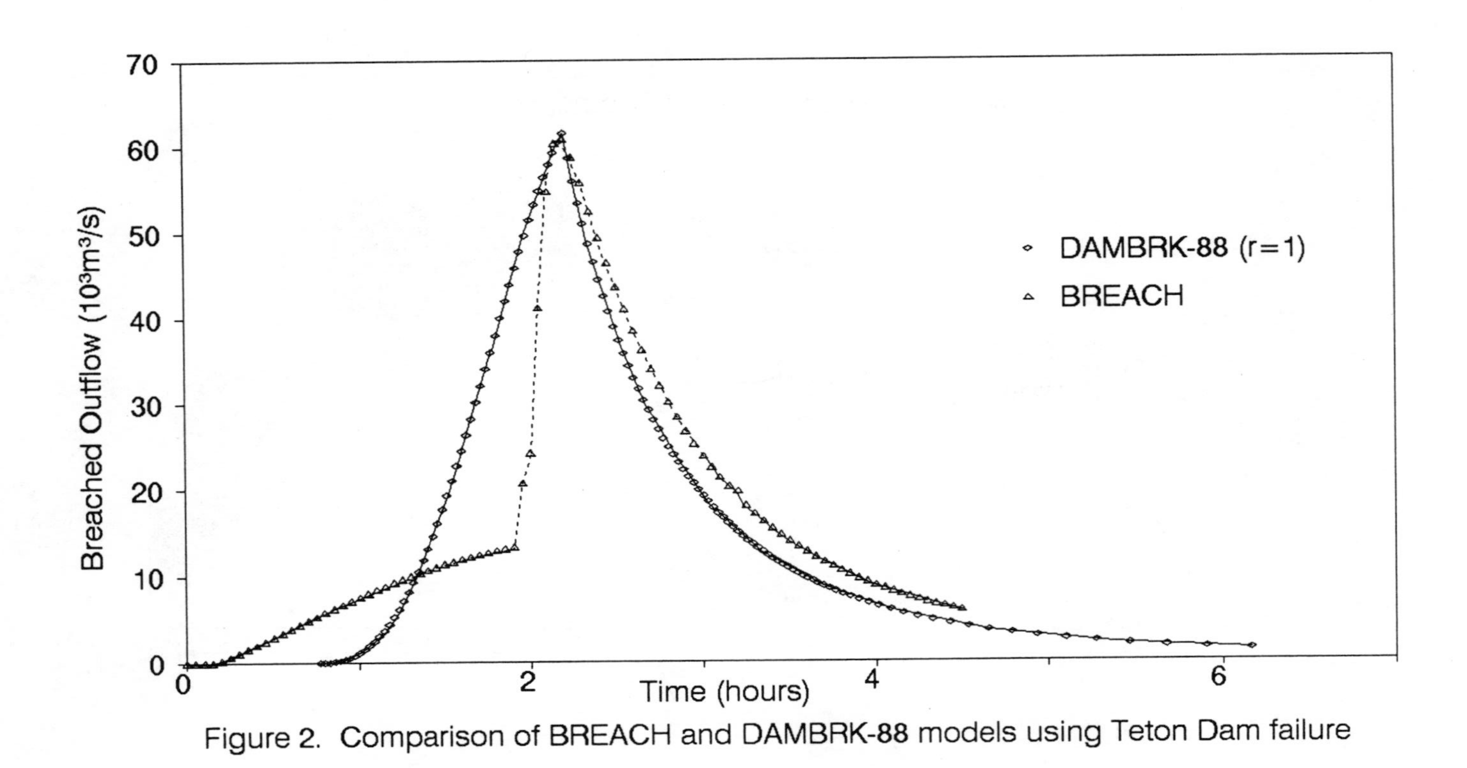

Figure 2. Comparison of BREACH and DAMBRK-88 models using Teton Dam failure

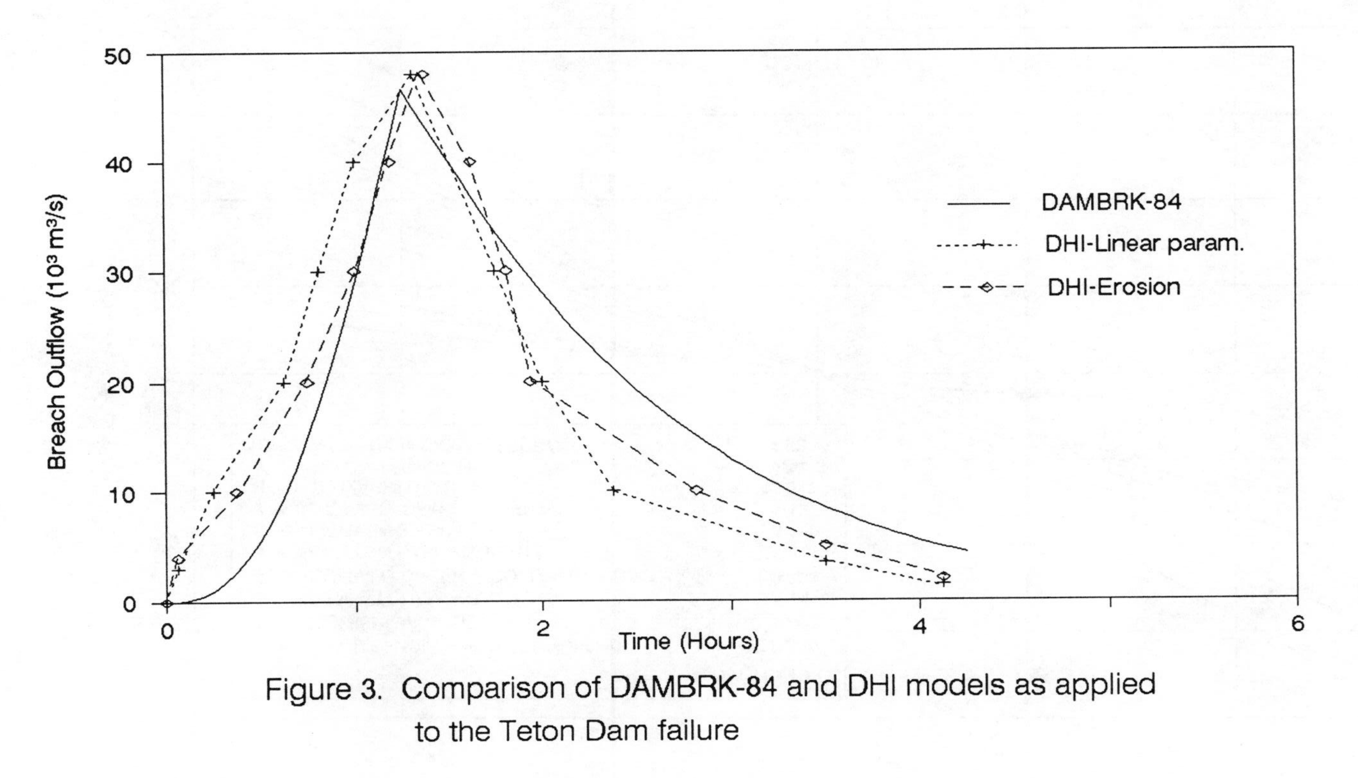

Figure 3. Comparison of DAMBRK-84 and DHI models as applied to the Teton Dam failure

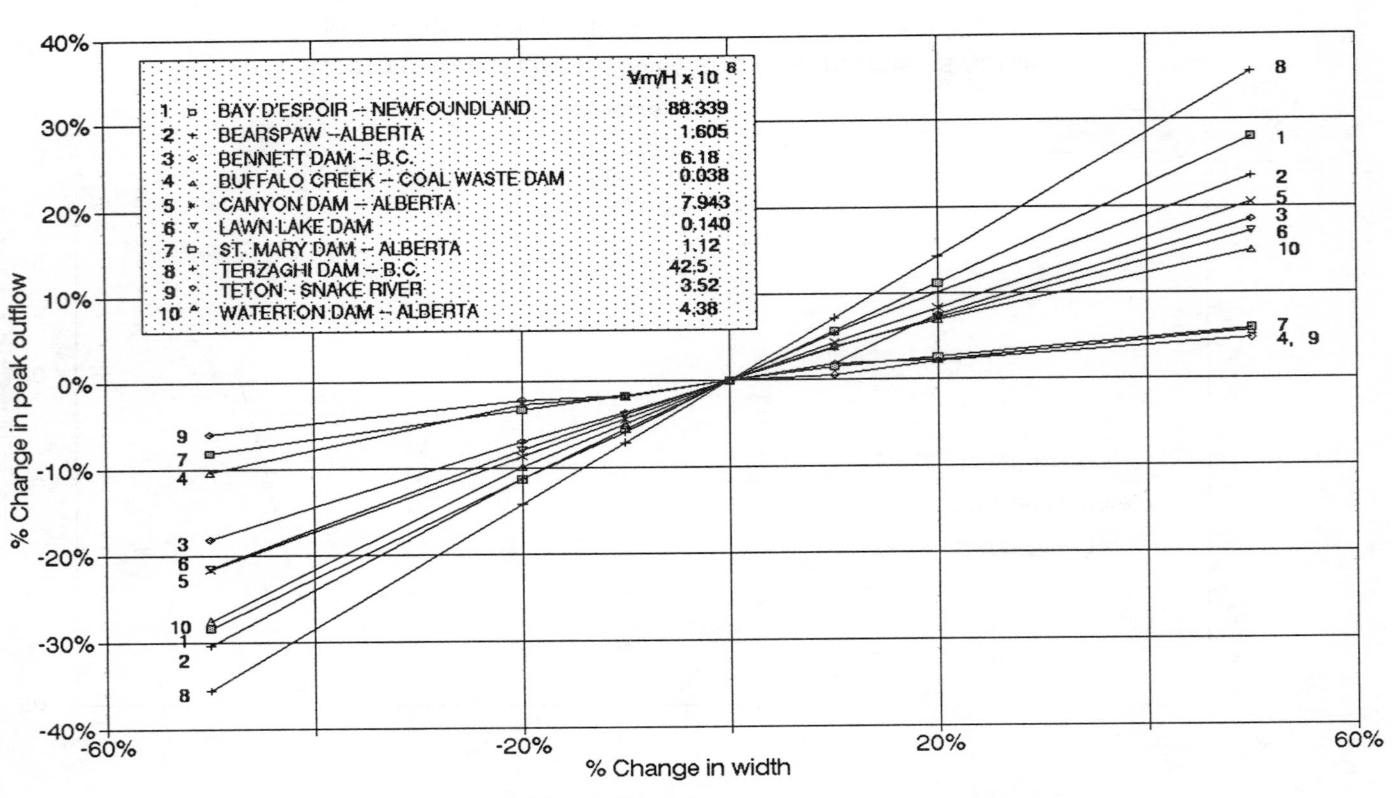

Figure 4. Sensitivity of peak outflow to the change in breach width only.

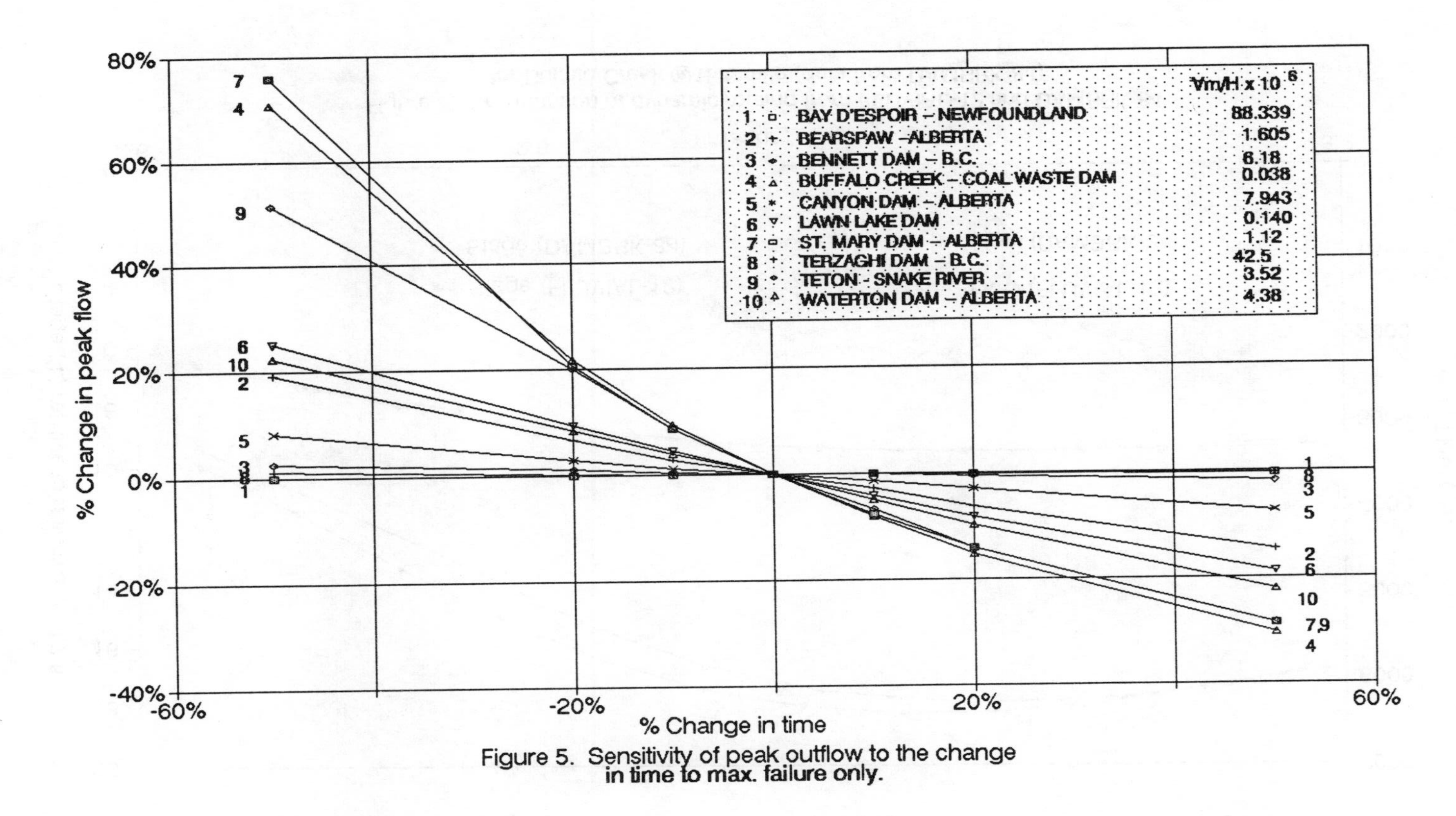

Figure 5. Sensitivity of peak outflow to the change in time to max. failure only.

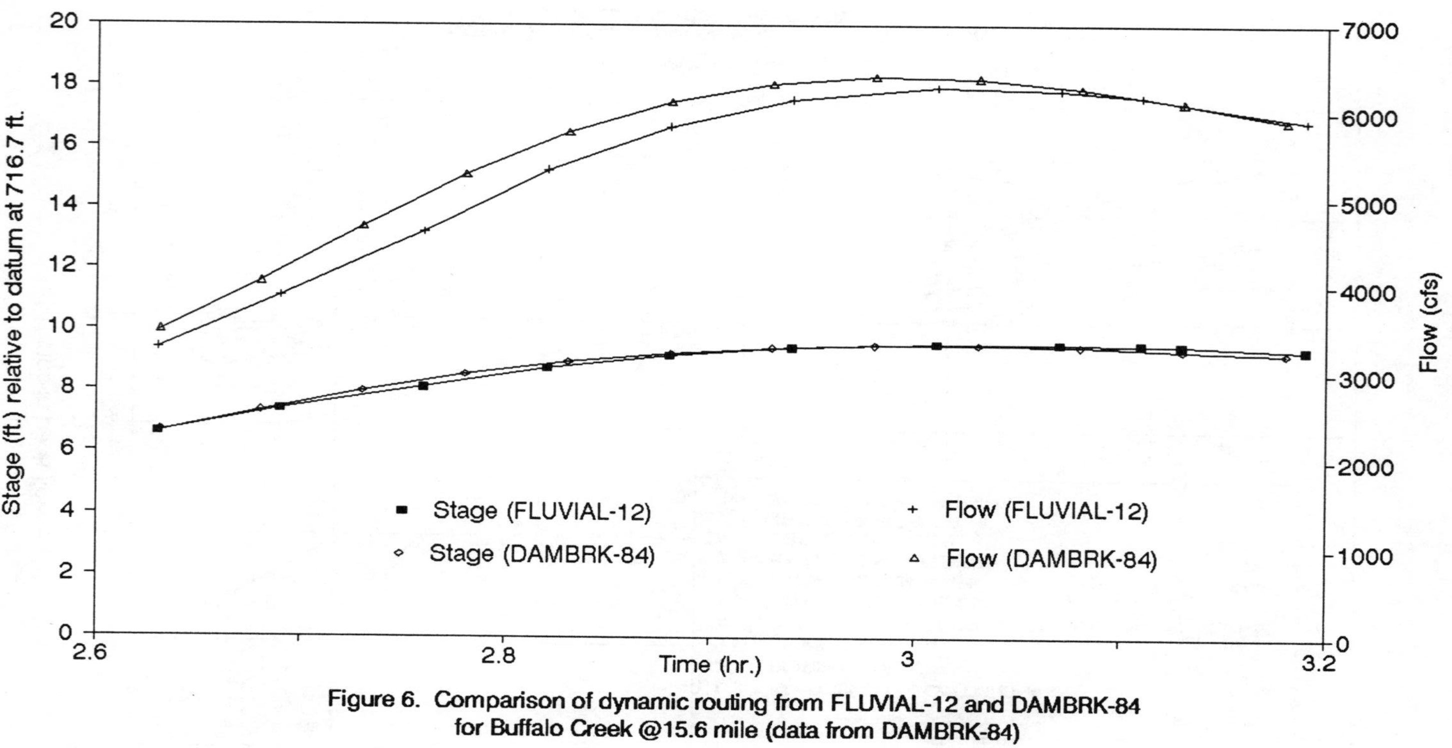

Figure 6. Comparison of dynamic routing from FLUVIAL-12 and DAMBRK-84 for Buffalo Creek @15.6 mile (data from DAMBRK-84)

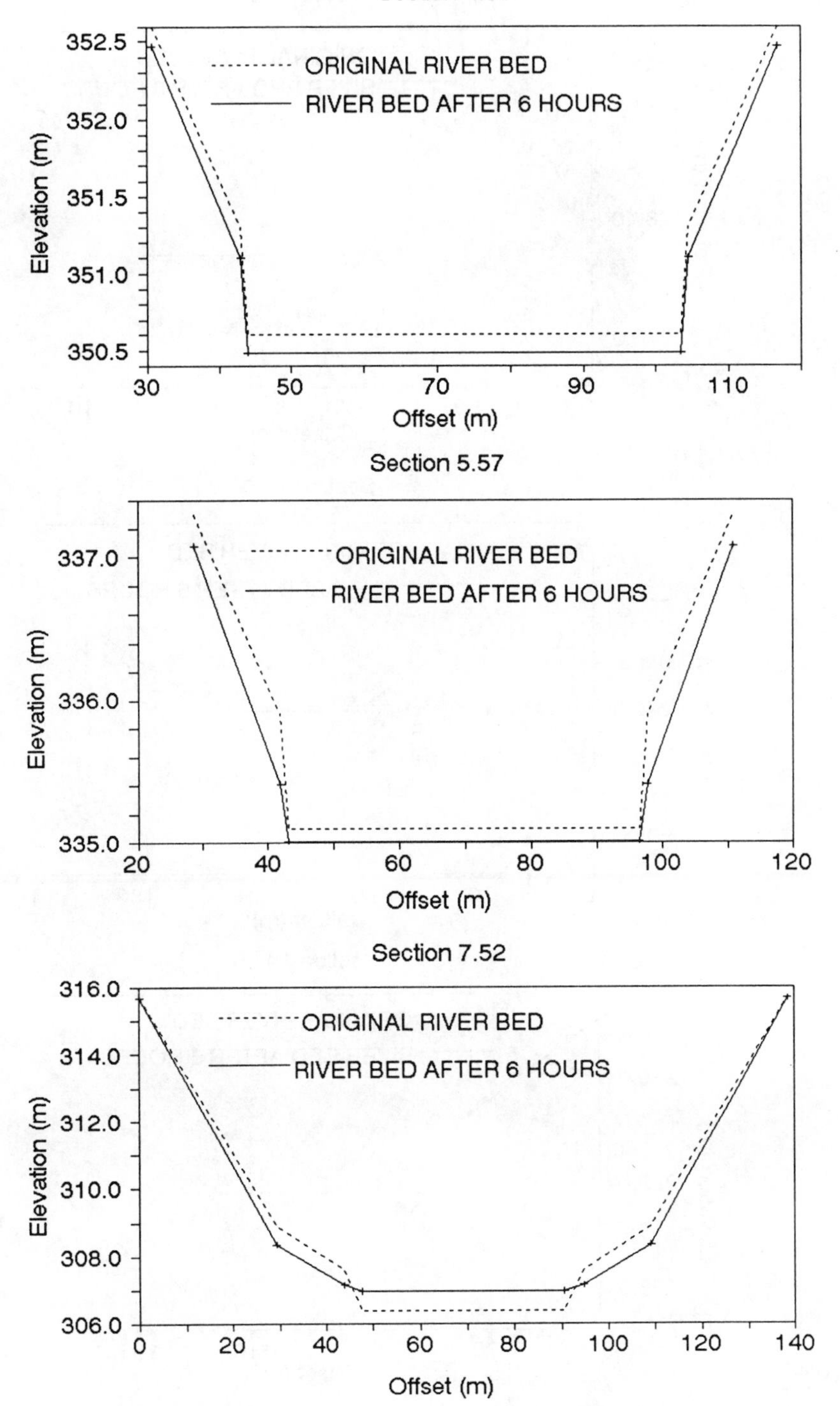

Figure 7a. Comparison of channel cross-sections after 6 hours

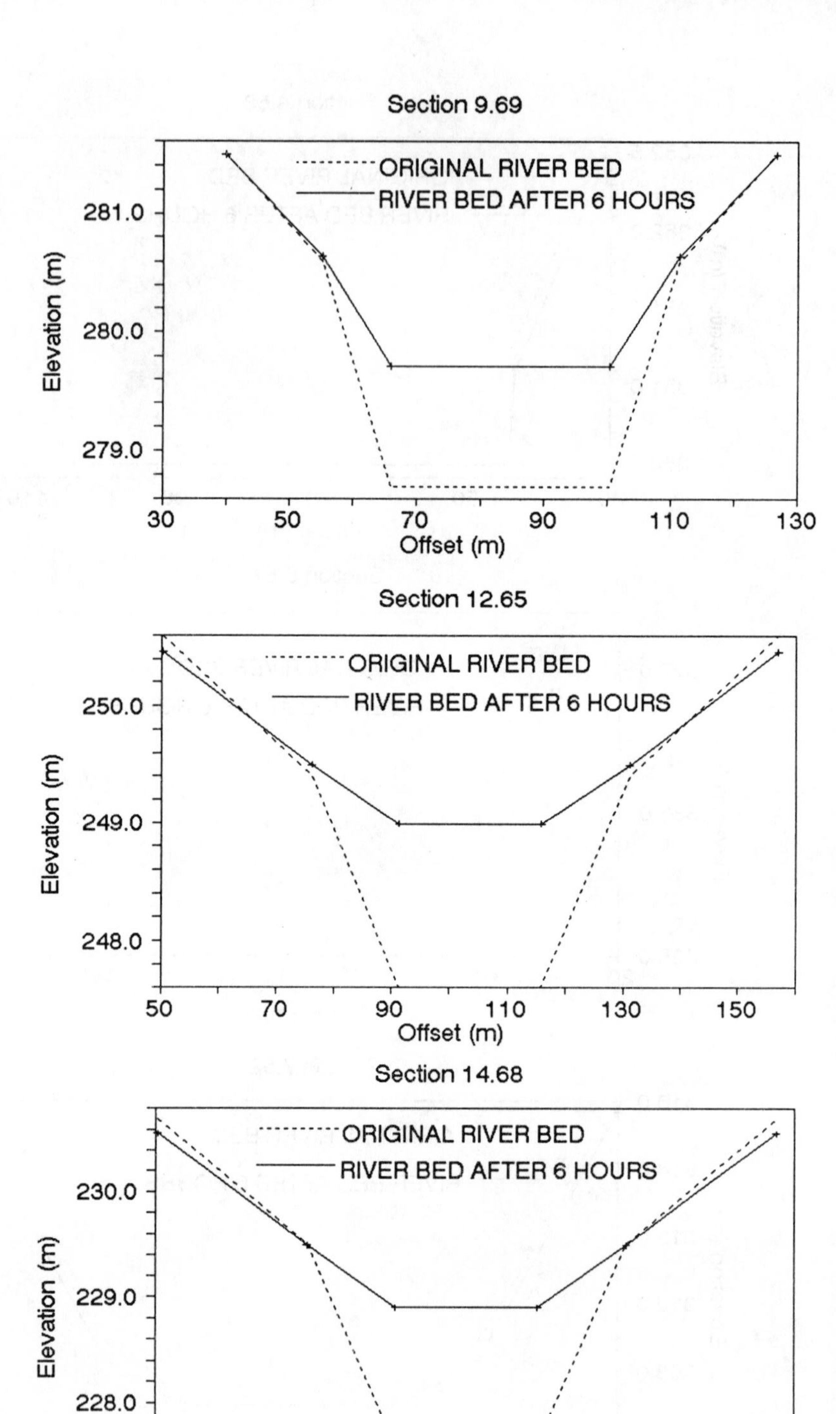

Figure 7b. Comparison of channel cross-sections after 6 hours

PAPER G3

International Conference on
RIVER FLOOD HYDRAULICS
17-20 September, 1990

CASCADE DAM RUPTURE ANALYSIS

A. BENTO FRANCO (Assistant at Instituto Superior Técnico, Technical University of Lisbon)

A. BETÂMIO DE ALMEIDA (Professor at Instituto Superior Técnico, Technical University of Lisbon)

1 - INTRODUCTION

For over a century, the so called DAM BREAK PROBLEM has attracted a large number of distinguished scientists and, more recently, of members of the computational hydraulic community. The published studies and results (as far as the authors of the present paper know at this date) can be grouped like this way:

- characterization of the mode of rupture of the dam (e.g. partial and gradual rupture of earth dams);
- analytical or classic solutions of the wave front near the dam site;
- computational simulation of the macro flood along irregular valleys (e.g. case studies);
- domains of validation for different mathematical models (e.g. fully dynamic or simplified models);
- comparisions of different numerical techniques (e.g. implicit, explicit) or basic computational methods (e.g. finite difference, characteristics or finite elements);
- detailed local phenomena simulations (e.g. 2.D modeling near the breach zone);
- physical modeling.

Practical case studies has been presented by different authors,some of them including the rupture of several dams in cascade: e.g. the numerical simulation of the rupture of 11 dams along the Douro river in Portugal and Spain (Almeida and Ornelas 1987); or the fast flooding of a plain in the Mondego river near Coimbra (Portugal) by using a mixed 1-D/2-D model (Almeida and Rodrigues 1984).

Different codes are available for numerical simulations of floods caused by dam failures: the most known being the DAMBRK developped by Dr. D. Fread in the National Weather Service of U.S.A. (FREAD 1979).

The objective of this paper is to present the first results of a systematic study made by the authors in order to define a methodology of analysis involving the rupture of several dams in cascade. The research work is going on covering other aspects.

After a short reference to the practical importance of this subject, the authors present the basic equations and the numerical scheme that has been developed. Finally, some numerical results are shown

International Conference on River Flood Hydraulics, edited by W.R.White

and the main conclusions are presented.

2 - THE IMPORTANCE OF THE PROBLEM

Currently, in most of the developed countries the most important rivers have several dams in cascade and, in most of the cases, the reservoirs fill completely the reachs between the dams. So, the failure of a dam will provoke a macro flood over sucessive deep reservoirs and dams. The published design charts or the very simplified codes are not useful for this kind of problem. Computer codes based on complete dynamic equations for unsteady flow and adequate internal boundary conditions must be used. However the systematic running of these heavy codes without a methodology will be very time consuming and the results can be unsafe in what concerns, by example, the highest water levels along the valley.

3 - COMPUTATIONAL MODEL

3.1 - Basic equations

The Saint-Venant equations were written under the so called conservation form (Richtmeyer and Morton, 1967):

$$\frac{\partial U}{\partial t} + \frac{\partial F(U)}{\partial x} = D(U) \qquad (1)$$

with:

$$U = \begin{vmatrix} A \\ Q \end{vmatrix} \qquad F(U) = \begin{vmatrix} Q \\ VQ + Fh/\rho \end{vmatrix} \qquad D(U) = \begin{vmatrix} 0 \\ -gA(J-i) \end{vmatrix}$$

were

A = cross-sectional flow area;
Q = water discharge;
V = flow velocity;
F_h = hydrostatic-pressure force on a cross section;
ρ = water mass density;
g = acceleration due to gravity;
J = slope of the energy grade line;
i = bottom slope.

3.2 - Numerical scheme

The matrix equation (1) is solved by the explicit MacCormack scheme (MacCormack 1971; Garcia and Kahawita 1986; Fennema and Chaudhry 1986; Belos and Sakkas 1987; Franco 1988). This scheme is based on two partial time steps:

- The predictor step:

$$\tilde{U}_i^{j+1} = U_i^j - \frac{\Delta t}{\Delta x}\left(F_{i+1}^j - F_i^j\right) + \Delta t\, D_i^j \qquad (2)$$

- The corrector step:

$$U_i^{j+1} = \frac{1}{2}\left[U_i^j + \tilde{U}_i^{j+1} - \frac{\Delta t}{\Delta x}(\tilde{F}_i^{j+1} - \tilde{F}_{i-1}^{j+1}) + \Delta t\, \tilde{D}_i^{j+1} \right] \qquad (3)$$

Δt = time step;
Δx = space step;
ij = indices of the nodes of the mesh on x-t plane;
$\sim$ = indicates that results from the predictor step should be used.

Following (Chaudhry and Hussaini 1983), the authors applied, for each step, the progressive and the regressive difference numerical technique in an alternate sequence along the numerical simulation.

In the boundary conditions (e.g. dams) this method was mixed with the method of the characteristics.

3.3 - Internal Boundary Conditions (Dams)

The rupture of each dam is characterized by the evolution of a rectangular breach whose area can increase more or less fast according with the type of the dam.

The following set of equations is solved in each time step:

- one upstream characteristic equation C^+
- one downstream characteristic equation C^-
- the continuity equation
- the equivalent discharge equation (corresponding to the breach, the spillway, the turbines and outlets).

The discharge through each breach is corrected by the factor atributed to Brater (Fread 1979) when submergence tailwater effects exists.

The system to be solved is a non-linear one with four equations and four unknowns which is solved by the Newton-Raphson technique.

3.4 - External boundary conditions

The upstream boundary conditions is a chosen hydrograph and the downstream condition is a static or a dynamic rating curve.

3.5 - Model validation

The computational model was validated by reproducing the classical dam break problem presented in (Fennema and Chaudhry, 1987). One of the results is presented in Fig. 1 (Franco 1988).

4 - CASCADE DAM BREAK

4.1 - General remarks

First of all, there are two different conditions for a cascade dam break: a simultaneous dam failure (due, by example, to a very strong regional earthquake) or a sucessive dam failure, like a domino failure (rupture in cascade). Among the different parameters involved, the most typical and important will be the time of complete collapse of each dam.

The engineer must also choose what are the most adverse effects that he want obtain with the numerical simulation. Just a few examples:

- maximum discharges and corresponding time?
- maximum water levels and corresponding time?
- time of arrival of the front wave or of the maximum water level?
- maximum submersion time of downstream plains?

For example,if the main objective of the study is to predict the safe level for the siting of a nuclear power plant, in a particular downstream valley section, it is sufficient to know the maximum water level in that section. But if the study is the main basis to establish an emergency rescue plan, the time of arrival of the wave front in the selected downstream sections will be also very important.

4.2 - Two dams case

Figure 2 shows two dams and their main characteristics. In Tables 1 and 2 are indicated the maximum discharges (Table 1) and the maximum water heights (Table 2) at each dam and at three downstream sections indicated in Figure 2.

In each Table the results are presented for three different times of rupture of each dam and also for a simultaneous rupture (results A) or for a cascade rupture (results B). Within brackets are presented the instants of occurrence of each maximum value after the first dam rupture.

The values of maximum discharges (QMAX) and of the maximum water heights (HMAX) are nondimensionalized dividing,respectively, by the maximum theoretical discharge at dam site ($QMAX = 8/27 . B . \sqrt{9,8} . H^{1,5}$, where B = width of rectangular cross section at dam site and H = = height of the dam) and by the initial height of the dam.

It can be concluded from these numerical results (Tables 1 and 2):

- The maximum discharge at dam B2 for a cascade rupture will occur for the minimum time of rupture of dam B1.
- For a simultaneous rupture, the maximum discharge at dam B2 will be greater if the respective time of rupture is different than the corresponding time at dam B1.
- Downstream of dam B2 (sections 181, 211 and 241), the maximum discharges occurs when this dam has a time of failure longer than the time of failure of dam B1. The most favourable situation in those river sections and in respect of the maximum flood discharges and water levels, will be for a longer time of failure of dam B1 together with lesser time of failure of dam B2. The longer the time of failure of the downstream dam the more unfavourable seems to be the flood characteristics downstream.
- As a rule, for a cascade rupture, the time of occurrence of the maximum water levels and discharges, at sections 181, 211 and 241, are greater than the corresponding time for a simultaneous rupture.
- For both different conditions of rupture (cascade or simultaneous) the minimum arrival time of the maximum values of discharges and water levels occur for the minimum time of rupture of two dams.
- These results indicate that a rupture in cascade will provoke more dangerous floods than a simultaneous rupture, in respect

Time of rupture of dam B_1 (sec.)	Time of rupture of dam B_2 (sec.)	SECTION AT DAM B_1		SECTION AT DAM B_2		SECTION 181		SECTION 211		SECTION 241	
		A	B	A	B	A	B	A	B	A	B
300	300	0.697 (0.08)	0.697 (0.08)	0.697 (0.08)	1.000 (0.73)	0.462 (1.86)	0.557 (2.00)	0.425 2.49)	0.482 (2.66)	0.397 (3.17)	0.435 (3.34)
	1800	0.697 (0.08)	0.697 (0.08)	0.787 (0.67)	0.990 (1.13)	0.514 (1.87)	0.586 (2.18)	0.455 (2.53)	0.503 (2.82)	0.416 (3.22)	0.450 (3.49)
	3600	0.697 (0.08)	0.697 (0.08)	0.888 (1.00)	0.888 (1.63)	0.561 (2.01)	0.607 (2.44)	0.485 (2.66)	0.522 (3.05)	0.436 (3.34)	0.465 (3.71)
1800	300	0.652 (0.50)	0.652 (0.50)	0.697 (0.08)	0.951 (0.99)	0.407 (2.28)	0.554 (2.25)	0.389 (2.83)	0.481 (2.90)	0.373 (3.44)	0.434 (3.58)
	1800	0.652 (0.50)	0.652 (0.50)	0.652 (0.50)	0.996 (1.34)	0.465 (2.13)	0.585 (2.41)	0.428 (2.77)	0.502 (3.05)	0.399 (3.43)	0.450 (3.72)
	3600	0.652 (0.50)	0.652 (0.50)	0.809 (1.00)	0.895 (1.84)	0.527 (2.16)	0.608 (2.67)	0.464 (2.82)	0.522 (3.28)	0.423 (3.51)	0.465 (3.93)
3600	300	0.589 (1.00)	0.589 (1.00)	0.697 (0.08)	0.726 (1.44)	0.352 (2.92)	0.526 (2.50)	0.342 (3.41)	0.465 (3.16)	0.334 (3.93)	0.424 (3.84)
	1800	0.589 (1.00)	0.589 (1.00)	0.652 (0.50)	0.954 (1.45)	0.393 (2.67)	0.566 (2.61)	0.379 (3.19)	0.489 (3.26)	0.366 (3.78)	0.440 (3.94)
	3600	0.589 (1.00)	0.589 (1.00)	0.599 (1.00)	0.910 (1.95)	0.464 (2.47)	0.599 (2.83)	0.428 (3.09)	0.513 (3.45)	0.400 (3.76)	0.458 (4.13)

A - Simultaneous dam failure B - Sucessive dam failure

Q^*MAX (TIME)

TABLE 1 - Maximum discharges - Q^*MAX - (dimensionless) and corresponding instants (hours) at five sections for two different conditions of cascade dam break.

Time of rupture of dam B_1 (sec.)	Time of rupture of dam B_2 (sec.)	SECTION AT DAM B_1		SECTION AT DAM B_2		SECTION 181		SECTION 211		SECTION 241	
		A	B	A	B	A	B	A	B	A	B
300	300	1.00 (0.00)	1.00 (0.00)	1.00 (0.00)	1.13 (0.67)	0.43 (2.03)	0.47 (2.19)	0.41 (2.67)	0.44 (2.84)	0.40 (3.17)	0.43 (3.34)
	1800	1.00 (0.00)	1.00 (0.00)	1.00 (0.00)	1.20 (0.68)	0.45 (2.06)	0.49 (2.37)	0.43 (2.72)	0.45 (3.01)	0.41 (3.22)	0.44 (3.49)
	3600	1.00 (0.00)	1.00 (0.00)	1.07 (0.68)	1.21 (0.68)	0.47 (2.20)	0.50 (2.62)	0.44 (2.85)	0.46 (3.23)	0.43 (3.34)	0.44 (3.71)
1800	300	1.00 (0.00)	1.00 (0.00)	1.00 (0.00)	1.00 (0.85)	0.40 (2.40)	0.47 (2.44)	0.39 (2.97)	0.44 (3.09)	0.39 (3.44)	0.43 (3.58)
	1800	1.00 (0.00)	1.00 (0.00)	1.00 (0.00)	1.17 (1.00)	0.43 (2.30)	0.49 (2.60)	0.41 (2.94)	0.45 (3.24)	0.40 (3.43)	0.43 (3.72)
	3600	1.00 (0.00)	1.00 (0.00)	1.00 (0.00)	1.19 (1.11)	0.46 (2.35)	0.50 (2.84)	0.43 (3.01)	0.46 (3.46)	0.42 (3.51)	0.44 (3.93)
3600	300	1.00 (0.00)	1.00 (0.00)	1.00 (0.00)	1.00 (0.95)	0.37 (3.00)	0.46 (2.69)	0.37 (3.51)	0.43 (3.34)	0.36 (3.83)	0.42 (3.84)
	1800	1.00 (0.00)	1.00 (0.00)	1.00 (0.00)	1.02 (1.18)	0.40 (2.78)	0.48 (2.80)	0.39 (3.33)	0.44 (3.44)	0.38 (3.78)	0.43 (3.94)
	3600	1.00 (0.00)	1.00 (0.00)	1.00 (0.00)	1.14 (1.47)	0.43 (2.63)	0.49 (3.01)	0.41 (3.27)	0.45 (3.64)	0.41 (3.76)	0.44 (4.13)

A - Simultaneous dam failure B - Sucessive dam failure

H^*MAX (TIME)

TABLE 2 - Maximum water heights - H^*MAX - (dimensionless) and corresponding instants (hours) at five sections for two different conditions of cascade dam break.

of the maximum water levels and maximum discharges at downstream sections but the contrary occur in respect of the arrival time of that peaks.

4.3 - Three dams case

With the increase in the number of the dams the general conclusions are more difficult. However for the case presented in Figure 3. The main results are presented graphically on Figures 4 to 7. For two situations: simultaneous rupture and rupture in cascade.

As a general remark it can be concluded that the rupture in cascade is more unfavourable in respect of the maximum water levels and maximum discharges at downstream sections but is more favourable in respect of the arrival time of the peaks of water levels and discharges.

5 - CONCLUDING REMARKS

The most unfavorable flood effects along a river valley, with several dams in cascade, is not always obtained by the simple consideration of the most severe rupture conditions at each of the dams. This can be explained by the different superposition effects of the flood waves generated in each dam.

The results presented by the authors in this paper show that it is important to select a methodology to choose the parameters values and rupture conditions in order to obtain the most conservative safety envelope according to the objective ofeach study.

The authors well recognize that a much more systematic computational work must be done in order to obtain more general and safe guidelines.

6 - REFERENCES

ALMEIDA, A.B. e RODRIGUES, D. (1984) - Dam failure flood. A case study: Aguieira dam. Proc. of the International Conference on Safety of Dams, Coimbra (paper C 1.4).

ALMEIDA, A.B.e Ornelas, R. (1987) - Simulação de cenários de rotura de barragens do Rio Douro. Conferência Ibero Americana sobre Aproveitamentos Hidráulicos, Lisboa.

BELLOS, V. and SAKKAS, J.G. (1987) - 1-D dam break flood-wave propagation on dry bed. Journal of Hydraulic Engineering, Vol. 113, No. 12, December, pp. 1510-1524.

CHAUDHRY, M.H., HUSSAINI, M.Y. (1983) - Second-order finite difference methods for transient-flow analysis. Applied Mechanics, Bioengineering, and Fluids Engineering Conference, Houston, Texas.

FENNEMA, R.J., and CHAUDHRY, M.H. (1986) - Explicit numerical schemes for unsteady free-surface flows with shocks. Water Resource. Res., 22(13), 1923-1930.

FRANCO, A.B. (1988) - Simulação Numérica de Cheias Provocadas por Roturas de Barragens em Série. A dissertation submitted in partial fulfillment of the requirements for the degree of

Master of Science. Instituto Superior Técnico, Technical University of Lisbon.

FREAD, D.L. (1979) - DAMBRK: The NWS Dam-Break Flood Forecasting Model. Office of Hydrology, National Weather Service (NWS), Silver Spring, Maryland 20910, November 9.

GARCIA, R. and KAHAWITA, R.A. (1986) - Numerical solution of the St. Venant equations with the MacCormack finite-difference scheme. Int. J. Numer. Meth. in Fluids, 6, 259-274.

MacCORMACK, R.W. (1971) - Numerical solution of the interaction of a shock wave with a laminar boundary layer. Lectures Notes in Physics. Springer-Verlag, Vol.8, pp. 151-163.

RICHTMYER, R.D. and MORTON, K.W. (1967) - Difference methods for initial value problems. 2nd Ed., Interscience Publishers, New York, N.Y.

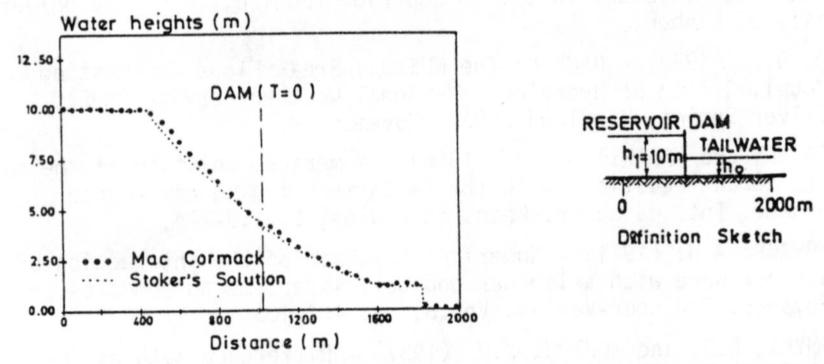

Fig.1 - Water-surface profile along the channel for T=60 s. The dam is instantaneously removed across its entire width. The channel is very wide, horizontal and frictionless. $h_0/h_1 = 0.004$. The example is reproduced from (Fennema and Chaudhry, 1987).

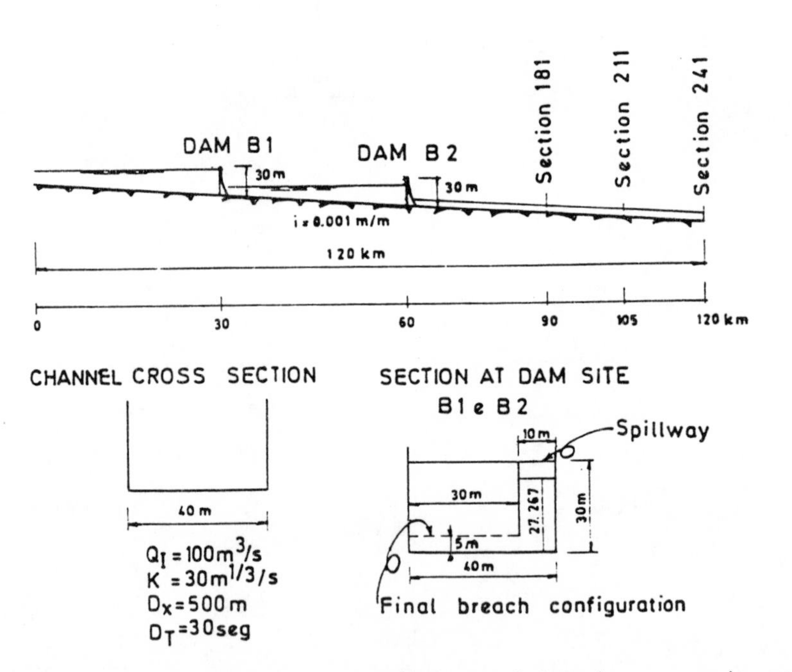

Fig. 2 - Definition conditions of two dams cascade rupture.

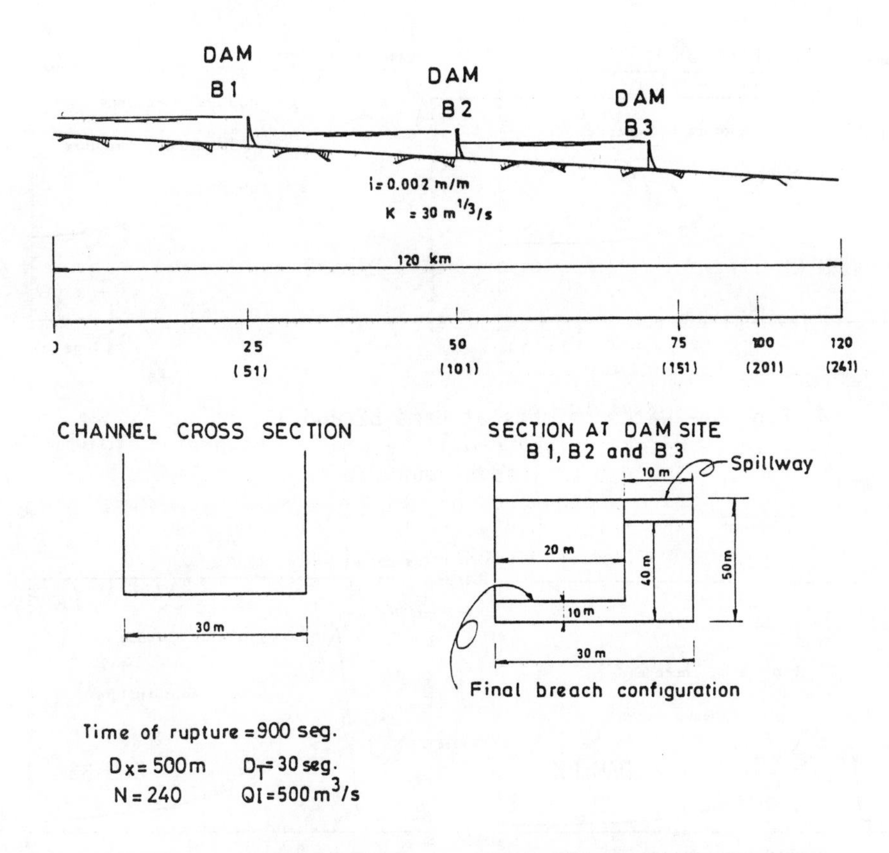

Fig. 3 - Definition conditions of three dams cascade rupture.

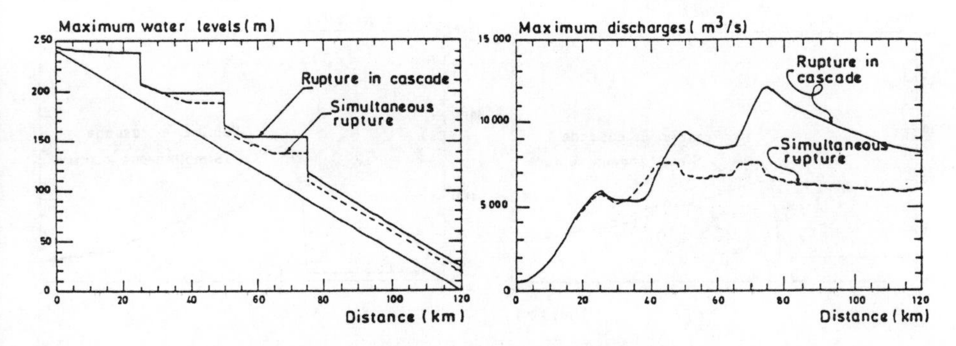

Fig.4 - Maximum water levels and maximum discharges along the channel.

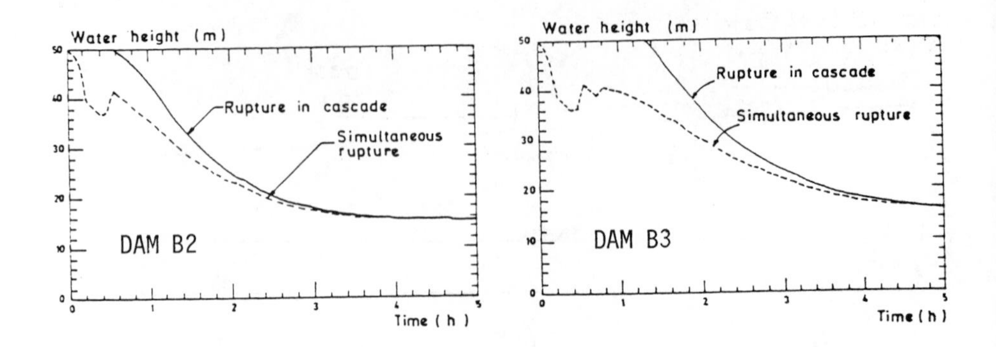

Fig. 5 - Water heights at dams B2 and B3.

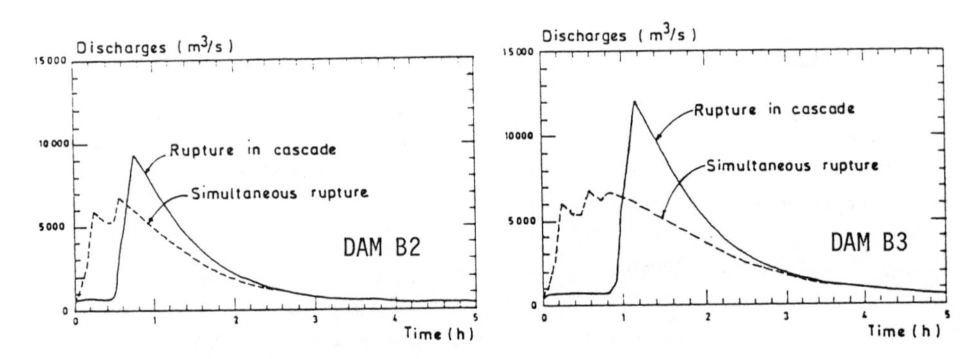

Fig. 6 - Discharges (m^3/s) at dams B2 and B3.

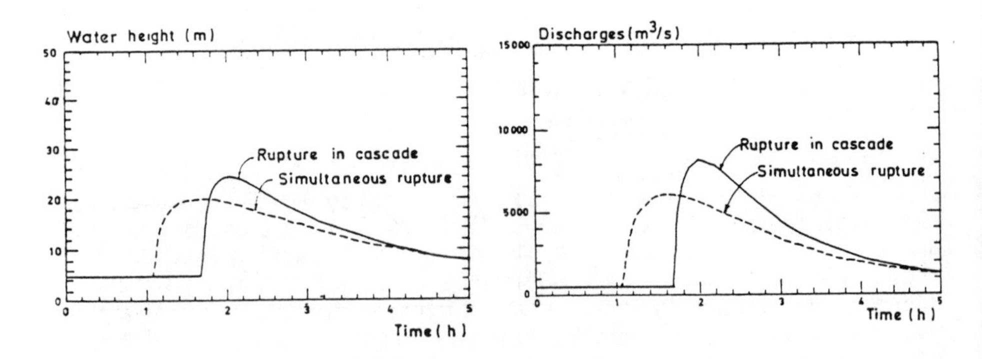

Fig. 7 - Water heights and discharges at section 241.

PAPER G4

International Conference on
RIVER FLOOD HYDRAULICS
17-20 September, 1990

CRITICAL FLOW IN A TWO STAGE CHANNEL

K.W.H. Yuen, L.G. Mouchel & Partners, Weybridge, Surrey
D.W. Knight, School of Civil Engineering, University of Birmingham, B15 2TT

SUMMARY: The results of an experimental investigation into critical flow in a two stage channel are presented. They indicate that for the particular geometry tested traditional methods tend to overestimate the critical depth. The method of Blalock & Sturm appears promising, but it relies heavily on knowing sub section friction factors accurately.

1. INTRODUCTION

With increasing use being made of two stage channels in flood alleviation schemes and a renewed interest in dambreak analysis applied to natural valley shapes, there is a need for a better understanding of the concept of critical flow in channels with complex geometries. The unique relationship between depth and discharge and the correct location of control points are important issues for hydraulic engineers. The authors have recently undertaken an experimental study of critical flow in a smooth trapezoidal compound channel as part of a larger study into Froude and Reynolds number influence on boundary shear stress distributions ($0.5 < Fr < 3.5$). In the critical flow studies some 50 depth values were observed in the compound channel for 9 sets of discharge, all in the out-of-bank condition. In general for each discharge, 5 values of bed slope were set taking the flow from just subcritical to just supercritical. Various parameters were measured (velocity field, energy, momentum, α, β, lateral variation of local Froude number, composite Froude number, undular waves, backwater profiles, etc.) in order to assess the appropriate criteria for critical flow. The analyses of **Petryk & Grant (1978)** and **Blalock & Sturm (1981)** and traditional methodologies (minimum E or M, etc.) were examined. This paper briefly presents some of the main results of this experimental work **(Yuen, 1989).**

2. THEORETICAL CONSIDERATIONS

2.1 Flow in two stage channels

A great deal of attention has recently been focussed on flows in compound or two stage channels because of their importance in river engineering, particularly in flood studies. (See for example **Knight & Demetriou, 1983; Knight & Hamed, 1984; Shiono & Knight, 1989; Knight, Shiono & Pirt, 1989; Knight, Samuels & Shiono, 1990; Elliott & Sellin, 1990; Knight & Shiono, 1990; Myers & Brennan, 1990; Wormleaton & Merrett, 1990).** It is clear that simple one-dimensional hydraulic theories are no longer capable of dealing with the complex flow structures that occur in natural rivers in which there are often significant changes of parameters in the lateral direction. Some knowledge of the general flow field, turbulence structure and boundary shear stress distribution in natural river sections is now often required and is a prerequisite for studying critical flow in these complex geometries.

International Conference on River Flood Hydraulics, edited by W.R.White

2.2 Critical flow in two stage channels

The concept of critical flow has been defined in various ways, **(Jaeger, 1956)** including **(i)** a change in the type of flow, i.e. change from subcritical to supercritical, **(ii)** when the discharge becomes a maximum, i.e. $\partial Q/\partial H = 0$ and **(iii)** when the energy becomes a minimum, i.e. $\partial E/\partial H = 0$. In the case of parallel stream tubes, i.e. in uniform, open channel flow, the numerical values of the critical depth given by all three criteria are identical. This also implies that the momentum is a minimum, i.e. $\partial M/\partial H = 0$. The specific energy, E, and the specific momentum, M, may be expressed in the form

$$E = H + \frac{\alpha Q^2}{2gA^2} \qquad (1) \qquad\qquad M = \bar{z}A + \frac{\beta Q^2}{gA} \qquad (2)$$

where the symbols have their usual meaning. Differentiation of equation **(1)** leads to

$$\frac{dE}{dH} = 1 - \frac{\alpha Q^2}{gA^3}\frac{dA}{dH} + \frac{Q^2}{2gA^2}\frac{d\alpha}{dH} \qquad (3)$$

and for minimum specific energy a compound channel Froude number may be given by

$$Fr_c = \left[\frac{\alpha Q^2 T}{gA^3} - \frac{Q^2}{2gA^2}\frac{d\alpha}{dH}\right]^{\frac{1}{2}} \qquad (4)$$

It has been suggested **(Blalock & Sturm, 1981)** that the non uniformity of the velocity within the cross section, which relates to the term $d\alpha/dH$, may be taken into account by the conveyance relationship

$$\alpha = \sum_{i=1}^{n}\left[\frac{K_i^3}{A_i^2}\right] \Bigg/ \left[\frac{K^3}{A^2}\right] \qquad (5)$$

to give

$$Fr_c = \left[\frac{Q^2}{2gK^3}\left(\frac{\sigma_2\sigma_3}{K} - \sigma_1\right)\right]^{\frac{1}{2}} \qquad (6)$$

where σ_1 - σ_3 are subsection parameters. Alternatively the gradually varied flow equation may be used **(Samuels, 1989)** to give

$$Fr_c = \left[\frac{Q^2 T}{gA^3}\left(\beta - \frac{A}{T}\frac{d\beta}{dH}\right)\right]^{\frac{1}{2}} \qquad (7)$$

Equations **(4)** & **(7)** reduce to the simple one-dimensional version

$$Fr = \left[\frac{Q^2 T}{gA^3}\right]^{\frac{1}{2}} \qquad (8)$$

for the case of $\alpha = \beta = 1$.

3. EXPERIMENTAL APPARATUS, PROCEDURE AND RESULTS

3.1 Experimental apparatus and procedure

The experiments were conducted at the University of Birmingham in a 22m long tilting flume with a specially constructed two stage channel the dimensions of which were b = h = 0.075m, B = 0.225m and s = 1.0. See **Fig.1**. Full details are available elsewhere **(Yuen, 1989)**. The bed slope of the channel was varied from 1.000 x 10^{-3} to 2.337 x 10^{-2} throughout the whole programme, but between 2.046 x 10^{-3} and 3.010 x 10^{-3} for the critical flow studies. Nine values of overbank flow were tested at relative depths, Dr (= (H-h)/H), between 0.05 and 0.5. Several preliminary tests were undertaken to observe the unstable water surface close to the critical flow condition. In general with the discharge fixed at a constant value different flow depths were obtained by varying the bed slope. The instabilities in the water surface were observed and the most significant disturbances were recorded. Because of the non-uniformity in the velocity distributions, the setting of critical flow, at which the cross sectional average Froude number is equal to unity, was difficult to achieve. Prior to detailed velocity measurements, several preliminary trials in which the lateral variation of depth averaged velocity was estimated using a single value at 0.4 of the depth were undertaken over a range of finely controlled discharges. The procedure which was finally adopted to identify the critical flow is summarised as follows:

- (i) Set uniform flow with a constant discharge and with the tailgate set below the main channel bed.
- (ii) Adjust the bed slope of the channel to give in turn S_o = 0.00301, 0.00278, 0.00269, 0.00257, 0.00241 and 0.00204, which was close to critical flow conditions and covered both subcritical and supercritical flow.
- (iii) Observe the pattern of waves on the free surface and record the significance of these disturbances at each setting of the bed slope. Particular notice was taken of undulations appearing on the flood plain adjacent to the main channel.
- (iv) Adjust tailgate until the transition zone appeared approximately 3-5m from the tailgate so that the surface profile was unaffected by the end drop.
- (v) Obtain the water surface profile using the pointer gauges along the whole channel checking the flow regime upstream and downstream of the jump.
- (vi) The surface profile measured in **(v)** was compared with the results from a backwater calculation with a constant resistance coefficient. The calculations were carried out both sides of the hydraulic jump.
- (vii) Point velocities over the full cross-section were measured at selected discharges at which the specific energy was close to a minimum. The depth-averaged velocities and local Froude numbers were evaluated.

3.2 Experimental results

A typical set of velocity data at critical flow is shown in **Fig.1,** and the corresponding α and β coefficients are shown in **Fig.2.** The depths and discharges at which the wave pattern was observed to be the most significant are shown in **Fig.3(a)** and the best fit curve through this data (measured curve) is reproduced in each of the other diagrams in order to aid comparisons . With the discharge held constant, the depth versus specific energy curve was obtained by varying the channel bed slope with particular emphasis being placed on obtaining values close to the minimum specific energy. **Fig.4(a)** shows values for α = 1.0 and **Fig.4(b)** for α = critical values (> 1.0) based on detailed velocity measurements. Similar plots were obtained of momentum, and a representative set for in-bank and out-of-bank flows are shown in **Fig.5** ($\alpha = \beta$ = 1.0 case only). The depths corresponding to the minimum values shown in **Figs. 4 &**

5 are shown plotted against discharge in **Figs. 3(b) & (c)**, together with the fiducial values based on observation from **Fig.3(a)**. **Fig.3(d)** shows the results based on computed backwater profiles through a weak hydraulic jump created in the flume by small adjustments of the slope and tailgate for a given discharge. Backwater calculations were undertaken in both subcritical and supercritical regimes and the critical depth estimated by progressively diminishing the height of the jump.

The velocity measurements were depth averaged at each vertical to give the local Froude number, Fr_d $(=U_{di}\sqrt{(gH_i)})$. The lateral variation of this Froude number is shown in **Fig.(6)** for the 9 depths tested, together with the area mean Froude number based on equation **(8)**. **Fig.7** shows how the average specific energy E_{av}, which was evaluated from averaging the local specific energy E_i $(= H_i + U^2_{di}/2g)$ across the width of the channel, varies with depth. Also shown in **Fig.7** are the specific energy values based on equation **(1)**. **Fig.8** shows the variation of the composite Froude number, Fr_c, based on equation **(6)** for the range of slopes and discharges tested. For each discharge value the depth at which $Fr_c = 1.0$ was noted and these are shown together in **Fig.3(f)**. Also shown on the left hand side of **Fig.8** are some subcritical composite Froude numbers corresponding to $S_o = 0.001$ together with measured values. **Fig.9** shows a direct comparison between all the methodologies and the curves shown in **Figs. 3(a) - (f)**.

4. DISCUSSION OF RESULTS

It is clear from the observation of the undular waves that the flow goes locally supercritical on the edge of the flood plain adjacent to the main channel where the depths are low and the local velocities high. This is borne out by the large measured values of local Froude numbers (up to 1.7) in **Fig.6** and the few pictures that are available of flood flows in natural rivers **(Petryk & Grant, 1978)**. This being so, the appropriate definition of critical flow for the whole channel is open to debate. The data presented here represents the first attempt by the authors to study critical flow experimentally and are somewhat limited by the choice of cross section chosen, since this section was chosen for another but related study. However the results do serve to clarify certain concepts and to compare different methodologies for determining critical flow.

The specific energy depth relationship for a two stage channel does exhibit a single minimum for overbank flow the value of which varies fairly systematically with relative depth as **Figs. 4, 5 & 7** show. However the E_{min} values based on equation **(1)** are significantly larger than those based on laterally integrating the local specific energy values. **Figs.3 (b) & (c)** show that the minimum specific energy or momentum values tend to give larger critical depths than those observed in practice. Use of the actual α and β values does not make a significant difference in this particular channel due to the relatively small flood plain width and deep main channel ($B/b = 3.0$, $b/h = 1.0$). However very large α and β values have been recorded elsewhere in different geometries. The terms $d\alpha/dH$ and $d\beta/dH$ may be determined from **Fig.2**. It is interesting to note that the critical flow α and β values are slightly larger than those for subcritical flow at comparable depths in the same geometry, possibly due to the different turbulence levels affecting the primary and secondary flow fields.

The area average Froude number, Fr_{av}, based on equation **(8)** was generally close to unity at observed critical conditions as **Fig.6** shows ($0.904 < Fr_{av} < 1.024$). However the local values based on depth averaged velocities depart significantly from unity ($0.5 < Fr_d < 1.7$) and indicate regions of subcritical and supercritical flow occurring at different lateral positions within the channel for a given discharge. The variations of these local Froude numbers with relative depth ($0.1 < Dr < 0.5$) at a given lateral position is complex. The composite Froude number given by equation **(6)** is difficult to evaluate on account of the sub area friction factors and choice of division planes. Using vertical division planes and excluding momentum transfer effects, **Figs. 3(f)** and **8** show that the critical depths are reasonably close to those observed for the condition $Fr_C = 1$.

5. CONCLUSIONS

Critical flow in a two stage channel is difficult to determine to within ±10% either experimentally or theoretically. Based on the local Froude number it is clear that regions of supercritical and sub critical flow can exist simultaneously within the same channel section. There is a strong tendency for critical flow to first occur on the edge of the flood plain adjacent to the main river channel, particularly at low submergence depths. Further experimental studies are required with different geometries to understand this interesting flow phenomenon.

6. REFERENCES

Blalock M E and Sturm T W, 1981, Minimum specific energy in compound open channel flow, ASCE, J.Hyd Div, 107, HY6, pp 699-717

Elliott S C A and Sellin R H J, 1990, The SERC flood channel facility: skewed channel experiments, IAHR, J.Hyd Res, 28, No.3.

Jaeger C, 1956, Engineering Fluid Mechanics, Chapter III, Blackie & Sons Ltd.

Knight D W Demetriou J D, 1983 , Flood plain and main channel flow interaction, ASCE, J.Hyd Eng, 109, HY8, pp 1073-1092.

Knight D W and Hamed M E, 1984, Boundary shear in symmetrical compound channels, ASCE, J.Hyd Eng, 110 , HY10, pp 1412-1430.

Knight D W, Shiono K and Pirt J, 1989, Prediction of depth mean velocity and discharge in natural rivers with overbank flow, in Hydraulic and Environmental Modelling of Coastal, Estuarine and River Waters, ed. Falconer, Goodwin & Matthew, Gower Technical Press, pp 419-428.

Knight D W, Samuels P G and Shiono K, 1990, River flow simulation : research and developments, J.Inst.Water and Environmental Management, 4, No.2.

Knight D W and Shiono K, 1990, Turbulence measurements in a shear layer region of a compound channel, J. IAHR, 28, No.3.

Myers W R C and Brennan, 1990, Flow resistance in compound channels, IAHR, J.Hyd Res, 28,No.3.

Petryk S and Grant E U, 1978, Critical flow in rivers with flood plains, ASCE, J.Hyd Div, 104, HY5, pp 583-594.

Samuels P G, 1989, Backwater lengths in rivers, Proc I CE, Part 2, 87, December, pp 571 - 582.

Shiono K and Knight D W, 1989, Vertical and transverse measurements of Reynolds stress in a shear region of a compound channel, 7th Int.Symp. on Turbulent Shear Flows, Stanford, USA, August, Vol.2, Paper 28-1.

Wormleaton P R and Merret D, 1990, An improved method of calculation for steady uniform flow in prismatic main channel/flood plain sections, IAHR, J.Hyd.Res. 28 No.3

Yuen, K W H, 1989, A study of boundary shear stress, flow resistance and momentum transfer in open channels with simple and compound trapezoidal cross section, PhD thesis, University of Birmingham.

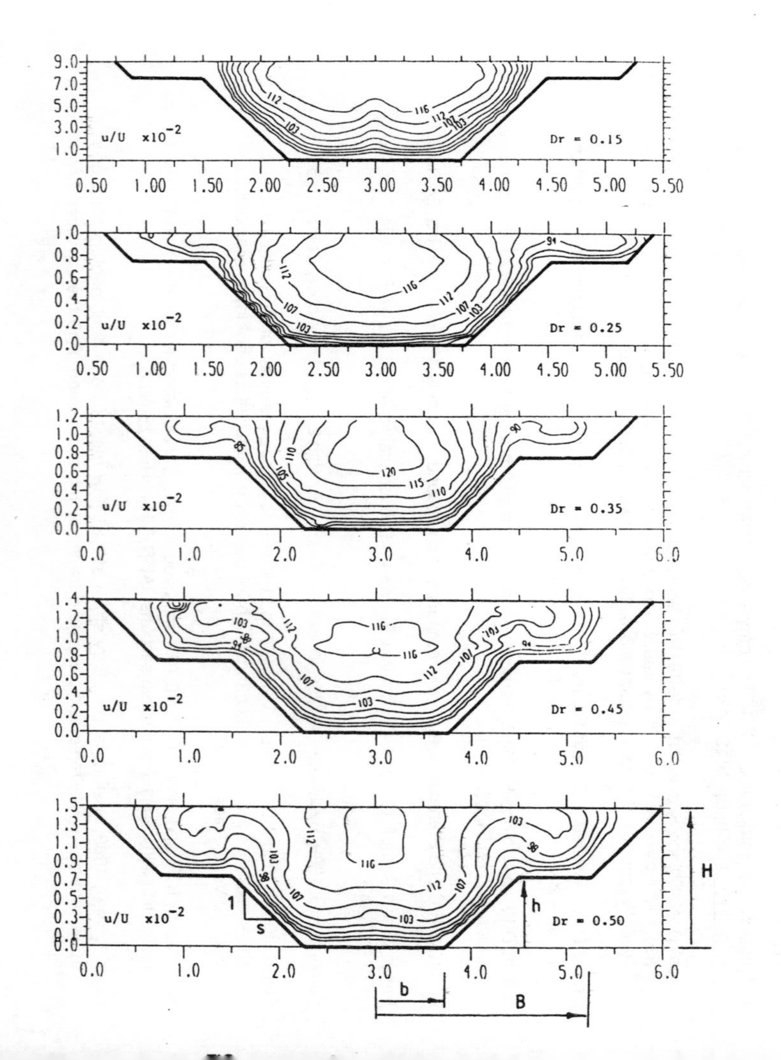

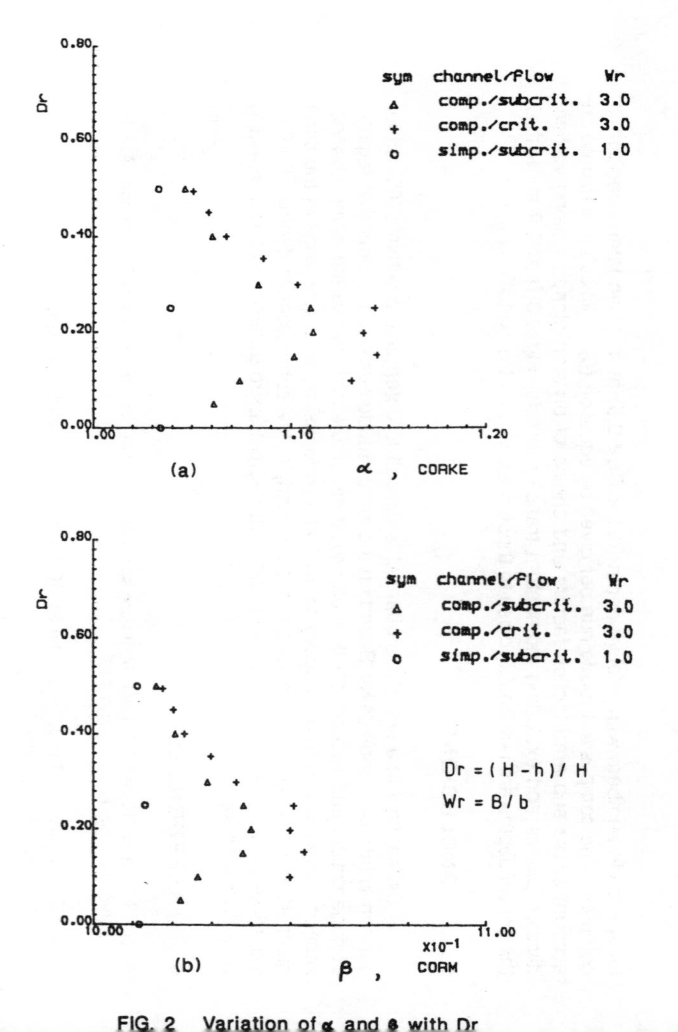

FIG. 2 Variation of α and β with Dr

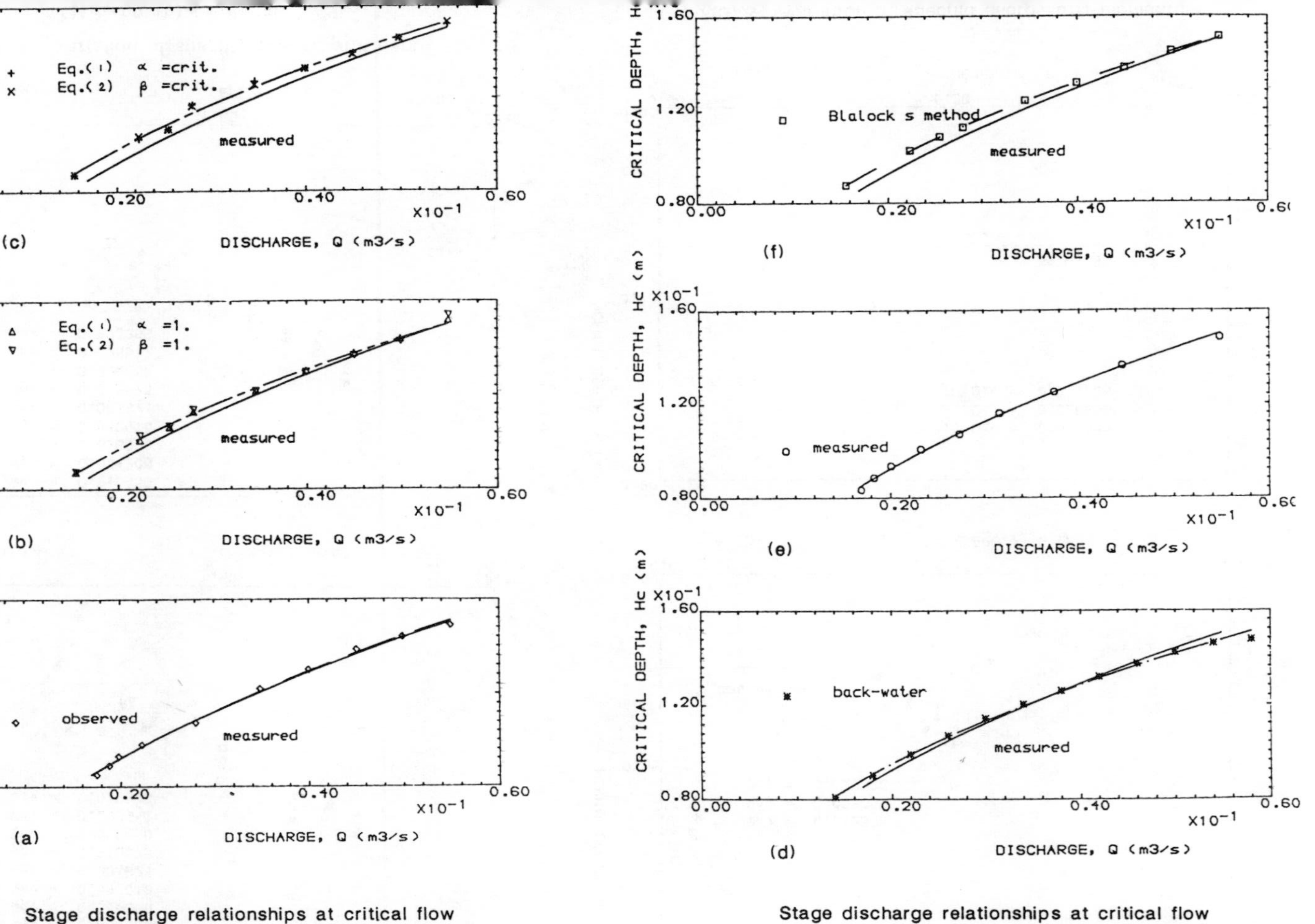

FIG. 3 Stage discharge relationships at critical flow

Stage discharge relationships at critical flow

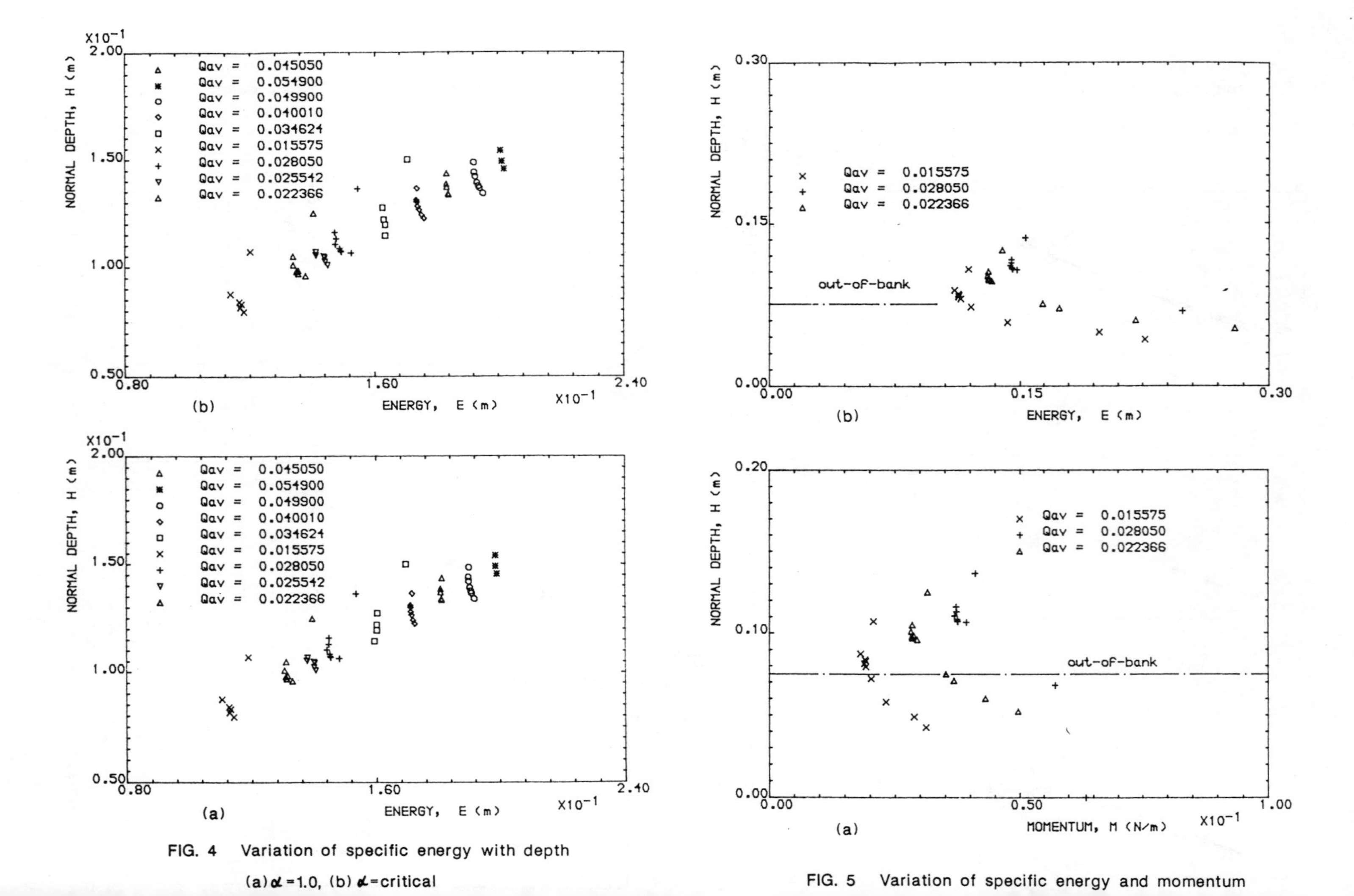

FIG. 4 Variation of specific energy with depth

(a) $\alpha = 1.0$, (b) α=critical

FIG. 5 Variation of specific energy and momentum

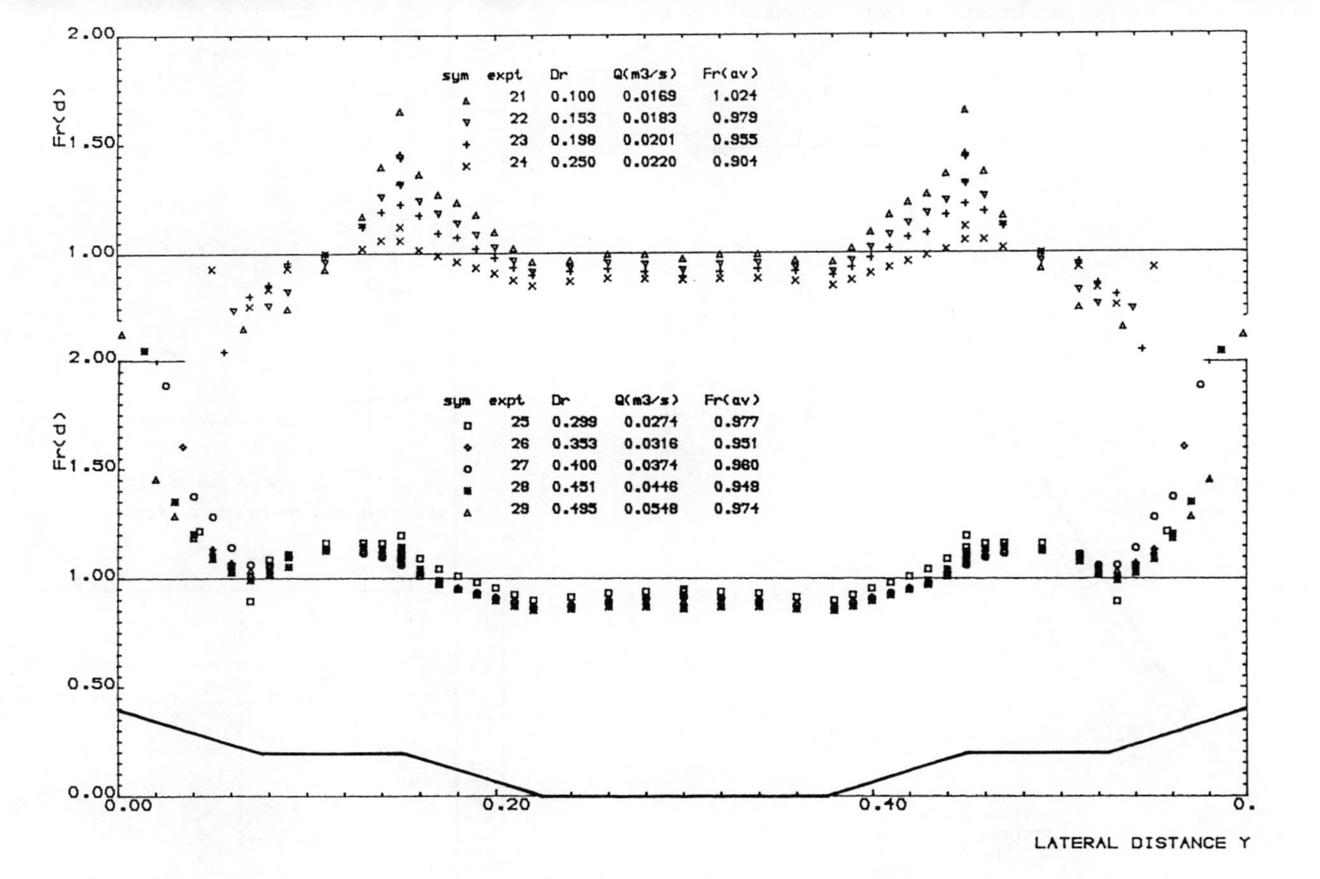

FIG. 6 Lateral distribution of local Froude number at critical flow

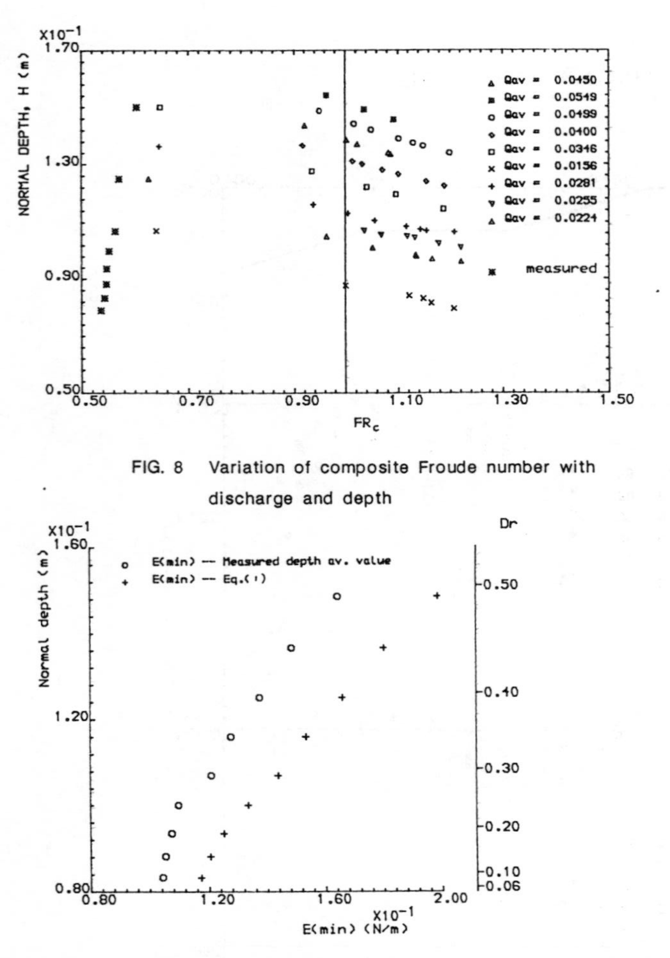

FIG. 8 Variation of composite Froude number with discharge and depth

FIG. 7 Comparison of minimum specific energy values

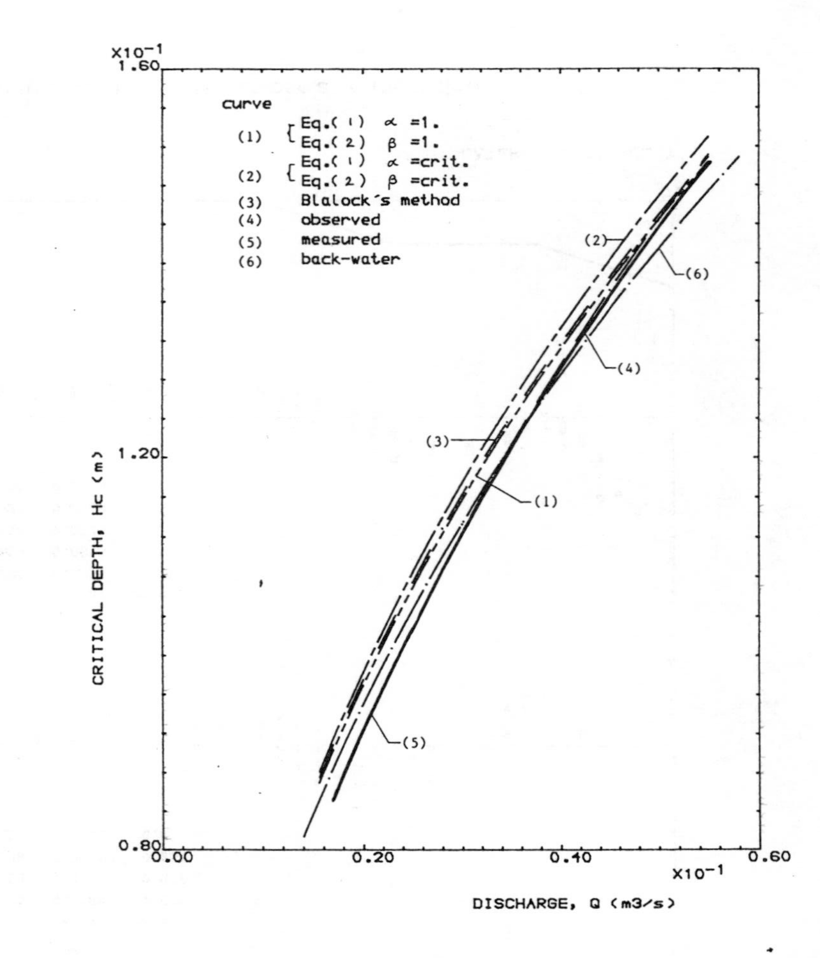

FIG. 9 Comparison of stage discharge relationships at critical flow

Sediment Transport and Morphological Effects

International Conference on
RIVER FLOOD HYDRAULICS
17-20 September, 1990

HYDRAULIC PERFORMANCE OF ENVIRONMENTALLY ACCEPTABLE CHANNELS

Dr C E Reeve and Dr R Bettess

Hydraulics Research Ltd, Wallingford

ABSTRACT

In recent years, environmental, ecological and recreational issues have been impinging more forcibly on the design of land drainage and flood protection schemes. Engineers have been asked to design schemes with conservation and enhancement of the environment as one of the important criteria. This has encouraged the adoption of 'natural' looking water courses. For example, the retention of river bends and aquatic vegetation growth are desirable from an environmental viewpoint, as is vegetation on the flood plain.

Several schemes have been constructed with these considerations in mind, for example, River Roding and River Leam.

The hydraulic analysis of such schemes, however, can be complicated.

In the work described in this paper the most widely used environmentally acceptable design options are identified and the hydraulic problems associated with them described.

As a first stage to providing guidelines HR have been funded, by eight of the UK Water Authorities, to identify methods which will allow the hydraulic performance of environmentally acceptable channels to be assessed.

Methods were identified from the available literature. Unfortunately there was no opportunity under the scope of the project to test the methods either in the field or in the laboratory. Though we believe that these methods are as far as we can tell the best available, this does not imply that they are completely satisfactory.

There is a danger in producing guidelines such as these that they tend to fix ideas and approaches to particular problems. We hope that in this case, by demonstrating the paucity of information on some of the topics, this paper will act to encourage further work and the generation of new ideas.

International Conference on River Flood Hydraulics, edited by W.R.White

INTRODUCTION

The most efficient engineering solution for conveying water may not always be the most acceptable environmental solution. Whereas the hydraulically most efficient channel may be a straight, regular channel this is rarely the most acceptable environmental option. In recent years, environmental, ecological and recreational issues have impinged more forcibly on the design of land drainage and flood protection schemes. Engineers have been asked to design schemes with conservation and enhancement of the environment as one of the important criteria. This has encouraged the adoption of watercourses which are the best environmental solution viz water courses which provide the best balance from hydraulic, ecological, morphological and maintenance viewpoints. For example, the retention of river bends and aquatic vegetation growth are desirable from environmental considerations as is vegetation on the floodplain.

Brookes (1988) and Purseglove (1988) give details of the physical effects of conventional river channel engineering methods.

Several schemes have been constructed with these considerations in mind, for example, River Roding and River Leam.

At present appropriate methods to analyse the hydraulics of such channels are lacking.

ENVIRONMENTALLY ACCEPTABLE CHANNEL FEATURES

Some of the most important environmentally acceptable channel features, which have been identified in the literature, are described in this section. More information on practices which can further the conservation of wildlife on rivers can be found in Water Space Amenity Commission, 1983; Lewis and Williams, 1984; Nature Conservancy Council, 1983; Countryside Commission, 1987, 1988; Brookes, 1988; Purseglove, 1988. Figure 1 indicates the hydraulic problems associated with these channel features.

Multi-stage/Compound channels The principle of multistage channels is that flood alleviation is achieved by containing high flows within wide flood berms above the normal water level. With care, this can be achieved with no disturbance to the existing river channel. The creation of flood berms may result in a reduction in the self-scouring capacity of the low flow channel which may lead to sediment deposition. Advantages of multi-stage channels to wildlife include the retention of existing channel habitats and the re-creation of low-lying river margins. The advantages to wildlife conservation and fisheries of leaving the channel untouched may be lost if the banks are totally disturbed. If possible, berms should be created on one bank only, or on alternate banks, so that only 30-50% of the bank community is disturbed at any point.

Shallow-water berms The principle behind this technique is the creation of a shallow underwater marginal shelf to the river channel. Engineering advantages include the provision of additional flood capacity, whilst maintaining the existing lowflow channel and bank toe protection through the establishment of marginal beds of emergent plants. Biologically berms increase the variety of water depth and flow conditions in the river channel and form important marginal habitats in their own right. From an engineering viewpoint shallow-water berms have the disadvantage that they may cause siltation.

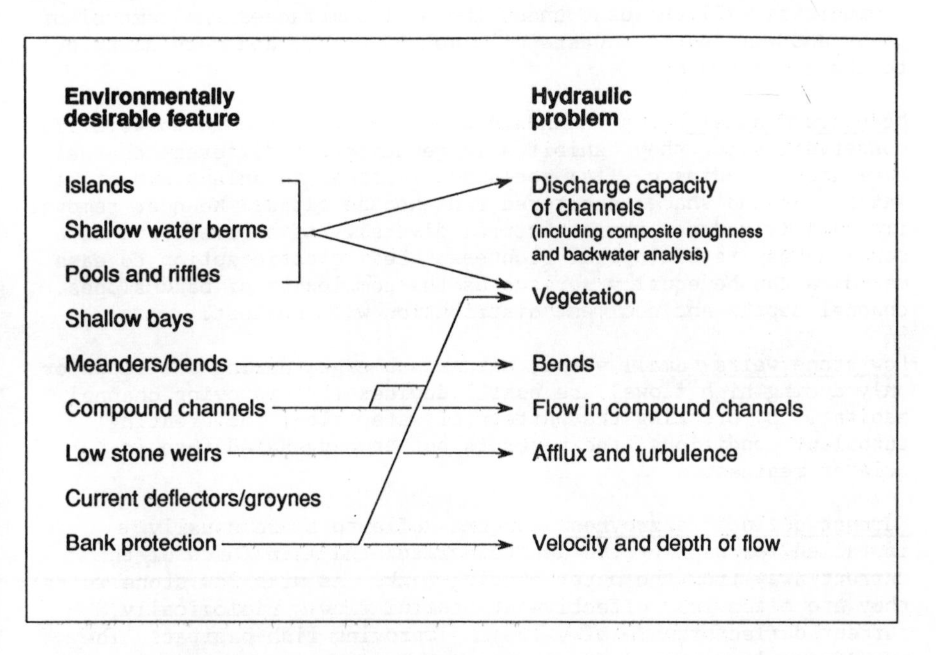

Figure 1 Hydraulic problems associated with environmentally desirable channel features

Islands Islands, large or small, are important refuges for animals and plants. Remote from human disturbance and grazing animals, islands may support different plant communities compared with more accessible banks. By increasing the length of river bank, islands increase the richness or diversity of 'edge' habitats for wildlife.

Shallow bays Sheltered from the main water flow, shallow bays add further to the diversity of river habitats. Fish fry benefit from the rich feeding conditions provided by shallow bays; the shallow water also protects them from large predators such as pike.

Pools and riffles A smooth, uniform bed is reflected by low species diversity: to encourage a wide variety of wildlife it is essential to have a variety of physical habitats. If a channel has to be regraded therefore every effort should be made to leave riffles and deep pools untouched. Turbulent, shallow water in riffles increases oxygenation of the water. The channel bed is usually gravel or coarse sediment which provides the right conditions for spawning form any fish species; and the right habitat for a variety of insect larvae, which may later provide fish with food. Deep, quiet pools provide the opposite: less rich in oxygen, but more stable and rich in organic matter and sheltered. The two extremes of bed conditions support different communities and in part provide the different requirements of fish at different stages of their life cycle. In alluvial rivers, if pools and riffles are removed they may reform naturally but all the communities will be lost; under these circumstances the removal of pools and riffles is a waste of time and money, and very damaging to the environment.

Meanders/Channel bends Meanders are of key importance to wildlife conservation for they exhibit a large number of different channel habitats - eroding cliffs; pools and riffles; turbulent and still water; sun and shade; sheltered and exposed sites. Meander removal immediately reduces the structural diversity of a river, and as a consequence its biological richness. Less drastic action to ease meanders can be equally serious as the complexity of bank slopes, channel depths and sediment distribution will be lost.

Low stone weirs Small weirs, either submerged during all flows or only during high flows, are useful devices for improving channel habitat. By breaking the pattern of water flow, and creating turbulent conditions, the water is better oxygenated than in quieter reaches.

Current deflectors/groynes Current deflectors are usually installed for bank protection to deflect the main force of the current away from the outer eroding bank. As with low stone weirs they are often less effective at bankful flow. Biologically, current deflectors are of value in improving fish habitat. They provide shelter from fast flowing water as well as increasing flow velocities in other sectors of the channel. In addition they provide hard substrate for colonization by algae and mosses. During low flows exposed groynes may simulate temporary shoal habitats - suitable for colonization by flowering plants. The introduction of groynes may increase the biological productivity of a reach since they increase the length of channel boundary where most of the biological activity occurs.

Bank protection Biologically the channel margins are the most productive zone. It is important when considering bank protection that attempts are made to retain or permit the reestablishment of natural plant and animal communities. Given that bank protection is required it is preferable on both aesthetic and wildlife conservation grounds that natural materials - either living or dead - are used rather than man-made materials. The benefits of using natural materials are two-fold. Firstly they provide a variability of character that enables more rapid establishment of plant and animal communities. Secondly, since all bank protection materials will eventually deteriorate, it is preferable to use natural materials since the degradation of this material will present less of a hazard.

A wide variety of natural bank protection is available. Lewis and Williams (1984) give many examples. Which type of bank protection is used in a given situation will depend on local, especially soil conditions. For example, plant types must be chosen for the soil type, water table condition, bank profile etc. which are present.

Hemphill and Bramley (1989) give details of the protection offered by both natural and man-made bank protection.

ASSESSING HYDRAULIC PERFORMANCE

The plan of a river reach which incorporates several of the environmentally desirable features described in the previous section is given in Figure 2. The water level along this reach under both low and high flow conditions is required. In this section the procedure by which this can be achieved is outlined.

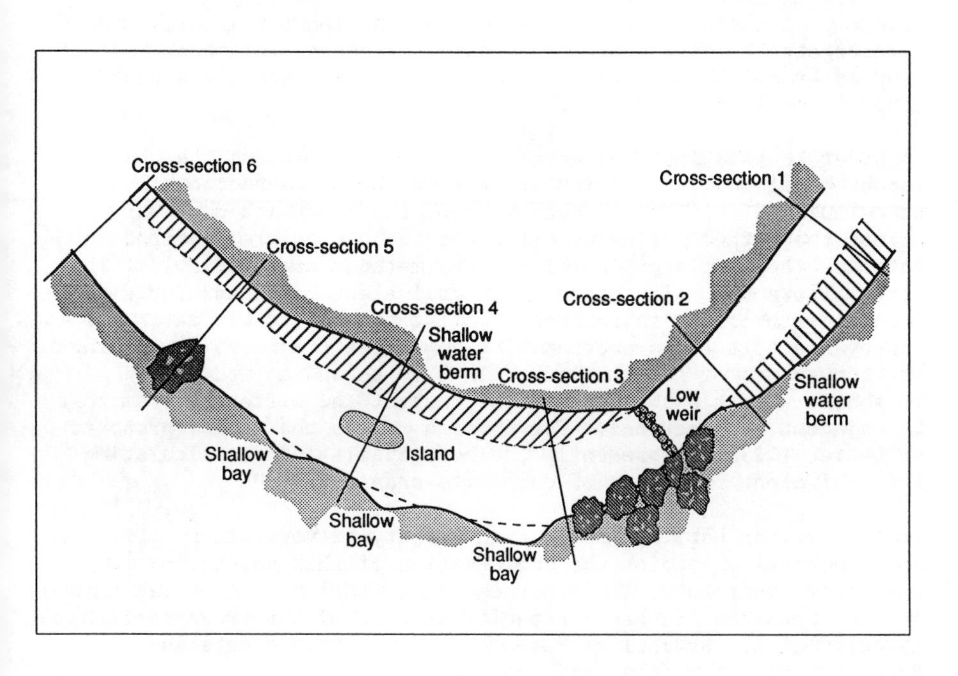

Figure 2 Plan of a hypothetical environmentally acceptable channel

If a straight, uniform channel was being considered the hydraulic calculations and water levels could be determined from a steady flow, backwater, equation or from unsteady flow calculations. The philosophy that we have adopted is that for a channel with environmental features the same calculation procedure can be adopted but the calculation of conveyance at each cross-section must be modified to take account of the different features. Thus allowance must be made for the extra head loss at bends, the conveyance must be calculated for a non-regular channel shape and must take account of variations in roughness across the section due to differences in vegetation. A detailed description of how these calculations may be performed is not given here; recommended techniques for carrying out these calculations are given in Hydraulics Research (1989).

It is assumed that the variation in channel geometry and roughness characteristics along the channel are known; cross-sections at which data is given are shown on Figure 2. The discharge and stage at the downstream section are required.

The river reach includes a number of shallow bays. These have minimal influence on the main channel flow and thus their presence can be ignored in the hydraulic analysis.

The existence of a bend in the channel reach will result in an increase in the resistance relative to that in a straight channel. A number of studies have been carried out in order to investigate the flow resistance caused by bends. Of these that of Leopold et al (1960) requires least information about the bend under investigation and is the simplest to use.

In order to establish the water level variation along the channel reach the discharge capacity at each of the cross-sections must be calculated. If, on the other hand, the roughness does vary across the wetted perimeter different techniques are required to estimate the discharge capacity. Two methods are available. The first allows the calculation of an equivalent roughness for a channel with composite roughness whilst the second estimates the conveyance of a cross-section with composite roughness by summing the conveyance of sub-sections. In this second method the roughness within a sub-section is constant and different from that in adjacent sub-sections. For British rivers the method proposed by Lotter (1933) is presently the best available for calculating the equivalent roughness of composite channels.

Rivers provide habitats for a rich variety of vegetation. From an environmental viewpoint the conservation of this vegetation is extremely important. The presence of vegetation must be taken into account when the discharge capacity at each of the cross-sections is calculated. Hydraulics Research (1989) gives a detailed description of the flow resistance due to vegetation.

If there is dense vegetation growth on the shallow water berms at cross-sections 2 and 4 there will be minimal flow through this part of the cross-section; the discharge capacity of this part of the section should be set to zero.

When calculating the discharge capacity at cross-sections 3, 4 and 5 the extra flow resistance due to the channel bend must be taken into account.

At cross-section 4 the presence of the island and the vegetation on the island must be taken into account when assessing the discharge capacity.

In many cases the flow behaviour in natural channels can be considered to be steady and backwater analysis techniques used to calculate the water surface profile.

The low stone weir upstream of cross-section 2 will lead to an increase in water level at cross-section 3. Flow across low stone weirs should be analysed using standard weir equations. Which of these equations to use depends on the ratio of upstream head to the weir length in the direction of flow.

Using the stage at cross-section 3, calculated by considering the effect of the low weir, as a downstream stage and the discharge capacity of cross-sections 4, 5 and 6 a backwater calculation can be used to calculate the stage at cross-sections 4, 5 and 6.

Morphological effects In their natural state rivers are often considered to be in regime. This is a state of dynamic equilibrium where the channel dimensions are determined by sediment supply and type and the magnitude and frequency of occurrence of discharge. River improvement schemes often change the capacity of a channel to transport sediment causing areas of deposition and erosion. These effects can in some cases lead to a long term maintenance commitment by the drainage authority. Brookes (1988) and Hydraulics Research (1987) describe the morphological effect of different river engineering works.

Since river work can affect channel morphology it is important that an estimate of the rate of sediment transport is made at the design stage of new channels or when channel improvements are planned. There are many sediment transport theories. White, Milli and Crabbe (1975) compared nineteen of these theories. They concluded that the most reliable theory, over a wide range of flow conditions and particle characteristics, is that of Ackers and White (1973).

SUMMARY

In this paper the hydraulic problems associated with the most commonly used environmentally desirable channel features are identified. The procedure required to assess the hydraulic performance of a channel reach which incorporates a number of thesefeatures is outlined. Hydraulics Research (1989) recommends suitable techniques for carrying out the detailed analysis.

RECOMMENDATIONS

Further research is essential to validate and improve the recommended procedures. The first stage of this further research should be to assemble all existing information on the hydraulic performance of environmentally acceptable designs.

Specific research projects should be initiated to investigate the following :

* Discharge capacity/conveyance of channels with composite roughness
* Multi-stage channels
* Flow resistance due to vegetation
* Flow resistance due to channel bends
* Low stone weirs

It would be beneficial if present and future schemes that incorporate environmentally acceptable design options are monitored. This data will allow the hydraulic impact of environmentally acceptable design options, under prototype conditions, to be ascertained. Armed with this information improved procedures can be developed.

ACKNOWLEDGEMENTS

The work described in this paper was funded by eight of the UK Water Authorities each of which contributed a member to a steering group. The authors would like to thank the members of the steering group for their assistance and encouragement.

REFERENCES

Ackers P and W R White, 1973. Sediment transport : a new approach and analysis. ASCE. Journal of Hydraulics Division. HY11. 99. pp2041-2060.

Brookes A, 1988. Channelised Rivers : Perspectives for environmental management. John Wiley and Sons.

Countryside Commission, 1987. Changing river landscapes : A study of river valley landscapes. Publication number CCP 238.

Countryside Commission, 1988. The water industry in the countryside. Publication number CCP 239.

Hemphill R and M Bramley, 1989. Protection of river and Canal banks. Butterworths.

Hydraulics Research report SR116, 1987. Morphological effects of river works. A review of current practice.

Hydraulics Research report EX1799, 1989. Assessing the hydraulic performance of environmentally acceptable channels.

Leopold L B, R A Bagnold, M G Wolman and L M Brush, 1960. Flow resistance in sinuous or irregular channels. United States Geological Survey Prof. Paper 282-D. pp 111-134

Lewis G and G Williams, 1984. Rivers and Wildlife handbook : A guide to practices which further the conservation of wildlife on rivers. RSPB and RSNC.

Lotter G K, 1933. Considerations on hydraulic design of channels with different roughness on walls. Trans, All-Union Scientific Research Institute of Hydraulic Engineering, Leningrad. 9. pp238-241.

Nature Conservancy Council, 1983. Nature conservation and river engineering.

Purseglove J, 1988. Taming the flood : A history and natural history of rivers and wetlands. Oxford University Press.

Water Space Amenity Commission, 1983. Conservation and land drainage guidelines.

White W R, H Milli and A D Crabbe, 1975. Sediment transport theories : a review. Proc. ICE, Part 2, 59, pp265-292.

International Conference on
RIVER FLOOD HYDRAULICS
17-20 September, 1990

PARTIAL CUT-OFF OF MEANDER LOOPS - A COMPARISON OF MATHEMATICAL AND PHYSICAL MODEL RESULTS

Y.R. Fares, School of Civil Engineering,
University of Birmingham, Birmingham, England, U.K.
J.G. Herbertson, Department of Civil Engineering,
University of Glasgow, Glasgow, Scotland, U.K.

SUMMARY

Typical results from a mathematical and a physical model which simulate conditions at the upstream end of a partially cut-off meander loop are presented in the form of water surface and depth-averaged velocity profiles. These are compared and found to very adequately verify the mathematical model when the cut-off channel bed is relatively high compared with that of the main channel.

INTRODUCTION

Following from a proposal to use partial neck cut-off of a meander to stabilize conditions in the meander loop, the authors undertook an investigation of the effects of the cut-off on the main channel flow at the upstream end of the cut-off channel. Both mathematical and physical models were constructed. The river channel was represented by a wide gentle bend and the flow entering the cut-off channel was modelled as flow spilling over a broad crested side weir.

The basis of the 2D depth averaged mathematical model has been reported previously (Herbertson and Fares 1988a and 1988b). The model has since undergone further development (Fares 1989). The present paper gives the comparison between the results of the modified model and those obtained from the physical laboratory model. Attention is concentrated on comparisons of measured and predicted water surface and depth-averaged velocity profiles. Where appropriate mention is made of corresponding results from a bend only series of tests.

THE LABORATORY MODEL AND TEST PROGRAMME

The principal dimensions of the laboratory model are shown on Fig. 1. Two series of tests were run, the first with the side weir closed off to give bend only conditions and the second with discharge permitted over the weir, representing flow into a partial cut-off channel. In the latter case 13 runs were made

International Conference on River Flood Hydraulics, edited by W.R.White

for water surface profile measurements and 5 for the measurement of velocity distributions (Fares 1989). For the purposes of this paper, results from only two test runs in each category will be considered. Details of these are given in Tables 1 and 2. These particular tests have been chosen in order to demonstrate the effect of high and low side weirs.

WATER SURFACE PROFILES

High side weir - as may be seen from Fig. 2 there is very good agreement throughout between the mathematical and physical model results. The following discussion will consider the regions upstream of, along and downstream of the intersection separately and will, in addition to the results shown on Fig. 2, draw on the results obtained from the bend only tests. It should be noted that the region downstream of the intersection is outwith the scope of the mathematical model and hence only the laboratory model results will be considered.

(i) Upstream of the intersection (bend angles 0° to 25°) the radial and longitudinal profiles are virtually the same as for the bend without side overflow. Superelevation effects predominate to such an extent that flow diversity effects produced by the overflow are negligible. The latter effect would be shown by a drawing down of the water surface on the outer side of the bend.

(ii) Along the intersection (bend angles 25° to 35°), despite the spilling of water on the outer side of the bend, the superelevation effect continues to dominate the profiles. The remarkably good agreement between measured and predicted profiles justifies the assumption of constant specific energy made in the mathematical model. This taken along with the fact that the mathematical model predicts a linear variation of longitudinal water surface gradient would suggest that the gradient of the local kinetic energy is also linear i.e. that the reduction of the local longitudinal depth-averaged velocity gradient is also linear.

(iii) Downstream of the intersection (bend angles 35° to 60°) the profiles again follow the same trend as in the case of the bend alone. The superelevation reduces steadily as the flow proceeds to the bend exit.

Low side weir - as may be seen from Fig. 3 agreement between the predicted and measured profiles is much poorer than in the base of the high side weir. As before the following discussion draws on corresponding results from the bend only tests.

(i) Upstream of the intersection the measured profiles show a reduction in superelevation due to the increased drawing of the flow towards the overflow. This results in an increase in the kinetic energy of the flow near the outer bank.

(ii) Along the intersection the actual surface profiles are greatly influenced by the formation of a stagnation zone along the inner bank and a separation zone on the outer side of the channel. The separation zone occupies almost half the width of the main channel and extends about half way along the weir crest. As can be seen from Fig. 3 the separation zone is effective in eliminating all superelevation between bend angles 25° and 30°.

(iii) Downstream of the intersection, indeed from about half way along the intersection, superelevation becomes re-established and then steadily reduces towards the bend exit - as in the case of the high weir.

DEPTH-AVERAGED VELOCITIES

High side weir - Fig. 4 shows that once again there is very good agreement between the mathematical and the physical model results both upstream of and along the intersection for this channel/weir configuration. Agreement is such that discussion of the results under headings of upstream of, along and downstream of the intersection is considered unnecessary. Compared with the corresponding results from the bend only tests there is little difference in the shapes of the velocity profiles from bend angle 0° to almost 30°. Thereafter, the slight concavity found in the bend only profiles is eliminated and indeed the indication is that this trend is reversed towards the bend exit.

Low wide weir - as shown in Fig. 5, as in the case of the water surface profiles agreement between measured and predicted values is poorer with this weir configuration. Considerable local differences are also found when comparing results with those of the bend only tests. A region by region discussion is once again justified.

(i) Upstream of the intersection there is a tendency for the increased flow diversity to move the maximum velocity from the inner bank towards the central region of the channel. A tendency which is not reproduced by the mathematical model.

(ii) Along the intersection the flow and the depth-averaged velocities are greatly influenced by the strong cross currents and the development of both stagnation and separation zones. The development of the latter two features can be seen in the profiles from bend angle 25° onwards. No account of these features is taken in the formulation of the mathematical model and hence the increasing discrepancy between measured and predicted results.

(iii) Downstream of the intersection the effect of the stagnation zone is particularly strong as may be seen by comparing the profiles shown on Figs. 4 and 5. As a result of the increasing extent of the stagnation zone there is a concentration of the flow and the velocities towards the centre and outer side of the bend. From this it may be deduced that in a natural river scour and bank erosion may be anticipated in this region.

CONCLUSIONS

(1) It is considered that conditions at the upstream junction of a meander and partial neck cut-off channel can be simulated by a wide gentle bend with a broad crested side overflow weir.

(2) By comparison of water surface and depth-averaged velocity profiles obtained from a mathematical and a physical model it has been shown that the mathematical model is very adequate for use in high weir crest conditions.

(3) Under low weir crest conditions the model performs much less satisfactorily due to the formation of very marked stagnation and separation zones.

(4) Compared with corresponding tests in a bend only channel little change occurs in either water surface or depth-averaged velocities when a relatively high side weir is introduced. However significant changes occur with the introduction of a low side weir.

(5) In the case of the low side weir the concentration of velocites towards the centre and outer side of the bend would probably result in significant bed and bank erosion in a natural river just downstream of the bend/cut-off channel intersection.

REFERENCES

Fares, Y.R., Effects of a cut-off (flood relief) channel intersection on bend flow characertistics, Ph.D. Thesis, Department of Civil Engineering, Univ. of Glasgow, Glasgow, Scotland, U.K., 1989.

Herbertson, J.G. and Y.R. Fares, Characteristics of flow at the intersection of river meanders and flood relief (cut-off) channels, Proc. Int. Conf. on River Regime, W.R. White (Ed.), Wiley and Sons, Chichester, U.K., 1988a, pp 191-202.

Herbertson, J.G. and Y.R. Fares, The effect of flood relief channels on the flow pattern at channel bends, Proc. Int. Conf. on Fluvial Hydraulics, Res. Centre for Water Resources Department, Budapest, Hungary, 1988b, pp 280-285.

TABLE 1 - Water surface profile test conditions.

Test run	Flow ℓ/s	Depth at entry to bend mm	Weir crest height mm	Flow over weir ℓ/s
WF13	7.22	88.0	65.0	1.33
WF 5	7.94	76.8	25.0	5.71

TABLE 2 - Velocity test conditions.

Test run	Flow ℓ/s	Depth at entry to bend mm	Weir crest height mm	Flow over weir ℓ/s
A5-V5	6.40	80.0	65.0	0.64
A1-V1	5.38	55.5	25.0	2.24

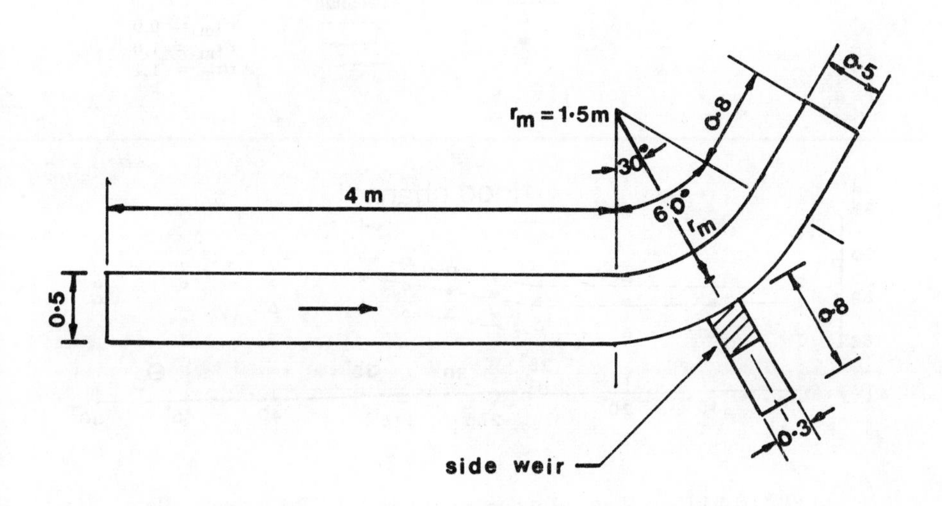

FIG. 1 - Dimensions of laboratory model.

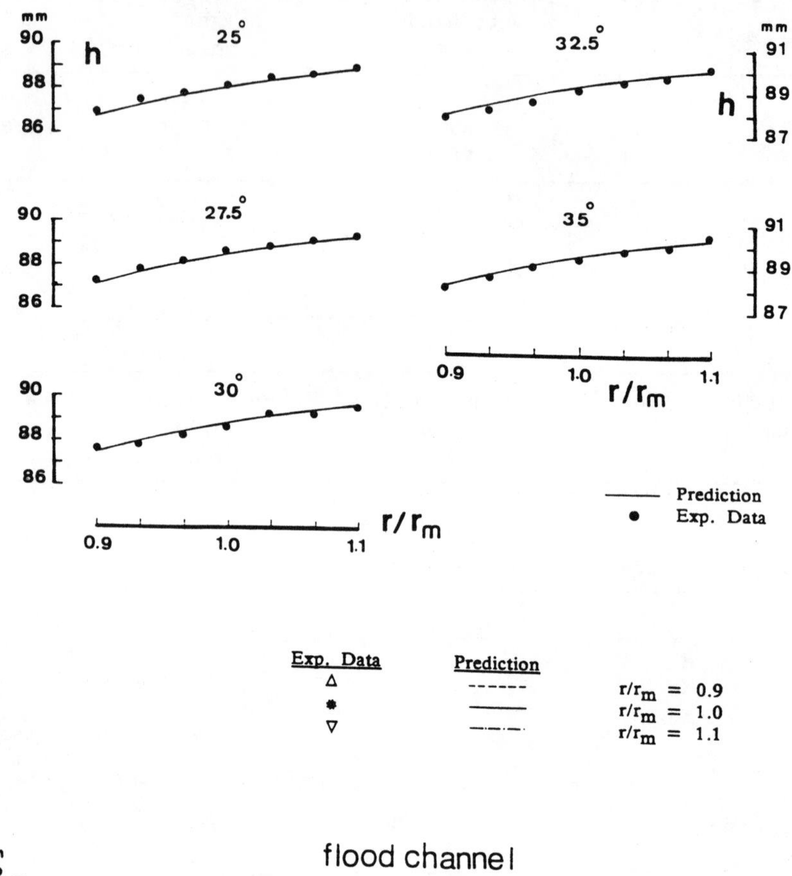

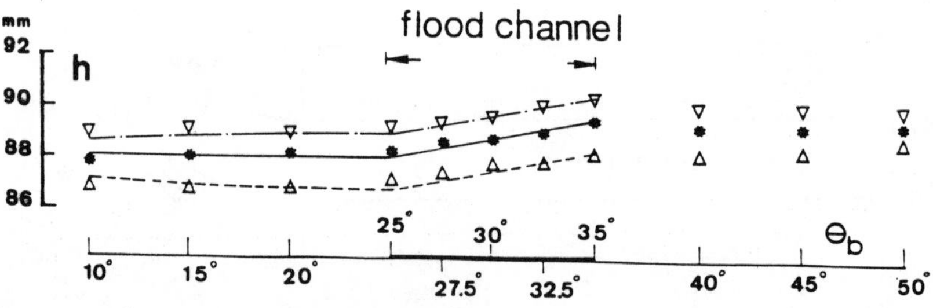

FIG. 2 - Water surface profiles - high side weir (Test WF 13).

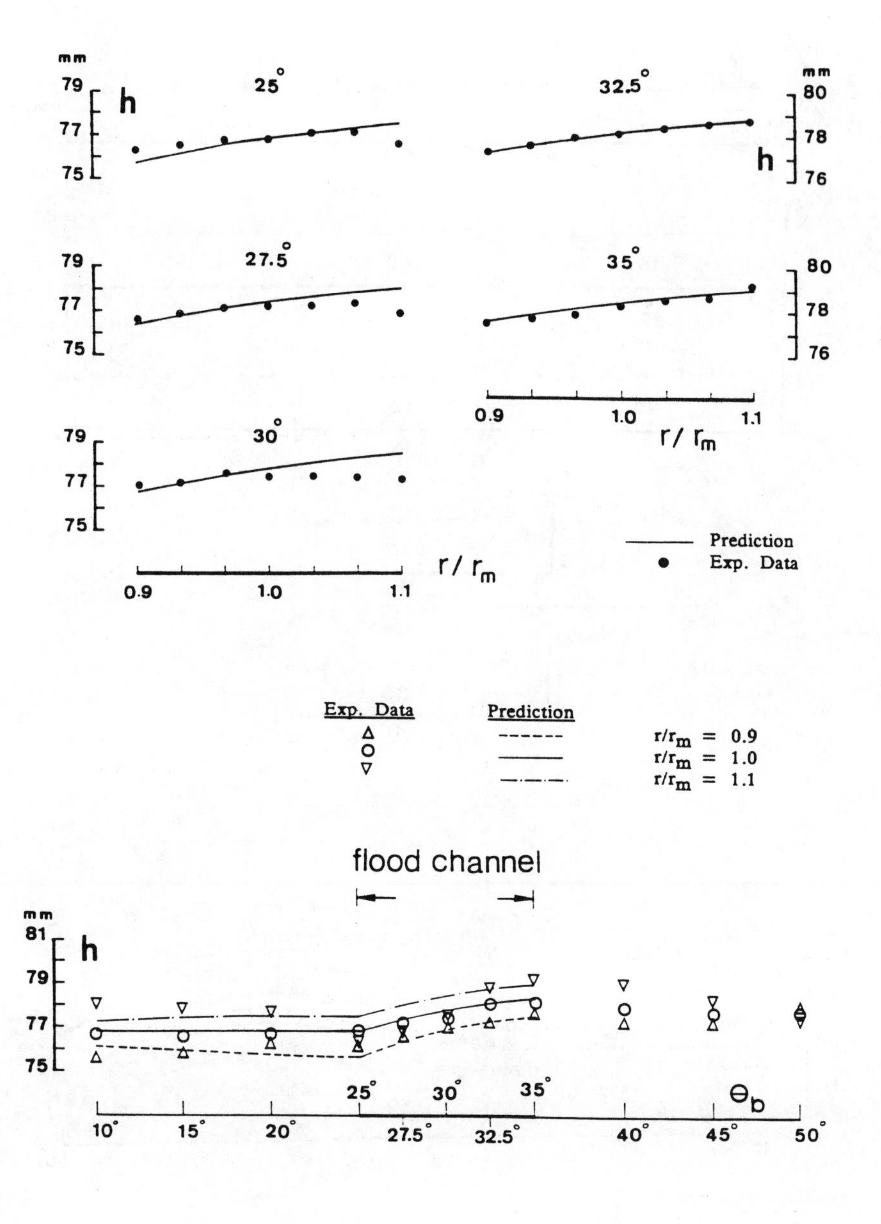

FIG. 3 - Water surface profiles - low side weir
(Test WF 5).

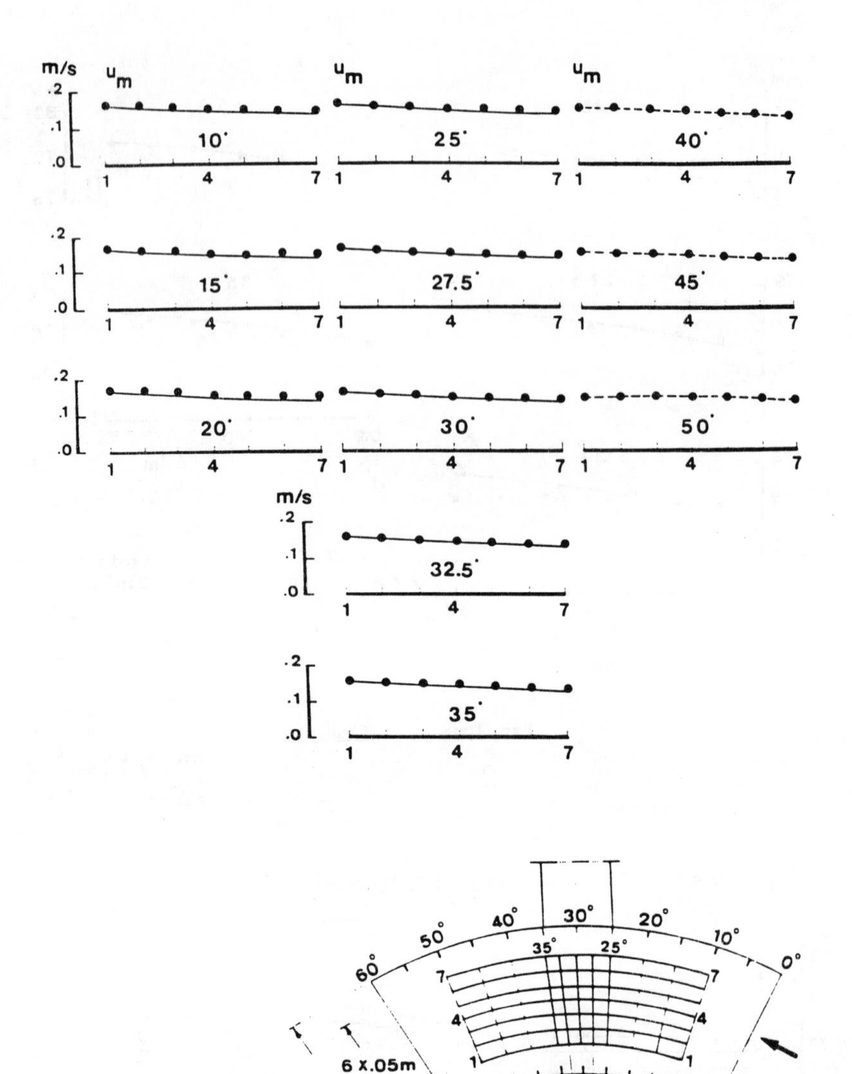

$h_w/h = .19$

—— Prediction
● Exp. Data ($\theta_b = 10° \rightarrow 35°$)
●----● Exp. Data ($\theta_b = 40° \rightarrow 50°$)

FIG. 4 - Depth-averaged velocities - high side weir (Test A5-V5).

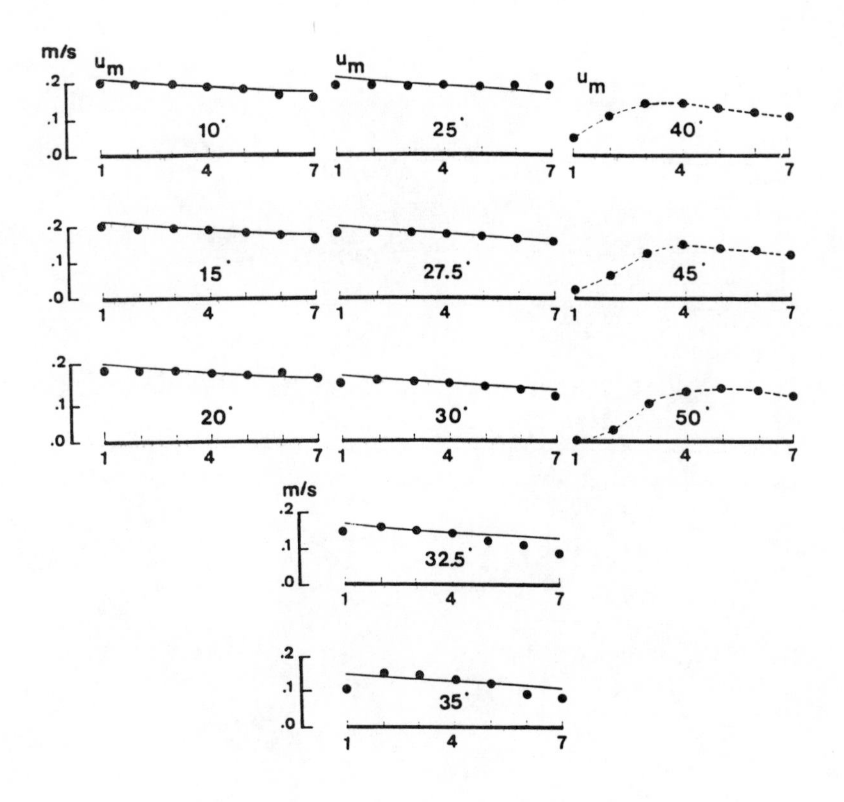

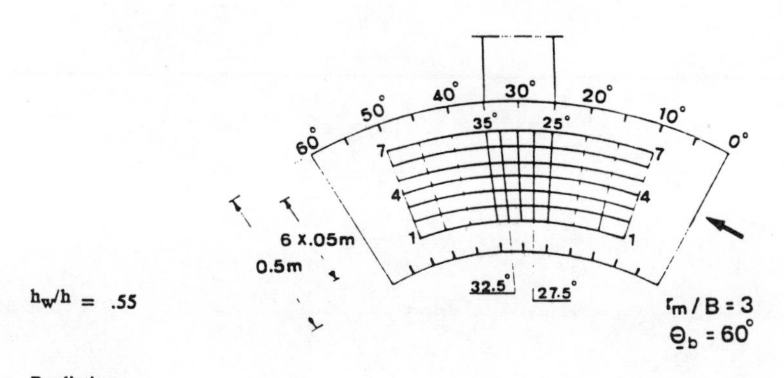

—— Prediction
● Exp. Data ($\Theta_b = 10° \rightarrow 35°$)
●----● Exp. Data ($\Theta_b = 40° \rightarrow 50°$)

FIG. 5 - Depth averaged velocities - low side weir (Test A1-V1).

PAPER H3

International Conference on
RIVER FLOOD HYDRAULICS
17-20 September, 1990

Experimental study on transport rate of graded sediment

Wang Shiqiang Zhang Ren

Department of Hydraulic Engineering, Tsinghua University, Beijing, China

SUMMARY

An investigation of the sediment transport rate of graded sand has been conducted in a 60m tilting flume in the Sediment Research Laboratory of Tsinghua University. The results of the experiments were used to verify the model which the authors proposed in 1989 for computing the transport rate of non-uniform sediment. In this model, mechanics of grain saltation, vertical distribution of velocity and sediment concentration and the interaction between coarse and fine grains at the river bed were considered. Good agreement is obtained in the comparison between the experimental data and the predictions of the model.

INTRODUCTION

The sediment in natural rivers is generally non-uniform in grain size. But so far, most equations for sediment transport rate are suitable only to uniform sediment and are not able to predict correctly the transport rate of non-uniform sediment for various size fractions, especially under rapidly sorting conditions. H A Einstein and Ning Chien started the studies on the transport rate for non-uniform sediment in the early fifties (H A Einstein, 1950, H A Einstein and Ning Chien, 1953) but their analysis did not consider in sufficient detail the hydrodynamics of the grain movement in water. As a result, some hypotheses in Einstein's theory are still controversial. A model proposed by the authors (Wang and Zhang, 1987, 1989) for predicting the transporting capacity of non-uniform sediment is introduced in this paper. The model has been verified by both flume data (Einstein and Chien) and river data (rivers in USA and China). There is however little flume data for graded sediments, particularly for fine sands. The experiment described in this paper is regarded as a further verification of the model.

PROCEDURE AND RESULTS OF EXPERIMENT

The experiments were carried out in the Sediment Research Laboratory of Tsinghua University with a tilting flume 60m long and 1.2m wide. The discharges used in experiment were up to 500 l/s supplied and regulated by two large and one small pumps. Natural sand was used

International Conference on River Flood Hydraulics, edited by W.R.White

and its D_{50} and D_{65} were 0.078 and 0.086mm respectively with a non-uniformity coefficient σ (= 0.5 (D_{84}/D_{50} + D_{50}/D_{16})) of 1.44. The gradation curve is shown in Fig 1.

At the beginning of each test, a sand layer 15cm thick was placed on the flume bed. The discharge Q and the water depth h were considered as independent variables in the experiments. Following self-adjustment of the bed configuration, the equilibrium energy slope S and the sediment concentration C were formed dependently. The duration of each test depended mainly on the flow intensity. It ranged from 4 to 20 hours in which the equilibrium state of fluvial adjustment could be reached. The discharge was measured by an electro-magnetic current meter which was calibrated against a weir. The longitudinal water surface profile was measured at 36 locations along a working the section of 50m using an automatic water surface follower. Due to the existence of a long working section, the accuracy in determining the energy slope was much greater than that which can be achieved in a short flume. Both sides of the flume are made of glass. This enabled the flow depth to be measured at 36 locations in the 50m working section on both sides of the flume using a ruler. The sediment concentration in the flow was determined using a siphon tube at nine points in a cross-section at the entry of the flume where the flow is very turbulent and the distribution of sediment concentration is quite uniform. The volume of each sediment sample was approximately of 1000cc.

The average water surface slope was calculated from the measured water level using a least-squares linear regression. The average flow depth was calculated by averaging the 36 measured depths.

Twenty-seven sets of experiment on the transport capacity of sediment in the flow were carried out and the main results of the experiment are summarised in Table 1. The ranges of discharge, water depth, energy slope and sediment concentration varied from 32 to 410 l/s, 0.100 to 0.365m, 0.554 to 3.054×10^{-3} and 4.71 to 188.95kg/cu.m respectively. According to the size distribution of bed material, 0.025m can be roughly regarded as the critical diameter between wash load and bed material load in flow. In Table 1, C is the measured total sediment concentration, T is the temperature, S is the energy slope, h is the water depth and Q is the discharge.

The composition of bed material changes to some extent when the flow intensity changed. But, for simplification we used a constant bed material size distribution as shown in Table 2 in the calculation thereafter.

MODEL OF TRANSPORT RATE FOR NON-UNIFORM SAND

Based on hydrodynamic and probabilistic analyses on grain saltation, equations of dimensionless transport rate N, relative thickness y_m/D and velocity u_b/u_* of the bedload as functions of the parameters M and r_s/r have been obtained by authors (Wang and Zhang, 1987). The functional relationship between M and N for various r_s/r is shown in Fig 2, in which

$M = ((r_s - r)/r)\ D/RS$, $N = q_b/D^{3/2}\ g^{1/2}\ r_s\ ((r_s - r)/r)^{1/2}$
q_b is bedload transport rate per width,
D is the diameter of grain,
u_b is the average velocity of bedload,
u_* is shear velocity
R is hydraulic radius
r and r_s are the specific weight of water and grain

Under the condition of natural sand with r_s/r equal to 2.68, the equations of bedload transport rate can be simplified as follows,

$$N = 1.19\text{x}10^{-4}\ (26-M)^{4.11}\ (M/0.3)^{m_1} \qquad (1)$$

in which, $m_1 = 0.1018-9.7707\text{x}10^{-3}\ M+6.752\text{x}10^{-4}\ M^2-2.93\text{x}10^{-5}\ M^3$

$$\frac{u_b}{u_*} = 2.54(26-M)^{0.5}\ (M/0.3)^{m_2} \qquad (2)$$

in which, $m_2 = -0.0394 - 0.01452\ M+6.024\text{x}10^{-4}\ M^2-2.76\text{x}10^{-5}\ M^3$

$$\frac{y_m}{D} = 0.62\ (26-M)^{0.95}\ (M/0.3)^{m_3} \qquad (3)$$

In which, $m_3 = -0.0941 - 0.02\ M+1.045\text{x}10^{-3}\ M^2-3.8\text{x}10^{-5}\ M^3$

where y_m is the height of grain saltation, or the thickness of bed load. Based on the diffusion theory given by H Rouse, the vertical distribution of sediment concentration in suspension can be obtained if the concentration S_a at the interface between the suspended load and the bed load is determined. According to the experiments conducted by Fu Xiao (Fu Xiao, 1988), the distribution of the probability density of jump heights of bedload is close to an exponential function. This means that the concentration in the bedload layer decreases with increasing distance y from the bed. The distribution of the flow velocity u(y) near bed surface is proportional to $u_*\ (y/D)^{0.234}$. Based on the observed data, the velocity of the grains $u_b(y)$ is proportional to the flow velocity u(y), thus, $u_b \sim 0.81\ u_*\ (y_m/D)^{0.234}$, $u_b(y)/u_b = 1.234\ (y/y_m)^{0.234}$. With the assumption of constant transport rate in the depth for the bedload, $S_a = 0.81\bar{S}$, where $\bar{S}$ is the average bedload concentration. The transport rate q_T of total bed material load can be obtained by the following equation

$$q_T = q_s + q_b = q_b\ (1 + 9.4\ u_*/u_b\ (PI_1 + I_2)) \qquad (4)$$

The transport rate of bed material load for specific grain size group is

$$i_T q_T = i_b q_b + i_s q_s = i_b q_b (1 + 9.4 u_*/u_b (PI_2 + I_2)) \quad (5)$$

where i_o, i_T, i_b and i_s are the fractions of the given size group for bed material, total bed material load, bedload and suspended load respectively. P, I_1 and I_2 are parameters as defined by Einstein.

From the analysis of flume and field data, the authors found that fine and coarse grains of non-uniform mixtures interacted with each other in bedload transport. The fine grains are protected by coarse grains and have a lower transport rate than that in a uniform sediment. In addition, the coarse grains are subjected to more tractive force due to their greater exposure to the flow. A modification of the transport rate for different grain size groups should therefore be made to take account of the interaction between grains with different sizes. A relationship between relative grain size D_k, relative water depth h/D_{50}, dimensionless unit stream power U_E and the modifying factor K_D has been suggested by the authors (Wang and Zhang, 1989) on the basis of the analysis of flume and river data, as shown in Figure 3. D_k is the ratio of specific diameter D_i to D_{65}, K_D is the ratio between observed bed load transport rate for the graded sand and calculated bed-load transport rate for a uniform sand. This relationship reflects the hiding and exposing effects in non-uniform sediment mixtures.

Considering the modifying coefficient K_D due to the non-uniformity of the sediment, $i_b q_b$ in equation (5) should be calculated by equation (6)

$$i_b q_b = K_D i_o N D^{3/2} g^{1/2} r_s [(r_s - r)/r]^{1/2} \quad (6)$$

where $K_D = D_k^m$ (7)

when $U_E > 0.011$

$$m = 0.02323 + 0.91414 D_k - 0.3542 D_k^2 + 0.0455 D_k^3$$

when $U_E \leq 0.011$

$D_k > 1$: $m = 2.1176 - 1.7376 D_k + 1.2646 D_k^2$

$D_k \leq 1$: $\frac{H}{D_{50}} < 35000$: $m = 1.0$

$= 35000 - 60000$: $m = 1.5$

$= 60000 - 70000$: $m = 2.0$

> 75000 : $m = 2.5$

where $U_E = V S / ((g V_i)^{1/3} Dgr]$ (8)

$Dgr = [g (r_s - r)/r/V_i^2]^{1/3} D_{50}$

V_i is the kinematic viscosity

COMPARISON BETWEEN EXPERIMENT RESULTS AND MODEL PREDICTION

By using the model described above and the hydraulic factors measured in the experiment, the transport rate of the total bed material load for different size groups can be predicted. The results of the calculation were then compared with the data on transport rates measured in experiment. The result of the comparison is shown in Table 3 in which, K_A is the ratio of observed transport rate to the predicted one for a given set and the $\bar{K}_A$ is the average value of K_A for 27 sets.

From Table 3, it can be seen that though the average $\bar{K}_A$ is less than one by 20%, the percentage of data points between K_A of 0.67-1.50 and 0.5-2.0 reached 59% and 85% respectively that might be an acceptable accuracy in prediction of transport rate for non-uniform sediment. It is better than that predicted by a lot of other sediment transport equations. As for different size groups, the larger deviation on accuracy in coarse group (0.10-0.20mm) might be attributed to the accuracy of measurement because it usually occupied a very small portion of the total bed material load. If more data for non-uniform sediment transport could be obtained the K_D - D_k relationship reflecting the comprehensive interactions between the fine and coarse grains in motion would be further improved.

CONCLUSIONS

1. The model suggested by the authors can predict the transport rate of bedload, suspended load and total bed material load in flume and natural rivers.

2. The model can predict not only the total transport rate of sediment but also the transport rate of various grain size groups with acceptable accuracy in practice.

3. The K_D - D_k relationship shown in Fig 3 correctly reflect the hiding and exposing effects in non-uniform sediment mixtures and is fundamentally verified by the experimental results obtained in the long tilting flume of Tsinghua University.

REFERENCES

Einstein, H A. The bed load function for sediment transportation in open channel flow, US Dept Agr, Tech Bull 1026, 1950.

Einstein, H A and Ning Chien. Transport of sediment mixtures with large ranges of grain size, Missouri river Division Sediment Series No 2, US Corps Engrs, 1953.

Fu Xiao (instructor : Zhang Ren and Wang Shiqiang). The experimental study on saltation of grain of bed load in water, Thesis for Masters degree, Tsinghua University, Beijing, 1988.

Wang Shiqiang and Zhang Ren, A new equation of bedload transport, Proc 22 Congress IAHR, 1987.

Wang Shiqiang and Zhang Ren, Sediment Transport rate for non-uniform sand, Proc Int Symp Sediment Transport Modelling, New Orleans, USA, 1989.

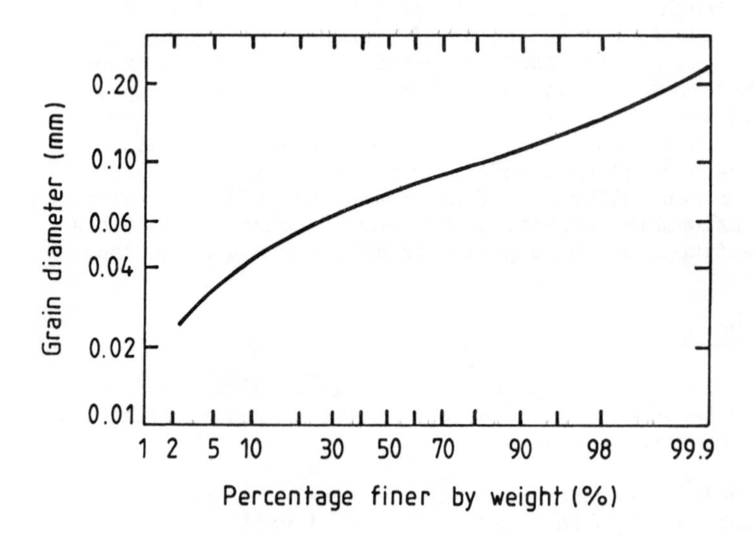

Fig 1 : Size distribution of model sand

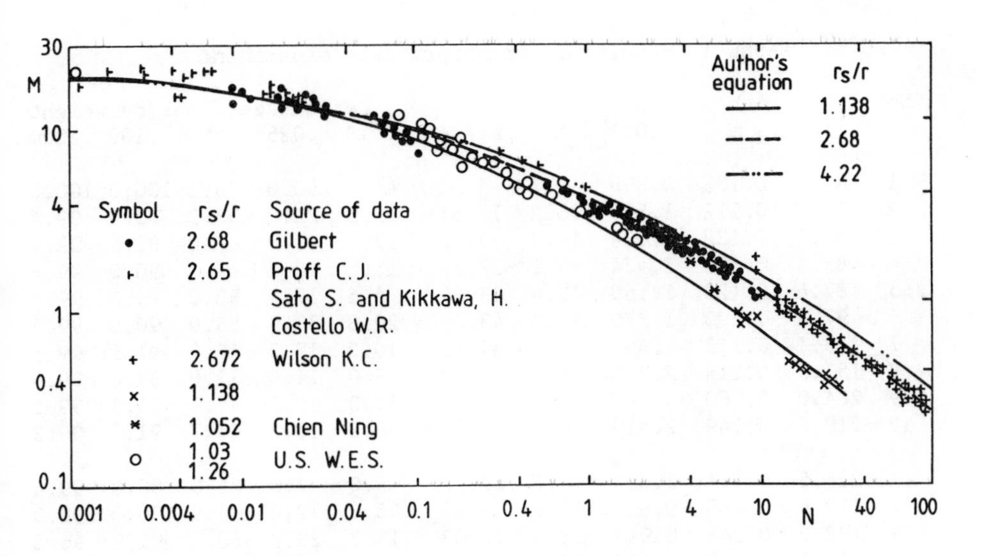

Fig 2 : N as a function of M and r_s/r

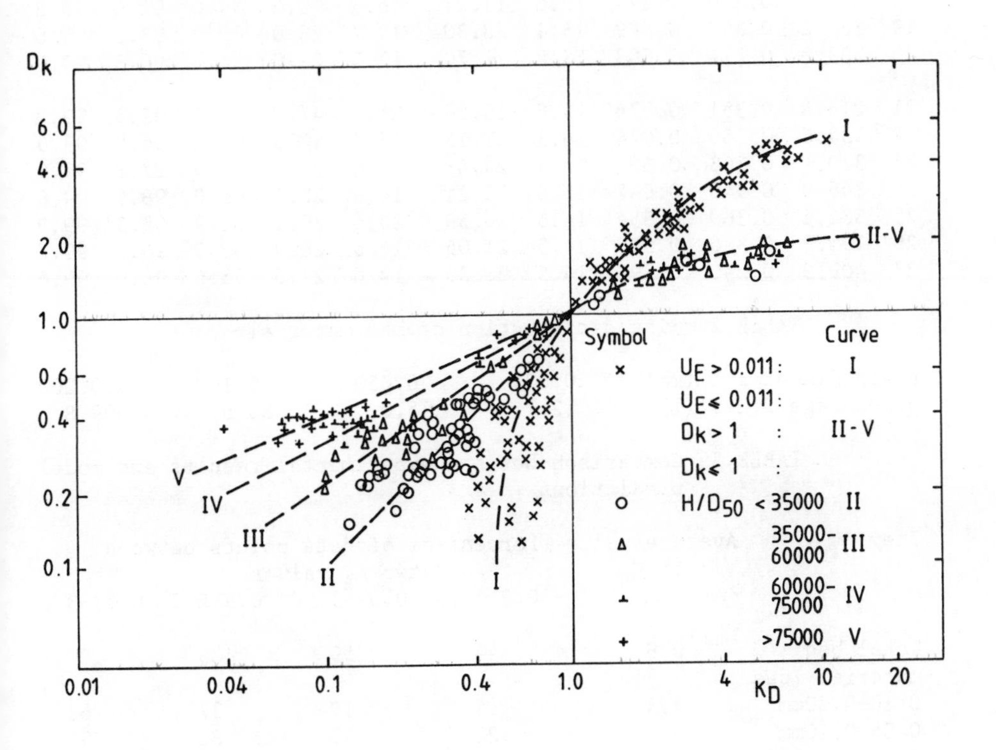

Fig 3 : Relationship of K_D to D_K

TABLE 1 Results of transport rate experiment

No	Q l/s	h m	S 10^{-3}	T °C	C kg/m³	Percentage finer by weight .010	.025	.050	.100	.200mm
1	32.0	0.103	0.898	13.7	4.71	44.1	50.0	75.1	100.0	100.0
2	52.8	0.112	1.530	16.2	13.61	15.5	22.0	53.2	93.0	99.4
3	64.5	0.122	1.624	14.0	25.83	13.1	23.0	47.0	88.5	99.4
4	83.4	0.134	1.454	15.1	27.74	11.5	18.2	44.1	90.0	99.4
5	87.6	0.120	1.150	13.4	33.82	5.6	17.7	52.0	95.2	99.6
6	97.3	0.100	1.376	16.2	43.65	20.8	33.9	53.0	90.5	99.5
7	125.1	0.113	1.496	14.5	49.26	10.2	17.3	42.0	91.5	99.5
8	151.5	0.114	2.226	14.5	81.94	8.0	11.6	32.0	88.0	99.4
9	204.0	0.160	1.347	14.9	61.08	11.0	15.0	45.9	94.3	99.5
10	219.6	0.149	2.410	16.0	104.57	9.9	16.2	39.7	91.7	99.3
11	215.5	0.144	3.054	13.7	188.95	5.0	7.9	25.0	80.0	99.4
12	110.6	0.245	0.611	13.6	9.35	56.0	72.0	84.9	100.0	100.0
13	182.2	0.248	0.941	18.4	22.03	14.5	28.9	60.2	91.9	96.2
14	193.1	0.245	0.850	17.8	18.90	25.7	41.0	70.8	100.0	100.0
15	193.1	0.251	0.866	17.1	21.11	18.8	33.8	62.6	95.5	98.8
16	198.8	0.232	0.825	14.9	31.91	15.1	29.2	58.8	92.0	98.1
17	310.4	0.208	1.624	12.8	82.16	7.3	14.0	44.0	93.4	99.7
18	348.0	0.220	2.171	12.6	111.21	6.5	9.9	34.0	92.0	98.8
19	367.2	0.357	0.589	15.1	28.30	14.7	28.0	60.2	97.1	99.6
20	383.6	0.274	1.003	13.8	41.70	13.8	22.0	51.0	95.3	99.9
21	216.8	0.351	0.574	15.8	10.59	26.8	47.0	69.8	92.6	99.8
22	300.6	0.365	0.674	16.3	23.15	17.2	31.0	64.0	96.8	99.9
23	310.4	0.363	0.685	16.5	24.43	11.6	28.5	66.5	97.8	99.9
24	346.8	0.340	0.642	15.8	25.21	14.5	28.4	69.0	98.5	99.6
25	382.1	0.360	0.554	14.5	20.59	20.6	30.1	61.9	95.3	99.8
26	391.8	0.336	0.586	14.5	21.05	16.5	29.9	62.0	95.6	99.7
27	409.9	0.240	0.596	14.5	23.39	14.6	27.0	56.6	98.0	99.6

TABLE 2 Size distribution of bed material

grain diameter (mm)	0.025	0.050	0.100	0.200
percentage finer (%)	2.7	15.0	80.5	99.8

TABLE 3 Comparison between experimental results and model predictions

Item	Average value of K_A	Percentage of data points between two K_A values 0.8-1.25	0.67-1.50	0.5-2.0	0.33-3.0
Total bed material load	0.8	44	59	85	100
0.10-0.20mm	3.3	15	19	37	63
0.05-0.10mm	0.8	22	59	82	96
0.025-0.05mm	0.74	41	63	85	100

PAPER J1

International Conference on
RIVER FLOOD HYDRAULICS
17-20 September, 1990

CLIMATE CHANGE AND FLOODS IN NORTHERN BASINS

Lars Bengtsson
Water Resources Engrg. Lund University, Sweden

Laszlo Iritz
Dept.Hydrology Uppsala University, Sweden

ABSTRACT

Two different rainfall-runoff models are applied to river basins in northern Sweden and Finland to study the effect of changed climate on peak flows. Hypothetical meteorological data series are constructed by increasing observed values by given amounts and fractions. In a Swedish moderately large basin snowmelt and daily precipitation were considered, and in two small Finnish basins, hourly precipitation. The winter temperature is found to be crucial for the runoff peak in the spring. Increased daily winter temperatures of a few degrees result in considerably reduced peak flows. The annual runoff increases in a climate of increasing precipitation, as does the autumn peak runoff. However, the rain intensity and the soil moisture conditions at the time of the rainfall are found to be much more important for the runoff peaks than the seasonal rainfall depth.

INTRODUCTION

The growing atmospheric concentrations of carbon dioxide and other trace gases are expected to lead to changes of the climate on Earth. The hydrologic regime is likely to be altered in river basins, maybe especially where some of the snow precipitation of today instead is going to fall as rain. This is expected to happen in the rivers in northern Sweden and Finland. Since many of the rivers are regulated for hydraulic power generation, it is essential that the river flow in the spring and in the autumn can be stored in reservoirs. In the non-regulated river basins much land is innundated during spring and may hinder agcricultural work. Because of the influence of river peak flows on the society along the northern rivers, this paper focus on the climate change effect on peak floods. Mathematical models have been developed to describe the phenomena that make up the climate. These general circulation models, GCMs, e.g. Manabe and Stouffer (1980), could be used to estimate changes in

International Conference on River Flood Hydraulics, edited by W.R.White

water resources. In practice, however, the spatial resolution is too large to provide information on a river basin scale. Instead, temperature and precipitation estimates from GCMs are used as inputs to river basin models. The outcome of these models is to be evaluated as trends of changes of the present hydrologic conditions not as absolute changes.

SIMULATING HYDROLOGICAL CONSEQUENCES

Hypothetical scenarios is most often used to asses the behavior of rivers in relation to changed climatic conditions, e.g. Nemec and Schaake (1982), Gleick (1987), Bultot et al. (1988). The scenarios chosen must be consistent with the output of the GCMs. Gleick (1986, 1989) suggested a number of factors to be considered when selecting a hydrologic model to study the impacts of changes in climate on regional water resources, of which the most important may be model adaptability to diverse hydrologic conditions. Nemec and Schaake (1982) and Bultot and Gellens (1989) mean that the natural variations over the period a model is calibrated for include the rather moderate changes in precipitation and temperature which are expected to occur as a result of increasing CO_2. Therefore, the result obtained from a well calibrated rainfall-runoff model should provide valuable information about responses of hydrologic systems to CO_2 caused weather changes.

In a study of the Sacramento Basin in California Gleick (1986, 1987) found that warmer climate would lead to decreases in summer soil moisture and summer runoff volumes, large increases in winter runoff and earlier snowmelt runoff. Because of higher temperatures less of the winter precipitation is snow, leading to less spring snowmelt runoff and earlier depletion of the soil moisture. Very much the same response to climate change has been simulated to occur in other regions, Bultot et al. (1988) and Martinec and Rango (1989). The annual runoff is found to be sensitive to changes in precipitation, Flaschka et al. (1987), while the seasonal distribution of snowmelt runoff is very sensitive to temperature, Gleick (1987) and Bultot et al. (1988).

FLUCTUATIONS OF CLIMATE AND RUNOFF

Climate fluctuations in Sweden over the last 100 years have been studied by Alexandersson and Eriksson (1989). The temperature records show a negative trend since the 1940-ies in contrast to general observations from the Northern Hemispere. The precipitation climate has been stable. GCMs show that doubling of CO_2 in the atmosphere will result in global warming in the range 1.5-4° C, higher near the poles and in the winter than at low latidues. The precipitation in Scandinavia will increase, Manabe et al. (1981), at least in the winter. An expected increase of the precipitation of about 10 mm/month during winter is small compared to the natural variations. A monthly temparature change of 4° C is significant. Observed seasonal variations are shown in Table 1.

TABLE 1. Seasonal precipitation and temperature variations in the period 1940 - 1988 in northern Sweden. From data presented by Alexandersson and Eriksson (1989).

	Dec-Feb	March-May	June-Aug	Sept-Nov
prec mean	120	90	180	170
prec range	50-220	30-150	100-320	90-250
temp mean	-	-1	-	-
temp range	-17-(-4)	-4-(+1)	-	-

RUNOFF MODELS USED IN THE PRESENT STUDY

Two different hydrological models were used in the present study. Since the study focused on peak flows and short term events, computations were performed with time steps of hours or up to one day. The first model, which was applied to the Råne River in Sweden, is basically the Swedish HBV model, Bergström (1976), but this new model called HBR, Hydrological Boxes and Reaches, has a higher degree of discretization depending on land use and elevation, and includes river and lake routing.

The other model is based on the Nash (1957) cascade. Rainfall in excess of infiltration and evaporation form the input to the first resevoir, Kutchment (1972). In Sweden and Finland infiltration is the governing factor forming runoff. The infiltration is assumed to be proportional to the saturation deficit of soil moisture, Iritz (1988). Runoff corresponds to the infiltration capacity if the saturation deficit is less than an empirically determined fraction of the soil moisture capacity. The soil moisture saturation deficit is accounting for all losses including interception. Thus, it is rather an index of total wetness of the basin than a detailed description of the soil conditions.

CASE STUDY-RÅNE RIVER

The Råne River basin is in northern Sweden. The river is running in a southeasterly direction through a land of forests and mires towards the Bothnian Bay. The basin is marked on the map shown in Figure 1. The area of the basin is 3768 km^2. The basin is snow covered from mid November until May. The annual precipitation is 600-650 mm. Almost half of the precipitation falls as snow. The river flow in the spring is extremely peaked, as is shown in Figure 2. As already mentioned the conceptual hydrological model HBR was used to simulate the flow in the Råne River. The model was calibrated for the period 1968-1972. Parameters were chosen so that the peak flows were computed correctely. One particular year, considered to be representative for the flow regime of the Råne River, was chosen for further analysis. The meteorological data of the hydrological year 1973-74 were repeatedly used as input to the model so that a quasi steady-state hydrograph was obtained, cf. Figure 2.

The Råne River flow regime is largely controlled by snow conditions. Changed temparatures may be expected to influence the runoff. When the daily air temperatures throughout the year were increased in the range 1-4° C, neither the annual nor the autumn runoff were computed to change much, but the spring discharge was considerably reduced. Already at an increased winter temperature of 2° C, the peak discharge was estimated to decrease from about 300 to 200 m^3/s. The amount of snow is reduced as compared to present conditions, and the snow disappeares before it gets very warm. The evaporative losses is concentrated to the summer, which means that the soil moisture does not decrease as much as found in the studies of regions 20 degrees latitude or more south of the Arctic Circle, e.g. Gleick (1987) and Bultot et al. (1988).

The observed daily precipitation was simply increased by given percentages. Increased precipitation manifested itself in increased annual runoff and in increased autumn peak flows. A 14 % precipitation increase was found to cause a 100 % increased autumn peak flow from about 100 to 200 m^3/s. However, the spring discharge peak was hardly affected at all. Thus, snowmelt induced peak flows is controlled by the temperature, while the autumn peak discharge is strongly affected by increased seasonal precipitation. If the precipitation throughout the year increases by 14 %, and the winter temperature increases by 2° C, the peak discharges in the spring and in the autumn are expected to be equally high, as shown in Figure 2. The computations are summarized in Table 2.

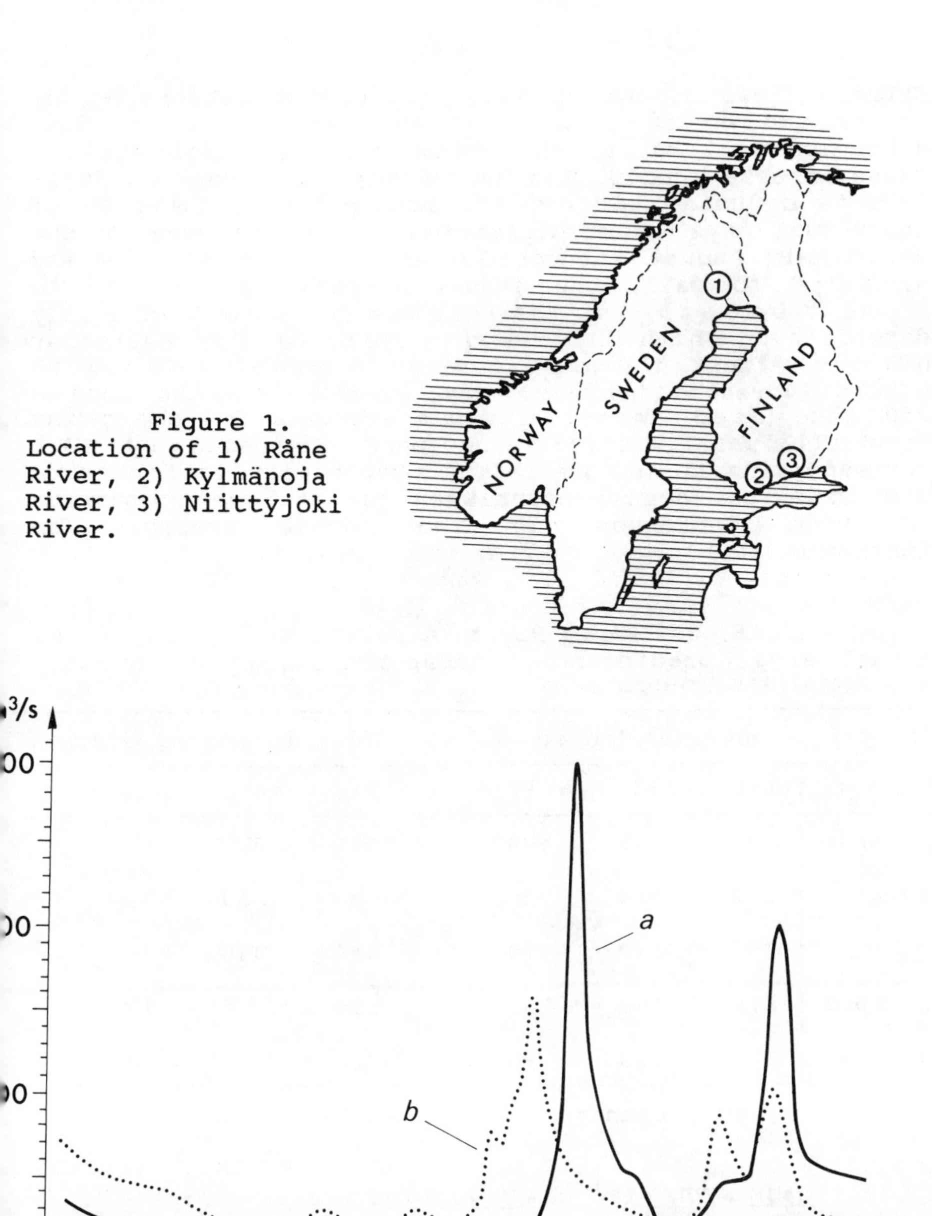

Figure 1. Location of 1) Råne River, 2) Kylmänoja River, 3) Niittyjoki River.

Figure 2. Observed (a) discharge in Råne River, and simulated (b) for 14 % increase of daily precipitation and 2° C temperature increase.

Extreme flows depend on the character of meteorological events and on the timing of the events. Storms just after snowmelt or in the autumn when the soil is wet cause intense runoff. The Råne River hydrograph of 1973-1974 was used to study the runoff influence of individual days of precipitation. If on any day in the period mid August through September 50 mm of rain was simulated to fall, the annual runoff was computed to increase by 50 mm, but the peak was found to be crucialy dependent on which day the rain fell. Rain in September did not affect the peak, while 50 mm of rain on 20 August increased the peak discharge from about 100 to 250 m^3/s. If 2 mm of rain was added when the spring discharge peak occured, the peak increased by 10 % corresponding to 0.7 mm/d. The probability that extreme meteorological events occur when the soil water storage is high, increases, if the annual precipitation increases.

TABLE 2. Råne River simulations. p,e,q = mm annual areal precipitation, evapotranspiration, runoff, Q = max discharge in m^3/s.

	unchanged prec			14 % increased prec		
T	0°C	+2°C	+4°C	+2°C	+4°C	+4°C *
p	590	590	590	670	670	670
e	310	320	320	330	330	330
q	280	270	270	340	340	340
Qspring	310	190	160	190	170	170
Qautumn	110	110	90	220	210	220

*) only temperature increase in winter

CASE STUDY-TWO SMALL FINNISH BASINS

The cascade model developed to include soil moisture processes, Iritz (1988), was applied to two experimental basins in Finland. The Kylmänoja basin is 4.0 km^2. It is mainly forested, 65 %, while 25 % is cultivated land and 10 % peatland. The mean slope is 8 %. The most common soil types are sand and sandy moraine. The Niittyoki basin has a drainage area of 29.7 km^2. Forests on firm land dominate, 59 %. Cultivated land constitutes 35 %. Niittyoki basin is more flat, slope 5 %, than Kylmänoja basin. Much of the land consists of clayey soils, 32 %. The location of the basins is shown in Figure 1.

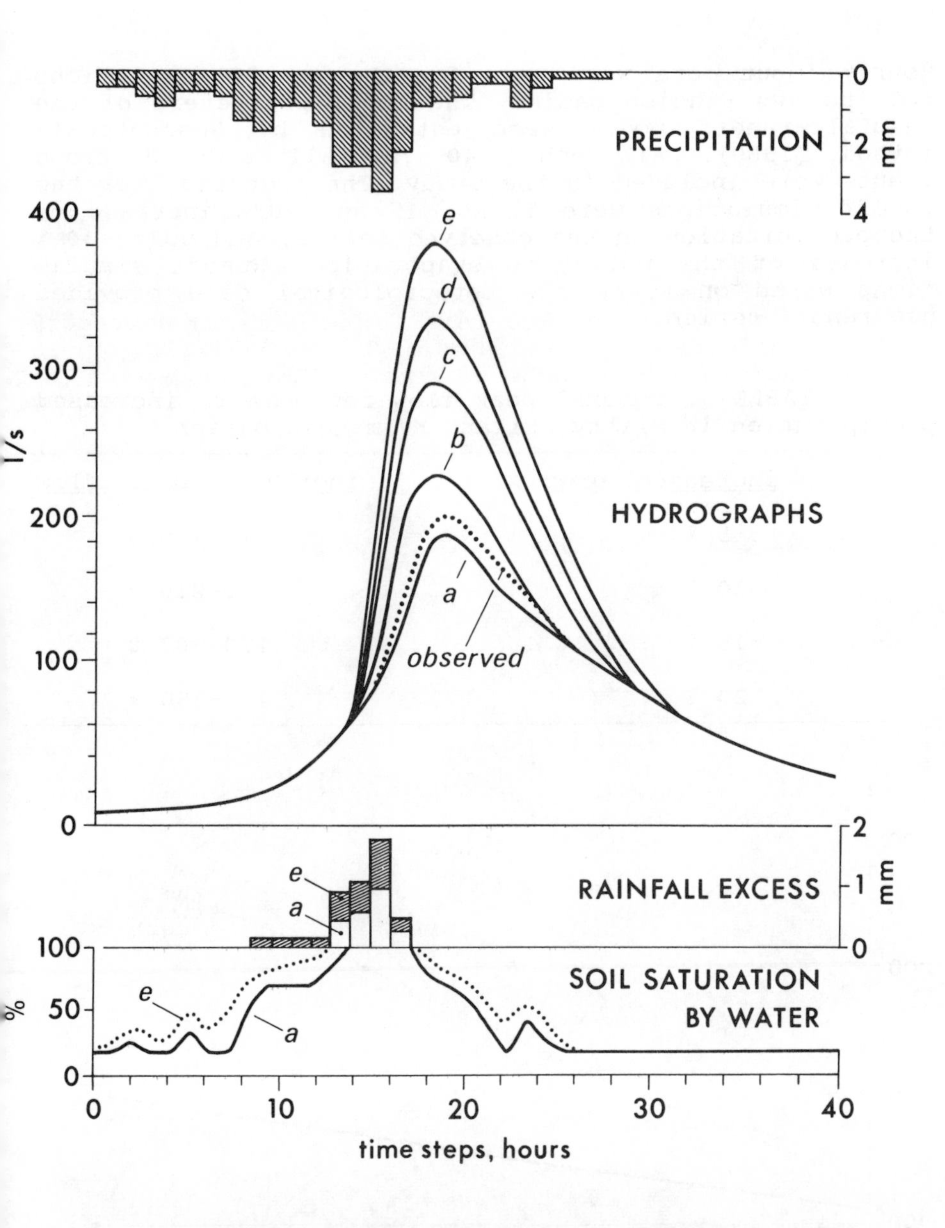

Figure 3. Observed (a) and simulated hydrograhs for Kylmänoja River; 5 % increased precipitation (b), 10 % (c), 15 % (d), 20 % (e).

Hourly input data were used for the runoff simulations for the two Finnish basins. The model parameters of the rainfall-runoff model were estimated by Rosenbrock's method (1960). Altogether 40 rainfall induced flood events were included in the study. The scenarios for the runoff simulations were 5, 10, 15 and 20 % increase of the precipitation in the observed series, and up to 30 % increase of the potential evaporation. Runoff simulations based on these new meteorological data provided new runoff series.

TABLE 3. General peak flow response to increased precipitation in Niittyjoki and Kylmänoja basins.

increased prec	increased peak flow
5 %	110-120 %
10 %	150-210 %
15 %	170-300 %
20 %	200-380 %

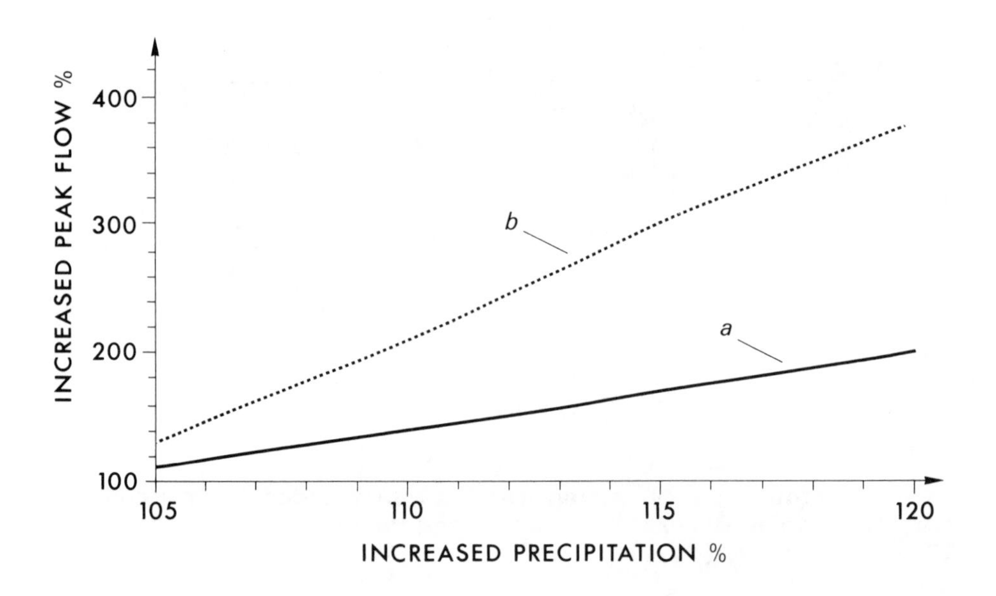

Figure 4. Relations between runoff and increased precipitation in Kylmänoja basin, 13 Oct 1963-- , and 1 Sept 1968-- .

Simulated hydrographs for 20 % increased precipitation

are shown in Figure 3 and compared with the observed hydrographs. Also the soil moisture content and the rainfall excess as computed by the model are shown. The simulations confirm that the hydrological regime is vulnerable to climatic changes; relatively small changes in precipitation depth have amplifying consequences on peak flows. The computed peak flows for the Finnish basins are summarized in Table 3.

The simulations show that the same percentage of increased precipitation may result in very different increase of runoff. The simulated peak flows of two different events are shown in Figure 4. At both occasions the observed precipitation depth was about 30 mm, but the duration of the rainfall differed being one day in the first case and only 2 hours in the other case. As seen in the figure, the runoff responses of the scenarios are quite different. Thus, timing and intensity of future storms are more important for the runoff peaks than average changes.

CONCLUSIONS

Rainfall-runoff models were applied to one river in Sweden and two brooks in Finland in order to investigate how peak flows may change in changing climatic conditions. It was found that increased winter temperatures have a very significant influence on the snowmelt induced runoff. Less snowcover and early melt result in reduced peak flows. Already a temperature increase of 2° C is computed to reduce the spring discharge peak by 30 %. Changing rainfall depth influences annual runoff and river discharge peaks in the autumn. However, especially in the two small basins, the timing and the intensity of the storms are crucial for the runoff response. Rainfall induced peak flows are likely to change more as a result of changed rain distribution in time than as a result of increased annual or seasonal precipitation. Still, in northern latitudes, where there are significant evaporative losses only in summer, the soil moisture in the autumn is going to increase with increasing seasonal rainfall, which means that extreme rainfall events more often than in a less wet climate may cause extreme flood events.

ACKNOWLEDGEMENT

We wish to acknowledge dr Pertti Seuna and mr Teppo Jarvi, National Board of Waters and the Environment, Helsinki, Finland for making the data from the Finnish basins available to us.

REFERENCES

Alexanderson, A. and Eriksson, B (1989) Climate fluctuations in 1860-1987, SMHI, Rept.RMK No.58, Norrköping.

Bergström, S. (1976) Development and application of a conceptual runoff model for Scandinavian catchments, Univ. Lund, Dept.Water Resour.Eng., Bull.A No.52, pp 124.

Bultot, F., Coppens, A., Dupriez, G.L.,Gellens, D. and Meulenberghs, F. (1988) Repercussions of CO_2 doubling on the water cycle and on the water balance - A case study for Belgium, J. Hydrol. 99, 319-347.

Bultot, F. and Gellens, D. (1989) Simulation of the impact of CO_2 atmospheric doubling on precipitation and evapotranspiration - study of the sensitivity to various hypothesis, Proc. Conf. Climate and Water, Helsinki, 73-91.

Flashka, I., Stockton, C.W. and Boggess, W.R. (1987) Climatic variation and surface water resources in the Great Basin region, Water Resour.Bull. 23, 47-57.

Gleick, P.H. (1986) Methods evaluating the regional hydrological impacts of global climatic changes, J.Hydrol. 88, 99-116.

Gleick, P.H (1987) The development and testing of a water balance model for climate impacts assesment: Modeling the Sacramento Basin, Water Resour.Res.23, 1049-1061.

Gleick, P.H. (1989) Climate change, hydrology and water resouces. Reviews of Geophysics, 27,329-344

Iritz, L. (1988) Recursive algorithm for computations of lateral flow in an adaptive forecast scheme, Proc. Nordic Hydrol. Conf., Rovaniemi, 77-88.

Kutchment, L.C. (1972) Mathematical Modeling of River Runoff (in Russian), Gidromet., Leningrad, 190 pp

Manabe, S. and Stouffer, R.J. (1980) Sensitivity of a global climate model to an increase of CO_2 concentration in the atmosphere, J. Geophys. Res. 85, 5529-5554.

Manabe, S., Wetherald, R.T. and Stouffer, R.J. (1981) Summer dryness due to an increase of atmopheric CO_2 concentration, Clim.Change, 3, 347-386.

Martinec, J and Rango, A. (1989) Effects of climate change on snowmelt runoff patterns, Remote Sensing and Large Scale Global Processes, IAHS Publ. 186.

Nash, J.E. (1957) The form of the instantaneous unit hydrograph, Hydr. Sci. Bull.3, 114-121.

Nemec, J. and Schaake (1982) Sensitivity of water resource systems to climate variations, J. Hydrol. Sci. 27, 327-343.

Rosenbrock, H.H. (1960) An automatic method for finding the greatest or least value of a function, The Computer J. 7, 175-184.

PAPER J2

International Conference on
RIVER FLOOD HYDRAULICS
17-20 September, 1990

THE REUSS RIVER FLOOD OF 1987 - HYDRAULIC MODEL TESTS AND RECONSTRUCTION CONCEPTS

G.R. Bezzola, P. Kuster, S. Pellandini

Laboratory of Hydraulics, Hydrology and Glaciology,
Swiss Federal Institute of Technology, Zurich

ABSTRACT

In August 1987, heavy rainfalls, together with a high zero degree isotherm caused extreme floods in the central part of Switzerland. The Canton of Uri was confounded by catastrophic damages caused by the Reuss River. The two reaches with major damages at Wassen and Gurtnellen were reproduced in two hydraulic models. These models presented here, served to develop and examine the reconstruction concepts for these two reaches. Model tests led to a better understanding of morphological changes and their reason. Knowledge of the dynamics of flood and the processes involved, together with the application of a differentiated flood protection scheme, permitted solutions for reconstruction, regarding the morphology and dynamics of this steep mountain river. Trough this, a higher degree of safety against flood can be achieved for the future.

THE REUSS RIVER VALLEY

From the source in the Gotthard pass region, the Reuss River flows north towards the Lake of Lucerne. The Reuss River Valley shows a typical, post glacial relief. Numerous loose materials fill the ancient valley, originally formed by the Reuss glacier. The valley bottom therefore consists mainly of morainic material, changing with deposits from rock falls or land slides. At some sections rock outcrops are found. The slope of the river varies between 2.5 and 7.0 %, the mean slope being about 3.5 %. Coarse sediment and large residual boulders with mean diameters of up to 5 m and more form the river bed. These residual boulders are typical for the middle reach of the Reuss River delt with here. Over the last century the river bed remained stable. River banks were therefore protected only in some short reaches.

The catchment area in this middle reach is about 320 km^2 at Wassen and 420 km^2 at Gurtnellen. Mean discharges range between about 15 m^3/s and 20 m^3/s. Before the flood event of 1987, the 100-year flood was estimated to be in a range of 400 to 450 m^3/s.

Since historical times the Gotthard pass and the Reuss River Valley play an important role as north-south axis through the Swiss Alps. The importance as an european arterial route led to the construction of the Gotthard railway line at the end of the last century. After 1960, the construction of the Gotthard motorway signified the opening of a new axis of european importance through the Alps. Together with the old main road through the Reuss River Valley and over the Gotthard pass, an important traffic network leads today through this narrow valley and competes with the agricultural use and colonization of landscape.

International Conference on River Flood Hydraulics, edited by W.R.White

THE FLOOD EVENT OF AUGUST 1987

The flood event in 1987 with estimated peak discharges of about 500 m^3/s at Wassen and 600 m^3/s at Gurtnellen (Faeh et al. in these Proceedings) changed the valleys appearance considerably. The strong armour layer of the river bed was broken up, and further increasing discharge caused severe bank erosion. Where bank erosion was not limited, the river width grew up to 2-3 times the original size. Often, this was combined with a changement of the river's course. As a particular phenomenon, the forming of new meanders and the migraton of existing ones could be observed, which is quite unusual for mountain rivers with the above described slopes and a widely spread grain size distribution of bed material. Yet unknown is the influence of the residual boulder on these processes.

During the construction of the railway line, and later of the motorway, it was necessary to throw up banks of earth at several points. Due to of the narrowness of the valley and its steep flanks, this was necessary to gain space for these traffic lines. These banks, consisting of finer material could easily be eroded by the river when changing its course. This caused damage and destruction of these traffic lines and further, led to additional, heavy sediment input in the river. Aggradation of the river bed due to exceeding the transport capacity was the consequence. This again increased bank erosion processes and caused further damages.

At Wassen, the erosion of the left river bank exposed the foundation of one of the motorway bridge piers. The pier sank 1.2 m, and the whole bridge was in danger of collapse. Downstream of the motorway bridge, the main road was destroyed and thus interrupted. About 1 km upstream of the motorway bridge, the railway line was undermined by the flood. Hence, all traffic lines through the Reuss River Valley were interrupted at Wassen. Fig. 1 shows the situation at Wassen before and after the event as well as the damaged or destroyed objects. Fig. 2 gives an impression of the situation at Wassen after the flood.

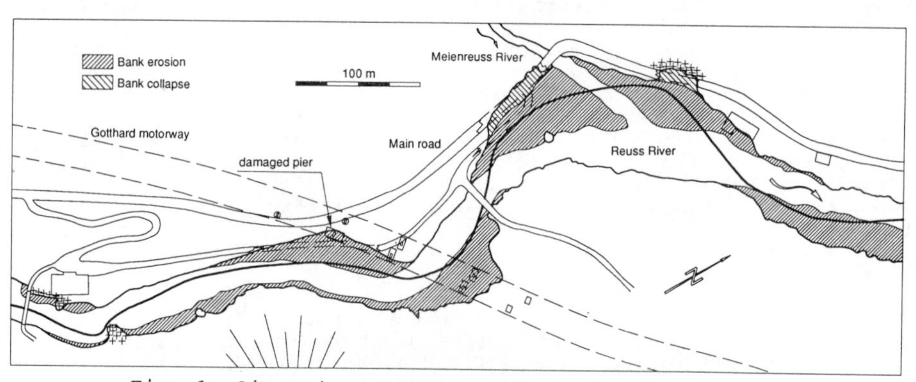

Fig. 1. Situation at Wassen after the flood event. The bold line represents the new thalweg.

At Gurtnellen, during the construction of the railway line, a part of a river bend above the village had been cut off and parts of a rock shelf had been removed. This led to the elemination of an assumed, previous fixing of the river's course. As Fig. 3 shows, the extreme discharge caused the reactivation of the existing meanders, combined with their migration downstream. The resulting, severe erosion at the outer banks of the meander bends caused the major damages. The Gotthard railway line was destroyed at the point, where the river bend had been cut off during the construction of the Gotthard railway line. The main road was destroyed at the upper end of Gurtnellen. A part of the cemetery and the presbytery were washed away completely and a second house was severly damaged. The arch bridge crossing the Reuss River at Gurtnellen was overflown, but did not collapse. Damages to agricultural land and landscape resulted also.

Fig. 2. Bank erosion and land slides at the confluence of the Reuss River and the Meienreuss River downstream of the damaged motorway bridge.

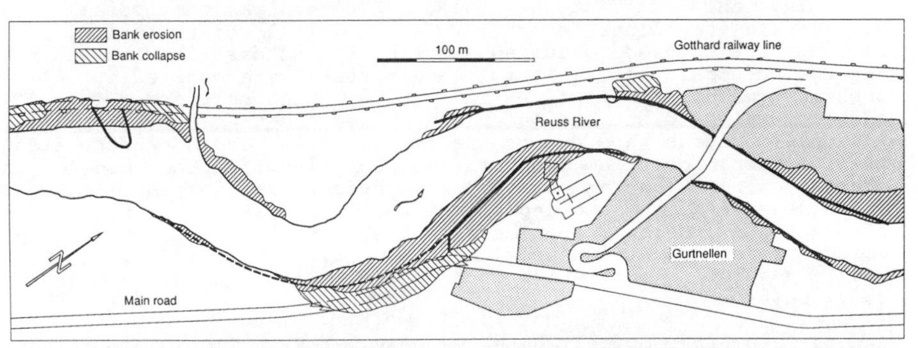

Fig. 3. Situation of the Gurtnellen reach after the flood event. Bank erosion due to meander migration caused major damages here. The figure also shows the main project elements for reconstruction (refer to text).

THE HYDRAULIC MODELS

After the immediate safety measures carried out with the help of Swiss Army units, the local government of Uri ordered extensive studies. Aim of these studies was to discover the causes of the catastrophy. Further studies should elaborate and examine the measures to be taken for the forthcoming reconstruction. Within the bounds of these extensive reconstruction projects, it was decided to investigate the two reaches at Wassen and Gurtnellen in hydraulic models.

A model scale of 1:60 was chosen for these models. They both are non-distorted models, based on the Froude law, in order to simulate the morphology correctly. Each of them reproduces a reach of about 1.5 km length of the Reuss River. The section at Wassen shows morphological forms, which are typical for steep alpine rivers with almost torrential regime. The mean slope is about 3.5 %. The central part of the model, just below the highway bridge, is characterized by its slope of about 6 % and a great concentration of residual boulders with mean diameters up to 4 m. These boulders form large step-pool systems, when rearranged at high discharges. At Gurtnellen the slope is more uniform and ranges between 2.5 and 3.5 %. Here the presence of many residual boulders (mean diameters up to 5 m) also characterizes the river's appearance. Typical for the section at Gurtnellen is the meandering course of the river. The meander length is about 350 m, the meander width about 120 m.

Special attention was given to the reproduction of sediment. The widely spread, coarse granulometry of bed material was recorded in nature by help of frequency-by-number transect sampling. This easy method allows quick samples of the top layer. It consists of measuring the diameter (b-axis) of all grains, which lie along a straight line across the sampling area. Anastasi (1984) and especially Fehr (1987) developed a model to convert the frequency-by-number transect sample to a sieve-by-weight distribution. This method also allows to take into account, whether the sample was made on a paved or a non-paved river bed. For practical use, sampling size d is limited to a range of $1 \text{ cm} < d < 1 \text{ m}$. A Fuller distribution is proposed to complete the sieve-by-weight distribution for smaller grain sizes.

Recording the sizes of the residual boulders was only possible by area-by-size sampling. In order to get a final distribution, including the aboved obtained sieve-by-weight distribution and the residual boulders, special preliminary tests were carried out. In a separate model, a mixture was put in, which corresponded to the sieve-by-weight distribution obtained from the transect samplings. Residual boulders were put on the top layer, according to the area-by-size samplings. Flow discharge was supplied to the model, in order to form an armour layer by hydraulical sorting. An areal frequency-by-weight sampling of the top layer was then taken including the residual boulders. This last sample was converted, using another conversion model proposed by Fehr (1987), to the sieze-by-weight distribution of the final mixture to be used in the model tests.

Strong geomorphological heterogeneity makes it impossible to have clear information about the internal composition of the river's steep banks. Here field analysis (for example by drilling) is almost impossible. Therefore, special tests had to be carried out in order to estimate the influence of variable assumptions concerning the percentage of the coarsest fractions. For practical use, a basic, finer sediment mixture was produced for both models. By adding a certain percentage of a second mixture of coarser particles only, the underground grain size distribution could be obtained, which was eventually varied locally and in time, according to the test results. A third, finer mixture corresponding to the mobile bed material was used to simulate the sediment input at the upstream end of both models. This mixture was determined by analyzing gravel banks which had been deposited during the flood event.

In order to obtain correct results, for example by measuring water-levels or scour depths, it is strongly advised to start the tests at an exact river bottom height. Correct conditions concerning channel roughness and resistance, (i.e. with an armoured layer formed before) are also necessary. Hence, before beginning a test, the river bed has to be built in on a higher level than the actual one in the field. Then flow discharge is supplied to the model. Finer grain sizes are washed out, and by hydraulical sorting, the armour layer is formed. This procedure requires time and the knowledge of the resulting movement of the river bed. In both models, armour layer forming is carried out with a discharge of 200-250 m^3/s during about 6-10 hours (model time). The sinking of the, initial river bed in the Gurtnellen model and the less steep reaches of the Wassen model is about 0.5-1 m. In the steeper reach of the Wassen model, the sinking is however about 3 m. Therefore a permanent surveillance and correction of river bed heights are necessary during these preparations.

MODEL TESTS AND DEVELOPMENT OF PROTECTION CONCEPTS

In a first phase, the immediate safety measures were examined in the hydraulic models. These tests showed that sufficient safety is ensured, until reconstruction works will begin.

Differentiated protection schemes for the definitive reconstruction concepts are now elaborated, based on the model test results. This happens in a close co-operation with the design engineers and the government of the Canton of Uri. One of the main points, is to allow different degrees of protection according to the importance of the object to be protected and the processes involved. This subject is treated further by Jaeggi and Zarn (in these Proceedings). Hence, if river control and reconstruction works can be adapted to this differentiated protection scheme, the resulting protection concept respects morphological conditions and river dynamics much better than classical river control works, which have to grant the same safety level on an entire river reach and often lead to exaggerated measures.

At Wassen, an upper design flood for the motorway bridge was fixed at 800 m^3/s, corresponding to the extreme flood. For the other objects in this area, design discharge was fixed at 500 m^3/s upstream of the confluence with the Meienreuss River and at 600 m^3/s downstream. This corresponds to the maximum observed flood in this reach. At Gurtnellen, design discharges are not yet fixed definitively, but will be somewhat higher, according to the hydrological conditions and the importance of the objects to be protected (village, international railway line).

The Wassen reach The first model tests served to examine and improve the immediate safety measures, which were mostly established before and during the construction of the hydraulic model. A riprap groyne had been built on the left bank upstream of the damaged motorway bridge pier. This groyne should guide the main current away from the left bank. Erosion of this bank, and thus a renewed endangering of the pier (which had meanwhile been lifted and underpinned), should be prevented. As a complementary measure, resulting from the first model tests, a new shaping of the river bottom was realised in this section. By blasting the residual boulders situated on the right half of the river bottom, the forming of a new thalweg was supported. This new shaping, together with the groyne, reduced the destructive action of the current at the left river bank considerably.

Two further piers of the bridge are situated on the outer bank of the following left-hand bend. Their foundation lies deeper than the river bed and the foundation of the damaged pier. Hidden in this bank, the concrete centring foundations had been left after the construction of the bridge. Together with the deep foundations of these two piers, they prevented the piers from being washed out in 1987. As an immediate measure this bank was protected by riprap.

Model tests had shown, that sufficient safety can be obtained by these immediate measures up to a discharge of about 350 m^3/s. At higher discharges, bank erosion started again. The resulting situation corresponded to the one observed in nature during the flood event. This confirmed the accuracy of the model and especially of the sediment mixtures used, as a reproduction of the morphological changes was very well possible.

The basic ideas for construction of the immediate measures and the above described tests led to the definite river control project. Upstream of the motorway bridge, the current should be guided away from the left bank. In the following left-hand bend, the outer bank should be protected against erosion completely. Downstream of the bridge, shaping of the river course and bank protection should support design discharges without greater damages. At higher discharges, limited damages in this area are allowed.

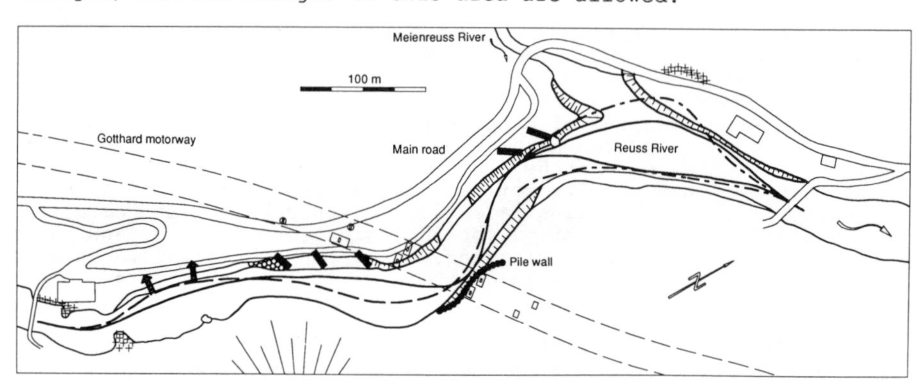

Fig. 4. Reconstruction project at Wassen. By the main protection elements (groynes, pile wall), flow is guided in such a way, that bank erosion is controlled (further explanations see text).

The main protection elements were designed in the following model tests. These elements are shown in Fig. 4. Three concrete groynes (weighing about 500 t), hidden in the left river bank, replace the riprap groyne and resist higher discharges. A reduction of the flow stress on these concrete groynes can be achieved by widening the river's course upstream of the groyne section. At this point, weak bank protection allows bank erosion. Through this, a weak right-hand bend is created, which leads the main current in the groyne section more towards the right bank. This can be seen, comparing the corresponding thalwegs in Fig. 4, which illustrate this dynamic behaviour. The current pressure on the concrete groynes also strongly depends on the behavior of the opposite, right bank at the groyne section. If bank erosion can take place here easily, this causes a further relief of the groynes. The erosion resistance of this bank is strongly influenced by its internal structure. Therefore, special tests were carried out by varying the erosion resistance of this bank. Even for extreme assumptions, the function of the groynes was checked.

The outer bank of the left-hand bend just below the bridge can be protected against erosion only by a rigid element. A 80 m long pile wall, with a foundation on rock, protects this bank and the piers resting on it even at discharges exceeding the extreme flood. The pile wall is hidden by riprap, which is washed away at discharges of about 400-450 m^3/s.

Downstream of the motorway bridge, at the confluence of the Reuss River and the Meienreuss River (a tributary with discharges of about 1/5 of those of the Reuss River), the forming of different branches can be observed. The dashed-dotted lines in Fig. 4 represent thalwegs, corresponding to the basic river dynamics without the influence of groynes in this area. The inner branch carries low and mean flows. The outer branch develops at high discharges approaching the extreme flood. This behavior corresponds to the observations made in nature. The outer branch is almost identical with the one formed in 1987.

Fig. 5. Upstream view of the Wassen model from a similar viewpoint as in Figure 2.

The solid lines in Fig. 4 represent the corresponding branches, forming under the influence of two additional concrete groynes in this area. At high discharges, the current is guided by these two groynes in a way, that the inner branch takes up a considerable part of the flood. This reduces the erosion tendency on the left river bank, which is then able to withstand discharges of about 500 m^3/s of the Reuss River, together with a discharge of 100 m^3/s of the Meienreuss River. The riprap protection on this bank consists of blocks with a mean weight of 4 t. Fig. 5 shows the model after a test with discharges ges up to the maximum observed flood.

The Gurtnellen reach At Gurtnellen, the immediate safety measures consisted basically of two elements. A concrete wall, founded on piles reaching rock, was built to separate the railway line and the river at the left bank upstream of the village. In the area of the village itself and on the outher bank of the large left-hand river bend at the entrance of Gurtnellen, temporary wooden bank protections were built. The first model tests showed a resistance to flow, up to a discharge of about 350-450 m^3/s of these wooden protections.

In the village, the Reuss River is crossed by an arch bridge, which narrows the flow section considerably. Discharges exceeding 500 m^3/s cause an overflow of the bridge and thus flooding parts of the village. This mainly is due to the fact, that main current hits the left abutment of the bridge instead of arriving at the bridge at the middle of its opening. This behavior, corresponding to what had happened in 1987, could be reproduced very precisely in the model. In 1987, the bridge had not been destroyed because of its extreme strong foundation on rock. During the first tests, an effect was noticed, which was not realised as much as during and after the flood event. It was the exposure of a rock shelf on the outer bank of the left-hand bend, which had partly been cut off during the construction of the railway line. Here, it should be mentioned, that in both models rock structures in the underground had also been reproduced, according to the geologist. Fig. 6 shows the rock shelf on a picture, taken shortly after the flood event. This shelf, together with the ancient, now cut off part of the river bend, presumeably fixed the meanders at Gurtnellen in earlier times.

Fig. 6. Exposed rock shelf and damaged railway line upstream of Gurtnellen. Here a part of an ancient river bend had been cut off (courtesy T.R. Schneider, Uerikon).

One of the main project ideas at Gurtnellen, was to use the shelf as an element of meander fixing by increasing its height with concrete. Fig. 7 shows the proposed shape of tis raised shelf in the hydraulic model.

The outer bank of the following left-hand bend had been strongly eroded in 1987 (see Fig. 3). A careful shaping of this bend and a riprap protection, which will be covered with earth and vegetation, garantees a stable river bank up to a discharge of the maximum observed flood. At higher discharges bank erosion is tolerated at this point.

Another most important point was the above described arch bridge in the center of the village. With its relatively small area of flow, it represents a flow constriction. Discharges even smaller than the maximum observed flood occupy the entire flow section. If discharge then further increases, this leads to flow under pressure and overflow of the bridge. The historical arch bridge characterizes the appearance of the village. Therefore the decision was made, to keep the ancient bridge. This decision and an expected design discharge for the village reach being greater than the maximum observed flood led to the necessety of careful guidance of flood through the village. This can only be achieved by vertical walls, leaving enough space between them. Careful shaping of the wall on the left bank upstream of the bridge guides the current more away from the bridge's left abutment to its middle. Roughness elements (vertical concrete bars) are added on the walls. They reduce the flow velocity near the wall, hence flow is concentrated more to the middle of the flume. By this measure, flow guiding to the middle of the bridge remains optimal even at extreme flows; overflow of the bridge now occurs at a discharge of about 700 m^3/s. Further, the roughness elements reduce the scour at the base of the walls considerably.

Fig. 7. Downstream view of the Gurtnellen model. In the foreground, the enlarged rock shelf can be seen. In the village, the arch bridge crosses the Reuss River.

As mentioned above, much consideration is given to the appearance of the village. From this point of view, a solution with a wide 'channel' through the village does not satisfy. Therefore the vertical walls will be hidden by riprap, which again will be covered for esthetic reasons. The resulting appearance will not much differ from that of Gurtnellen before August 1987. Special consideration was given to the designing of this riprap. At a discharge of about 400 m^3/s it has to be eroded, in order to garantee the full cross section between the walls being free for higher discharges.

The solution with a bridge, where design flood passes under pressure is unusual. This is only possible, if such a situation does not lead to greater damages at extreme discharges even when carrying floating wood. Tests concerning this aspect showed that at high discharges, due to the elevated velocity of flow in the middle of the river, tree-trunks arrive parallel to the flow direction at the middle of the bridge. They pass below it without problems, even when the bridge is overflown. At discharges approaching the design flood, overflow of the bridge, and thus flooding parts of the village is tolerated. Measurments of flow depth and velocity will provide the information to establish danger zones, according to the separation in extreme flooded areas and moderate flooded areas, as described by Jaeggi and Zarn (in these Proceedings).

CONCLUSIONS

Hydraulic models of steep mountain rivers require a lot of preparation work for each test, especially if tests are carried out up to discharches which exceed maximum observed flood. Wide grain size distribution demands special procedures to form the initial river bed before beginning each test. Superelevation of the river bottom and a following hydraulical sorting of bed material are necessary each time, in order to form an armour layer at the desired river bed level.

A correct modelling of the river dynamics and morphological changes is necessary when projects are based on these processes. Hence, undistorted model have to be used.

Attention has to be paid to the internal composition of river banks. Its influence can be estimated by testing extreme assumptions concerning erosion resistance of river banks.

The described reconstruction projects show how a protection concept against floods, based on differentiated degrees of protections may admit projects, which respect morphological conditions and river dynamics better than projects based on uniform degrees of protection. Knowledge of the processes involved during floods and the river dynamics at extreme discharges are the base to design protection elements which show their effect according to the magnitude of flow corresponding to the the discharge they are designed for.

At Wassen, bank erosion as a main damage process can be controlled by hidden protection elements. At Gurtnellen, an unconventional solution is proposed to control and stop meander migration and thus limit further damages due to bank erosion resulting from this process.

The aspect of the Reuss River will not be changed essentially by the reconstruction works, necessary after the flood of 1987. Even, if for the future a higher safety against flood can be achieved.

REFERENCES

Anastasi, G. (1984): "Geschiebeanalysen im Felde unter Berücksichtigung von Grobkomponenten", Mitteilungen der Versuchsanstalt für Wasserbau, Hydrologie und Glaziologie, ETH Zürich, Nr. 70

Faeh, R., Koella, E., Naef F. (In press): "The flood in the Reuss Valley in August 1987 - A Computer Aided Reconstruction of a Flood in a Mountain Region", Proc. Int. Conference on River Flood Hydraulics, Wallingford, England

Fehr, R. (1987): "Geschiebeanalysen in Gebirgsflüssen", Mitteilungen der Versuchsanstalt für Wasserbau, Hydrologie und Glaziologie, ETH Zürich, Nr. 92

Jaeggi, M.N.R. and Zarn, B. (In press): "A New Policy in Designing a Flood Protection Scheme as a Consequence of the 1987 Floods in the Swiss Alps", Proc. Int. Conference on River Flood Hydraulics, Wallingford, England

PAPER J3

International Conference on
RIVER FLOOD HYDRAULICS
17-20 September, 1990

Bed Topographies and Sediment Transport during Flood in Mountainous Rivers

Kazuyoshi Hasegawa Dept. of Civil Enginrng.
Hokkaido University
Akio Mori ditto
Shinn Ishikawa ditto

ABSTRACT

Effects of bed topographies and plane forms of mountainous rivers on sediment transport during floods were analyzed from observations of two streams, Shiramizu and Ogawa, in Hokkaido, Japan. It was found through the observations that longitudinal bed forms in mountainous rivers consist of three kinds of topographical units with different characters, classified with magnitudes of wave lengths: The first is the large channel unit with 100-400m wave length, which is formed by large earth transfers, like debris flows, and is accompanied with channel branches; the second is the medium channel unit with 20-80m wave length, which has two kinds of origins of antidunes and alternating bars; the third is the small channel unit called "ribs" or "step-pools" with 2-20m wave length, which also has two kinds of origins of antidunes and standing waves on the water surface. A large quantity of sediment moves through channel change on large channel unit during large floods. The medium channel unit initiates migrations to yield sediments caused by the breaking of ribs by a flood.
Ribs or step-pools play a role in controlling the discharge of fine materials like suspended sediment.

INTRODUCTION

Recently, bed topographies and flow resistance in mountainous rivers have become the subject of wider and wider investigation, due to the necessity to predict high water level or the amount of yielded sediments during a flood. Bed topographies closely relate to the flow resistance and sediment transport. Several criteria for bed configuration in mountainous rivers have been proposed. However, classification into configurations seems not yet to be complete, and the origins of the configurations are not well enough clarified for a satisfactory understanding of the relations between each configuration and sediment transport. In this paper, investigations of three study sections in two mountainous streams are reported, and the origins of bed configurations and the mechanisms of sediment yield or transport through flood are analyzed.

STUDY SECTIONS

The two streams studied, Shiramizu River and Ogawa River, are located near Sapporo western Hokkaido as shown in Fig.1. The basins are constituted of rocks of the tertiary period, and both streams flow down from Mt. Muine, an extinct volcano, as can be seen in

International Conference on River Flood Hydraulics, edited by W.R.White

Fig.2. There are great differences between two streams at the following points. While the Ogawa basin is covered with thick deposition layer caused by a major land slide which is estimated to have occurred seven to ten thousand years ago and the stream is dissecting the debris to form steep valley wall, no deposition layer is seen and the dissected valley is wider in the Shiramizu basin; the stream flows spread to often braid in the flood plane. Catchment areas and length of the two streams are shown in TABLE 1. One study section is adopted in Ogawa (hereafter called OS) and two sections are in Shiramizu (hereafter called S-I and S-II). Characteristics for these study sections are also indicated in TABLE 1. Both streams experienced a medium flood in September 1985 within the observation term, whose recurrence interval is estimated at approximately 10-years or less (hereafter written as '1985/9 flood'). The large flood nearest the observation term occurred in August 1981 (hereafter written as '1981/8 flood'). The recurrence interval for peak discharge is evaluated over 10-years although that for total rainfalls during this flood is evaluated over 100-years. Peak discharges with respect to the both and snow melting flood are listed in TABLE 2.

RESULTS OF TOPOGRAPHICAL SURVEY FOR STUDY SECTIONS

Three topographical units in the Ogawa study section Fig.3 (b) shows longitudinal bed profile in OS, from which the altitude of mean bed slope (=0.102) is subtracted. The wave forms can be classified into three kinds of topographical units: Saw teeth-like shapes in the figure are the smallest of the channel units. The number of these undulations amounts to 242 individuals in this study section. Average wavelength of them is 4.2m long. Fig.4 shows a plane form of a part of the OS (OS-1; corresponds to 100-300m reach of Fig.3). It is found from the figure that these small channel units consist of rounded steps and pools surrounded by the steps. This kind of channel unit is often called "step-pool" (Whittaker & Jaeggi(1982)); however, this seems to correspond with "Cascades" proposed by Grant et al.(in print.), judging from the bed slope. Medium channel units with 43m mean wavelength are found in Fig.3(b). This kind of undulation has a shape steep front slope and gentle back slope. The height of the front of this undulation exceeds 1m. The five real lines in Fig.4 transversing the channel indicate the

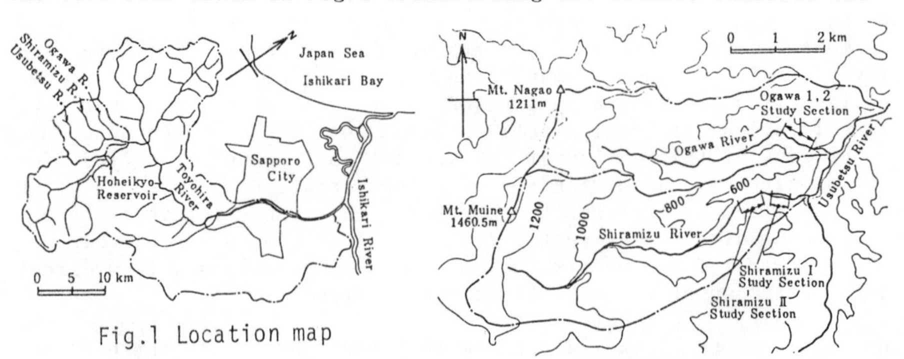

Fig.1 Location map

Fig.2 Sketch of study section

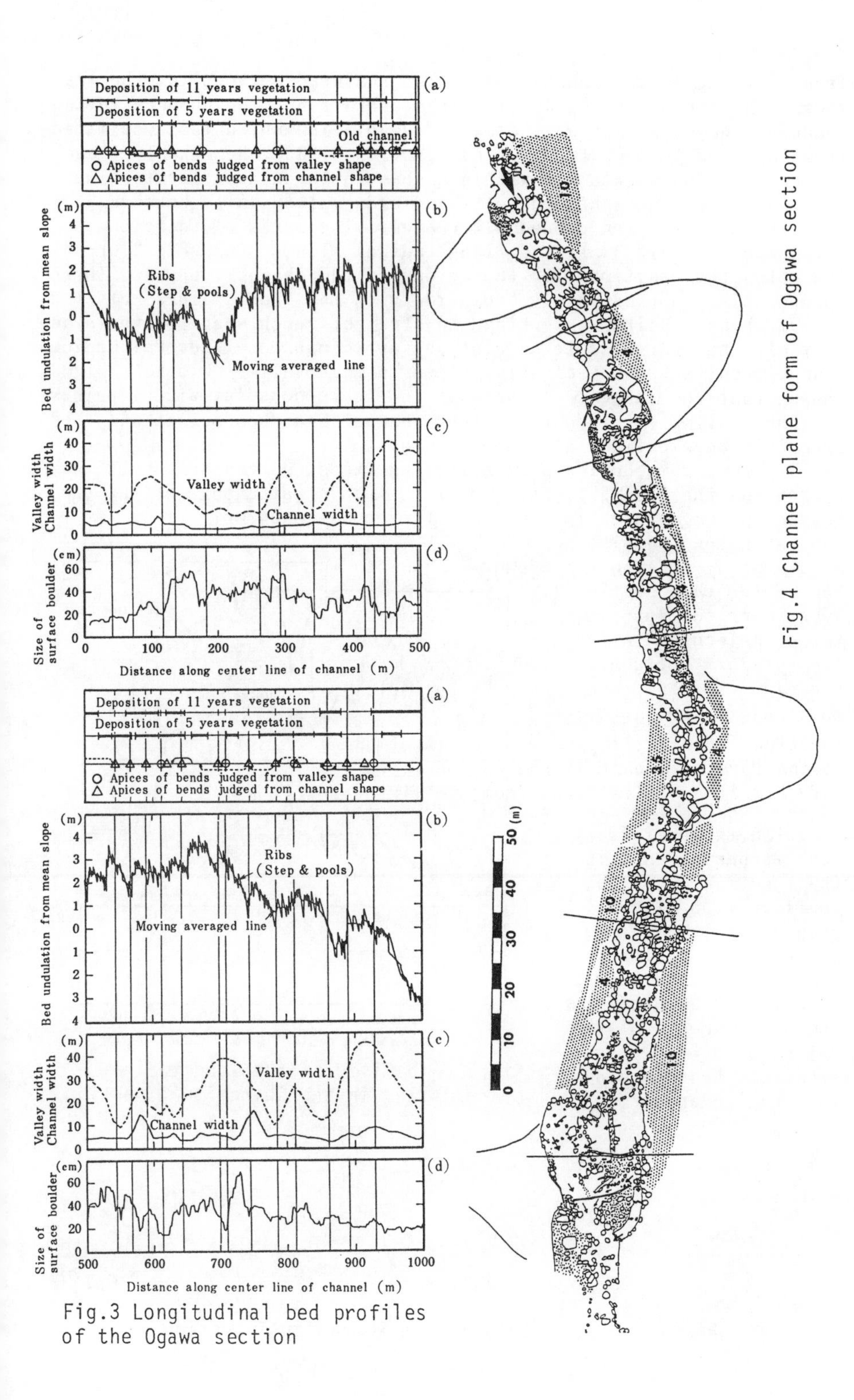

Fig.3 Longitudinal bed profiles of the Ogawa section

Fig.4 Channel plane form of Ogawa section

front of the medium channel unit. The shadowed segment in the map shows the deposition of debris with vegetation. The numbers in the shadowed segments express the age of vegetation which was estimated from the diameters of trees at survey time (1985). Remarkably, each segment is just contained within a space between two front lines, and further, the right and left hand side valley walls between the two front lines are eroded alternately. The marks of circles and triangles in Fig.3(a) and longitudinal lines in Fig.3(b)-(d) indicate the positions for the apices of the channel bends. These points also approximately coincide with the front lines of the medium channel units, excepting the straight reach where there is no apex of bend. Large scale undulations are composed of several medium channel units. They closely relate to the valley width. Fig.3 shows that the large scale undulation crests occur at wider points of the valley. It is notable that channel branches arise and bed materials become finer at these points.

Except for some boulders constituting steps, no channel unit was broken by the 1985/9 flood. Besides, no great change of the bed topography is apparently caused by the annual snow melt flood.

Bed variation in Shiramizu-I study section

Survey for this section were carried out in twice, before and after the 1985/9 flood. Fig.5(a) is the comparison of the longitudinal bed profiles before and after the flood. It is possible as in the OS to distinguish three kinds of bed topographies in the section, but the configuration of small channel unit is considerably different from that of the OS. As seen in Fig.6, boulders composing crests of the units or steps align straight transversing to the channel.

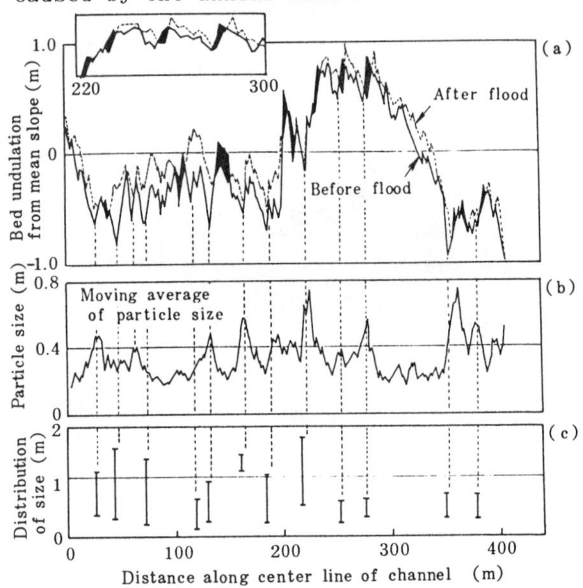

Fig.5 Comparison of the longitudinal bed profiles in the Shiramizu I section

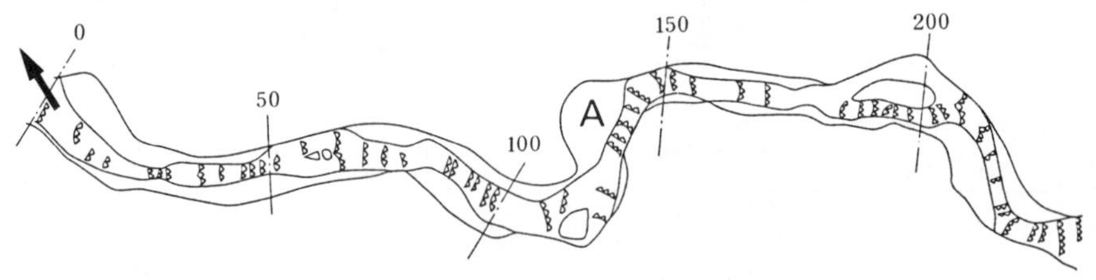

Fig.6 Crests of ribs in the Shiramizu I section

This type of channel unit is often called "ribs" (McDonald & Day (1978)). The 1985/9 flood made 3 ribs advance in the downstream direction and 4 ribs retreat in the upstream direction, and 7 ribs within the study section broke. Furthermore, it yielded 26 new ribs in the section. On the other hand, undulations of medium scale with 20-40m wavelengths showed very characteristic change as the frontage of crest was scoured and the rear of crest was accreted to. As a result, they ascended in the upstream direction. Fig.5(b) illustrates the spatial moving average for the size of surface boulders. The place where large boulders gather often corresponds to a trough of the medium channel unit. The reason why has not been determined so far; however, it seems likely that the ribs composed of large boulders tend to bring about this kind of medium channel unit.
It is seen in Fig.5(a) and Fig.6 that the large channel unit with about 200m average wave length closely relates to the channel plan form, especially in the curvature of bend. In fact, accretion over 2m height was observed near the 130m point (marked A in Fig.6) after the flood, where the channel suddenly bends and flow rushes through the upper straight reach to strike against bank. But, the large channel unit in S-I section is not associated with any channel branches, and is considered to have originally been formed by a large meandering which had had some other origin.

Shiramizu-II study section with well developed branch channels

Fig.8 shows the braided channels of S-II section. There lie remarkable complex branches in the channels. However, water does not always run through all branch channels. Ordinary, only one or a few channels are filled by flow and the others are abandoned. Fig.7 is a longitudinal bed profile seen along the main channel. Three kinds of bed undulations can be seen similarly as in other study sections. In this survey, small channel units with 5.0m average wave length seen in a partial section were similar to ribs. And ones in other partial sections resemble step-pools in OS. The medium channel unit which has a 30-100m wave length presents a different aspect; it is accompanied by the small scale branched channels which are surrounded by islands covered by comparatively young vegetation. the large channel units which stand at peaks A,B,C are closely relate to branching of the channels: While many branches are developed in the area from back-slope with gentle inclination to the crest, the branches are arranged such that they combine together from the crest to the front-slope with steep inclination. Concerning this matter, the width between river terraces also correlates to large scale bed undulations and the development of channel branches.

DISCUSSION OF ORIGINS OF CHANNEL UNITS AND SEDIMENT TRANSPORTS

Small channel units The origin of ribs or step-pools was considered as coarsening of the top layer and formation of antidunes by Whittaker(1982), and after that, by Ashida et al.(1984). Fig.9 is the regime criteria for dunes, flat bed and antidunes proposed by Hayashi(1970). When the data are plotted from small channel units of S-I section using the hydraulics condition for a half of the peak discharge in 1985/9 flood, they drop in the antidunes area, as shown by the white circles in the figure. However, if the hydraulics conditions for the peak discharge are used, the resulting plots are

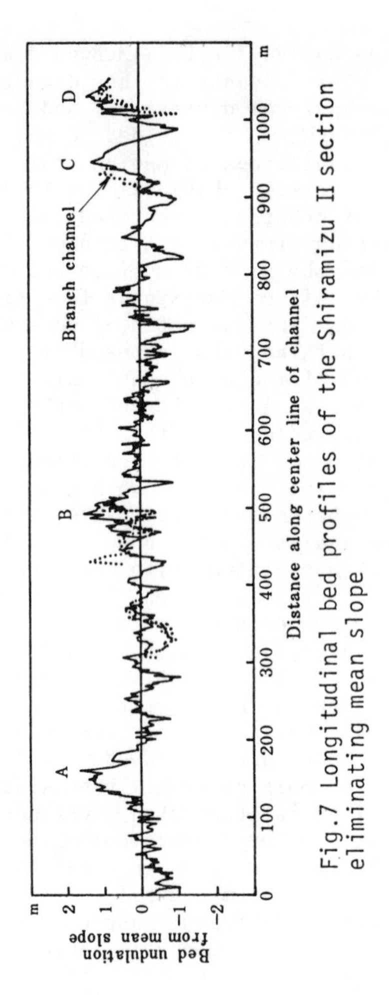

Fig.7 Longitudinal bed profiles of the Shiramizu II section eliminating mean slope

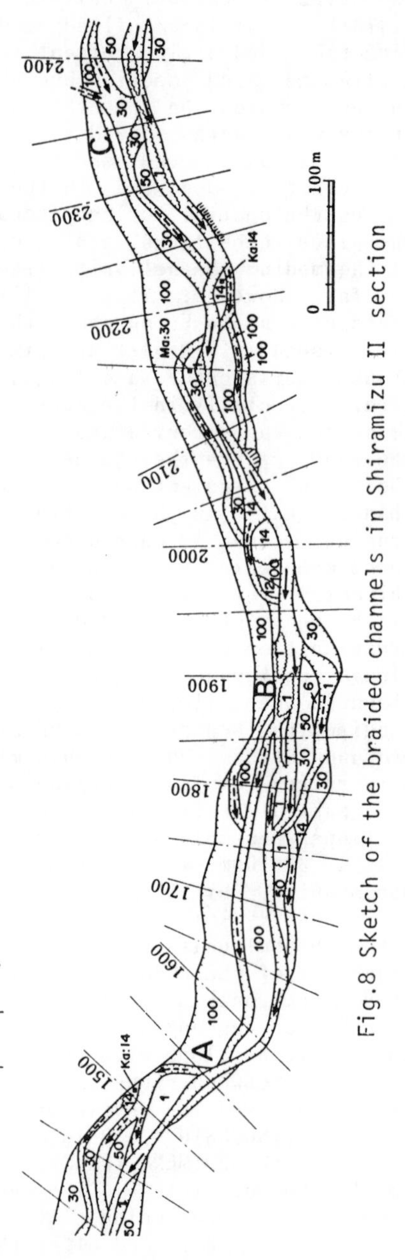

Fig.8 Sketch of the braided channels in Shiramizu II section

out of the antidunes area. Therefore, the small channel units seen in S-I section originate from antidunes generated by approximately half of the peak discharge in a flood with a 10-year recurrence interval (hereafter 10-year flood) or a flood with an over 10-year recurrence interval (over 10-year flood). Because their features are roughly 2-dimensional with no accompanying pools, they do not function as storage mechanisms for fine sediments.

On the other hand, small channel units in OS and S-II section show a different nature: Fig.10 shows the spectral density for the bed undulation within S-II calculated by MEM. Interestingly, dominant wavelengths seem to be integral multiples of 2 of the minimum dominant wavelengths. The same tendency appears in the case of OS. This suggests the origin of small channel units in OS etc. relates to the surface waves on supercritical flow. Fig.11 illustrates the theoretical relations between lateral mode number N and the longitudinal wave length λ_N in Airy waves where the primary wave length in the lateral direction was chosen at 1.8H (H= mean water depth). Used discharge was 42 m^3/s in S-II and 40 m^3/s in OS respectively and mean velocities were calculated from the Hey(1979) equation. When investigating the abscissas corresponding to the ordinates for observed dominant wavelengths on the curves, they seem to take discrete integral values. Conversely, the above discharges and primary wavelength were sought in order to satisfy the relations. It is noteworthy that the chosen discharges are considerably large (corresponding to the 1981/8 flood), and both Froude Numbers take values slightly over unity, under which standing waves often occur. Fig.12 shows an example of our experimental results to confirm the influence of surface waves upon bed shear stresses. Obviously even high frequency components for water surface displacements are reflected in the variation of bed shear stresses with opposite phase. Therefore, the hypothesis for standing waves to form a step-pool system is quite valid. This kind of channel unit is 3-dimensional accompanied with a deep pools, and it may play a role as storage to keep fine sediments (Ashida, Takahashi & Sawada (1976)).

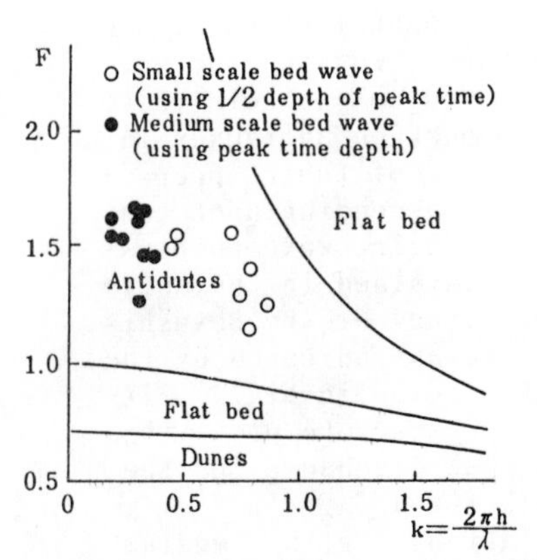

Fig.9 Regime criteria on small scale bed waves by Hayashi(1970)

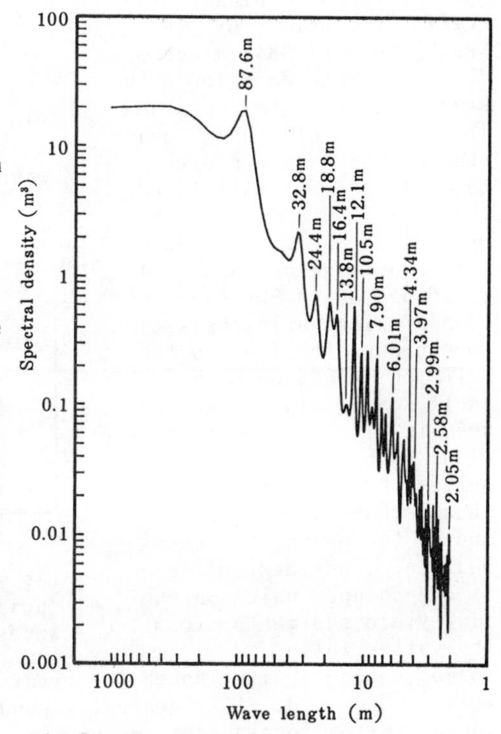

Fig.10 Spectral density for the bed profile of the Shiramizu II section calculated by MEM

Medium channel units These also have two kinds of origins: Medium channel units in S-I must be antidunes in the light of their properties of ascending upstream and for their wave numbers to be contained in the antidunes area of the Hayashi criteria as indicated by the black circles in Fig.9. It was necessary to plot the data peak discharge for the 1985/9 flood.

Undulations with medium scales in OS and S-II can be considered as single row alternating bars and double rows alternating bars respectively. According to the regime criteria by the Kuroki- Kishi(1984) diagram (Fig.13), the data for both study sections are contained in the areas of single and double row bars in either case, large or small flood, though S-I data fall in the area of no bars. Alternative wall scours seen in Fig.4 would be caused by the action of alternating bars to concentrate the flow to the left or right bank. Next, small scale islands such as seen in Fig.8 can be thought of as double row bars themselves. Depositions forming these channel units become one of the major sources of sediments; besides, effects of the channel units on the flow yield sediments from the valley walls.

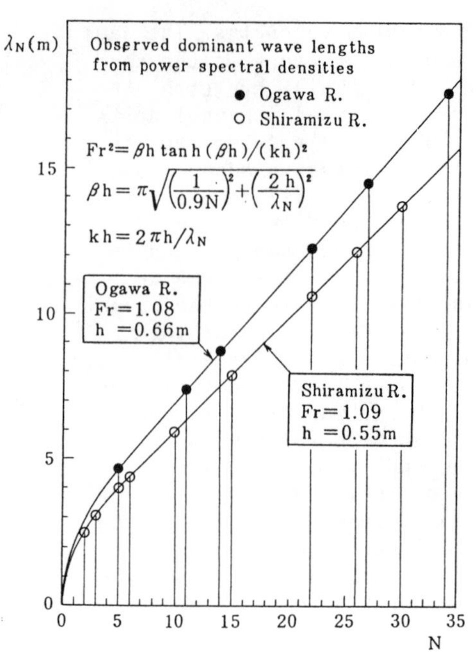

Fig.11 Relation between lateral mode number and flow directional wave length of the bed form

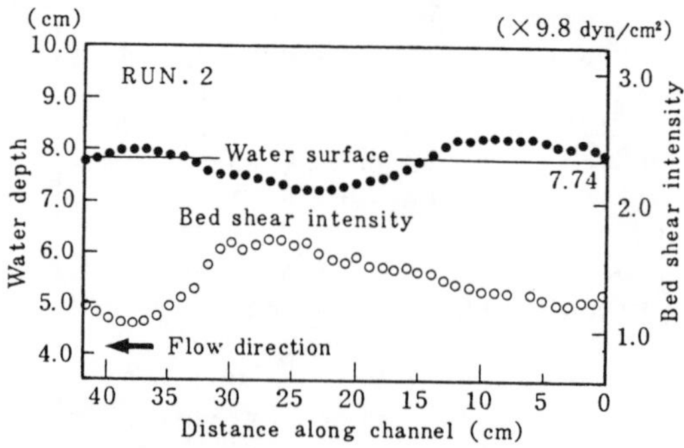

Fig.12 Relation between water surface profile of standing waves and bed shear stress

Large channel units Though the origin of this kind of unit is not well understood, it is generally assumed that they were formed by large valley-forming soil movements, such as landslides. However, variations on this channel unit proceed through alterations in branched channels, whose mechanisms may depend upon the fact that flood flow in mountainous river is in supercritical state in almost all reaches. One can find the following characteristics with supercritical flow near a junction with a mountainous river: First, as the upstream state of flow does not depend upon the downstream conditions, the ratio of distributed discharge to main flow discharge can be decided arbitrarily within a limited range, according to the entrance conditions. Second, abrupt width change sudden distribution change at a junction tend to introduce a hydraulic jump. Fig.14 is the model for braided channels in S-II, and Fig.15 is the simulation result for flow by means of the conservation finite differences method for the 1-dimensional momentum equation giving a discharge close to peak discharge in a 10-year flood. Obviously, there occurs a hydraulic jump at the junction point: It is easy to consider that a great quantity of sediments will be rapidly deposited there and the present channels will be blocked, with a strong possibility the flow will rush into new channels. Thus, sometimes scouring or dissecting old islands, the large channel unit transforms the landscape of the riverbed, transporting large amounts of sediments to lower areas.

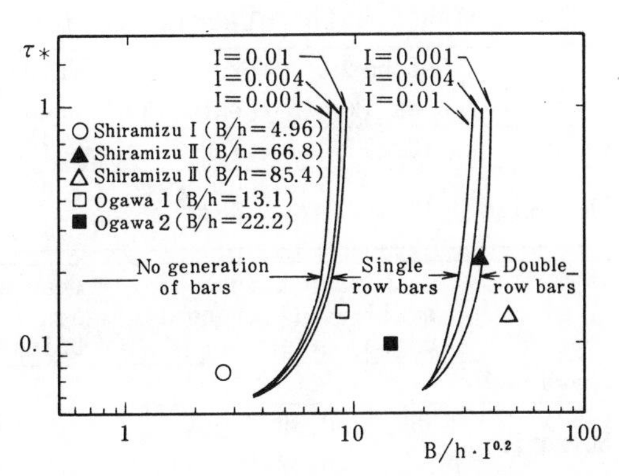

Fig.13 Regime criteria to distinguish small and medium scale bed waves by Kuroki and Kishi(1984)

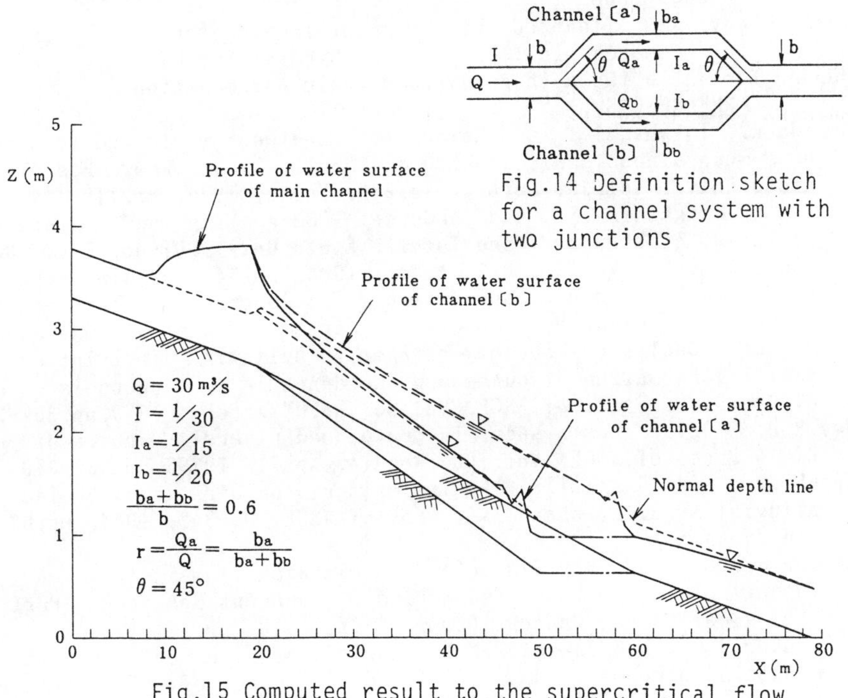

Fig.14 Definition sketch for a channel system with two junctions

Fig.15 Computed result to the supercritical flow of the channel system with two junctions

TABLE 1 Characteristics for two study sections

	Catchment area (km^2)	Total length (km)	Values of study sections Length (km)	Mean slope	D_{84} (m)	D_{50} (m)
Ogawa	10.08	7.0	1.0	0.102	0.54	0.17
Shiramizu	16.46	8.2	I 0.4	0.0436	0.36	0.18
			II 1.0	0.0495	0.25	0.07

		Mean wave height of small scale channel units (m)	Mean wave length of small scale channel units (m)	Width in peak flood (m)
Ogawa		0.58	4.2	22.2
Shiramizu	I	0.39	5.5	9.0
	II	0.42	5.4	31.8

TABLE 2 Experimented floods

		Run off discharge from snow melting (Obserbed)	Peak discharge for 1985/9 flood (Observed in Sept.1st 1985)	Peak discharge for 1981/8 flood (Estimated from precipitation data)
Ogawa		9.0 (m^3/sec)	12.0 (m^3/sec)	40.0 (m^3/sec)
Shiramizu	I	15.0 (m^3/sec)	42.0 (m^3/sec)	100.0 (m^3/sec)
	II	12.0 (m^3/sec)	33.0 (m^3/sec)	80.0 (m^3/sec)

ACKNOWLEDGMENT

This study was financed by a grant-in-aid for developmental scientific research in 1989 provided by Ministry of Education in Japan, for which the authors express their appreciation.

REFERENCES

Ashida, K., Takahashi, T. and Sawada, T.: 'Sediment yield and transport on a mountainous small watershed', Bull. Disas. Prev. Res. Inst., Kyoto Univ., Vol.26, Part 3, No.240, Sept., 1976, pp.119-144

Ashida, K., Egashira, S. and Ando, N.: 'Generation and geometric features of step-pool bed forms', Kyoto Univ., Disas. Prev. Res. Inst. Annuals, Vol.27, B-2, April, 1984, pp.341-353 (in Japanese)

Grant, G.E., Swanson, F.J. and Wolman, M.G.: 'Morphology and morphogenesis of boulder-bed mountain streams, Western Cascades, Oregon', Geological Society of America Bulletin, (in printing)

Hayashi, T.: 'Formation of dunes and antidunes in open channels', Jour. of Hy. Div., Proc. of ASCE, Vol.96, No.HY2, Feb., 1970, pp.357-366

Hey, R.D.: 'Flow resistance in gravel-bed rivers', Jour. of Hy. Div., Proc. of ASCE, Vol.105, No.HY4, April, 1979, pp.365-379

Kuroki, M. and Kishi, T.: 'Regime criteria on bars and braids in alluvial straight channels', Proc. of JSCE, No.342, 1984, pp.87-96 (in Japanese)

McDonald, B.C. and Day, T.J.: 'An experimental flume study on the formation of transverse ribs', Current Research, Part A, Geological Survey Canada, Paper 78-1a, 1978, pp.441-451

Whittaker, J.G. and Jaeggi, M.N.R.: 'Origin of step-pool systems in mountain streams', Jour. of Hy. Div., Proc. of ASCE, Vol.108, No.HY6, June, 1982, pp.758-773

Physical and Numerical Modelling

PAPER K1

International Conference on

RIVER FLOOD HYDRAULICS

17-20 September, 1990

Cross-section location in 1-D models

Dr P G Samuels CEng MICE MIWEM
Section Manager, River Engineering Department

Hydraulics Research, Wallingford, UK

ABSTRACT

The fundamental analytic tool for many river flood studies is a one dimensional (1-D) model of flow in an open channel. Several models are in widespread use which have originated from government agencies, universities, specialist hydraulic laboratories or in-house research by consulting engineers. All the models, however, are built from similar components; the St Venant equations, a numerical discretisation method such as the Preissmann scheme or the Abbott-Ionescu scheme, other computational algorithms and data for the site of application. The success or otherwise of an application depends to a large extent on the selection of suitable cross sections to form the discrete representation of the natural river geometry. This selection is part of the art of river modelling and it is likely that no two experts would choose precisely the same location for the cross-sections. The reason for this is that the complexity of the flow equations and natural geometry render full analytic study impossible. Each expert will have his own set of rules based on experience. This paper gives some rules for cross section location developed at Hydraulics Research Ltd and discusses the interaction between numerical methods, section location, flow conditions and calculation stability.

1 INTRODUCTION

The choice of spacing of river cross sections is fundamental to the success of the application of a computational hydrodynamic model. The art is to choose sufficiently frequent sections to describe the hydraulic behaviour of the channel or system of channels with acceptable precision but on the other hand giving a project which the client can afford and the consultant (if any) can run at a profit. Requiring too much data gives unnecessary expense in its collection, processing and simulation and too little data may lead to calculation instabilities and gross inaccuracies. Hitherto the selection of cross sections has been based on the experience of the modeller of similar applications and knowing the idiosyncrasies of his modelling system. If the client has invited competitive tenders for a modelling project then he has to decide whether the model data density specified are sufficient to deliver the

International Conference on River Flood Hydraulics, edited by W.R.White

confidence he requires in the simulation or whether the modelling programme and cost are likely to be extended to deliver the result.

This paper gives some guidelines used at Hydraulics Research Ltd (HR) to select cross sections in 1-D river models. These have been developed over a number of years from a mixture of theoretical analysis and experience. It is assumed that the channel hydraulics are represented by the St Venant equations of open channel flow and that approximate numerical solutions are generated using a consistent and stable method such as the Preissmann box scheme or the Abbott-Ionescu scheme. Details of these standard equations and schemes are widely available, see for example Abbott (1979) and Cunge et al (1980).

2 STATING THE OBVIOUS

At the outset of a study the location of some model sections is patently obvious. Sections should be sited at:

(1) the model limits;

(2) either side of structures (which act as internal boundaries);

(3) at sites of prime importance to the client; and

(4) at all flow and level measurement stations.

Only rarely will these sections be sufficient to undertake hydraulic simulations. More sections are needed but where should they be put?

3 APPLYING COMMON SENSE

Some further rules can be established from considering for what the cross section data is going to be used. The propagation of flood waves (or tides) along a river broadly is determined by storage, conveyance and controls. In a model storage and conveyance are eventually averaged between pairs of cross sections whereas controls are at discrete locations. Here there is a potential conflict. The low flow profile in a river is often a sequence of pools and riffles, with the water level in the pools being controlled by critical flow over the riffles. This indicates that sections should be located at the riffles but these are not then representative of the river as a whole. Hence a model designed for flood flow computation may not reproduce low flow profiles correctly and vice-versa.

Often a natural river will have areas of static offbank storage in flood conditions which are not described by the model cross sections. These may be included by introducing a fictitious "mathematical" width of cross section, see Cunge et al (1980) pp23,4, or from a more detailed treatment of the equivalent river;

see Samuels and Gray (1982) and Samuels (1990). A natural river will often meander in its valley floor which will cause the effective water surface slope on the floodplains to differ from that along the main channel. In a one-dimensional model with freely draining flood plains (ie not protected by an embankment), the section lines must be normal to the approximate direction of flow. The flood plain section lines should not intersect within the flood envelope. This will constrain the layout of cross sections in channels that have a high sinuosity. Of course it is proper to question whether the flow can be treated adequately as one dimensional in such cases. Figure 1 illustrates this problem for the River Teme near its confluence with the River Severn at Worcester.

A further common sense argument is that it should be possible to use larger space steps in larger rivers. An intuitive criterion of this sort may take the form:

$$\Delta x \approx kB \tag{1}$$

where Δx is the space step (distance between cross sections), k is a constant and B is the surface width. At HR Ltd for a number of years the value of k has been taken as 10 to 20 and B to be the bankfull width of the main channel. Cunge et al (1980) pp143 to 174 discuss quite fully how to choose representative cross-sections for 1-D river models.

4 APPLYING MATHEMATICS

4.1 The backwater length

A characteristic length scale, L, for a river flowing subcritically is derived by Samuels (1989) as

$$L = 0.7\ D/s \tag{2}$$

where D is the (bankfull) depth of flow and s is the surface or main channel slope. Over this length, the backwater upstream of a control or other disturbance decays to 0.1 of the original value. The backwater curve is approximately an exponential perturbation to the normal depth line. It may be reasoned that, since the water surface profile in a computational model is fitted most accurately by a series of straight line segments (for Preissmann's scheme), then this exponential should be represented by several segments. To allow about four cross sections in the backwater length we set

$$\Delta x < 0.2\ D/s$$

or $$\Delta x < 0.2\ D/[s\ (1-Fr^2)]$$

if the Froude number Fr is appreciable. The form of this estimate shows two things:

(1) for shallow flows, less than bankfull, a smaller space step may be required; and

(2) for flows that are nearly critical the distance steps in the model need to be smaller.

Having assumed subcritical flow in this analysis, it gives no indication of the step size required for modelling supercritical flow.

4.2 Representation of physical waves

In a model of unsteady flow in an open channel, either or both of two physical waves are likely to be of importance:

(a) flood wave; and

(b) a tide propagating along an estuary.

The length scales of these waves may be estimated as follows:

	Flood*	Tide
propagation speed (m/s) c	1 to 0.5	3
period (hours) T	24 to 200	12.5
wave length cT (km)	50 to 800	~ 120

* These values are typical of UK conditions

A good representation of the wave will require say at least 8 to 10 grid points to the wave length. Assuming these physical waves to be sinusoidal would give quite generous upper limits on space steps. However in the upper part of an estuary the tidewave becomes distorted with a much shorter rise time than ebb. A typical river flood hydrograph is also skewed with the rise being about 30% to 40% of the total flood duration. Hence if the Fourier components of these waves are determined, higher modes are present and it will be important to represent these within the simulation. The number of space steps required for each wave will depend upon:

(1) the amplitude and phase portraits of the numerical method, see Abbott (1979) or Skeels and Samuels (1989)

(2) the Courant number C_N of the numerical simulation

$$C_N = c\ \Delta t/\Delta x$$

(3) the degree of distortion of the physical wave from a sinusoid.

Although in the limit of the formation of a tidal bore this analysis suggests that an arbitrarily small space map will be required, this is not the case. The correct simulation of a bore or the failure of the model computation for this case, will be determined by the detailed representation of the non-linear terms within the scheme. A useful guide for the number of grid points to the fundamental harmonic of a physical wave is, say, 30 to 50 which would allow a reasonable representation (for low to moderate Courant numbers) for the 4th or 5th harmonics.

4.3 The effect of rounding error

Although most limits on the cross section spacing given in this paper will set a maximum for the distance between sections, the influence of rounding error in the computations will be to set a minimum space step. During the computation, real numbers are only determined to $\pm 10^{-q}$ where q is the number of decimal digits of precision. For example, using 32 bit (4 byte) reals for single precision, gives $q \approx 6$. Suppose that a relative error ϵ_s on surface slope can be tolerated in the computation. Then to achieve this accuracy we require

$$\Delta x > 10^{-q}/(s\ \epsilon_s)$$

However, if d digits of precision are lost due to cancellation of the leading digits of the stage values then the limit is

$$\Delta x > 10^{d-q}/(s\ \epsilon_s)$$

If $d = 2$, $q = 6$, $s \sim 10^{-3}$ and $\epsilon_s \sim 10^{-3}$ then

$$\Delta x > 100\text{m}$$

which may be of significance. This calculation shows the need to adjust the section data to a local datum for computation if possible.

4.4 Friction slope averaging and the small depth problem

These two topics have been analysed separately in the past but they are both linked to the truncation error of the numerical scheme for the dynamic equation. Tavener (1973) and Laurenson (1985) have discussed for steady flow different means of approximating the average friction slope in a river reach based upon data at the cross sections at the two ends. Tavener (1973) assumes that the friction slope line between the sections can be approximated by a parabola in space whereas Laurenson (1985) assumes a cubic spline approximation. Laurenson concludes that a reasonable, but not universally satisfactory rule is to define the mean friction slope for a reach by the arithmetic average of the values at two ends, ie to use trapezium integration to solve the backwater equation. This is consistent with Preissmann's difference scheme for unsteady flow. Cunge et al (1980) pp175 to 178 examine the small depth problem which in unsteady flow manifests itself by stage at an upstream section rising whilst the stage downstream and discharge decrease. The cause is identified as the trapezium rule approximation used for friction slope and the solution is to weight the friction slope towards the upstream section. The analysis below shows that the calculation accuracy and stability (in the sense of avoiding the small depth problem) are determined by an interlinking of the choice of the friction slope averaging method and the appropriate model section spacings.

The dynamic equation for unsteady flow is

$$\partial_t Q + \partial_x(\beta Q^2/A) + gA\,(\partial_x h + Q|Q|/K^2) \qquad (3)$$

where the symbols have their usual meaning and are as defined in the appendix to the paper. We focus our attention on the surface and friction slope terms giving the approximate dynamics (for low Froude numbers)

$$\partial_x h + Q|Q|/K^2 = 0 \qquad (4)$$

Integrating this gives for steady flow

$$h_2 - h_1 = \int_{x_1}^{x_2} (Q^2/K^2)\,dx \qquad (5)$$

Here x_2 is the upstream section, x_1 is the downstream section. The integral may be written as

$$\int_{x_1}^{x_2} (Q^2/K^2) = \bar{s}_f\,\Delta x = (rs_{f_2} + (1-r)s_{f_1})\,\Delta x \qquad (6)$$

where r is a space weighting coefficient; setting $r = ½$ gives the trapezium rule. Cunge et al (1980) argue from the flow physics that (dQ/dh_1) must be negative (ie increasing the downstream depth will decrease the discharge for a fixed upstream level). Expanding equation (6) gives the following constraint

$$\bar{s}_f > 2s\Delta x\,(1-r)\,s_{f_1}\,\{\frac{1}{K_1}\,\frac{dk_1}{dh_1}\} \qquad (7)$$

where s is the mean water surface slope

This constraint is satisfied by weighting r towards 1 ie upstream as identified by Cunge et al <u>or</u> by decreasing Δx, the section spacing. This analysis gives substance to the tentative conclusion in Section 4.1 above that for shallow flows a closer sections may be required. Here the section spacing that is necessary to avoid the small depth problem and the integration rule for the friction slope integral are clearly interlinked.

The case for some upstream weighting can also be made by considering the first order pertubation of the M_2 profile which is an exponentially decaying disturbance to the normal depth profile, see Samuels (1989). The trapezium rule or weighted trapezium rule is endeavouring to match the slope of a chord of the exponential by an arithmetic (or weighted) average of the slope at either end, see Fig 2. It is relatively straightforward to show the optimum weighting, r, to use in equation (6) is given by

$$r = \frac{p}{p - 1} - [\log_e p]^{-1} \tag{8}$$

where p depends upon the friction slopes at the two sections and the slope, s_n, of the normal depth line thus

$$p = \frac{s_{f_1} - s_n}{s_{f_2} - s_n} \tag{9}$$

With this value of r the numerical integration proceeds exactly at each cross section for the exponential profile. If $p = 2$ then $r = 0.56$ implying an error of about 4% in the slope of the chord if the trapezium rule, $r = 0.5$, is used. This value of p corresponds to the limit $\Delta x < 0.2\ D/s$ given in section 4.1 above. Research as yet unpublished at HR Ltd has shown that by using the rule, eq 8, the section spacing required to give a certain accuracy in water surface level is about twice that which is needed when the trapezium rule is used.

From Fig 2 it is clear that if Δx is too large then using the trapezium rule will cause the computation of the M_2 profile to overshoot the normal depth line and continue on an M_1 profile. Although this is stable computationally, it is obviously erroneous.

4.5 The numerical "energy" equation

Whereas Section 4.4 treated the interaction between the surface slope and friction slope terms, Samuels (1985) shows that in some circumstances there is an important relation between the convective acceleration $\partial_x(Q^2/A)$ in equation (3) and the pressure term $gA\partial_x h$. Both these terms are non linear and so the effects of differing treatments of the terms do not show up in linear Fourier analysis, see Cunge et al (1980) and Skeels and Samuels (1989). For frictionless flow the dynamic equation may be written as an energy equation

$$E = h + U^2/2g = \text{constant} \tag{10}$$

Following Samuels (1985), any numerical scheme for the steady flow equation can be rearranged as

$$h_2 = h_1 + \lambda(\mu)\ (U_1^2 - U_2^2)/2g \tag{11}$$

where $\mu = A_2/A_1$ is the ratio of the areas at the two sections. Obviously if $\lambda(\mu) = 1$ then the scheme obeys the energy equation (10); otherwise the numerical energy may rise above or fall below the physical energy line. Figure 3 shows the situation for steady flow through a contraction with E_c being the critical energy. If $\lambda < 1$ then the numerical energy rises and falls as the critical energy rises or falls. If $\lambda > 1$ then the numerical energy falls as the critical energy rises and vice-versa. In this case it is possible for the numerical energy line to cross the critical energy line and the non-linear algebraic finite difference equations in such a case have no solution. This situation is easy to demonstrate with a pocket calculator. If, however, an unsteady flow simulation is being undertaken then the difference between the critical and numerical energy will appear as wild oscillation in water surface level and discharge. The key point is that this behaviour is forced by making the ratio between successive cross section areas too large and the cure is to reduce the section spacing.

It can be shown that if the convective acceleration term is expanded as

$$\partial_x (Q^2/A) = 2 \frac{Q}{A} \frac{\partial Q}{\partial x} - \frac{Q^2}{A^2} \frac{\partial A}{\partial x} \tag{12}$$

and arithmetic averages used for Q/A, Q^2/A^2, and gA in the dynamic equation, then $\lambda > 1$. This rearrangement is often made in using Abbott's scheme since Q, or $U = Q/A$, and A are not available at the same computational points. This potential for non-linear instability of Abbott's scheme coupled with its more restricted range of linear stability causes practical difficulties. These are resolved in practice by removing the velocity head terms as critical flow is approached thereby falsifying the physics of the flow simulation. In describing the DHI model System II based on the Abbott scheme, Havno et al (1985) state; "During the transition to supercritical flow the centering is gradually moved upstream and forward in time alongside with the convective momentum term being taken out". For models based on a conservative form of Preissmann's scheme no such crude reduction of the physical basis of the model is necessary. In the author's opinion the Abbott scheme should only be used with extreme caution where the flow may approach critical conditions as is the case in several UK rivers. The cross section spacing for stable computation with the Abbott scheme is likely to be much more restrictive than for the Preissmann scheme in steep rivers unless the code has been doctored as described by Havno et al (1985). In this case the accuracy of the water level simulation is likely to be suspect. Samuels (1985) shows that when using the form of Preissmann's scheme he describes, the ratio between successive cross section areas should lie in the range 2/3 to 3/2. This ensures that the error in total numerical energy does not exceed 5% of the velocity head difference between the adjacent sections in the model. For Abbott's scheme, the same limiting ratio of flow areas leads to the same error tolerance, but there is no guarantee that the error in energy level will not force a catastrophic instability in the computation near critical flow conditions.

5 CONCLUSIONS

The rules identified in this paper for selecting cross sections may be summarised as

(1) all sites of key interest

(2) adjacent to major structures

(3) representative of the river geometry

(4) about 20 B apart (a first estimate only)

(5) a <u>maximum</u> of 0.2D/s apart (Section 4.1)

(6) a <u>maximum</u> L/30 apart where L is the length scale of the physically important wave (flood or tide) (Section 4.2)

(7) a <u>minimum</u> of $10^{d-q}/(\epsilon_s\ s)$ apart (section 4.3)

(8) so that the area ratio lies between 2/3 and 3/2 for successive sections. (Section 4.5).

Furthermore it has been argued that

(9) The section spacing may need to be reduced to avoid the small depth problem when modelling shallow flows if the averaging rule for the friction slope is fixed within the model.

(10) In steep rivers, the Abbott scheme may require a closer section spacing than the implementation of Preissmann's scheme described by Samuels (1985) since the Abbott scheme is inherently less robust near critical flow.

(11) The averaging for friction slope on a M_2 profile should be weighted upstream to improve the representation of the exponential decay of the M_2 profile into the normal depth line.

Finally it will be appreciated that the arguments given in this paper do not purport to be a rigorous treatment of selecting cross sections to give a specified overall accuracy of the computation. Only the interaction of key terms in the St Venant equations have been compared for some particular cases. The topological discretization of the floodplain and its linking to the channel flow can pose further problems which have not been addressed in this paper.

6 ACKNOWLEDGEMENTS

This work has been supported by The Ministry of Agriculture Fisheries and Food under Research Commission is on River Flood Protection at Hydraulics Research Ltd. This paper reflects neither the opinion not the policy of the Ministry. I am grateful to Mrs J E Slade for her comments on the first draft of this paper.

7 REFERENCES

(1) Abbott M B (1979). "Computational Hydraulics", Pitman, London.

(2) Cunge J A, Holly F M, Verwey A (1980), "Practical Aspects of Computational River Hydraulics" Pitman, London.

(3) Havno K, Brorsen M and Refsgaard J C (1985), "Generalized mathematical modelling system for flood analysis and flood control design". Paper F3 presented at 2nd Int Conf on the Hydraulics of floods and flood control. Cambridge UK. Published by BHRA Cranfield, Beds, UK.

(4) Laurenson E M (1985), "Friction slope averaging in Backwater Calculations". Jnl Hydr Engng, Proc ASCE, vol 112, No 12, pp1151-1163.

(5) Samuels P G (1985), "Modelling Open Channel Flow using Preissmann's scheme". Paper B2 presented at 2nd Int Conf on Hydraulics of floods and flood control. Cambridge, Beds, UK.

(6) Samuels P G (1989), Backwater lengths in Rivers, Proc Instn Civ Engrs (Land), Pt 2, Vol 87, pp571-582.

(7) Samuels P G (1990), "Volume Conservation in 1-D River Models" submitted to Jnl Hydr Engng. Proc ASCE (in press).

(8) Samuels P G and Gray M P (1982), "The FLUCOMP river model package - an engineers guide". Report EX 999. HR Ltd, Wallingford, UK.

(9) Skeels C P and Samuels P G (1989), "Stability and Accuracy analysis of numerical schemes modelling open channel flow". Paper presented at HYDROCOMP 89. Held at Dubrovnik, Yugoslavia, conference proceedings published by Elsevier Applied Science.

(10) Tavener G F (1973), "Stability and Reach length in water surface profile determination". Wat Res Bull Vol 9, pp950-962.

Appendix Notation

A	area
B	surface width
c	wave speed
C_N	Courant number
D	(bankfull) depth
d	integer part of $\log_{10}(h)$
Fr	Froude number
g	acceleration due to gravity
h	stage (water surface elevation)
K	conveyance
k	constant (between 10 and 20, Section 3)
L	backwater length 0.7D/s (Section 4.1)
L	length scale of physical wave (Section 4.2)
p	ratio of friction slope
Q	discharge
q	machine precision (decimal digits)
r	weighting coefficient for friction slope
s	water surface slope
s_f	friction slope
s_n	slope of normal depth line
T	time scale of physical wave
t	time
U	area mean velocity (Q/A)
x	distance
β	momentum coefficient
Δt	time step
Δx	space step
ϵ_s	relative error in slope
λ	numerical energy factor
μ	ratio of cross section areas

Subscripts

$_1$	downstream section
$_2$	upstream section

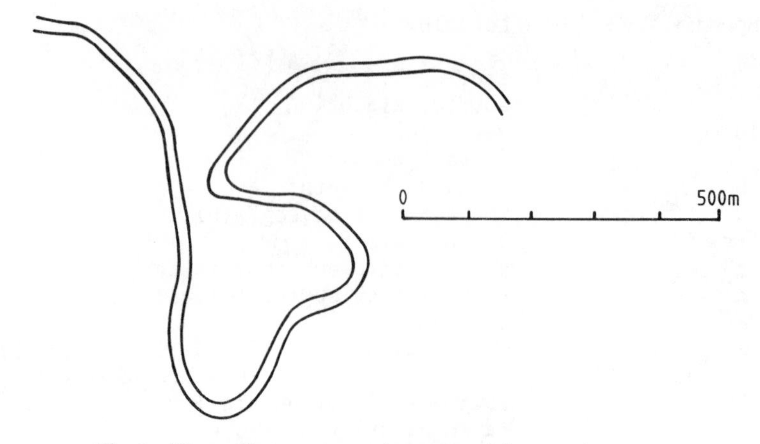

Fig 1 River Teme meander near Worcester

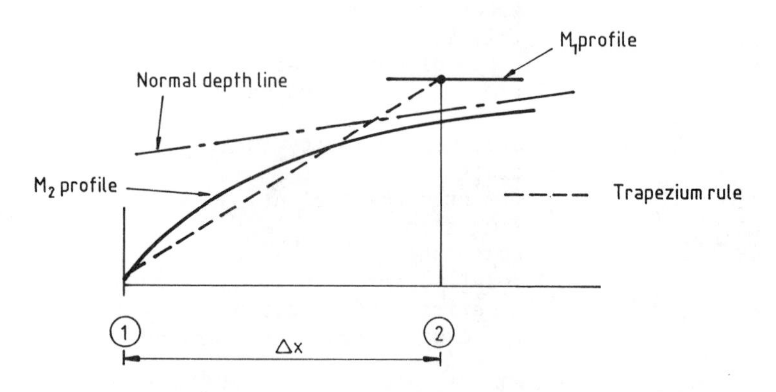

Fig 2 The trapezium rule approximation for friction slope

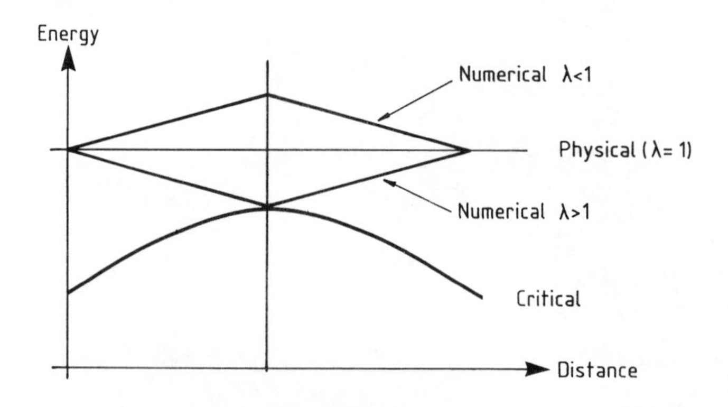

Fig 3 Energy levels for flow through a contraction

PAPER K2

International Conference on
RIVER FLOOD HYDRAULICS
17-20 September, 1990

MODELLING COMPLEX RIVER NETWORKS

J E Slade MA and Dr P G Samuels CEng MICE MIWEM

Hydraulics Research Limited, Wallingford, Oxon, UK.

ABSTRACT

As the power and versatility of computational models increases and they become applicable to new situations, the user encounters new problems, arising from the characteristics of the systems now amenable for study. Many are related specifically to the vast volume of data needed to describe and calibrate the model area. In practice, this is never available, throwing ever increasing importance on the natural realism of the hydraulics embodied in the software, rather than the range of features included. This paper concentrates on some typical difficulties experienced in modelling large river networks taking as examples studies in the UK and Bangladesh.

INTRODUCTION

In the past twenty years there has been an explosion in the development of computational hydraulic models, stimulated by the growth in the size and power of the computer systems on which they run. The expansion has included both the complexity and the size (area and duration) of the problems addressed. Today one can not assume automatically that it will be the program or computer resources which will provide the limiting constraint, rather than peculiarities of the study area, the stability of some important feature or the availability of historic data. Three components of a successful study are :

- Consistent and reliable data
- Correct calculation procedures
- Intelligent interpretation of results

Advanced network and cell models as are now applied to river systems in major studies require far more care and diligence on behalf of the user than the simple one dimensional backwater and unsteady flow models of a decade or more ago. This paper addresses three problems typical of simulating flows in extended river networks:

a) the estimation of significant local runoff;
b) the topographic database;

International Conference on River Flood Hydraulics, edited by W.R.White

c) the division of flow between channels and flood plains in overbank floods

It is not our intention necessarily to highlight and advertise successful applications of the particular model used but give examples to warn inexperienced practitioners of the potential pitfalls that may await them in moving from simple models to evaluating the hydraulic behaviour of a complex river basin. Perhaps what follows could be considered as modern equivalents of the cautionary tales told by Victorian parents to guide and instruct their children.

THE LORIS COMPUTATIONAL MODEL

LORIS is a fixed bed model for looped river networks developed at Hydraulics Research Ltd (HR). Flow in the channels is represented by the St Venant equations; for the embanked washlands a quasi two-dimensional representation is obtained, by simplifying the flow dynamics to a balance between the water surface and friction slopes. The equations are solved by using Preissmann's four-point finite difference scheme, and sparse matrix software from the Harwell Subroutine Library. The computational units are organised in a modular way, to make it easy to represent any topological layout. The model can include a variety of structures; bridges, pumps, sluices, syphons, weirs. The sluices may have one-way flaps to prevent tidal penetration upstream or be operated according to an automatic policy. Modelling is carried out in several phases: topological definition, topographic data analysis, bridge afflux estimation; hydrological assessment; main simulation and results post processing. The model has been implemented on a number of computers including an ICL2972 under VME; DEC microVAX under VMS and an IBM PS2 model 80 and COMPAQ 386 both under extended DOS. This model has been used for areas as diverse as a pumped fenland drainage system and river basins covering 10000km^2 in Bangladesh.

NETWORK CHARACTERISTICS

When studying complex river systems, one encounters problems which do not arise or are unimportant in simpler topologies. Some stem from the characteristics associated with networks or the need for embanking, whilst others stem from the increased volume of data - topographical, hydrometric and historic - needed to represent and calibrate any network model.

LATERAL INFLOW

For any model, the measured tributary inflows must be supplemented by lateral inflow from ungauged tributaries, small ditches and land drains. It may be necessary also to include incident rainfall, evapotranspiration and groundwater losses. Providing these options in the computational model is easy compared with estimating numerical values. In most applications, the contribution from lateral inflow is small compared with the gauged inflows, so that the estimate of its magnitude need not be very precise. There are two important exceptions, the developing industrial or residential area, and the low-lying polder area. For the former, the urban runoff will have faster response than the river flood, and may either have to be considered separately, or may be dominant. Any ongoing pattern of development will make the evaluation of design conditions difficult. A low lying area is likely to contain a network of channels, many of which function as storage rather than main carriers, and which are embanked to protect washlands and agricultural enclaves. Abstractions for industrial, domestic or agricultural use may further reduce the average flow. The estimation of river discharge is a problem in its own right in lowland areas, because gauging structures may be drowned or outflanked. At the same time, the magnitude of the lateral inflow will probably be large, particularly if the area is dependent on artificial drainage schemes. Figures 1 and 2 show the River Great Ouse as it was in the sixteenth century, and as it is today. Tributary inflows are intercepted, and returned to a new tidal channel near its mouth, thereby dispersing flood discharges through five parallel routes. Ninety two pumping stations have been located in the study area, most of them discharging into the by-passed Ely River system, where they account for over 50% of the total discharge. Many of the pumps are diesel powered, with a continuously variable output, recorded in millions of gallons a day, or in terms of energy consumption.

It is easier to explain which methods of estimating the inflow were not satisfactory for the Great Ouse, and why, than it is to make a recommendation. Scaling the output from one station in the ratio of the areas drained into each reach was unacceptable. Suitable data were only available for the very largest stations, and the discharge was therefore lagged and aggregated compared with the distributed inflows from the minor drains. Figure 3 shows the results of this approach with the first peak on the hydrograph being correctly captured as a diversion of water through a sluice. The second spurious hump is generated by inappropriate lateral runoff. Another approach, balancing the total inflow to and outflow from the system also failed. Apart from the difficulty of setting an appropriate lag for each gauged inflow site, this method assumed a neutral balance in the area at all times, whereas it is known that the river operation engineers draw down levels in anticipation of a flood. It is suggested that the most reliable method is to use a rainfall-runoff model, although setting catchment parameters remains a problem, especially in a man-made topography. Previous work has shown that fenland runoff has a delayed flat response described by a trapezoidal unit hydrograph. (IWEM manual, 1987).

CHANNEL GEOMETRY

The combination of small gradients and high tidal penetration in the Ouse system leads to short term geometrical instability, with fine sand being carried upstream during periods of low discharge, and redistributed during fluvial floods. This effect has been monitored since 1921, in a survey which provide values of the bed level averaged over each mile of river from Earith to the Wash. Whilst this effect does not cause hydraulic problems, it does lead to large variations in the geometry. These distort the apparent depths at high and low water, and the ratio between them, making a good calibration impossible. An algorithm was developed for generating section data combining a surveyed section shape with a minimum level taken from a contemporary record. Using this, it was possible to calibrate the Great Ouse model for five events, each with its own geometrical data, but using common roughness coefficients. Figures 4 and 5 show the simulated stage hydrographs at Denver, using the surveyed bed profile, and the modified bed respectively. (Slade 1989).

CONVEYANCE

The estimation of conveyance has its own literature. A reasonable calibration can be obtained for rough turbulent flow over a restricted depth range assuming the friction coefficient remains constant, and using any of the common formulae for the friction slope, (Ackers 1958). It is known that in general the friction coefficient is required to vary with depth, an effect which becomes more significant as the flow depth decreases (Knight, 1981). If a model is required to cover a wider range of flow depths and different flow regimes, the choice of friction law becomes important. The Colebrook White and Manning friction laws are both implemented in LORIS, but the former has consistently given a better representation of prototype data over a wider range of flow depths, and is not restricted to turbulent flow. In the Great Ouse simulations a further complication arose. The model was calibrated initially in the tidal zone against observations of a neap tide. A close match was achieved for high and low water levels and their times of occurence. Applying the same resistance coefficients to observations of a spring tide taken only weeks later produced errors of up to 0.5m in high water level but with low water being reproduced well as in the neap tide case. The resolution of this problem was to make the effective roughness depend on the flow velocity to mirror the physical changes in the alluvial bed features which dominate the turbulence in the flow. A full account of this is given elsewhere. (Tagg and Samuels 1989).

The computational model also needs to account for the natural variability of river geometry, with many channels having a two stage section. It is well known that the hydraulic radius is not an appropriate descriptor of these geometries and so resistance equations based on this parameter will lead to erroneous results (Samuels 1989). The LORIS model is now being extended to include an ordinary differential equation to model the lateral variation of velocity (Wark et al, in these proceedings). This method is being tested against observations of velocity distribution at several UK gauging stations.

RIVER EMBANKMENTS AND FLOODPLAIN FLOWS

The representation of floodplain areas in embanked systems varies between the provision of large areas of off-line storage and a mosaic of floodplain cells bounded by the one-dimensional channel system, throughout which the flow is propagated in two dimensions.

The Gumti Titas Basin

Figure 6 shows a plan of the Gumti Titas basin, in Bangladesh, where most of the included area is subject to flooding, with the direction of floodplain flow depending on the relative levels in the tributaries, and in the Meghna River, which forms the western boundary of the region. Flow from the Meghna passes generally from north to south along the old spill channels of the Lower Titas and over the adjacent flood plain. The Meghna rises and falls comparatively slowly in the course of the flood season from July to September. The rivers draining the hills to the east of the catchment have a much more rapid response to the monsoon rains with several peaks distinguishable at Comilla for example on the Gumti River. The backwater from the Meghna affects levels over almost the entire basin making the determination of rating curves difficult at the flow gauging stations. In many channels the flow direction reverses during the course of a flood.

The calibration of the LORIS model on the Gumti Titas basin had many difficulties associated with the assembly of adequate topographic data from a variety of sources which indicated great variability of channel shape from year to year. One of the problems experienced had its origin in the complex two dimensional connectivity of the river channel and flood plain system. Whereas in one dimensional models the main parasitic numerical mode is an oscillation from section to section and time step to time step in water level, in a 2-D model spurious circulations can occur as solutions to the non-linear algebraic equations in the model.

Discharge over the river embankments is given by the equation for flow over a broad-crested weir.

$$Q = 1.7*C*b*f(h_u,h_d)*(h_u - c)^{1.5} \qquad (1)$$

where Q is the discharge in m^3s^{-1}, h_u and h_d are the stage upstream and downstream respectively, c is the crest level (all in m above a common datum), b is the crest length in m, f() is the drowning

function and C is a discharge coefficient. The effective crest level is calculated by integrating the surveyed bank levels over the river cell length. Further refinement can be provided by embankment structures - permanent or time-varying breaches, culverts and flapped outfalls. This is illustrated in Figure 7.
For floodplain/floodplain boundaries, the equation for flow over a broad crested weir is appropriate for the propagation of flow into a new, dry area, but as the depth increases, a friction based equation is used

$$Q = K*(h_i - h_k)^{0.5} \qquad (2)$$

where K is the conveyance/m evaluated on the boundary, and h_i, h_k are the stages in the adjacent cells.

The finite difference representation is critical to both the reliability and numerical stability of the simulation, particularly for the embankments. Because it embodies a power law, the weir equation can generate large discharges when applied over long boundaries, and it is extremely unlikely that detailed information will be available to facilitate the informed choice of discharge and drowning coefficients. Figure 8 shows the typical pattern for a spurious circulation encountered in the lower Titas area. The identification and explanation of the cause of this mode was quite difficult. The water level on the channel side of the embankment was represented by values at each section whereas on the flood plain cell centre values were used. The water levels at the centre river section of the patch of cells was found to be raised above those either side by 0.1m or more. In the bank flow formula equation (1) the head on the channel side of the bank was taken as the arithmetic average of the water level, at two adjacent cross sections, implying a piecewise linear continuous representation of water level. On the flood plain side the cell centre values are used directly in equation 1 implying a piecewise constant representation of the water level. The spurious mode was eliminated by allowing the bank flow calculation to use a single channel section stage value rather than the average of two in the bank flow equation. In our opinion this behaviour is probably similar in origin to the inter-element compatibility conditions often found in finite element analyses and identified by patch tests, (Zienkiewicz, 1977). A second potential problem in representing the floodplain flow arises if a coarser grid is used for the flood plain than in the channel, see figure 9. If the flood plain cell acts purely as storage then no problems occur, but, if the banks are well drowned then water can bypass the central channel section. It takes a route with no frictional resistance on the flood plain, since friction losses are only accounted for as the flow passes from one flood cell to another. Both these potential problems illustrate the importance of the choice of numerical representations of the basic hydraulic laws.

CONCLUSIONS

Modelling large river networks is becoming more common as the cost of computer resources reduces. Large models bring potential problems in that they require large volumes of data which need to be validated. Detailed calibration is usually impossible because the calibration data do not exist and are expensive to collect. The modeller therefore relies on the physical realism of the model he has chosen. The assumptions made in the derivation of the model need to be validated for each application, particularly if calibration data are sparse. In determing the causes of discrepancies noted during the calibration process, the modeller must keep an open mind, being prepared to question the topographic data, assumed roughness and discharge coefficients, the assessed inflows, the model assumptions, and complex interactions in the numerical hydraulics in the model. Obviously this process starts with data validation but it is wise not to accept anything at its face value.

ACKNOWLEDGEMENTS

This paper is based on project studies research and funded by the Ministry of Agriculture, Fisheries and Food, the National Rivers Authority, Anglian Region (previously Anglian Water), and the World Bank. This paper does not reflect the opinions or policies of any of these organisations. The work was undertaken in the River Engineering Department of Hydraulics Research, headed by Dr W R White.

REFERENCES

Ackers P, 'Resistance of fluids flowing in channels and pipes', Hydraulics Research Paper No 1, HMSO, London 1958.

IWEM, 'River Engineering - Part 1, Design Principles', Water Practice Manuals Book 7, IWEM, London, 1987.

Knight D W, 'Some field measurements concerned with the behaviour of resistance coefficients in a tidal channel', Estuarine and Coastal Shelf Science, Academic Press, London, 1981, p303.

Knight D W and Demetriou J D, 'Floodplain and main channel flow interaction', Journal of Hydraulic Engineering, ASCE, Vol 109 No 8, August 1984.

Myers W R C, 'Frictional resistance in channels with floodplains', Proc 1st Int Conf Hydraulic Design in Water Resource Engineering, Southampton, 1984.

Samuels P G, 'The Hydraulics of Two Stage Channels - review of current knowledge', Paper presented to Conference of River Engineers, Loughborough, 1989.

Slade J E, 'Bed level variation in a tidal river'. Proc Int Conf Hydraulic and Environmental Modelling of Coastal, Estuarine and River Waters, Bradford, 1989, p453.

Tagg A F and Samuels P G, 'Modelling flow resistance in tidal rivers', Proc Int Conf Hydraulic and Environmental Modelling of Coastal, Estuarine and River Waters, Bradford, 1989, p441.

Wark J B, Samuels P G, and Ervine D A, 'A practical method of estimating velocity and discharge in compound channels', in press.

Wormleaton P R, Allen J and Hadjipanos P, 'Discharge assessment in compound channels', Journal of the Hydraulics Division, ASCE, Vol 108, No HY9, September 1982.

Wormleaton P R, 'Determination of discharge in compound channels using the dynamic equation for lateral velocity distribution', Proc Int Conf on Fluvial Hydraulics, Vituli, Budapest, 1988.

Zienkiewicz O C, 'The Finite Element Method' (3rd Edition), McGraw Hill, London 1977.

PAPER K3

International Conference on
RIVER FLOOD HYDRAULICS
17-20 September, 1990

HYPERCONCENTRATED, SEDIMENT-LADEN, AND CLEAR-WATER FLOOD FLOW ROUTING USING NUMERICAL METHODS

M. NOUH
Department of Civil Engineering, Sultan Qaboos University,
P.O.Box 32483 Al-Khod, Muscat, Sultanate of Oman

SUMMARY: The accuracy and efficiency of three numerical methods for routing hyperconcentrated, sediment-laden, and clear-water flood flows were investigated. The numerical methods are the explicit finite difference formulation, the implicit finite difference formulation, and the method of characteristics. The results of the numerical methods were compared with results of fully controlled and careful physical model measurements. The accuracy and efficiency of the methods for routing clear-water flows, followed by those for sediment-laden flows, are higher than the same for hyperconcentrated flows. Generally, the accuracy and efficiency decrease as mean concentration of suspended sediment increases above 8.0 gpl.

INTRODUCTION

Flood flow routing is needed for accurate design of many water engineering works. It is used to forecast levels and flows along a given reach of a river. The routing could be done analytically or numerically. The numerical methods of flood routing are based on solutions of the full Saint-Venant equations for gradually varying flow. A review of the majority of these methods can be found elsewhere (Nouh, 1986). For a given level of computational error, the accuracy and the efficiency of the numerical methods may vary with the boundary conditions of problem (Price, 1974). However, based on field observations, Nouh (1988a, 1988b) found that the accuracy of some common flood routing methods; namely, the constant and variable parameter Muskingum-Cunge methods, and the constant and variable parameter diffusion methods, varies with the characteristics of flood flow as well as with the boundary conditions of problem. The present study is an extension to these previous studies on the accuracy of flood routing methods. Its main objective is to investigate the effects of large amounts of suspended fine sediment on the accuracy as well as on the efficiency of some other advanced numerical flood routing methods. Three numerical methods of flood routing were considered. These methods are the explicit finite difference formulation, the implicit finite difference formulation, and the method of characteristics.

As it has been found by many investigators, the presence of suspended sediment can affect the flow and channel form of natural streams. At large concentrations of suspended sediment, both physical and dynamic character of the flow are different from clear-water (with zero amount of suspended sediment) flow. The fluid viscosity and density are increased; and turbulence intensity, velocity and sediment concentration distribution, flow resistance and sediment transport capacities are changed. However, for flow having Reynolds number around 700,000 the changes in the velocity distribution is insignificant (Nouh, 1989). Since the considered flood routing methods include both channel and fluid parameters which in clear-water flows have values different from those in flows with suspended sediment, it is expected, therefore, that the numerical results of the methods for routing flows with sediment and for clear-water flows to be different. In this study, these numerical results were compared with results from a physical model designed for this purpose.

International Conference on River Flood Hydraulics, edited by W.R.White

THE PHYSICAL MODEL

The laboratory investigations were performed on a rigid 18.4 m long recirculating plexiglass straight tilting flume having a rectangular cross section 0.60 m wide by o.40 m deep. Micropropellers and limnimeters located at approximately 4.0 m intervals along the flume centerline provided a means to measure the velocity and the corresponding depth of flow at a certain time. Suspended sediment samples were collected during the rising and falling branches of hydrographs, and at the points of velocity measurements using a system of pumps and regulating valves. Detailed information on the flume can be found from elsewhere (Nouh, 1989). Discharge of water was supplied to the flume by a centrifugal pump. An automatically operated valve located in the supply line provided a means of obtaining flow rates which varied over time. Flow discharge, changing from 20 lps to 250 lps during a time interval of 300 seconds, measured by an electromagnetic flow meter, which was located 2.0 m from the flume entrance.

The flume was set to a desired slope and clear-water at a predetermined average rate, and at a predetermined ratio of hydrograph depth to hydrograph duration, was allowed into the flume. Flow velocities and depths were then measured during the rising and falling branches of the hydrograph. Keeping the average rate of discharge constant, another depth duration ratio of hydrograph was generated, and flow velocities and depths were measured during the rising and falling branches of the hydrograph. Three ratios of depth "D" (in meters) to duration "T" (in minutes) of hydrograph were considered. Then the average discharge rate was changed, and flow velocities and depths were measured under the effect of the above values of D/T. Five average rates of discharge were considered.

After the clear-water experiments, an increment of sediment at a predetermined size distribution was injected very slowly to the flow, that have a certain average flow rate and a certain ratio of hydrograph depth to hydrograph duration, ensuring that the sediment was completely in suspension and no deposition was allowed. The sediment was of constant gradation (standard deviation = 1.20) and variable median diameter, as shown in Table 1. Suspended sediment, and flow velocities and depths were then measured at the standard locations. These measurements were taken for the same average rates of discharge and for the same ratios of hydrograph depth to hydrograph duration as the rates and the ratios considered in the case of clear-water flows. Then, the above whole sequence of experimentation was repeated with another increment of sediment being added each time. The experimental series was terminated with an experiment in which no stationary sediment was observed anywhere along the flume. Table 1 shows the range of data collected during the experiments.

TABLE 1. Range of Data Collected During the Experiments.

Type of flow	Number of experiments	Average rate of discharge (lps)	Ratio of hydrograph depth to duration (meter/minute)	Mean concentration of suspended sediment (gpl)	Median diameter of suspended sediment (mm)
Hyper-concentrated	60	120-200	0.02-0.06	4.20-58.74	0.01
Sediment-Laden	60	120-200	0.02-0.06	8.21-51.80	0.10
Clear-Water	15	120-200	0.02-0.06	00	00

THE NUMERICAL METHODS OF FLOOD ROUTING

The considered numerical methods of flood routing are the Leap-Frog finite difference explicit method, the four-point finite difference implicit method as developed by Amein and Fang (1970), and the fixed mesh characteristic method. Brief review of these methods can be found elsewhere (Price, 1974). These methods are of second-order accuracy, meaning that the finite difference schemes for basic equations use Taylor expansions for the terms in the equations and these expansions are truncated after the second order. These particular methods were selected because they are normally used by design engineers. They are based on the following Saint-Venant equations for gradually varying flow in open channels:

$$dA/dt + dQ/dx = q \tag{1}$$

$$dQ/dt + d/dx\,(Q^2/A) + gA\,(dy/dx) = gA\,(S_o - S_f) \tag{2}$$

in which A is the wetted cross-sectional area of channel, Q is the discharge, q is the lateral inflow per unit length, g is the gravitational acceleration, y is the stage, S_o and S_f are the bottom slope and friction slope of channel, respectively, x is the distance from upstream section, and t is the time.

To examine the accuracy and efficiency of the above flood routing methods, the numerical results were compared to the results from the physical model. The input at the upstream section (2.0 m from the flume entrance) was the stage as a function of time, and the accuracy test on the numerical methods was made from the comparison between the computed and observed stage hydrographs at the downstream section (about 1.00 m from the flume exit).

RESULTS AND DISCUSSIONS

As it has been mentioned earlier, the main objective of this study is to compare the accuracy and efficiency of three numerical methods for routing hyperconcentrated, sediment-laden, and clear-water flood flow. It has to be mentioned here to the fact that these methods have been examined before (Price, 1974) for accuracy and efficiency by comparing the numerical results of the methods with the exact analytical solution of the basic equations used to describe the clear-water flow. The present study extends the work of Price (1974) to include other types of flow of completely different physical and dynamic characteristics (i.e. hyperconcentrated and sediment-laden flows), and to examine the appropriateness of the methods by comparing the numerical results with results from a physical model.

Experimental Results: The experiments have shown that the physical and dynamic characteristics of flows with large amounts of suspended sediment are different from those of clear-water flows. In addition, velocity and suspended sediment distributions under unsteady flow conditions are different from those under steady flow conditions.

Samples of hyperconcentrated, and sediment-laden flows were collected during the rising and falling branches of hydrograph, and then used to determine the dynamic viscosity "u". Details of such experimentation are not given here, but would be provided during the presentation at the conference. The relative dynamic viscosity at depth y, u_{yr}, defined as the dynamic viscosity of the flow at depth y from the channel bottom divided by the dynamic viscosity of clear-water at the same temperature of the flow, was evaluated at different points. Figure 1 shows a typical variation of u_{yr} with y/y_T, where y_T is the total depth of flow. Inspection of the figure indicates that: (1) for the same mean concentration of suspended sediment "C", the dynamic viscosity of hyperconcentrated (finer gain size diameters) flows is generally larger towards the water surface, but smaller towards the channel bed, than that of sediment-laden (relatively coarser grain size diameters) flows; (2) the viscosity of hyperconcentrated and sediment-laden flows is larger in the rising branch than that in the falling branch of hydrograph; (3) the viscosity of hyperconcentrated flows, followed by that of sediment-laden flows, is larger than that of clear-water flows; and (4) the dynamic viscosity of hyperconcentrated and sediment-laden flows increases as mean concentration of suspended sediment "C" increases.

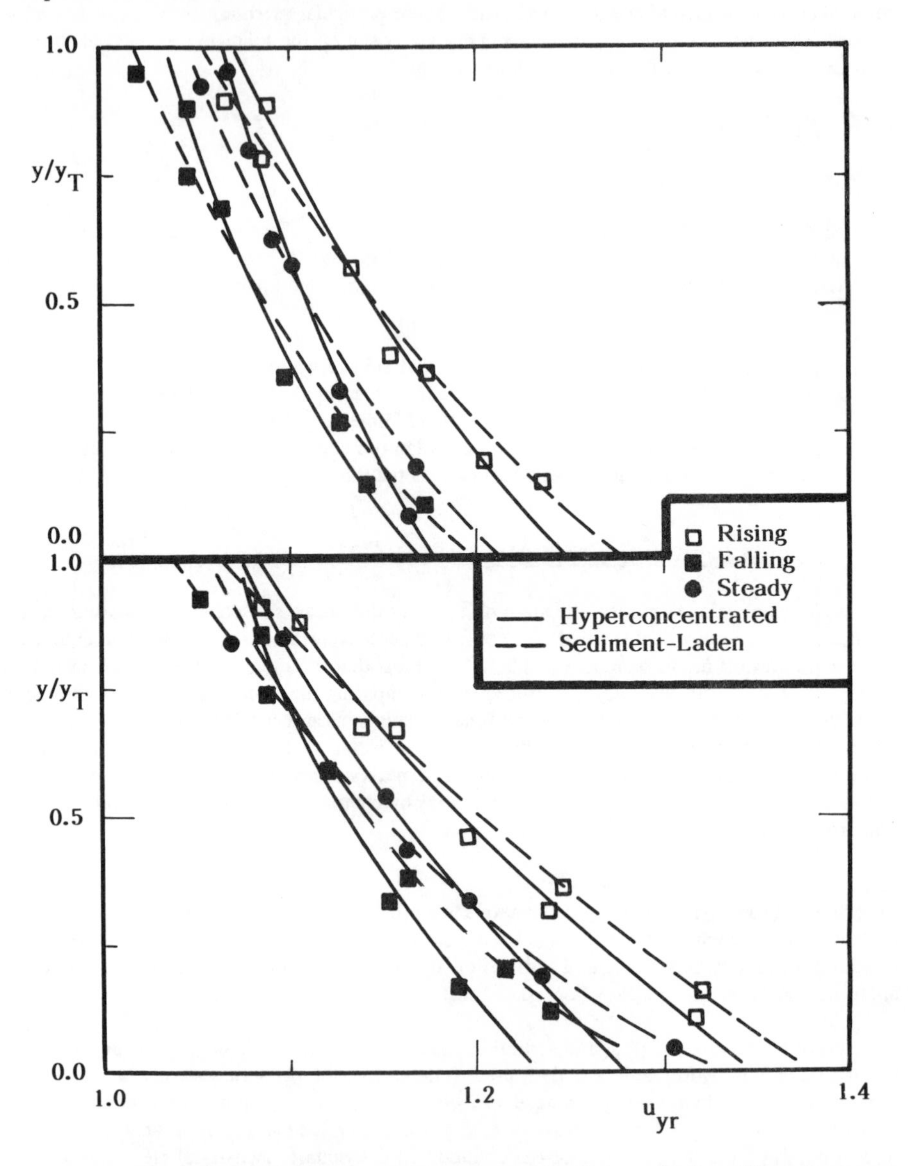

Figure 1. Variation of Hyperconcentrated and Sediment-Laden Flow Dynamic Viscosity with Depth of Flow Under Steady and Unsteady Flow Conditions [D/T= 0.06 meter/minute] and for C=20 gpl (top) and C=39.5 gpl (bottom).

The relative mean value of dynamic viscosity at a vertical "u_r" (defined as the ratio of the mean value of dynamic viscosities measured along the vertical divided by the dynamic viscosity of clear-water at the same temperature) was evaluated and plotted against C in Figure 2 for various shapes of hydrograph. It can be seen that: (1) for a certain value of C, the mean value of the dynamic viscosity of hyperconcentrated flow is larger than that of sediment-laden flow; (2) as mean concentration of suspended sediment increases the dynamic viscosity of hyperconcentrated and sediment-laden flow increases; and (3) the sensitivity of mean dynamic viscosity to mean concentration of suspended sediment in case of the hyperconcentrated flows is higher than that in case of the sediment-laden flows; and (4) the sensitivity of mean dynamic viscosity to mean concentration of suspended sediment increases as D/T of hydrograph increases.

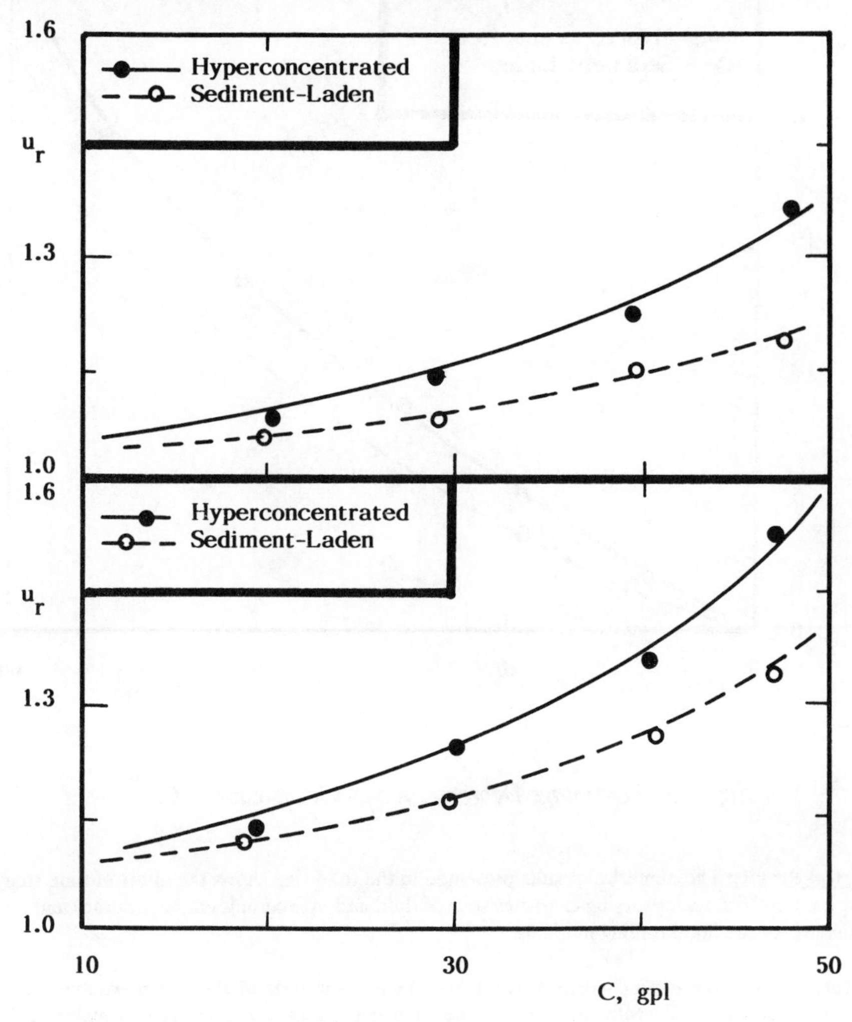

Figure 2. Variation of u_r with C for D/T = 0.02 meter/minute (top) and for D/T = 0.06 meter/minute (bottom).

The experiments have also shown that the presence of suspended sediment in a flow decreases the friction slope S_f of the channels. The results of the experiments, which confirmed the results of previous studies (Nouh, 1987, 1990), are shown in Figure 3. It can be seen that the decrease in the friction slope of channel due to the presence of suspended sediment is larger in case of hyperconcentrated flows (very fine grains of suspended sediment) than in case of sediment-laden flows (relatively coarse grains of suspended sediment). Such changes in S_f may affect the results of the considered routing methods, which solve equations depends on the value of S_f (i.e. Eq. 2).

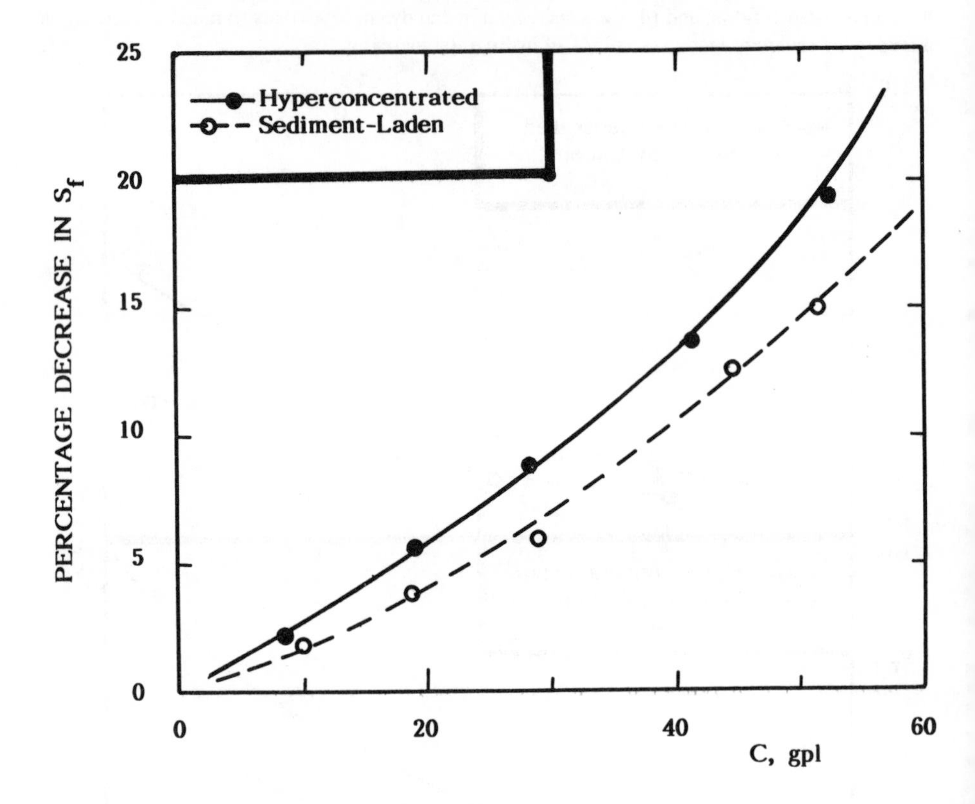

Figure 3. Percentage Decrease in S_f with Increase in C.

<u>Numerical Results:</u> The numerical results presented in the following shows the effect of time step "Dt", space step "Dx" under varying characteristics of fluid and hydrograph on the accuracy and on the efficiency of the flood routing methods.

First, consider the fixed mesh characteristic method. Typical variation of absolute maximum error "E" and computer time "C_t" with variation of time step, space step, and D/T ratio of hydrograph are shown in Figure 4 and Figure 5, respectively. It can be seen that: (1) the accuracy (measured by the absolute maximum error) is sensitive more than the efficiency (measured by the computer time) to the variation of time step, space step, and D/T hydrograph ratio; (2) the accuracy of the method for routing the clear-water flood flows, followed by that of the method for routing the sediment-laden flood flows, are higher than the same for routing the hyperconcentrated flood flows; (3) the accuracy decreases but the efficiency increases (i.e. E increases and C_t decreases, respectively) as mean concentration of suspended sediment "C" increases; (4) the sensitivity of both accuracy and efficiency to variation in Dt, Dx, and in D/T is higher in case of the hyperconcentrated floods than that in case of sediment-laden floods; and (5) the sensitivity of both accuracy and efficiency to the variation in D/T and in Dt is higher than that in Dx.

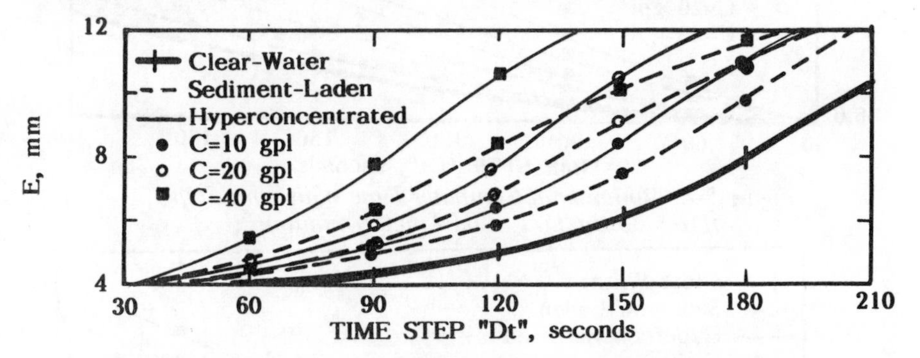

Figure 4-A. Variation of Absolute Maximum Error With Time Step (Dx = 30 cm, and D/T = 0.04 meter/minute).

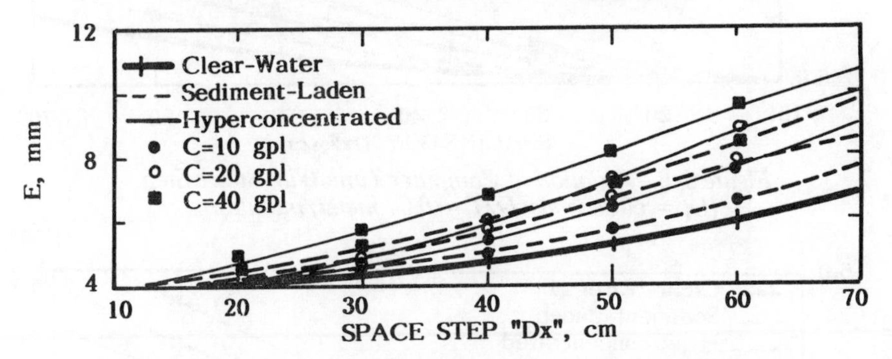

Figure 4-B. Variation of Absolute Maximum Error With Space Step (Dt = 60 seconds, D/T = 0.04 meter/minute).

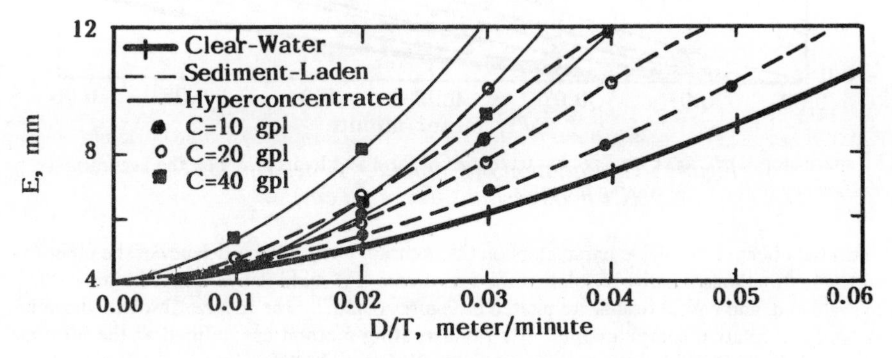

Figure 4-C. Variation of Absolute Maximum Error With D/T (Dt = 60 seconds, Dx = 30 cm).

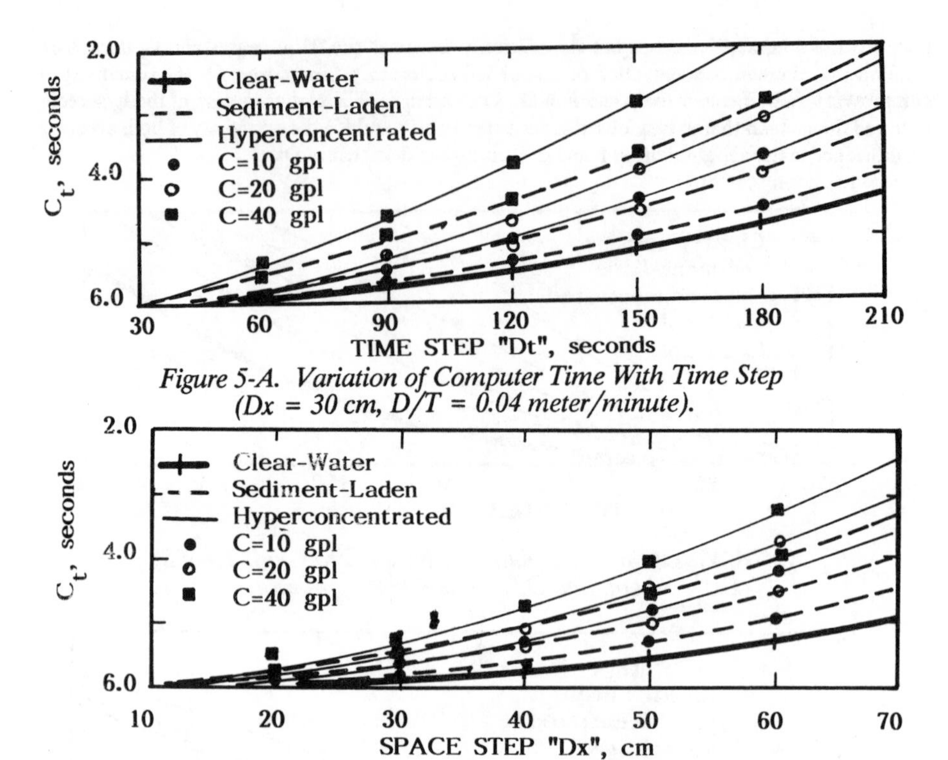

Figure 5-A. Variation of Computer Time With Time Step (Dx = 30 cm, D/T = 0.04 meter/minute).

Figure 5-B. Variation of Computer Time With Space Step (Dt = 60 seconds, D/T = 0.04 meter/minute).

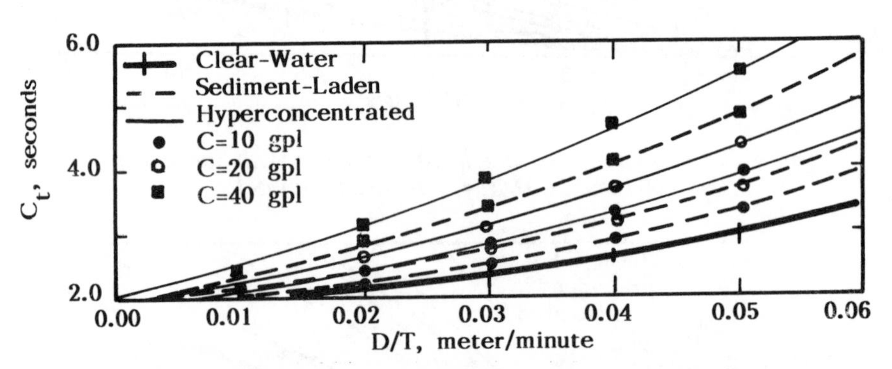

Figure 5-C. Variation of Computer Time With D/T (Dt = 60 seconds, Dx = 30 cm).

To show the effect of the above parameters on the accuracy and on the efficiency of the other two flood routing methods, relative absolute maximum errors "E_r" and relative computer times "C_{tr}" were evaluated, and typical results are plotted in Figures 6 and 7. The relative absolute maximum error and the relative computer time of a flood routing method are defined as the absolute maximum error and the computer time for given Dt, Dx, and D/T values of the flood routing method divided by the same of the fixed mesh characteristic method of flood routing. Figure 6 and 7 show the typical results of the Leap-Frog explicit finite difference method and the four-point finite difference implicit method, respectively. Inspection of the figures indicates that: (1) all the flood routing methods produce results of similar accuracy and efficiency in case of routing clear-water flows; (2) the accuracy as well as the efficiency of the flood routing methods decrease as mean concentration of suspended sediment increases; (3) the accuracy as well as the efficiency of any of the methods for routing hyperconcentrated flows, followed by those for routing sediment-laden flows, are lower than the same for routing clear-water flows; and (4) the accuracy as well as the efficiency of explicit finite difference formulation, followed by those of the implicit finite difference formulation, are higher than the same of the fixed mesh characteristic method. The results (which are not presented here) have indicated that the effect on the accuracy and on the efficiency of Dt and D/T is greater than that of Dx.

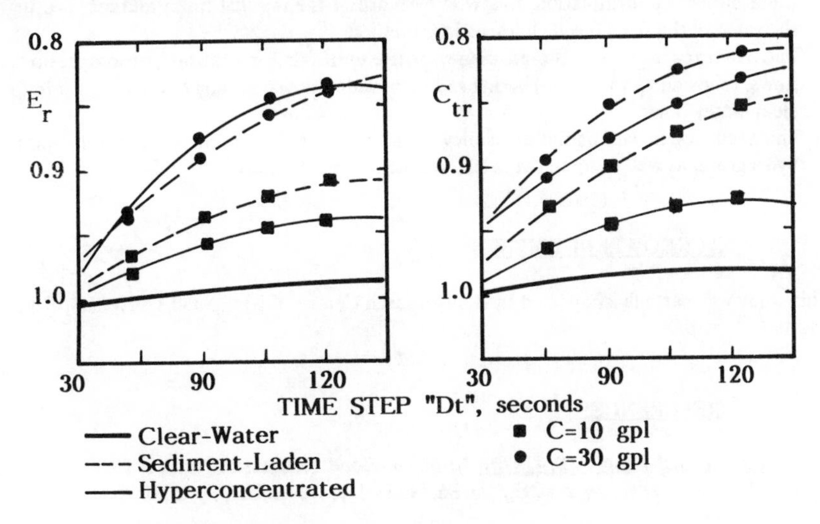

Figure 6. Variation of E_r (Left) and C_{tr} (Right) With Time Step (Dx = 30 cm, D/T = 0.04 meter/minute).

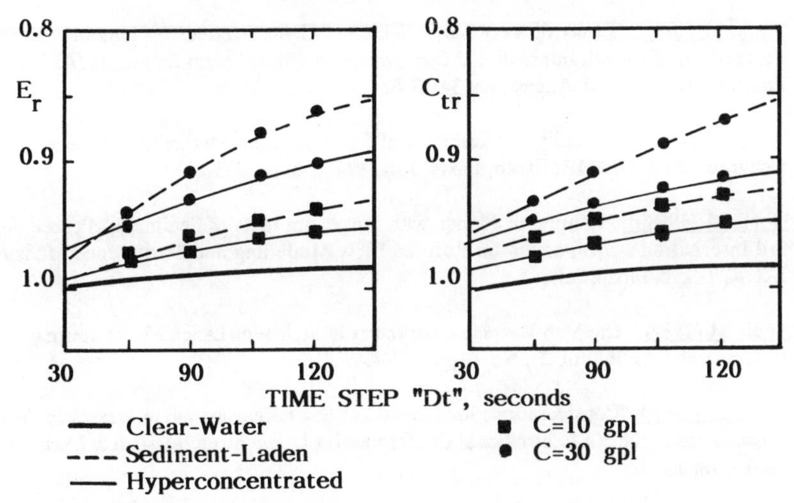

Figure 7. Variation of E_r (Left) and C_{tr} (Right) With Time Step (Dx = 30 cm, D/T = 0.04 meter/minute).

CONCLUSIONS

The accuracy and the efficiency of the explicit finite difference formulation, the implicit finite difference formulation, and the fixed mesh characteristic method for routing hyperconcentrated, sediment-laden, and clear-water flows were examined by comparing the numerical results with results from a physical models. From the results obtained the following conclusions are made:

1. The flood routing methods are of almost similar accuracy and efficiency in case of routing clear-water flood flows.
2. As mean concentration of suspended sediment increases, the accuracy as well as the efficiency of the methods decrease. In such cases, the accuracy as well as the efficiency of the explicit finite difference formulation, followed by those of the implicit finite method, are higher than the same of the fixed mesh characteristic method.
3. The accuracy as well as the efficiency of the methods for routing hyperconcentrated flood flows, followed by those for routing sediment-laden flows, are lower than the same for routing clear-water flows.
4. The accuracy as well as the efficiency of the flood routing methods depends upon shape of hydrograph as well as upon the selected time and space steps.

ACKNOWLEDGEMENTS

This study was partially supported by the Research Centre of King Saud University, Riyadh, Saudi Arabia.

REFERENCES

1. Amein, M. and Fang C. S. (1970): "Implicit Flood Routing in Natural Channels," Journal of the Hydraulics Division, ASCE, Vol. 96, No.HY12, December, pp. 2481-2500.

2. Nouh, M (1986): "Mathematical Modeling of Surface Water in Saudi Arabia," Final Technical Report Number 4/1401, Research Center, King Saud University, Riyadh, Saudi Arabia, 127p.

3. Nouh, M (1987): "Effect of Very Large Sediment Concentrations on Highway Sewer Flows," Proceedings of the 4th International Conference on Urban Storm Drainage, IAHR/IAWPRC, Laussane, Switzerland, August, pp. 343-348.

4. Nouh, M (1988a): "Relative Performance of Flood Routing Methods," Proceedings of the 6th Congress of APD-IAHR, Kyoto, Japan, July, Vol. II-1, pp. 333-340.

5. Nouh, M (1988b): "Routing of Floods with Large Amounts of Sediment," Proceedings of the 3rd International Symposium on Refined Flow Modelling and Turbulence Measurements, IAHR, Tokyo, Japan, July.

6. Nouh, M (1989): "The Von-Karman Coefficient in Sediment Laden Flow," Journal of Hydraulic Research, IAHR, Vol. 27, No. 4, pp. 477-499.

7. Nouh, M (1990): "Considerations for Least-Cost Storm Sewer System Design in Arid Areas," Proceedings of the 5th International Conference on Urban Storm Drainage, IAHR/IAWPRC, Osaka, Japan, July.

8. Price, R K (1974): "Comparison of Four Numerical Methods for Flood Routing," Journal of Hydraulics Division, ASCE, Vol. 100, No.HY7, July, pp. 879-899.

PAPER K4

International Conference on
RIVER FLOOD HYDRAULICS
17-20 September, 1990

THE DEVELOPMENT OF CRITERIA FOR PREDICTING DAMBREAK FLOOD DAMAGES USING MODELLING OF HISTORICAL DAM FAILURES

L. Clausen and P.B. Clark
Binnie & Partners
Grosvenor House, Redhill, Surrey, UK.

SUMMARY: A flood released by the failure of a dam could cause extensive damage. Criteria are developed from the analysis of a past failure event to enable prediction of the extent and levels of damage that would occur. The estimation of the cost of that damage and the potential loss of life are discussed.

INTRODUCTION

In the UK the safety record of dams in recent years has been very good: the last incidents involving loss of life occurring over sixty years ago. These failures took place in 1925 at Dolgarrog in Wales and at Skelmorlie in Scotland, causing a total of twenty fatalities. However, the capacity for damage is still available: there are between 5000 and 6000 reservoirs in the UK, of which about 2400 contain volumes of water greater than 25 Ml (5.5 million gallons) and come under the requirements of the UK Reservoirs Act (1975). Some of these reservoirs are located in small upland valleys above populated areas.

The consequences of a dam failure could, however, be disastrous, with potentially great loss of life and damage. There have been a number of failures throughout the world in which casualties have run into thousands. Even during the 1970's some 600 people died in the USA as a result of dam failures.

The emphasis in reporting failures by the media has naturally been directed at the loss of life, but the extent and costs of damage may also be very considerable even if the loss of life is small. For example the failure of the Teton dam in the USA in 1976 caused destruction and damage to nearly 4000 houses and 250 businesses, though warnings limited the loss of life to 11.

Much work has been directed at developing methods for predicting the magnitude and characteristics of the flood wave consequent upon a potential dam failure, and in routing that flood wave downstream. Using numerical simulation it is now possible to predict with reasonable accuracy the potential extent of inundation, should a particular dam fail. A number of countries require inundation maps

International Conference on River Flood Hydraulics, edited by W.R.White

for all major reservoirs.

One use of dambreak is thus in the preparation of contingency plans where knowledge of the potential extent and degree of damage would be extremely useful to the emergency services. Dambreak analyses are also used widely in some countries in risk and hazard studies to determine expenditure on dam safety improvements and, in particular, the choice of site-specific spillway standards. Such studies require estimation of the costs of potential damage. A knowledge of the potential loss of life and cost of damage caused by a dam failure is required in the assessment of third party insurance premiums, though such insurance is not generally taken out by UK owners at present. Such information would also enable the implications of development downstream of existing and proposed reservoirs to be properly considered.

In view of the widespread use and application of dambreak analysis it is surprising how little information is available on the physical impact of such high-velocity flow and the related costs of damage. There is much information available in the UK on the damage caused by flood inundation - i.e. where the effects of velocity are negligible - primarily from the work of the Flood Hazard Research Centre at Middlesex Polytechnic. Similar information exists in a number of other countries and it appears that most studies involving an estimation of the costs of potential damage following a dam failure have used an approach based on such data. If so the costs of the damage may have been significantly underestimated. A study in Australia by Smith and Greenaway (1987) suggested that, for the particular case they studied, the costs of damage in high velocity flow when structural failure of buildings was accounted for could be as much as nine times greater than when inundation only was assumed.

DEVELOPMENT OF DAMAGE CRITERIA

The amount of damage caused by low-velocity flooding is primarily a function of the depth and duration of inundation. A number of additional damage mechanisms are involved when the flow has a high velocity, including:-

- differential pressure e.g. between the inside and outside of a building;
- dynamic drag on an obstruction;
- wave action;
- scour around the foundations of a building;
- erosion of river banks and slumping of side slopes;
- debris battering.

The damage might thus be related to many hydraulic parameters including depth and velocity of the flow, bed shear stress, flow momentum and stream power, and rate of flood rise. Moreover in the prediction of damage to a specific building other factors such as the structure's location within the flood plain, its orientation to the flow, the extent to which it may be sheltered by other buildings or natural features and, of course, its structural condition, must all be considered. In addition, damage may be caused by battering from the debris carried in the flow which is affected by the availability of debris upstream and the capability of the flow for picking up and transporting that material.

Clearly the prediction of damage to this level of detail is not possible, nor indeed is it warranted given the inherent inaccuracies in predicting the characteristics of failure of a dam, in modelling the progression of the flood wave and, in particular, the details of the flow in a complex topography, and in transposing estimates of the damage into corresponding costs. A much more simplified model was therefore sought - one which would provide general guidance on the potential damage and which could utilise the typical output from a one-dimensional dambreak simulation program.

To develop and calibrate a simple model to predict the extent of damage, past floods were used to compare flow conditions in those events with the damage caused. Both dambreak and high-velocity river floods in the UK and elsewhere were considered, but only a few provided suitable results. To be of use the records of such events needed to have sufficient details of both the damage and the flood flows, and many cases considered were deficient in one or other aspect.

Moreover the conditions of particular interest were those which might provide information on the severity of flooding likely to initiate different levels of structural damage. There are a number of well-documented cases (e.g. the Lynmouth floods of 1952) in which the flow velocities and depths were such that, in the areas affected, buildings were totally destroyed. Such information provides no guide to the limiting conditions above which velocity-related damage occurs.

Only a few of the many cases considered could be used to produce useful results. Most of the data was provided by one British dam failure: that at Dale Dyke in 1864. The dam failed, probably due to internal erosion leading to settlement and overtopping during a storm, without any warning being issued and at night on 11 March 1864. The resulting flood was channelled down the narrow valley and through the city of Sheffield some 10 kms downstream. It resulted in the loss of 245 lives and caused considerable damage both in the valley leading down to Sheffield and in that city itself. Sufficient details of the dam breach and subsequent flood wave were provided in an engineering report by Rawlinson (1864) to enable the calibration of a numerical model of the flood wave. Extensive descriptions, photographs and drawings of damaged buildings were published by a local journalist (Harrison, 1864) and these could be related to specific locations using maps of the area published in 1900.

Dale Dyke: failure simulation

Depths and velocities of flow were calculated using a numerical model developed specifically for modelling the flood wave released by a dam failure: the USA National Weather Service's DAMBRK program (Fread, 1984). This program is a widely accepted and recommended model (e.g. Wurbs, 1987) which is capable of dealing with the complexities of flood propagation in both sub- and supercritical conditions. The program has subsequently been improved (Fread, 1988) and a version developed specifically for the conditions of steep, narrow valleys with the near-critical flow conditions encountered in the UK (Binnie & Partners, 1990).

Dambreak flood modelling can be considered in two parts: the outflow from the dam and the flood routing down the valley. The former involves some of the main uncertainties in dambreak floodwave prediction, as the potential failure mode is not known. The floodwave is affected by the failure mode, breach dimensions and time of failure. However, for modelling the Dale Dyke flood, reasonable estimates of these factors could be obtained from records of the disaster investigations. The accuracy of the data required for the flood routing was open to greater variation. A plan of the inundated area at a scale of 6 inches to 1 mile was presented in the Rawlinson report, together with a selection of valley cross-sections. Further cross-sections were required to model the valley; these were taken from 1:25000 scale contoured plans. The contour interval of 5 m was inadequate for accurate modelling of the valley topography and caused a few problems when calibrating the computer model. These were solved by changing the assumed dimensions of the river channel in line with the more accurate details on those cross-sections provided by Rawlinson. The flood was routed for 15 kms, which is as far as Rawlinson's plan extends. At this distance from the dam, the maximum depths had reduced to 3 metres (above the river bed) and the velocities were about 1.5 metres/sec.

Some difficulties were experienced with the calibration. The initial data set produced errors in the maximum depths of up to 30% of those reported in the Rawlinson report. This is perhaps indicative of the sort of accuracy that might be expected in trying to predict the progression of a potential dam break flood in steep, narrow upland valleys typical of many sites of reservoirs in the UK. Much of the problem was found to lie with the details of the cross-sections, as noted above. The valley topography was uneven and the cross-sections varied considerably. Roughness appeared to have a less significant influence on the water levels within the range of values considered reasonable for Manning's 'n'. Final values adopted in the calibration were generally no higher than about 0.050.

Figure 1 shows the comparison between water depths in the model, with the best calibration that could be achieved with those recorded by Rawlinson. With two or three exceptions the depths as modelled are within 10% of those recorded. Part of the reason for the larger errors was instability of the model - the 1984 version of DAMBRK not coping well with flows near critical depth, as noted earlier. This was particularly noticeable with the peak velocities and some smoothing of both of these and the maximum depths were carried out for use in the damage correlation.

Damage analysis of Dale Dyke flood

Using the calibrated DAMBRK simulation, peak flow conditions could be determined throughout the inundated area and a correlation sought with the damage that occurred to properties. The locations of about 70 damaged structures, excluding bridges, were determined from the details published by Harrison (1864) and the damage suffered by each of these buildings was assessed according to the following categories:-

INUNDATION DAMAGE: Damage similar to that caused by a natural low-velocity river flood. No immediate structural damage (longer term damage may occur as a result of saturation of foundations or structural timber).

PARTIAL (OR MINOR) DAMAGE: Moderate structural damage i.e. windows and doors knocked out but with little damage to the major structural elements of the building.

TOTAL DESTRUCTION (OR MAJOR DAMAGE): Total structural collapse or major damage to the structure necessitating demolition and rebuilding.

The output from DAMBRK provides information on the average velocities and the water levels at each defined section and at intermediate cross-sections defined by the program. Values corresponding to the cross-section at each structure were interpolated linearly. It is not feasible to infer any lateral velocity distribution from a one-dimensional model but the local water depth (referred to as 'point depth') can be calculated at each structure and this is a more relevant parameter than maximum or averaged section depths.

During the passage of the flood wave, depths and velocities vary. In order to keep the criteria for assessing the level of damage as simple as possible and to relate the damage to definable output parameters from the model, the maximum velocities and the maximum depths only were considered in the damage analysis. In the following discussion it is the maximum average velocity across the section and the maximum point depth that occurred which is referred to in all cases. Various functions of these parameters were correlated to the level of damage at each structure, though the maximum values of each do not necessarily occur at the same time during the flood.

There was very poor correlation between velocity alone and damage, as might be expected. The velocity as averaged across the section would provide no differentiation between the damage caused by the faster, deeper flows in the central part of the valley and the lower levels of damage in the slower, shallow regions at the sides.

The inclusion of the point depth provides a measure of the lateral variation, and makes the use of the average section velocity more reasonable. As noted, several possible functions of point depth (d) and average section velocity (v) were considered but the function giving the best correlation was also the simplest - i.e. velocity times depth. Figure 2 shows the results from Dale Dyke plotted as depth v. velocity for each structure with the corresponding level of damage indicated. As might be expected with such data there is some overlap between the levels of damage but the boundaries between these regions, denoting inundation, partial and total damage, can reasonably be delineated by curves of constant d.v. Thus the boundary between inundation and partial damage can be defined as

$$d.v = 3 \text{ m}^2/\text{s} \qquad \ldots. \ (1)$$

and that between partial and total damage can be defined as

$$d.v = 7 \text{ m}^2/\text{s} \qquad \ldots. \ (2)$$

A simplification, eliminating the region of partial damage would be to define the boundary between total and inundation damage as:-

$$d.v = 6 \text{ m}^2/\text{s} \qquad \ldots. \ (3)$$

The lack of damage information for $v < 2$ m/s implies that all damage in the corresponding region was unremarkable - i.e. inundation damage only. Based on this evidence, therefore, an additional criterion should be that the damage should be categorised as inundation damage if

$$v < 2 \text{ m/s} \qquad \ldots. \ (4)$$

These criteria defining the regions in which each type of damage occurs are shown in Figure 3 and compared with the similar form of criteria proposed by Black (1975), and the US Army Corps of Engineers (USACE, 1988) for total structural damage of timber-framed houses. The former compares well with the criteria defined by equations (1) and (2), as does the USACE criteria for one-storied buildings. USACE criteria for damage to two-storied buildings suggests that a significant increase in the depth and/or the velocity is required to cause such damage, within the range of velocities to which the data applied. The data from Dale Dyke does not indicate any discernible distinction between one and two storey masonry buildings and, moreover, Sangrey's data (1975)suggest that the USACE criteria for 2-storied buildings - i.e. the depth times velocity value necessary to cause total structural damage - is high (see Figure 3). It is interesting to note that the USACE results also suggest that no structural damage occurs with velocities below about 2 m/s.

APPLICATION OF CRITERIA

Figure 4 shows the application of these criteria to part of the area that would be inundated from the potential failure of an actual reservoir. Again the dambreak wave and its propagation downstream were modelled using DAMBRK (Fread, 1984). From the output data the locations were calculated on each cross-section, denoting the boundaries between the types of damage, using equations (1) and (2). These were then marked on a map of the valley and the areas, or regions, likely to suffer the different types of damage delineated.

In the recent version of DAMBRK, modified for particular application in the UK (Binnie & Partners, 1990) an output post-processor has been added to calculate and to print out the values of peak section velocity times maximum depth for each point across each section (defined with x-y coordinates), and the corresponding type of damage to be expected.

DAMAGE COSTS

The detailed calculation of the costs of the damage caused by the flood released by the failure of a dam can be a time consuming and laborious process. The assessment of the costs of damage due to inundation - i.e. low velocity flooding - have been discussed in many publications. In the UK, as noted earlier, much of the methodology has been established by the Flood Hazard Research Centre at Middlesex Polytechnic and reference should be made to their many publications and papers; in particular, Penning-Rowsell & Chatterton (1977) and Parker et al (1987). Those methods have been extended and simplified for the estimation of total damage (Binnie & Partners/FHRC, 1990). It is not the purpose of this paper to review that whole body of work, however a few points should be made in relation to the damage criteria presented above.

The type of damage that is related to the hydraulics of the flow is the 'direct' damage only, i.e. that caused by the direct impact of the flood on the structures and properties in question. The total costs of the damage caused by any such flood must include the 'indirect damages', such as those caused by interruption of transportation and services, loss of production, provision of emergency services etc. These may be a substantial part of the total cost attributable to the flood. Moreover there are 'intangible' costs which, at present, cannot be quantified. They include such costs as those associated with ill-health following a disaster. Because they cannot be quantified they tend to be ignored but studies by Green et al (1983) on riverine and marine flooding suggests they may be comparable or even greater than the tangible flood costs.

In view of the uncertainties in the overall cost estimates, great accuracy in the calculation of direct damage costs is unwarranted. In many cases it would be sufficient to distinguish only between the areas of total damage and inundation damage using equation (3). Where there are significant areas of flooding in which partial damage might be expected - such as in a town located where the valley, containing the reservoir, opens out - then the delineation of such areas may be worthwhile.

The cost of the damage to a building in such a 'partial damage' zone can be assumed to be proportional to d.v, between the total damage cost at d.v = 7 m^2/s and the inundation cost at d.v = 3 m^2/s.

LOSS OF LIFE

As discussed in the introduction, the loss of life in a dam failure flood is rightly the major concern. Certainly in the UK, and in many other countries as well, decisions on dam safety criteria and expenditure are dictated by considerations of public safety rather than economic ones. It is a matter of considerable debate as to whether potential casualties should be assigned a monetary cost and included into the total damage cost calculation. The consensus of opinion, with which the authors concur, appears to be that the estimate of potential loss of life should not be expressed in monetary terms but presented, in any analysis of the consequences of the failure of a dam, as a separate figure.

The other difficulty is in actually estimating the potential loss of life. It depends greatly on the time of warning available to effect evacuation, and this is a function not only of the type of failure of the dam but also on the time of failure (i.e. day or night), degree of instrumentation and monitoring, and readiness or otherwise of emergency services to heed and act on any warning.

Research carried out by the US Bureau of Reclamation (1986) in analysing a number of past events suggests that 1½ hours is a critical minimum time for effective evacuation. In events in which this warning time was not available the average loss of life (LOL) was related to the population at risk (PAR) by the function:-

$$LOL = PAR^{0.6} \quad \ldots. (5)$$

When 90 minutes warning was available:-

$$LOL = PAR \times 0.0002 \qquad \ldots . (6)$$

Clearly effective monitoring of dams and the preparation of contingency plans can have a major effect in reducing casualties.

CONCLUSIONS

Much work has gone on in recently years in improving the understanding of the mechanisms of dam failure and in developing methods to analyse the progression of the flood wave released. Much less attention, however, has been paid to the accuracy of the analysis of the consequences of failure though the results of such analyses may be used to determine major capital works programmes for improving dam safety, and have other important uses including contingency planning.

One way in which flood damage costs may have been underestimated is in the assessment of the level of structural damage that occurs in high-velocity flow. The criteria presented in this paper as equations (1), (2) and (4) provide a means of identifying the areas, in the path of the flood released from a dam failure, in which structural damage is likely to occur to brick and masonry buildings such as are the great majority of buildings in the UK. It is appreciated that the criteria are based largely on the data from one historical event and they may need review and modification if further data becomes available.

ACKNOWLEDGEMENTS

The work on which this paper is based was carried out under a research contract for the UK Department of the Environmental. The guidance of Mr J Phillips, Mr C Wright and other members of the steering committee is much appreciated.

REFERENCES

BINNIE & PARTNERS (1990): "DAMBRK UK: Dambreak flood simulation program manual", UK Department of the Environment.

BINNIE & PARTNERS/FLOOD HAZARD RESEARCH CENTRE (1990): "Estimation of flood damage following potential dam failure: Guidelines", Contract Report for the UK Department of the Environment.

BLACK R (1975): "Flood proofing rural residences", a project 'Agnes' report, no EDA 77-088, US Dept of Commerce, EDA.

FREAD D L (1984): "DAMBRK: The NWS dam-break flood forecasting model", US National Weather Service, Silver Spring, Maryland, USA.

FREAD D L (1988) "The NWS DAMBRK Model: Theoretical background/user documentation", US National Weather Service, Silver Spring, Maryland, USA.

GREEN C H, PARKER D J and EMERY P J (1983): "The real costs of flooding to households: intangible costs", Geography and Planning Paper No 12; Middlesex Polytechnic, Enfield, UK.

HARRISON S (1864): "A complete history of the great flood at Sheffield on March 11 and 12, 1864", S Harrison, Sheffield.

PARKER D J, GREEN C H and THOMPSON P M (1987): "Urban flood protection benefits: a project appraisal guide", Gower Technical Press, Aldershot.

PENNING-ROWSEL E C and CHATTERTON J B (1977): "The benefits of flood alleviation: a manual of assessment techniques", Gower Technical Press, Aldershot.

RAWLINSON R and BEARDMORE N (1864): "Report on the failure and bursting of a reservoir embankment belonging to the Sheffield Waterworks Company, on the night of Friday 11 March 1864", Report (in Inst. of Civil Eng. library, London)

SANGREY D A et al (1975): "Evaluating the impact of structurally interrupted flood plain flows", Technical Report No 98, Cornell University, prepared for the Office of Water Research and Technology, US Dept of the Interior.

SMITH D I and GREENAWAY M (1987): "Dam failure, the estimation of direct flood damage. A study of Queanbeyan, NSW", Australian National University, Centre for Resource and Environmental Studies (CRES) working paper 1987/23, Canberra.

US ARMY CORPS OF ENGINEERS (1988): "Flood damage analysis package: users manual", USACE, Hydrualic Engineering Centre, Davis, CA.

US BUREAU OF RECLAMATION (1986): "Guidelines to decision analysis", ACER Technical Memorandum No 7, Engineering and Research Centre, Denver, Colorado.

WURBS R A (1987): "Dam-breach wave models", Jrnl. of Hydraulics Div. ASCE Vol 113, HY1.

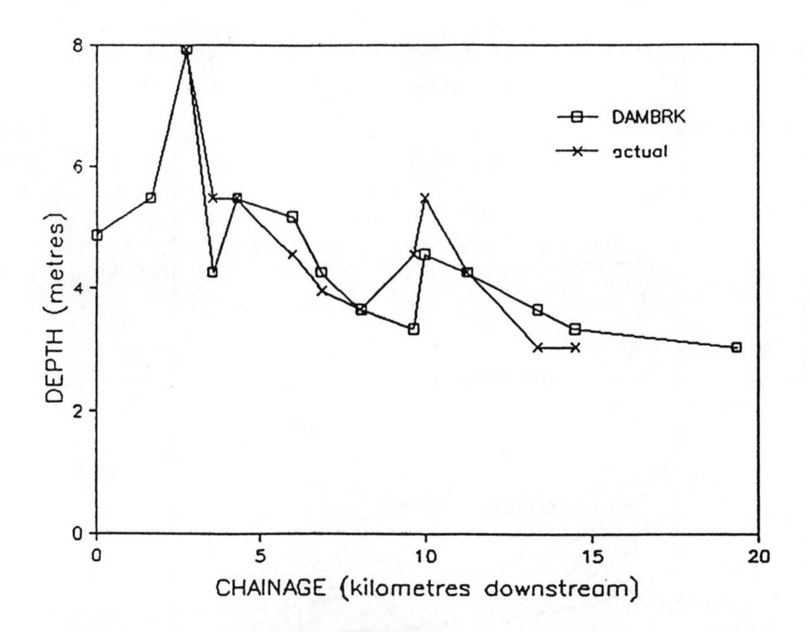

Fig. 1 Dale Dyke: comparison between actual and modelled depths

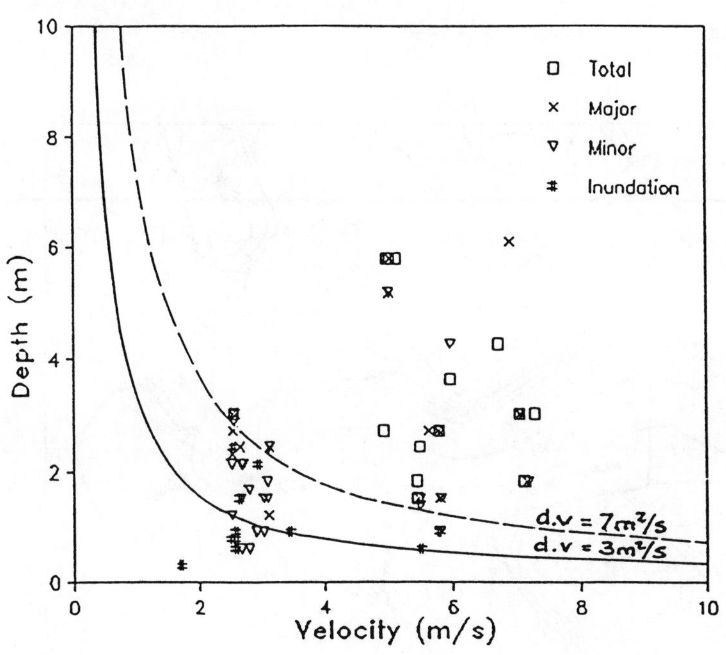

Fig. 2 Building damage in Dale Dyke flood

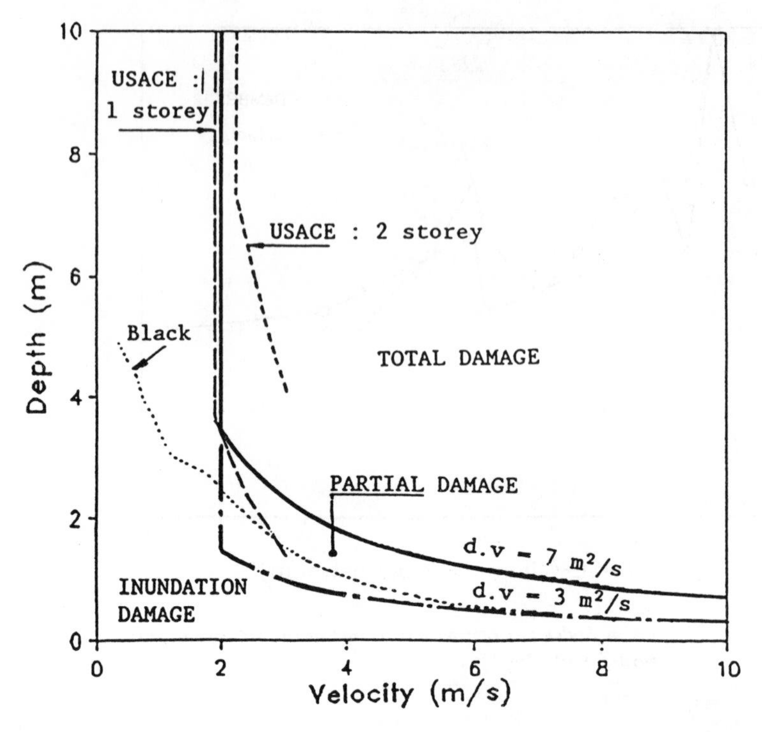

Fig. 3 Damage criteria

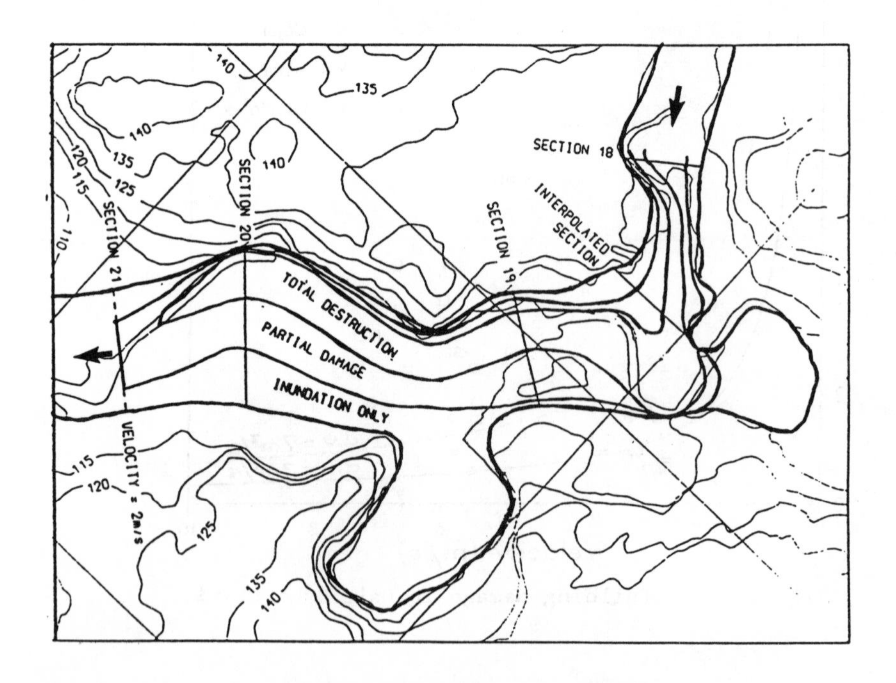

Fig. 4 Example of damage zones

PAPER L1

International Conference on
RIVER FLOOD HYDRAULICS
17-20 September, 1990

PHYSICAL MODELLING OF A COMPOUND RIVER CHANNEL

By

Dr W.R.C. MYERS

Department of Civil Engineering & Transport

University of Ulster

ABSTRACT

Methods of discharge capacity prediction for compound channels and rivers lead to significant errors, if they are based on the extrapolation of inbank flow resistance data to overbank flows. Yet data capture of flood flows in compound river channels is difficult and expensive. Physical modelling helps to overcome these difficulties by allowing extension and generalisation of field data to cover variations of geometry and roughness.

The results of a 1:20 physical model study of a compound river channel are presented. Collection of field data is described, along with measures necessary to achieve model prototype conformity. The model has been used to test the effects of variable cross-sectional geometry and boundary roughness. As such it provides general guidance on flow resistance relationships likely to prevail in compound river channels similar to that studied.

INTRODUCTION

Accurate prediction of discharge capacity is one of the fundamental problems of river engineering. While attempts at discharge assessment have a very long history, it is only in the last two centuries that the problem has been tackled in a scientific manner with the development of equations which relate discharge to other relevant parameters.

The simplest of these are the uniform flow equations attributable to Chezy, Manning and Darcy-Weisbach. These simple expressions find their way into more complex formulations which describe gradually varied steady and unsteady flow, which form the basis of sophisticated computational river models available to the engineer today.

However even the most sophisticated model is only as good as the equations and parameters it embodies. Of particular concern in river engineering is the determination of flow resistance, which usually takes the form of a roughness coefficient. This parameter which is often assumed constant, is in fact highly variable and depends on stage, discharge, Reynolds number, boundary roughness,

International Conference on River Flood Hydraulics, edited by W.R.White

plan geometry and cross-sectional geometry. Ideally, roughness coefficients should be determined experimentally; but frequently this is not possible and a prediction of some sort must be made.

Compound river channels consisting of a deep central channel and one or two side flood plains, represents a case where cross-sectional geometry undergoes a step change as stage rises above the bankfull value; and this in turn has a significant effect on flow resistance. This type of river cross-sectional geometry is quite common and is often used in channel redesign since it presents some advantages in terms of enhancing the amenity value of the river. However if inbank flow resistance data are used to predict overbank flows, these may be up to ±30% in error.

A significant and growing body of research has been carried out into the hydraulic behaviour of compound channels. The vast majority of this work is related to laboratory flumes of small size and often having smooth boundaries, and it is not yet clear how easily these results may be scaled up to give guidance on prototype river behaviour. Most recently a major focus for this work has been the SERC Flood Channel Facility at the laboratories of HR Ltd, Wallingford. The conception and planning the facility are described by Knight & Sellin (1987) while the first results of the study have been presented by Knight & Shiono (1990), Sellin & Elliott (1990), Wormleaton & Merritt (1990) and Myers & Brennan (1990). It is not possible to present a comprehensive review of the literature on compound channels in this short paper, but a very useful bibliography has been produced by Holinrake (1987-1989). Ramsbottom (1989) has presented the currently available field data on compound river channels.

PHYSICAL MODEL

The River Main in Northern Ireland has been reconstructed along part of its length to form a compound cross-section which is illustrated in Fig 1. An 800 km reach of the river is being studied using field data, computational modelling and physical modelling to provide flow resistance information which may be useful in river design. In particular, methods of discharge estimation are sought which will eliminate or minimise the errors commonly associated with compound river channels.

Physical models have a long history of service in river engineering. In the case of compound channels, they may be used to extrapolate field data to cover higher flows and different geometries from those measured. However scale effects in compound channels are not yet well understood, and in particular the laws governing the scaling of the momentum transfer from main channel to flood plains have not been fully developed.

The River Main model covering a 250 m length of river was built to a natural scale of 1:20, out of perspex and set to the river bed slope of 1.906×10^{-3} . Discharge was measured volumetrically at low flows, while higher flows were recorded using a Venturi meter.

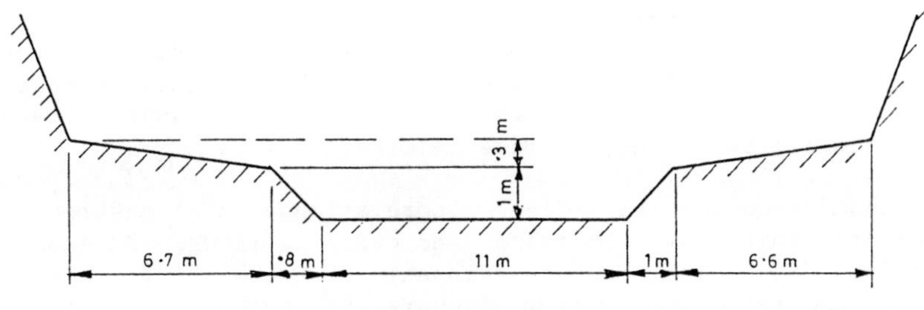

RIVER MAIN SECTION 14 UPSTREAM LIMIT

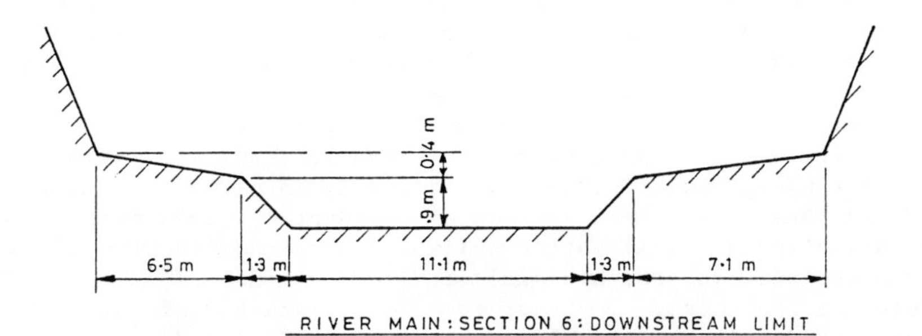

RIVER MAIN : SECTION 6 : DOWNSTREAM LIMIT

FIG 1 : RIVER MAIN CROSS-SECTIONAL GEOMETRIES

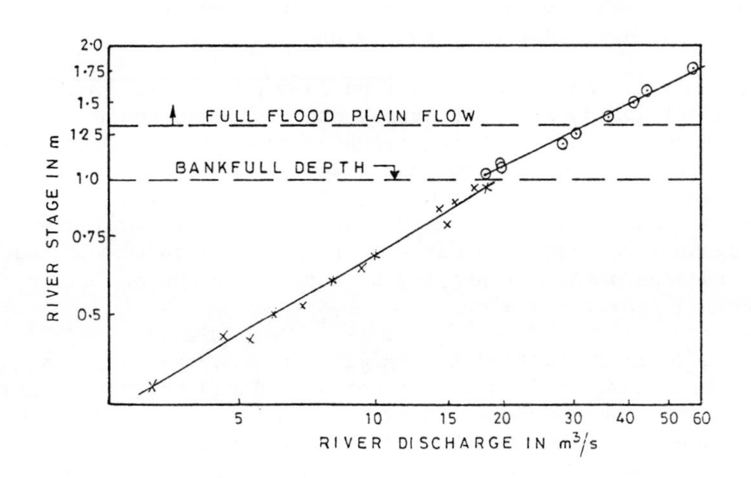

FIG 2 : STAGE DISCHARGE RELATIONSHIP FOR SECTION 14

Depth measurement was by means of digital scales reading to .01 mm.

Flow data from the river was collected from a bridge at the upstream end of the experimental reach. A current meter was used to measure point velocities at 60% of flow depth on some 30 verticals across the section. The velocity area method was then applied to calculate total discharge. Stage readings were taken at both upstream and downstream limits of the experimental reach.

Fig 2 and 3 show the stage discharge relationships at upstream and downstream limits for both inbank and overbank flows. As expected, there is a discontinuity of relationship at the bankfull depth, with an associated reduction in discharge at depths above bankfull. This is due to momentum transfer which reduces the capacity of the main channel and increases the discharge on the flood plains. Because the main channel carries the majority of the flow, its reduction is not compensated for by extra flood plain flow.

Artificial roughening of the model was necessary in order to achieve conformity with the prototype. This was achieved using 5 mm diameter wooden dowels inserted vertically into the flow, such that they penetrated the free surface at all depths. This system had the advantage of facilitating quick and easy modification of the roughness pattern, but obviously it did not model the shape of the prototype roughness. In order to achieve inbank conformity the roughness density had to be reduced for increasing depth as shown in Fig 4. This graph was then extrapolated to give guidance on the main channel roughness density applicable to overbank flows. The additional roughness required to achieve conformity at depths above bankfull was then provided by roughening the flood plains. It was found that a single flood plain roughness density was satisfactory at all overbank flow depths.

Conformity between model and prototype is shown in Fig 5 where the measured model depths and discharges, appropriately scaled are compared to the prototype stage discharge relationships. Overbank conformity is good, but at low inbank depths, model and prototype values begin to diverge. This was due to the increasing relative roughness of the river at low depths which necessitated increasing model roughness density to achieve conformity. A point was reached where increasing dowel bar density no longer had the desired effect of increasing flow resistance.

In addition to investigating the model at prototype roughness, it was considered desirable to extend the usefulness by investigating variations of roughness and geometry. A number of variations was considered, of which the most significant are detailed in Table 1.

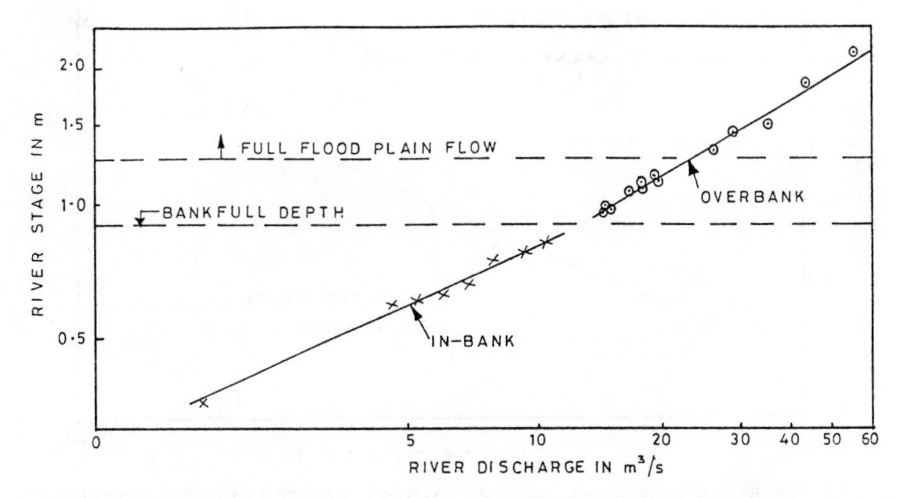

FIG 3 : STAGE DISCHARGE RELATIONSHIP FOR SECTION 6

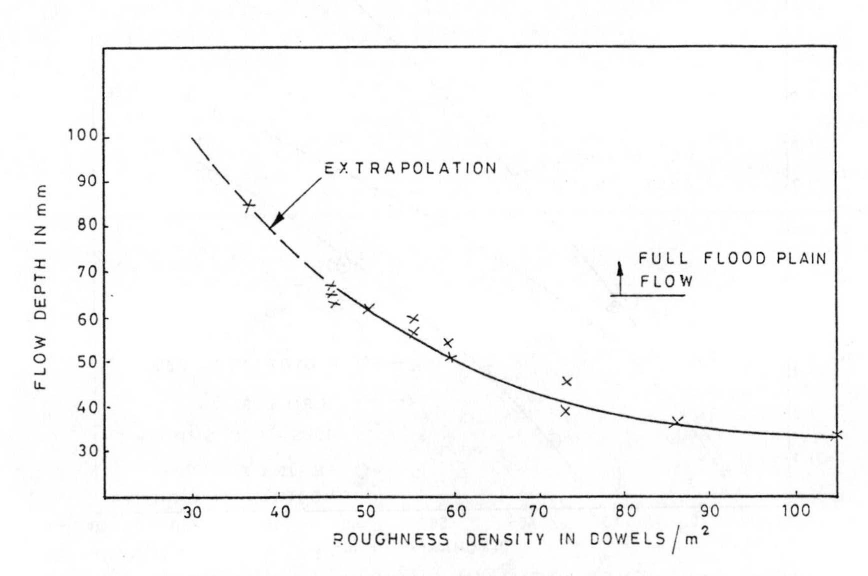

FIG 4 : RIVER MAIN MODEL : VARIATION OF MAIN CHANNEL ROUGHNESS DENSITY WITH FLOW DEPTH

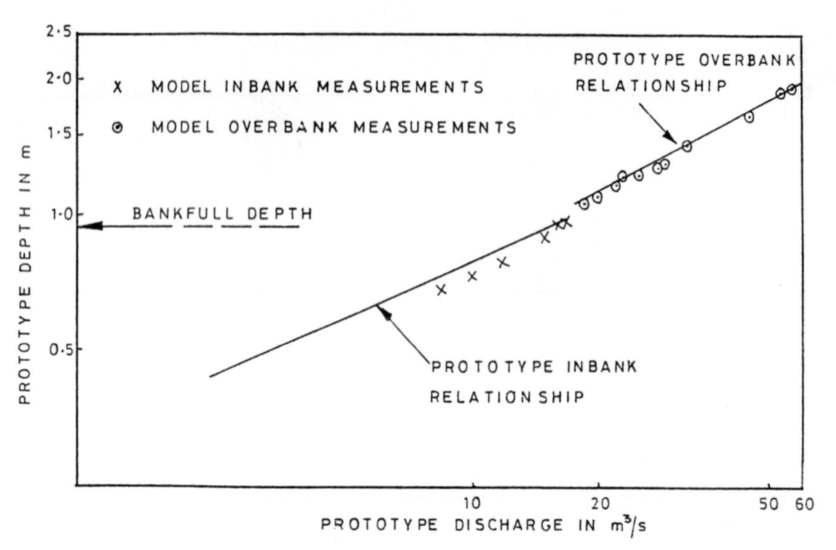

FIG 5 : RIVER MAIN MODEL: MODEL PROTOTYPE CONFORMITY

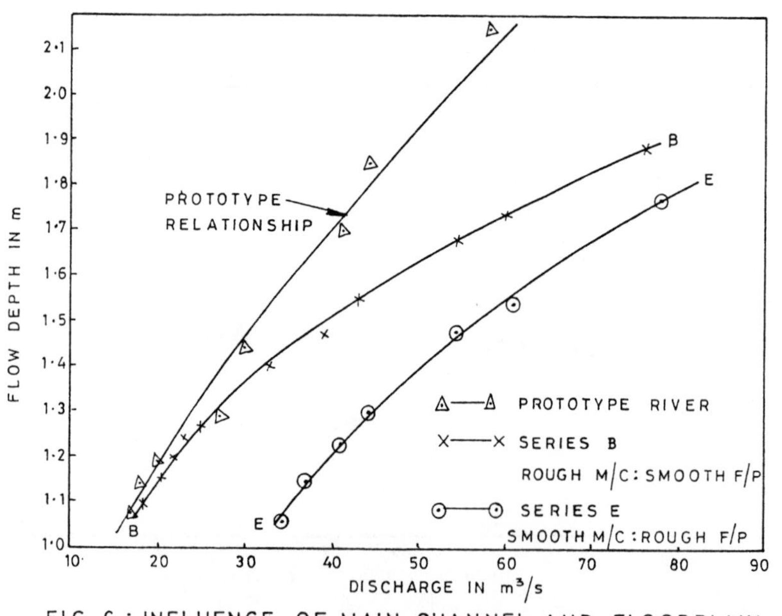

FIG 6 : INFLUENCE OF MAIN CHANNEL AND FLOODPLAIN ROUGHNESS ON STAGE-DISCHARGE RELATIONSHIPS

SERIES	CROSS-SECTION	MAIN CHANNEL BOUNDARY	FLOOD PLAIN BOUNDARIES	
B	Symmetrical	Rough	Smooth	
C	Symmetrical	Rough	Rough	Prototype
E	Symmetrical	Smooth	Rough	conformity
G	Asymmetrical	Rough	Rough	

TABLE 1: Details of Physical Model Tests

In Table 1, a "smooth" boundary indicates a perspex finish, while the designation "rough boundary" indicates "prototype roughness density" on either main channel or flood plains or both. The asymmetrical cross-section was achieved by inserting a flood wall at bankfull on the right flood plain, producing a compound section having a main channel and one flood plain.

STAGE-DISCHARGE RELATIONSHIPS

Using the scaling laws for depth and discharge it was possible therefore to generate stage discharge relationships for SERIES B, E and G, as shown in Figs 6 and 7. The river stage discharge relationship is shown for comparison. These figures illustrate the influence of variations of boundary roughness and cross-sectional geometry on stage discharge relationships of rivers similar to the River Main. While these predictions must be used with caution, nevertheless they do provide some general guidance on the limits within which rivers similar to that studied may behave. Hence such predictions may guide river engineers on the likely behaviour of compound channels such as the Main.

Fig 6 illustrates the influence of main channel and flood plain roughness on the stage discharge relationship. The reduction of flood plain roughness leads to a significant increase in compound channel capacity; around 60% increase at a flow depth of 1.9 m. Reduction of main channel roughness leads to an increase in bankfull discharge of around 100% and this increased percentage capacity is almost sustained throughout the depth range. Fig 7 shows, perhaps surprisingly, that an asymmetrical cross-section with the same roughness as that of the prototype, exhibits a greater discharge capacity at all depths considered. This is due to the reduction in momentum transfer to the flood plains effected by the insertion of a flood wall at bankfull depth on the right bank. Thus the reduced momentum transfer in the asymmetrical section leads to increased main channel velocities and discharge capacity.

FLOW RESISTANCE

Flow resistance is normally included in river engineering equations in the form of a roughness coefficient. Manning's equation is probably the most widely used uniform flow equation, which is also incorporated in gradually varied steady and unsteady flow equations as an expression of the friction slope. Thus a knowledge of

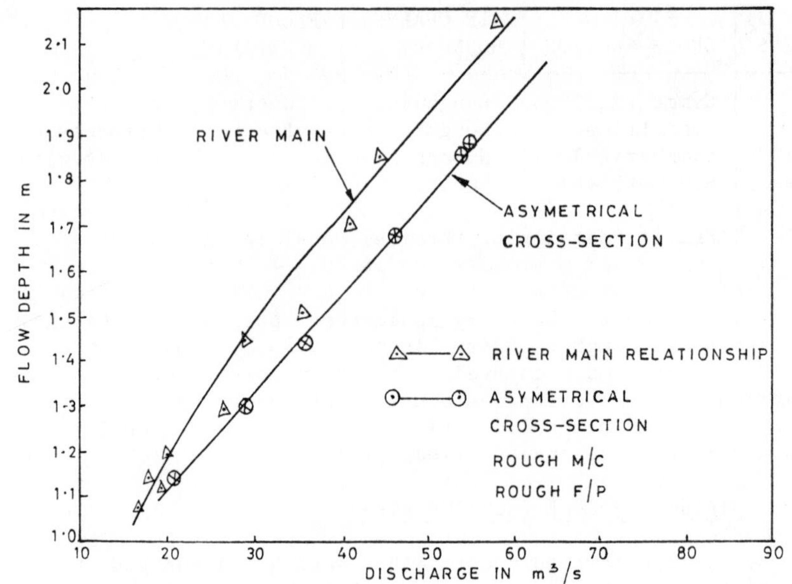

FIG 7: INFLUENCE OF GEOMETRY ON STAGE DISCHARGE RELATIONSHIPS

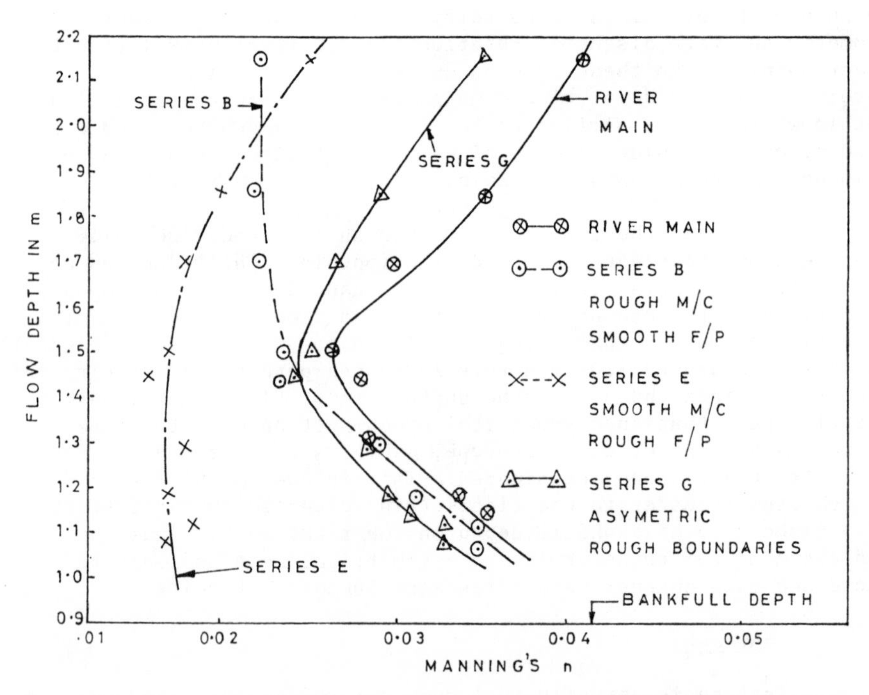

FIG 8 INFLUENCE OF BOUNDARY ROUGHNESS & GEOMETRY VARIATION OF MANNING'S ROUGHNESS COEFFICIENT

Manning's roughness coefficient is important.

Fig 8 shows values of roughness coefficient for the prototype river and also for the variations of boundary roughness and geometry considered using the physical model. Prototype river values were derived by incorporating the measured stage and discharge data into a gradually varied flow model of the experimental reach. The relationship shows a decreasing value of Manning's "n" with depth, to a flow depth of around 1.5 m, with an increase thereafter as flow depth increases. This minimum value of "n" is characteristic of compound channel geometries, although it normally occurs at depths immediately above bankfull. Its occurrence at a larger depth here is because the flood plain beds slope laterally inwards, and hence the minimum value occurs only when both flood plains are completely inundated.

Also shown in Fig 8 are the derived relationships for SERIES B, E and G of the test programme. The roughness coefficient values were calculated using stages and discharges measured on the physical model, combined with water surface slopes from the prototype river. Fig 8 must be interpreted with caution, especially in relation to the actual values of "n". But the relationships do indicate the influence of boundary roughness and channel geometry on the behaviour of roughness coefficients. They also illustrate the complexity of roughness coefficient behaviour in compound river channels, and warn of the danger of extrapolating inbank or bankfull values to overbank flows.

CONCLUSIONS

1. The results of a 1:20 scale physical model study of a compound river channel have been presented.

2. Conformity between model and prototype was achieved using artificial roughness in the form of 5 mm diameter wooden dowels, inserted vertically into the flow.

3. The physical model was used to predict stage - discharge relationship and Manning's roughness coefficient for variations of boundary roughness and cross-sectional geometry.

4. These predictions must be used with caution, but indicate the limits of discharge capacity within which compound river channels such as that studied may operate.

5. Model studies represent a powerful tool in extending and generalising scarce river data relating to compound geometries.

REFERENCES

Hollinrake P.G. (1987, 1988, 1989), "The Structure of Flow in Open Channels - a literature search", Vols 1, 2, 3; HR Ltd, Reports SR96, SR153, SR209.

Knight D.W. and Sellin R.H.J. (1987), "The SERC Flood Channel Facility", Jour. of Inst. Water and Environmental Management, Vol 41, No. 4, August, pp 198-204.

Knight D.W. and Shiono K. (1990), "Turbulence Measurements in Shear Layers of Compound Channels", Jour. Hyd. Research, IAHR, Vol 28, No. 1.

Myers W.R.C. and Brennan E.K. (1990), "Flow Resistance in Compound Channels", Jour. Hyd. Research, IAHR, Vol 28, No. 1.

Ramsbottom D.M. (1989), "Flood Discharge Assessment", HR Ltd, Report SR195, March, pp 1-148.

Sellin R.H.J. and Elliott S. (1990), "The SERC Flood Channel Facility: Skewed Channel Experiments", Jour. Hyd. Research, IAHR, Vol 28, No. 1.

Wormleaton P.R. and Merritt D. (1990), "Discharge Calculation Methods in Compound Channels", Jour. Hyd. Research, IAHR, Vol 28, No. 1.

ACKNOWLEDGEMENT

The author wishes to express his thanks to the Science and Engineering Research Council for their financial support of this research project. Thanks are also due to the Department of Agriculture for Northern Ireland for assistance at various stages of the project.

International Conference on
RIVER FLOOD HYDRAULICS
17-20 September, 1990

EFFECT OF SCALE DISTORTION IN A COMPOUND RIVER CHANNEL MODEL STUDY

Higginson, N.N.J.
Drainage Division, Department of Agriculture for N. Ireland
Johnston, H.T.
Civil Engineering Department, The Queen's University of Belfast
Myers, W.R.C.
Civil Engineering Department, University of Ulster

ABSTRACT

Distortion of the vertical scale in physical models of river systems is a common practice to increase water depths in the model. Where the channel section is compound, the momentum transfer from the deep primary channel to the flood plain is affected by the scale distortion. A natural scale and a distorted scale model of a compound channel are compared and contrasted with field measurements on the prototype river.

INTRODUCTION

Although the practice of physically modelling rivers has been used for over a century there are only a small number of handbooks on the design of river models available to the hydraulic engineer. There is even less literature to be found on the subject of scale effects, even though they play a key part in the design of physical models. [If large scale distortions are applied (5 or more) the similarity of the velocity profiles between a model and its prototype is limited.] Scale distortion is often necessary in physical modelling as scales for horizontal length are seldom appropriate for the vertical dimensions. The effect of scale distortion is often an increase in the proportion of model channel area influenced by boundary effects in comparison to the prototype.

The compound or two stage channel can be man made or occur naturally. In man made compound channels the secondary channel or berm is usually one or two times the width of the primary channel whereas in natural channels the secondary channel is usually many times the width of the primary channel. The compound channel has been developed for environmental and aesthetic reasons. During low flows the depth of water is kept high hence helping the migration of fish. The deep central section of the river ensures a high mean velocity which creates a self cleansing action preventing or inhibiting the growth of aquatic weeds. The berm area is used to provide storage in times of flood and this attenuates the flood peak.

In the compound channel the complicated processes of momentum transfer presents a problem to the engineer when he has to design the shape and size of the channel. The behaviour of the flow in the compound channel is not fully understood. The region between

International Conference on River Flood Hydraulics, edited by W.R.White

the fast flow in the primary channel and the shallower flow on the berm is referred to as the interface zone. This zone of high fluid shear makes it difficult to predict the distribution of velocity throughout the cross section. Various methods for estimating the discharge by sub dividing the area in sections have been put forward by a number of authors but when used for the compound channel they often result in large errors. This makes it difficult for the river engineer to accurately predict the carrying capacity of the channel. For this reason it is often desirable if not essential, to construct a physical model in order to investigate flooding to predict the stage discharge relationship.

Little is known about the effect of scale distortion on the modelling of the momentum transfer process. This process results in a line of vortices being set up along the interface and an associated loss of energy from the flow. At levels just above bankfull condition in the primary channel the momentum transfer process results in a reduction of the average velocity. There has been considerable experimental laboratory work done on compound channels. Unfortunately most of this work is based on rectangular sections and not related to prototype rivers which have sloping banks. Early work by Sellin (1964) noted the series of vortices with vertical axes which form along the interface area. Boundary shear and velocity distributions were studied by Elsawy and Myers (1975) in smooth models and they concluded that the interaction decreased the bed shear in the primary channel and increased it over the berms. Holden and James (1989) investigated the effect of the primary channel side slopes and concluded that the intensity of the interaction decreases slightly as the slope becomes milder.

PROTOTYPE CHANNEL

During the early seventies a drainage scheme was designed for the river Maine in Northern Ireland. The purpose was to provide adequate freeboard for agricultural land in the upper reaches of the catchment. In the lower reaches a large industrial complex was considered to be under threat from flooding, largely due to certain works being carried out upstream which included the removal of several weirs which had helped create pondage. The catchment at the industrial site was 250 Km^2 and the design requirements were such that a channel had to carry $210m^3/s$ with a freeboard of 900m and have a bankfull capacity of $342m^3/s$. [The mean annual flood for the site has been estimated at $80m^3/s$]. The presence of a factory on one bank, a main road and pumping station on the other bank acted as a restraint to the width of the channel. A compound channel was designed to accommodate the strong fishery interests. The longitudinal slope reduced from 1 in 270 to 1 in 1700 at the downstream end of the channel. The width of the channel varied and it was decided to study the reach which was the most vulnerable, i.e., the reach where the channel passes between the factory and the pumping station and hence the narrowest section.

At the section under study the primary channel was designed to have a width of 12m, a depth of 0.9m. Each berm is 7.5m wide and slopes towards the primary channel with a lateral gradient of 1 in 25. The slope at the reach chosen for study had a design slope of 1 in 520. The bed material consisted of a very coarse gravel with a D50 size varying from 100 to 200mm.

The side slopes of the primary channel consist of quarried stone of up to 0.5 tonne weight. The berms are usually covered with heavy weed growth and the channel banks are protected from erosion by a fabric called Enkamatt, which has been sown with long grasses.

FIELD INVESTIGATION

The water surface gradient at the study reach has been monitored by use of post gauges and found to be 0.0019 over a wide range of flows. An autographic water level recorder was installed in the reach and hydrographs obtained show no evidence of any effect on the rising limb of the change from inbank to compound channel. Over 50 river flow gaugings using propeller meters were taken over a wide range of flows and various rating equations were studied. It was decided that the best predictions over the complete range of flows could be made by using two equations. Equation (1) is applicable for low flows up to the primary channel bankfull condition and is given as:

$$Q = 16.057\,(H)^{2.187} \qquad (\text{For } H < .9\text{m}) \quad \ldots\ldots \text{ eqn (1)}$$

with $R^2 = 0.9928$

Using 27 gaugings for overbank conditions the following equation was obtained

$$Q = 16.839\,(H)^{1.537} \qquad (H > .9) \quad \ldots\ldots \text{ eqn (2)}$$

for which $R^2 = 0.9713$

The variation with depth of Manning's coefficient, n, averaged over the channel cross-section is shown in Fig. 2. It can be seen that the value of n decreases to 0.35 when the primary channel is full. From the bankfull condition to the top of berms the value of n continues to decrease to 0.020 up to a depth of 1.2m when the full compound section is utilised. As the depth increases further the value of n starts to increase and continues to increase to the maximum recorded depth of flow of 2.55m.

EXPERIMENTAL WORK

Two physical models have been constructed of the prototype channel, one with a scale distortion of 1.8 and the other to a natural scale.

Distorted Scale Model. The model was constructed in fibreglass having a smooth finish. The channel was 11.5m long and the scales were 1 in 25 vertically and 1 in 45 horizontally, giving a primary channel depth of 36mm. The discharge was measured using a vee-notch tank equipped to give a continuous readout of flow rate.

Depths of flow at the measuring section were measured using a sonic water level sensor with an accuracy of 0.2mm which could traverse the channel while the water surface slope was set parallel to the channel bed by use of an adjustable outfall gate.

A series of experiments have been carried out with the smooth boundary condition in which measurements of depth of flow, velocity distribution and discharge capacity of the berms and primary channel have been taken under various flow conditions. Point velocity measurements were obtained using a data logger scanning the output form a mini-propeller meter over a 50 second period to give average velocity. Table 1 shows the dimensions of the distorted scale model with fig. (1) showing a typical cross section.

As with the prototype two rating equations were found to be best for predicting discharges for all ranges of flow. However the change of point was found to be at a depth of 48mm and not 36mm which was the equivalent to bankfull on the prototype.

Using 18 values above 48mm a rating equation was derived which was

$$Q = 0.00635\, H^{2.505} \qquad H \geq 48\text{mm}$$

$$\text{for which } R^2 = 0.962$$

Using 13 values below 48 mm the rating equation obtained was

$$Q = 0.022695\, H^{1.578}$$

$$\text{with } R^2 = 0.9794$$

These rating equations are shown on Fig. 3.

The Natural Scale Model. This model is 20 m in length and made of perspex to a scale of 1:20. The principal dimensions are shown in Table 1. Discharge was measured volumetrically at low flows, and by means of a Venturi meter at higher discharges. Depth measurement was by means of digital scales reading to 0.01mm and uniform flow was arranged for each discharge using an adjustable weir at the downstream end of the model. Uniform flow was defined as a flow depth change along the model length of less than 0.5mm.

At overbank flows, point velocities were measured at 60% of depth at over 40 verticals across the section. These were taken as the depth averaged velocities for the verticals, and they were used to calculate the components of discharge in the main channel and on the flood plains. The integrated discharge could also be compared with the value measured volumetrically or by Venturi meter and these agreed to within ±5%.

Smooth and roughened boundary tests were undertaken, the later to achieve conformity with the prototype. Only the smooth tests are referred to herein, as a comparison with these arising from the distorted scale model, in the hope that this may yield conclusions as to the advisability of scale distortion in compound channel models.

The rating curves for inbank and overbank flow are as follows:-

INBANK $Q = 0.0114\ H^{1.876}$ Q in l/s .... eqn (5)
OVERBANK $Q = 0.0035\ H^{2.142}$ H in mm .... eqn (6)
Correlation coefficients for the regression analysis were 0.9995 and 0.9866 respectively.

DISCUSSION OF RESULTS

Although both models have been operated under both smooth and rough boundary conditions, only the smooth boundary tests are reviewed here, since only they allow direct comparison between natural and distorted scales. The aim of the exercise has been to illustrate the differences between natural and distorted scales in relation to compound river channel models.

Figure 2 shows lateral profiles of depth averaged velocity for both models, applicable to the same values of relative depth in each case. At all depths the natural scale model showed lower velocities, and this effect was particularly noticeable on the flood plains. The velocity profiles became closer as depth increased. These trends may be attributed to the fact that scale distortion produces larger depth to width ratios at all depths thereby yielding large velocities.

Full velocity distributions for the distorted scale model are shown in Figure 3. Unfortunately similar distributions were not available for the natural scale model. The distributions show clearly the differences in main channel and flood plain velocities at low depths, which give rise to momentum transfer. As depth increases floodplain velocities increase to similar values to that occurring in the main channel, with the emergence of a filament of maximum velocity close to the flood plain. This filament moves on to the flood plain at large depths.

The models were tested with smooth boundaries to examine the effect of velocity on momentum transfer across the interface between the primary channel and the berm. The variation with position across the channel of the depth averaged velocity divided by the mean velocity for the complete cross section is shown in Fig. 3, for different depths of flows. The same Yr ratio was used in both models for comparative purposes.

The variation in the average Manning's coefficient with depth of flow is shown on Fig. 1 and similar trends to that found in the prototype can be observed, except that the maximum value of n above bankfull condition occurs at a lower stage.

Velocity distribution for two depths of flow are shown in Fig. 4 for the distorted scale model. It can be seen that at the depths of flow above bankfull the maximum velocity in the primary channel is located in the interface zone. As the depth increases further the maximum value of velocity for the whole cross section was found to occur on the berm in the distorted scale model. This was not observed in the natural scale model.

Stage discharge relationships for the both models are shown in Fig. 4, and the values have been scaled up to prototype dimensions. Also shown for comparison is the data obtained from river gaugings. It is to be expected that neither model conforms to the prototype since model boundaries are smooth. However it is most interesting to note that the natural scale model lies significantly closer to the prototype than does the distorted model data. Furthermore this effect is particularly pronounced at overbank depths of flow. This is obviously due to the fact that the relative roughness of the distorted scale model is less than that of the natural scale; and hence the former will require considerably more roughening to achieve conformity, particularly in the overbank region. These results underline the potential dangers of scale distortion, which would appear to be accentuated in models of compound river channels. The design discharge is indicated on the figure.

The distribution of discharge between main channel and flood plains is another relevant aspect of river modelling and Fig. 5 illustrates the proportions measured in both models. Values are also given in Table 2. Also shown are similar data for the prototype river, and from previous laboratory studies for comparison. Not surprisingly, neither model precisely predicts flow proportions, since these are governed not only by geometry but also by roughness. However in general the natural scale model seems to fall closer to the prototype relationship at all but the lowest depths. This again underlines the departure of distorted scale models from prototype behaviour.

From the viewpoint of discharge estimation in compound river channels, flow resistance is of paramount importance. This is usually expressed as a roughness coefficient, with the most widely used being that attributed to Manning. Figure 6 shows the variation with flow depth of Manning's 'n' for both models and the prototype river. The river data exhibit complex behaviour with a minimum value of 'n' just as the flood plains become fully inundated. Thereafter Manning's 'n' increases with depth. The model data are much less variable with depth as expected, but do show the minimum value at the same depth as on the prototype. However at depths above 1.2m (prototype), Mannings 'n' is almost constant for the models as might be expected since boundaries are smooth.

Figure 7 presents a different representation of the flow resistance data in the form of the variation of Darcy-Weisbach friction factor with Reynolds number. This representation is traditionally associated with pipe flow, but is becoming more popular in relation to open channels in recent years. Both model and prototype data are presented. Inbank model data behaves as expected while there are slight differences in overbank behaviour when natural and distorted scales are compared. The prototype shows much larger absolute values as expected, and the overbank data exhibit the trend noted in Fig. 6 whereby friction factor increases with Reynolds number (and depth) above the depth at which the flood plains are fully inundated. Both Figs. 6 and 7 underline strongly the complex nature of flow resistance in compound river channels and the dangers inherent in extrapolating inbank values to overbank flows.

CONCLUSIONS

1. Natural and distorted scale models of a compound river channel have been compared for the smooth boundary case.

2. Distorted scale models exhibit higher velocities especially on the flood plains and at less depths.

3. Natural scale models exhibit stage discharge relationships which are significantly closer to the prototype curves in the unroughened condition. However both models require artificial roughness.

4. Natural scale models more closely predict proportions of discharge in main channel and flood plains.

5. Flow resistance behaviour of natural and distorted scale models is broadly similar, with the former exhibiting a maximum value of roughness coefficient at overbank flows which was not observed in the distorted scale model. Neither model accurately represented flow resistance behaviour in the prototype river.

6. Flow resistance relations in compound river channels exhibits complex relationships, and hence inbank values cannot be used to give accurate prediction of discharge capacity at overbank depths of flow.

REFERENCES

Holden, A.P. and James, C.S. (1989). "Boundary Shear Distribution on Flood Plains", Journal of Hydraulic Research Vol. 27 No. 1.

Myers, W.R.C. and Elsawy, E.M. (1975). "Boundary Shear in Channel with Flood Plain", Journal of Hydraulics Division A.S.C.E. 101, 933-946.

Sellin, R.H.J. (1964). "A Laboratory Investigation into the Interaction Between the Flow in the Channel of a River and that over its Floodplain". La Houille Blanche, 7, 793-801.

NOTATION

b	half width of primary channel
B_f	width of berm
H	Depth of flow
K	equivalent grain size roughness
n	Mannings roughness coefficient
Q	discharge
Q_b, Q_c, Q_T	discharge associated with berms, primary channel and total section
V	mean cross sectional velocity
Y_r	relative depth ratio

		Distorted Scale	Natural Scale
Primary Channel Depth (d)		36 mm	47
Bed Width	(2b)	266	550
Berm Width	(bf)	167	360
Berm Lateral Slope		7.2%	5%
Inner Bank Slope (Horz:Vertical		1 in 1.8	1 in 1

TABLE 1. PRINCIPLE MODEL DIMENSIONS

Y_r	Distorted Scale Qc/ Qt	Natural Scale Qc/ Qt
.36	.82	.89
.41	.75	.82
.46	.68	.75
.51	.63	.71

TABLE 2. PROPORTIONS OF FLOW IN MAIN CHANNEL AT VARIABLE RELATIVE DEPTHS

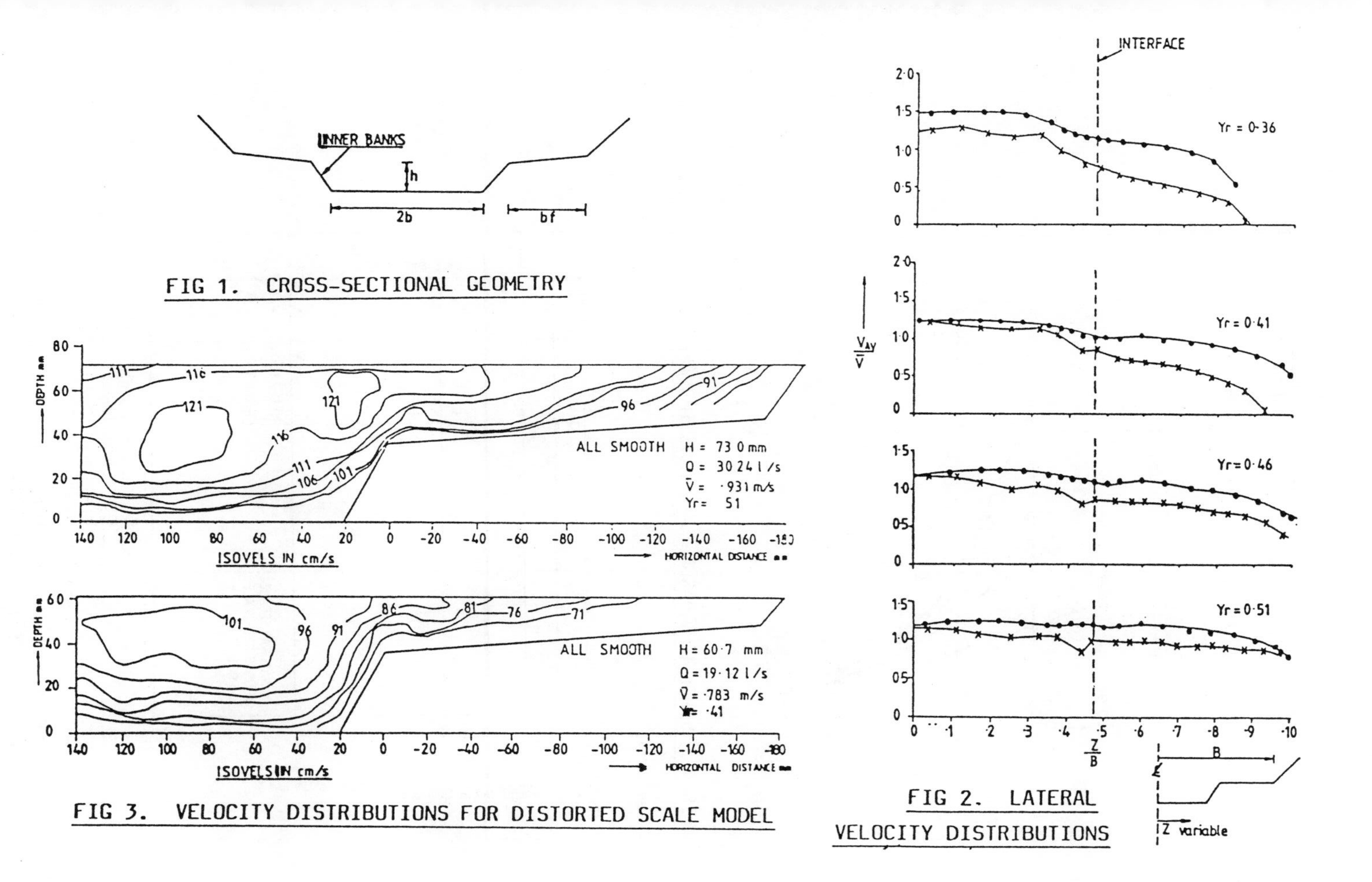

FIG 1. CROSS-SECTIONAL GEOMETRY

FIG 2. LATERAL VELOCITY DISTRIBUTIONS

FIG 3. VELOCITY DISTRIBUTIONS FOR DISTORTED SCALE MODEL

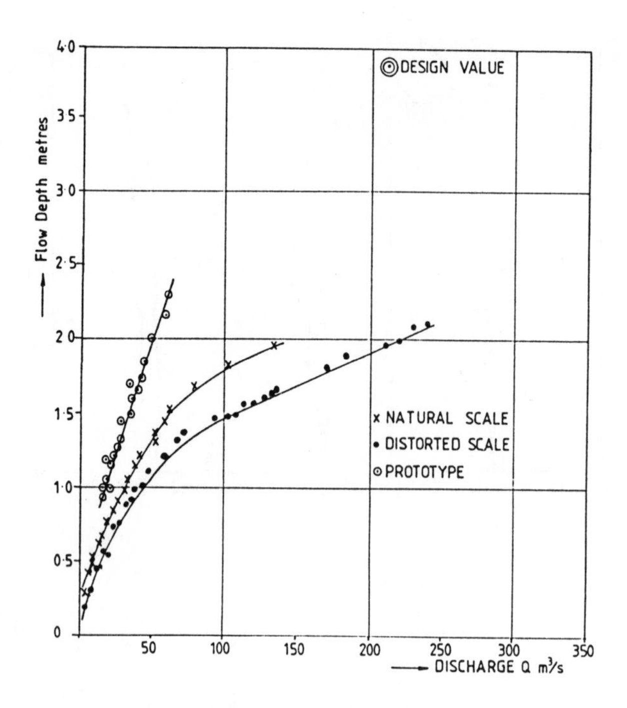

FIG 4. STAGE DISCHARGE RELATIONSHIPS (PROTOTYPE SCALE)

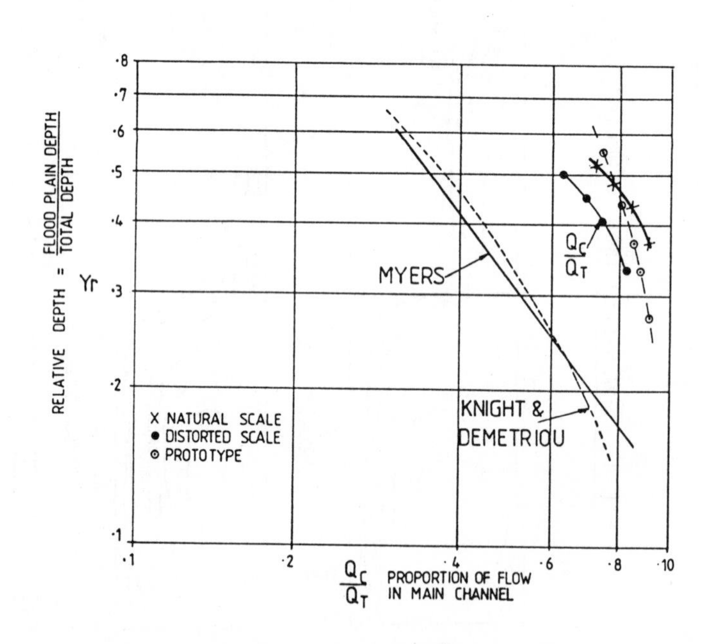

FIG 5. VARIATION WITH RELATIVE DEPTH OF RATIO OF MAIN CHANNEL TO FULL CROSS-SECTIONAL DISCHARGE

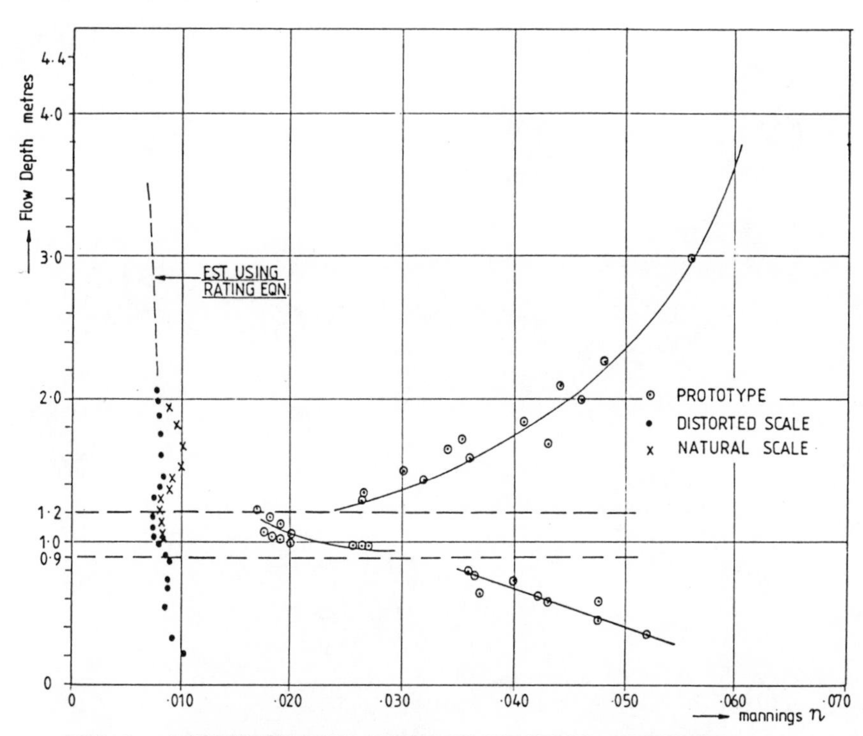

FIG 6. VARIATION WITH DEPTH OF MANNINGS ROUGHNESS COEFFICIENT

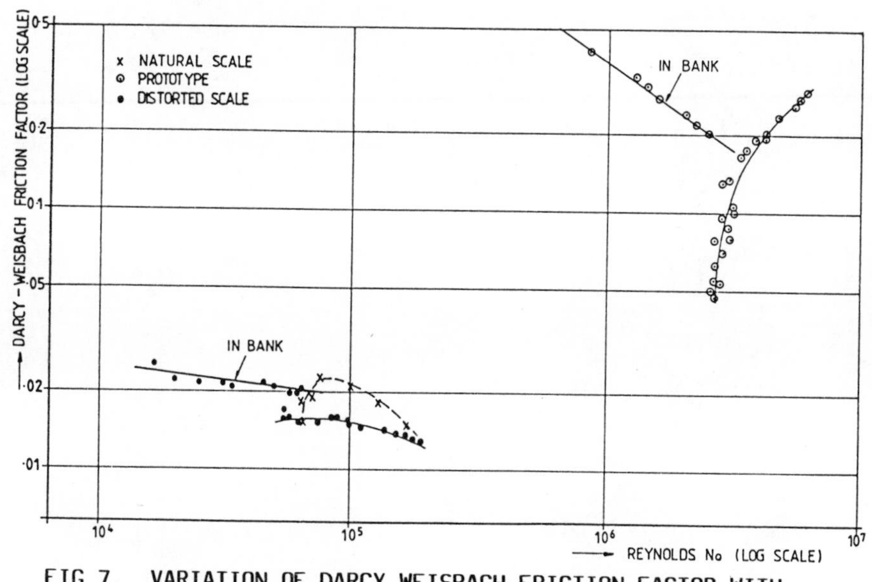

FIG 7. VARIATION OF DARCY WEISBACH FRICTION FACTOR WITH REYNOLDS NUMBER

PAPER L3

International Conference on
RIVER FLOOD HYDRAULICS
17-20 September, 1990

NUMERICAL SIMULATION OF OVER BANK FLOODING IN RIVERS

G. PENDER : Glasgow University
J. ELLIS : Private Consultant

ABSTRACT

Flood wave attenuation in embanked river systems depends on complex interaction between the main channel and it's flood plains. A flood plain algorithm is presented which simulates main channel flood plain interaction during periods of greater than bank full flow. Computation of changes in flood plain water level are based on an iterative explicit solution of the continuity equation.

INTRODUCTION

The manner in which water enters or leaves a river channel from adjacent flood plains is highly variable. In the case of an undeveloped river the geometrical characteristics of the interface may be relatively simple, however, the flow processes can be complex, see Ervine and Ellis (1987). An indication of how some of these physical phenomena can be included in one-dimensional numerical models was given by Wormleaton (1988). In rivers where flood protection work has taken place, the geometrical characteristics of the interface become complicated. Protective measures such as embankments may form a part of flood alleviation schemes and add to the difficulties of flood prediction.

Typically, the sequence of flooding such areas might follow the pattern depicted in figure 1. In figure 1(a) the river level is below the bank full level, but water may be lying in flood plains due to an antecedent flood event. The river level rises and commences spilling onto the flood plain, figure 1(b). Where an embankment exists, then for a time at least, the flow from the river will be independent of flood plain level. As the flood plain fills, figure 1(c), the flow between the river and the flood plain is increasingly influenced by flood plain water level, which is in turn dependent upon the hydraulic characteristics of the flood plain.

As flood levels subside, directions of flow change between flood plain and river, figure 1(d). Ultimately, a condition may be reached with water draining from the flood plains into the subsiding river, figure 1(e).

International Conference on River Flood Hydraulics, edited by W.R.White

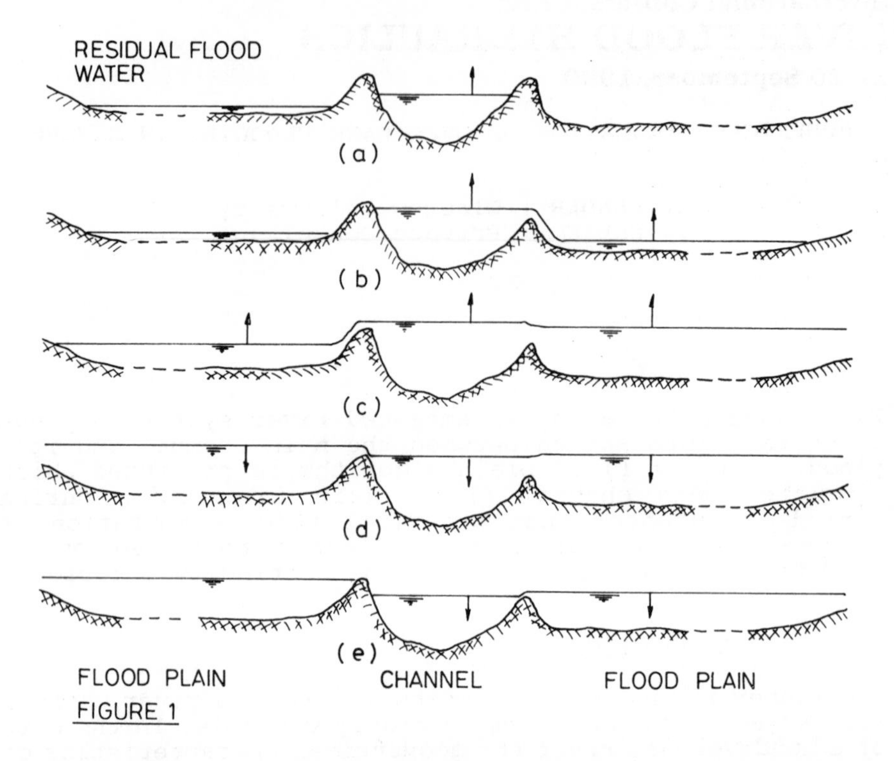

FIGURE 1

The flow process may become more complicated in the case of a meandering river, figure 2. In such cases, flow may leave the river upstream of the meander, between sections A and B, and re-enter the river downstream of the bend, between sections C and D. Thus part of the flow short-circuits the meander loop.

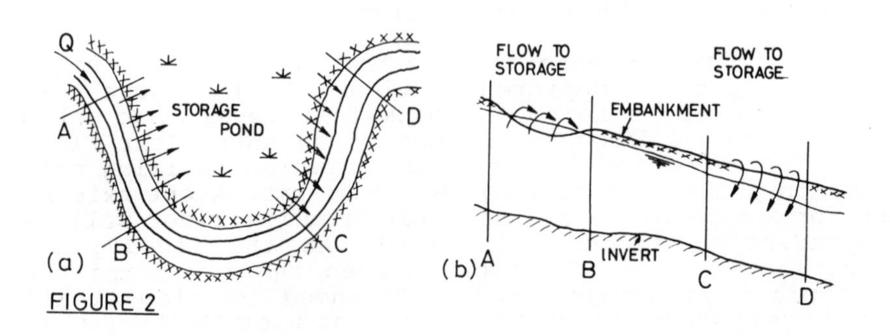

FIGURE 2

NUMERICAL SIMULATION OF FLOODS IN EMBANKED RIVERS

The numerical simulation of flood propagation in embanked river systems usually requires separate representation of the main channel and the flood plains, for example Samuels (1983). Simulation of flood wave propagation along the main channel normally proceeds through a numerical solution of the St. Venant equations. Of the finite difference schemes available, the Preissmann four point implicit scheme is the one most commonly employed for flood routing calculations. The advantages of this scheme are detailed by Abbott (1979) as:

i. unconditionally stable when the time weighting parameter $\theta \geqslant 0.5$,

ii. non-equidistant grid points can be employed,

iii. internal boundaries, such as weir conditions, can be conveniently introduced.

The numerical method used in the following is based on the Preissmann scheme. It has been extended to include an algorithm for analysing the formation, operation and drowning of natural control sections. The algorithm tests the Froude number at each solution node to determine if critical conditions exist. If flow through the section is critical then the solution domain is split and an additional internal boundary condition inserted. The internal boundary ensures weir type flow at this cross-section until the control is drowned by downstream influences. The internal boundary is then removed and the solution proceeds as previously.

A variety of options exist for representing flood plains. Cunge, Holly and Verwey (1980), present three possibilities:

i. one-dimensional non-inertial lateral storage ponds,

ii. two-dimensional non-inertial lateral storage ponds,

iii. looped two-dimensional inertial model.

The one-dimensional storage pond approach is appropriate where areas of flood plain act in isolation, with no longitudinal flow between flood plain elements. Such circumstances arise where the flood plain is crossed by road embankments and transverse dykes or contains areas of open cast mining.

One of the main problems with the storage pond representation of flood plains is numerical oscillations in pond water level during the initial stages of storage pond flooding or draining. These are caused by poor numerical representation of average lateral flow, or average flood plain area, over a time increment. The problem is described in detail by Cunge, Holly and Verwey (1980).

The oscillations can be controlled by reducing the time increment during critical stages of flood plain simulation. However, this approach reduces the economic advantage in using an implicit scheme for the main channel simulation, where choice of time increment is not restricted by stability requirements. There is therefore an economic benefit if changes in storage pond behaviour can be modelled using a time increment suitable for simulation of main channel conditions.

In the following a numerical algorithm is presented for simulating flood plain behaviour using a one-dimensional non-inertial storage pond model. The algorithm reduces pond oscillations by closely modelling the physical pond main channel interaction when calculating lateral flow.

FINITE DIFFERENCE STORAGE POND MODEL

The volume conservation equation for a storage pond can be written as:

$$ql = A_s \cdot dWl_p/dt \qquad 1.$$

where ql is the lateral flow between the main channel and the storage pond (based on a "weir" flow relationship of the form $ql \alpha H^{3/2}$), A_s is the surface area of the storage pond and Wl_p is the storage pond water level. Values of lateral flow verses main channel water level are calculated and stored in data tables.

Equation 1 can be written in finite difference form as:

$$\overline{ql}_j \cdot \Delta t/A_s = \Delta Wl_p \qquad 2.$$

Provided the average lateral inflow, $\overline{ql}_j$, can be calculated, equation 2 can be solved at each time increment to estimate changes in storage pond water level. Where the storage pond is fed by more than one main channel solution reach, the lateral over bank flows are summated over all reaches contributing to storage pond water levels.

The average lateral flow from reach j during a time increment can be calculated from;

$$\overline{ql}_j = 0.5(ql^n_j.sf^n_j + ql^{n+1}_j.sf^{n+1}_j) \qquad 3.$$

where the superscripts indicate the time increment and sf is a submergence reduction factor. Typical functions of sf verses submergence ratio are given in Ellis (1989). To improve numerical stability of the lateral storage pond calculations, we require to estimate changes in lateral flow arising from changes in pond water level occurring during a time increment.

Out flows from main channel. Calculation of outflows from the main channel into lateral storage can be obtained by using an iterative procedure. A first estimate is obtained by setting,

$$ql^{n+1}_j = ql^n_j$$

and iterating to find sf^{n+1}_j. The main channel equations are now solved to obtain the main channel water level, Wl^{n+1}. The value of lateral flow at time n+1 can now be revised and the iterative calculation repeated as necessary.

Inflows to main channel. Calculation of flows from lateral storage requires to take account of the reduction in lateral flow due to decreasing storage pond water level. This can be achieved by writing equation 3 in the form;

$$\overline{ql}_j = 0.5(ql^n_j.sf^n_j + (ql^n_j + \Delta ql).sf^{n+1}_j) \qquad 4.$$

Where Δql is the change in lateral outflow occurring during the time increment from n to n+1. From consideration of the rate of change of lateral flow with water level, we can write,

$$dql/dWl_p = \Delta ql/\Delta Wl_p \qquad 5.$$

An estimate of dql/dWl_p can be made from the calculated relationship between ql and Wl above bank level. Rearranging equation 5 and inserting into equation 4 gives,

$$\overline{ql}_j = 0.5(ql^n_j.sf^n_j + (ql^n_j + dql/dWl_p\,.\Delta Wl_p).sf^{n+1}_j) \qquad 6.$$

Inserting equation 6 into equation 2 and rearranging we obtain,

$$Wl_p = \Delta t.ql^n_j(sf^n_j + sf^{n+1}_j)/(2A_s - \Delta t.sf^{n+1}_j.(dql/dWl_p)) \qquad 7.$$

As with the case of flows into lateral storage, a first estimate of Wl_p^{n+1} is made and an iterative calculation undertaken to obtain sf^{n+1}_j. The main channel equations are then solved and the iteration repeated if necessary.

Lateral flows starting during a time increment. In storage ponds situated in river meanders, inflow and outflow can occur simultaneously. In these circumstances, inflows during a time increment can result in the storage pond water level rising above some sections of bank over which no initial lateral flow is occurring. It is desirable that lateral outflows occurring in such circumstances are estimated and their effect on storage pond water level calculated before beginning the calculations for the next time increment.

This can be achieved by first estimating the change in storage pond water level due to inflows. By comparing this with the lowest dry bank level, feeding the pond, the existence of an outflow beginning during the time increment can be determined. The outflow will cause a reduction in pond water level that can be determined from,

$$\Delta Wl_p = (0.5(Wl^{n+1}_p - cl).(dql/dWl_p).\Delta t.tf)/A_s \qquad 8.$$

where cl is the bank crest level, and tf is the proportion of the time increment for which the outflow exists estimated from,

$$(Wl^{n+1}_{p} - cl)/\Delta Wl^{n+1}_{p}$$

An iterative calculation is necessary to obtain a final value of Wl^{n+1}_{p}.

NUMERICAL VALIDATION OF STORAGE POND ALGORITHM

The lateral storage pond algorithm was tested by a number of numerical trials. A selection of these results are presented below.

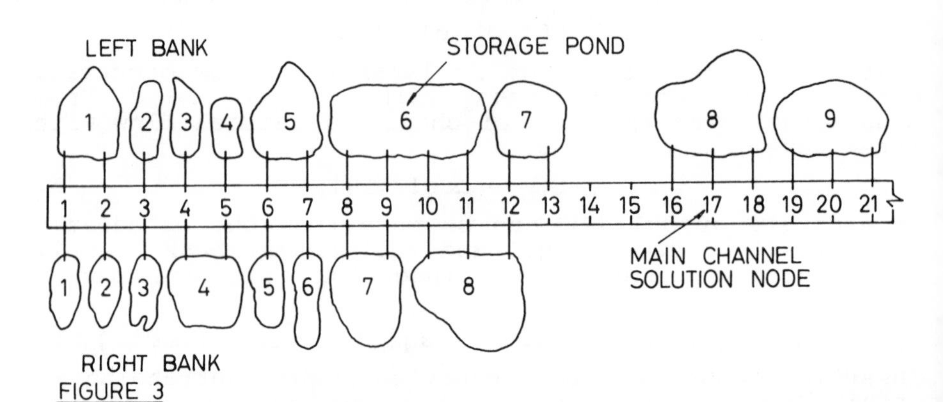

FIGURE 3

The channel and storage pond layout used are shown in figure 3. Distance increments between solution nodes were typically 250m. Two controls exist in this length of channel:

i. a permanent control formed by a weir at solution node 11,

ii. and, a natural control at solution node 16, this is drowned at high flows.

The downstream boundary condition employed was a single valued rating curve and the upstream boundary condition was a hydrograph with a peak flow of 102 m^3/s. Lateral "weir" flows were calculated assuming a Froude number of unity over the crest of the embankment. A time increment of 900 seconds was used throughout.

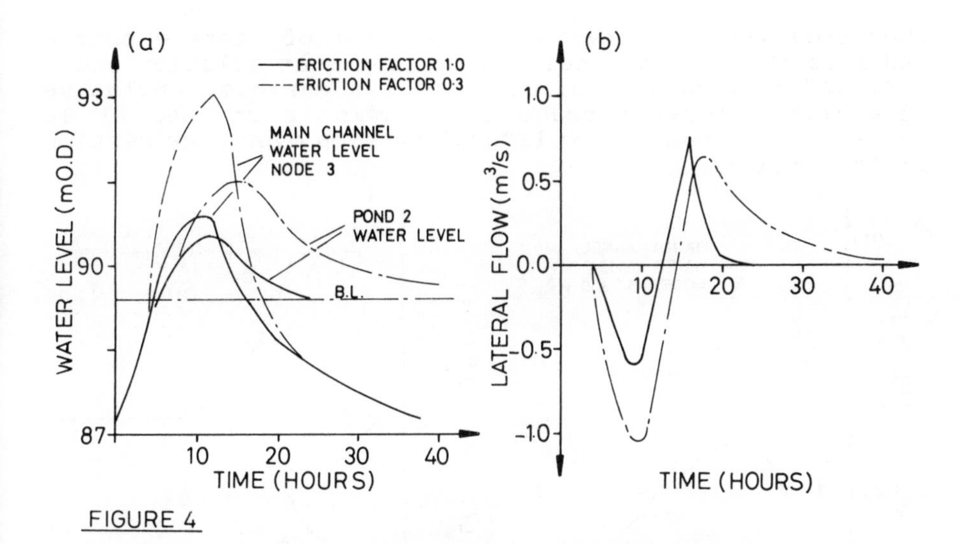

FIGURE 4

The behaviour of right bank storage pond 2 can be determined from the time histories of storage pond water level, the lateral flow and main channel water level at solution node 3, shown in figures 4 a and b.

From these it can be seen that no inter-action between the main channel and lateral storage occurs until 4.5 hours, when node 3 water level rises above the bank level. Free lateral flow then takes place between the main channel and pond 2 until 6 hours, when the storage pond water level rises above the bank level. Submerged lateral flow continues until 12.25 hours, when the storage pond water level reaches its maximum level of 90.66 m O.D. The corresponding main channel water level at this time is 90.82 m O.D. The maximum rate of change in storage pond water level is 0.28 m/s between 6 hours and 8 hours. This compares with a rate of change of main channel water level of 0.11 m/s over the same period. The main channel water levels then fall and water held in lateral storage returns to the main channel. Lateral outflows from storage are submerged "weir" flows until 16 hours when the main channel water level drops below bank level. Storage pond 2 continues to drain until 22.75 hours.

Storage pond behaviour during simultaneous inflows and outflows can be illustrated by examining left bank storage pond number 6 fed by solution nodes 8,9,10, and 11. Water levels at solution nodes 8,9, and 10 rise above their corresponding bank levels at 2 hours, resulting in lateral flows into the storage pond, see figure 5. These cause the lateral storage pond water level to rise above 88.1 m O.D., the level of bank 11, at time 8 hours. At this time main channel water level at solution node 11 is 87.25 m.

Thus free lateral flow takes place out of storage pond 6 and into the main channel. Water levels at solution nodes 8,9, and 10 continue to rise until a maximum cumulative flow into lateral storage of 24 m^3/s is reached at 10 hours. The corresponding lateral outflow over bank section 11 is 9 m^3/s.

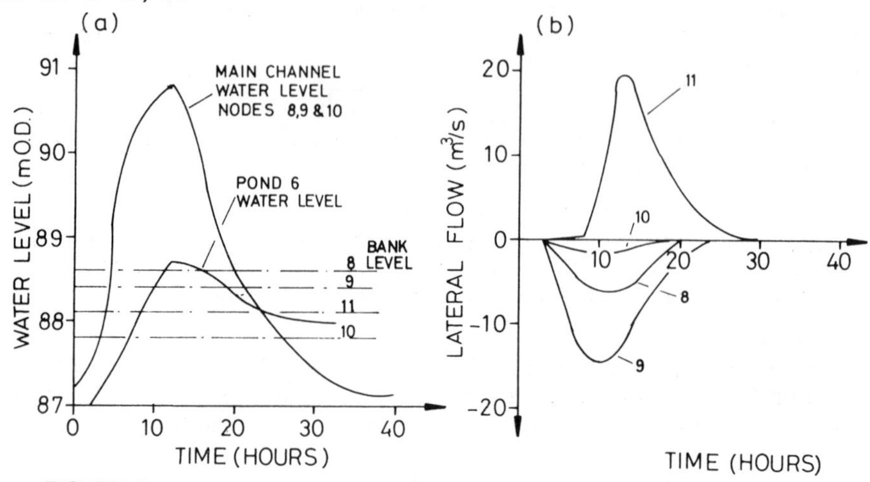

FIGURE 5

The lateral flow verses water level relationship used to obtain these results ignores frictional resistance of the bank. To examine the probable effect of over bank frictional resistance, the original values of lateral flow verses water level were reduced by 70%. The effect this has on water levels and lateral flows at pond 2 is shown in figures 4 a and b. As expected, the global reduction in values of lateral flow has resulted in increased main channel water level. However, in the case of pond 2 this increase in main channel water level has resulted in increased lateral flows from the main channel between 6 hours and 14 hours. Therefore, a greater volume of water is stored in pond 2 between 6 hours and 26 hours when lateral flow resistance is increased globally. This highlights an underlying difficulty in calibrating river models using the lateral storage pond approach to flood plain simulation. That is, adjustments to local over bank friction at one section of bank can significantly influence lateral flows and pond water levels throughout the model.

CONCLUSIONS

An algorithm is presented for the solution of one-dimensional non-inertial lateral storage ponds. The algorithm includes the gradient of the lateral head/discharge curve in the calculation of time averaged lateral flows. Numerical tests over a range of pond areas and rates of filling indicate that numerical stability has been improved.

REFERENCES

1. Abbott M.B. (1979)
"Computational Hydraulics: Elements of the Theory of Free Surface Flows", Pitman Publishing Limited, London.

2. Cunge J.A., Holly F.M. and Verwey A. (1980)
"Practical Aspects of Computational River Hydraulics", Pitman Publishing, London.

3. Ellis J. (1989)
"Guide to the analysis of open channel spillway flows", CIRIA Technical Note 134.

4. Ervine D.A. and Ellis J. (1987)
"Experimental and computational aspects of overbank floodplain flow", Transactions of the Royal Society of Edinburgh: Earth Sciences, Vol 78, pp 315-325.

5. Samuels P.G. (1983)
"Computational modelling of flood flows in embanked rivers", Proceedings of the International Conference on the Hydraulic aspects of Floods and Flood Control, London.

6. Wormleaton P.R. (1988)
"Determination of discharge in compound channels using the dynamic equation for lateral velocity distribution", Proceedings of the international Conference on Fluvial Hydraulics, Budapest.

PAPER L4

International Conference on
RIVER FLOOD HYDRAULICS
17-20 September, 1990

AN APPROXIMATE ONE-DIMENSIONAL STAGE-HYDROGRAPH ROUTING METHOD

Muthiah Perumal[1] and K.G. Ranga Raju[2]

[1]Department of Continuing Education and
[2]Department of Civil Engineering
University of Roorkee, Roorkee, India

Summary : Using a modified form of the concept used by Kalinin and Milyukov, a simplified method of routing a stage hydrograph in prismatic rectangular channels is developed.

1. INTRODUCTION

Flood routing in channels is often carried out on the assumption that the flood wave movement is one dimensional and that it is governed by the St. Venant's equations. For gradually varied unsteady flow in rigid channels with no lateral flow, these equations are written as (Henderson 1966)

$$\frac{\partial Q}{\partial x} + \frac{\partial A}{\partial t} = 0 \tag{1}$$

and

$$S_f = S_o - \frac{\partial y}{\partial x} - \frac{1}{g}\frac{\partial v}{\partial t} - \frac{v}{g}\frac{\partial v}{\partial x} \tag{2}$$

in which t = time; x = distance along the channel; y, v, A and Q are respectively depth, velocity, cross-sectional area and discharge; g = acceleration due to gravity; S_f = friction slope; and S_o = bed slope.

Examination of the assumptions of St. Venant's equations and their implications in natural channels have led many engineers to question the need to consider all the terms in Eq. (2). Many have sought to simplify Eq. (2) in order to reduce computation time and data requirements. Values of the various terms in Eq.(2) presented by Henderson (1966), and Wong and Laurenson (1983) indicate that some of these terms can be justifiably ignored or may be approximated by some procedures for studying many of the flood routing problems. The adoption of this concept has led to a group of simplified flood routing methods.

Various simplified flood routing methods are in vogue using discharge as the operating variable. A comprehensive review of such available methods has been presented by Weinmann and Laurenson (1979). However to the knowledge of the authors, there exists no simplified method which uses stage or flow depth as the operating

International Conference on River Flood Hydraulics, edited by W.R.White

variable for studying flood propagation. Stage hydrograph routing is useful for flood warning, for the planning and design of flood protection embankments, and for canal regulation.

This paper describes a technique based on the simplification of St. Venant's equations for routing stage hydrographs in rigid bed channels of uniform rectangular cross-section.

2. PHYSICAL BASIS OF THE PROPOSED THEORY

Steady flow in a channel is characterised by a unique relationship between stage and discharge at any cross-section. This situation is altered during unsteady flow resulting in the same unique relationship between the stage at the middle of the reach and the discharge not at the same location, but at some downstream location. This has been adopted by Kalinin and Milyukov (as quoted by Miller and Cunge 1975) to determine the 'unit reach length' required for flood routing in channel reaches having uniform cross-section, but with the hypothesis that the distance between the middle of the reach and the location downstream of it wherein the normal discharge corresponding to the flow depth at the middle of the reach is recorded, remains constant during unsteady flow. This consideration makes the Kalinin-Milyukov method not very flexible since the 'unit reach length' of the channel is fixed for a given flood wave and the end section of the 'unit reach length' may not coincide with the downstream section where the stage-discharge information is required, thus necessitating the interpolation of the routed hydrograph (Koussis 1980). Further the application of the Kalinin-Milyukov method is restricted to the routing problem wherein the wave celerity remains almost constant for all discharges. In the method proposed herein, the above limitations of the Kalinin-Milyukov method have been overcome.

3. DEVELOPMENT OF THE METHOD

The method is developed for a rectangular channel of constant width and bed slope with no lateral flow along the reach. The following assumptions have also been made :

1. The friction slope S_f and the water surface slope $\partial y / \partial x$ remain constant at any instant of time over the routing reach.

2. At any instant of time during unsteady flow, the steady uniform flow relationship is applicable between the stage at the middle of the reach and the discharge occurring somewhere downstream of it.

Fig. 1 shows the channel reach of length Δx and the input and output stage hydrographs. It is assumed that the stage at the middle of the reach corresponds to the normal depth of the discharge which is observed at the same instant of time at an unspecified distance ℓ downstream from the middle of the reach. Let this

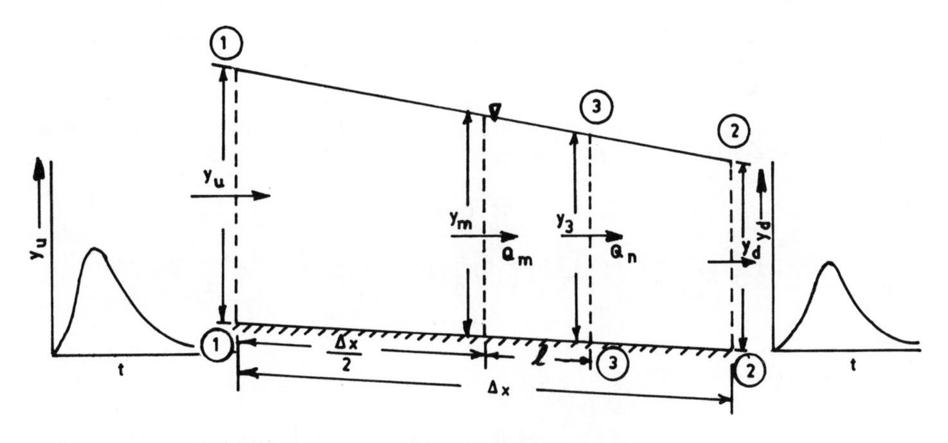

FIG. 1 DEFINITION SKETCH

discharge be denoted as Q_n and the section where it occurs be denoted as Section 3.

The discharge using Manning's equation is written as

$$Q = Av = \frac{A}{n} R^{\frac{2}{3}} S_f^{\frac{1}{2}} \tag{3}$$

where n is the Manning's roughness coefficient; R is the hydraulic radius; and P is the wetted perimeter. Differentiating Eq. (3) w.r.t. x after expressing A and R in terms of width and depth of flow, and invoking the assumption thet S_f is independent of x gives

$$\frac{\partial Q}{\partial x} = B \left[\frac{5}{3} - \frac{4}{3} \frac{y}{(B+2y)}\right] v \frac{\partial y}{\partial x} \tag{4}$$

The term $\left[\frac{5}{3} - \frac{4}{3} \frac{y}{(B+2y)}\right] v$ represents the celerity of the flood wave.

Differentiating Eq. (4) w.r.t. x gives

$$\frac{\partial^2 Q}{\partial x^2} = B\left[\frac{5}{3} - \frac{4}{3} \frac{y}{(B+2y)}\right]v \frac{\partial^2 y}{\partial x^2} + B\left[\frac{5}{3} - \frac{4}{3} \frac{y}{(B+2y)}\right] \frac{\partial v}{\partial x} \frac{\partial y}{\partial x}$$

$$- \frac{4}{3} \left(\frac{B}{B+2y}\right)^2 v \left(\frac{\partial y}{\partial x}\right)^2 \tag{5}$$

Assuming that the multiples of the differential terms are very small and may be neglected and assuming further that $\partial y/ \partial x$ remains constant at any instant of time over the reach under consideration, Eq. (5) reduces to

$$\frac{\partial^2 Q}{\partial x^2} = 0 \qquad (6)$$

This implies that at any instant of time the discharge also varies linearly over the routing reach.

Using Eqs. (1), (2), (3) and (4) one gets

$$S_f = S_o \{1 - \frac{1}{S_o} \frac{\partial y}{\partial x} [1 - \frac{4}{9} F^2 (\frac{B}{B+2y})^2]\} \qquad (7)$$

where

$$F = \frac{v}{\sqrt{gy}} \qquad (8)$$

Applying Eqs. (3) and (7) to the mid-section of the reach and simplifying

$$Q_m = \frac{By_m}{n} (\frac{By_m}{B+2y_m})^{\frac{2}{3}} S_o^{\frac{1}{2}} \{1 - \frac{1}{S_o} \frac{\partial y}{\partial x}\Big|_m [1 - \frac{4}{9} F_m^2 (\frac{B}{B+2y_m})^2]\}^{\frac{1}{2}} \qquad (9)$$

where $\frac{\partial y}{\partial x}\Big|_m$, y_m and F_m represent the water surface slope, the flow depth and the Froude number at the middle of the reach. The normal discharge Q_n corresponding to y_m occurs at distance ℓ downstream of the middle of the reach and it is expressed as

$$Q_n = \frac{By_m}{n} (\frac{By_m}{B+2y_m})^{\frac{2}{3}} S_o^{\frac{1}{2}} \qquad (10)$$

Thus Eq. (9) is modified as

$$Q_m = Q_n \{1 - \frac{1}{S_o} \frac{\partial y}{\partial x}\Big|_m [1 - \frac{4}{9} F_m^2 (\frac{B}{B+2y_m})^2]\}^{\frac{1}{2}} \qquad (11)$$

For the sake of brevity, let

$$\frac{1}{S_o} \frac{\partial y}{\partial x}\Big|_m [1 - \frac{4}{9} F_m^2 (\frac{B}{B + 2y_m})^2] = r \qquad (12)$$

Based on the typical values of S_o and $\partial y/\partial x$ in natural rivers (Henderson 1966), it may be deduced that $|r| \ll 1$. Under such condition expanding Eq. (11) in Binomial Series and then neglecting higher orders of r gives

$$Q_m = Q_n - \frac{Q_n}{2S_o} [1 - \frac{4}{9} F_m^2 (\frac{B}{B + 2y_m})^2] \frac{\partial y}{\partial x}\Big|_m \qquad (13)$$

Since $\partial y/\partial x$ is constant at any instant of time

$$\frac{\partial y}{\partial x}\Big|_m = \frac{\partial y}{\partial x}\Big|_3 \qquad (14)$$

where $\frac{\partial y}{\partial x}\big|_3$ is the water surface slope at Section 3.

Eq. (13) is rewritten using Eq.(4) and (14) as

$$Q_m = Q_n - \frac{Q_n\left[1 - \frac{4}{9} F_m^2 \left(\frac{B}{B + 2y_m}\right)^2\right]}{2S_o B\left[\frac{5}{3} - \frac{4}{3}\,\frac{y_3}{(B + 2y_3)}\right] v_3} \; \frac{\partial Q}{\partial x}\Big|_3 \qquad (15)$$

Since the discharge also varies linearly, the term adjunct to $\frac{\partial Q}{\partial x}\big|_3$ represents the distance ℓ between the mid-section and that downstream section where the normal discharge, corresponding to the depth at the mid-section, appears at the same instant of time.

i.e.
$$\ell = \frac{Q_n\left[1 - \frac{4}{9} F_m^2 \left(\frac{B}{B + 2y_m}\right)^2\right]}{2S_o B\left[\frac{5}{3} - \frac{4}{3}\,\frac{y_3}{(B + 2y_3)}\right] v_3} \qquad (16)$$

Using Eqs. (1) and (4), the following expression may be arrived at:

$$\frac{\partial y}{\partial t} + \left[\frac{5}{3} - \frac{4}{3}\,\frac{y}{(B + 2y)}\right] v\,\frac{\partial y}{\partial x} = 0 \qquad (17)$$

Applying the above equation at Section 3 and rearranging the terms, one gets

$$\left[\frac{5}{3} - \frac{4}{3}\,\frac{y_3}{(B + 2y_3)}\right] v_3\,\frac{\partial y}{\partial x}\Big|_3 = -\frac{\partial y}{\partial t}\Big|_3 \qquad (18)$$

But

$$\frac{\partial y}{\partial x}\Big|_3 = \frac{\partial y}{\partial x}\Big|_2 \simeq \frac{y_d - y_u}{\Delta x} \qquad (19)$$

where y_u and y_d are the flow depths at the input and output sections respectively. y_3 can be expressed as

$$y_3 = y_d + \left(\frac{1}{2} - \frac{\ell}{\Delta x}\right)(y_u - y_d) \qquad (20)$$

Substituting Eqs. (19) and (20) in Eq. (18) gives

$$y_u - y_d = \frac{\Delta x}{\left[\frac{5}{3} - \frac{4}{3}\,\frac{y_3}{(B + 2y_3)}\right] v_3}\,\frac{\partial}{\partial t}\left[y_d + \left(\frac{1}{2} - \frac{\ell}{\Delta x}\right)(y_u - y_d)\right] \qquad (21)$$

Eq. (21) is similar to the differential equation governing Muskingum method with the travel time K expressed as

$$K = \frac{\Delta x}{[\frac{5}{3} - \frac{4}{3} \frac{y_3}{(B + 2y_3)}] v_3} \tag{22}$$

and the weighting parameter θ after substituting for ℓ from Eq. (16) expressed as

$$\theta = \frac{1}{2} - \frac{Q_n [1 - \frac{4}{9} F_m^2 (\frac{B}{B + 2y_m})^2]}{2S_o B [\frac{5}{3} - \frac{4}{3} \frac{y_3}{(B + 2y_3)}] v_3 \Delta x} \tag{23}$$

Solving Eq. (21) using conventional Muskingum difference scheme gives

$$y_{d_2} = C_1 y_{u_2} + C_2 y_{u_1} + C_3 y_{d_1} \tag{24}$$

where y_{u_2} and y_{u_1} respectively are the input water stages at the beginning of present and immediately past routing steps, and y_{d_2} and y_{d_1} respectively are the output water stages at the beginning of the present and immediately past routing steps. The coefficients C_1, C_2 and C_3 are given as

$$C_1 = \frac{- K\theta + \Delta t/2}{K(1-\theta) + \Delta t/2}$$

$$C_2 = \frac{K\theta + \Delta t/2}{K(1-\theta) + \Delta t/2} \tag{25}$$

$$C_3 = \frac{- \Delta t/2 + K(1-\theta)}{K(1-\theta) + \Delta t/2}$$

where Δt is the routing time interval.

The algorithm followed to route the given inflow hydrograph using this method is described in the flow chart as shown in Fig. 2.

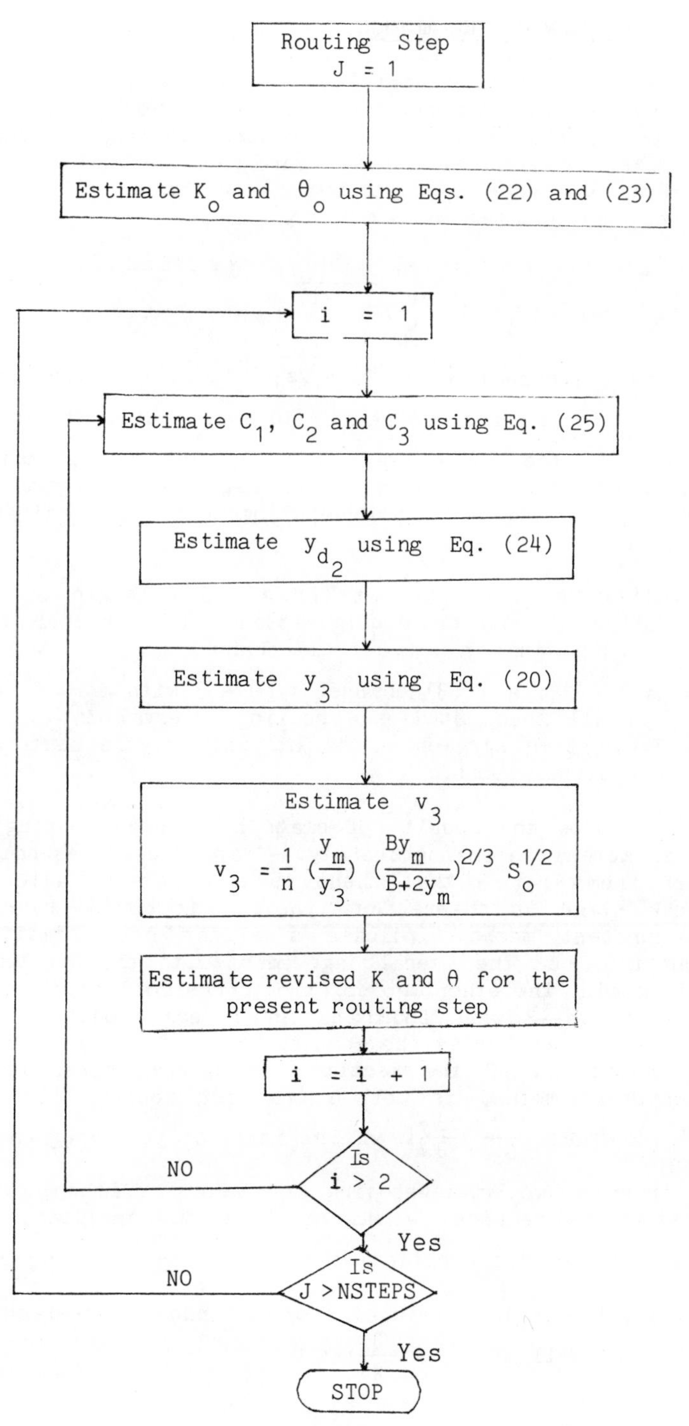

FIG. 2 ALGORITHM USED IN THE PRESENT ROUTING METHOD

4. APPLICATION OF THE METHOD

The method was verified by applying it for routing stage hydrographs in rectangular channels for a given reach length, and comparing its solution with that of the corresponding St. Venant's equations. The hypothetical inflow hydrograph defined by a four parameter Pearson type-III distribution (Weinmann 1977) of the following form was adopted in this study

$$Q(t) = Q_b + (Q_p - Q_b)\left(\frac{t}{t_p}\right)^{\frac{1}{(\gamma - 1)}} \exp\left[\frac{\left(1 - \frac{t}{t_p}\right)}{(\gamma - 1)}\right] \qquad (26)$$

where Q_b is the base flow = 100 m^3/s; Q_p is the peak inflow = 1000 m^3/s; t_p is the time to peak = 10 hrs.; and γ is the skew factor = 1.15. The input stage at any time corresponding to the above above inflow hydrograph was estimated using a finite difference form of Eq. (1) and adopting a backward difference scheme.

Routing studies were carried out for a reach length of 40 km with the following channel configurations: (1) Channel type - 1 with S_o = 0.0002 and n = 0.04; (2) channel type - 2 with S_o = 0.0002 and n = 0.02; and (3) channel type - 3 with S_o = 0.002 and n = 0.02. In all these studies a routing interval of 15 minutes was used. The entire stretch of 40 km. was treated as a single reach in these calculations.

Figs. 3 and 4 show the results of stage hydrograph routing using the proposed method in channels of type-1 and type-3 respectively. It is seen from Fig. 3 that there is considerable attenuation of the peak stage in channel of type-1. The routed hydrograph using the present method indicate a slight overestimation of the attenuation, but the overall agreement with the St. Venant's solution is good. The other two solutionscorresponding to channels of type-2 and type-3 were found to agree very closely with the St. Venant's solutions as may be seen in Fig. 4 for type-3 channel. Detailed examination of the results for several cases revealed that the present method is well suited for routing flood wave with small value of $\left|\frac{1}{S_o}\frac{\partial y}{\partial x}\right|$ of the input stage hydrograph. The same was inferred while developing the method. Although a more detailed study is required with regard to the applicability of this method based on the consideration of $\left|\frac{1}{S_o}\frac{\partial y}{\partial x}\right|$ of the input stage hydrograph, it is concluded from the runs carried out that the method works well if $\left|\frac{1}{S_o}\frac{\partial y}{\partial x}\right| < 0.5$.

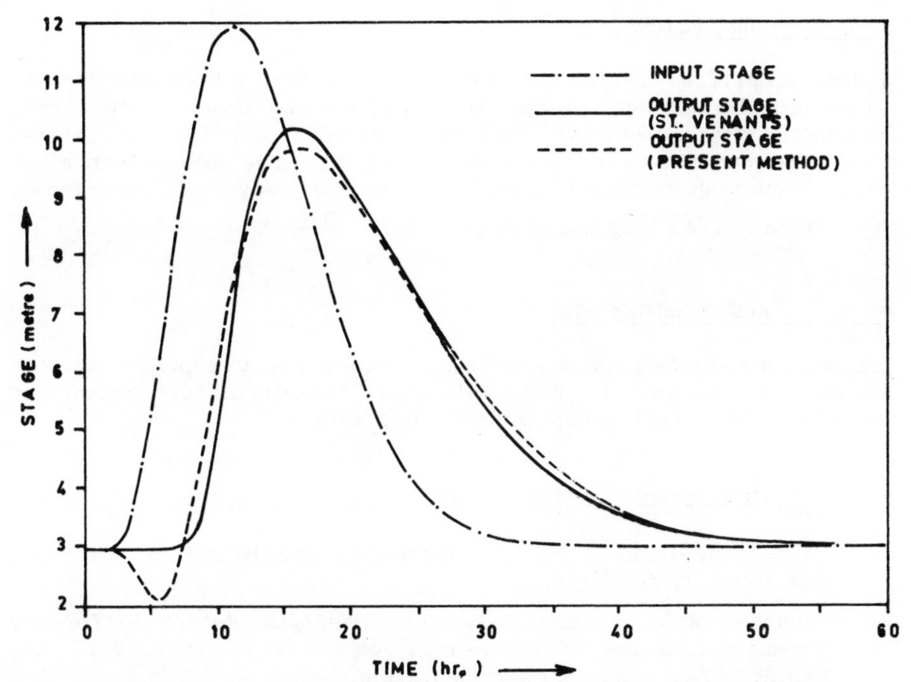

FIG. 3 STAGE HYDROGRAPH ROUTING (CHANNEL TYPE-1)

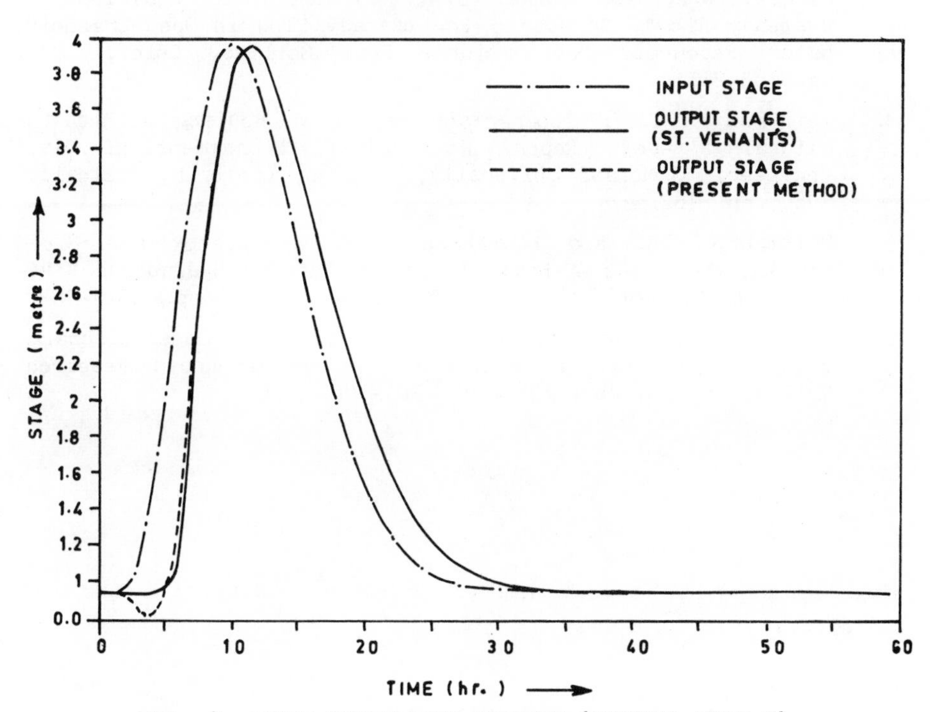

FIG. 4 STAGE HYDROGRAPH ROUTING (CHANNEL TYPE-3)

5. CONCLUSIONS

A new simplified hydraulic method for routing stage hydrographs in rectangular channel reaches with uniform bed slope and Manning's roughness coefficient is developed without considering lateral flow. The parameters of the method vary at each computation step, thus accounting for nonlinearity of the unsteady flow phenomenon. The method yields good results when $\left| \frac{1}{S_o} \frac{\partial y}{\partial x} \right| < 0.5$.

6. ACKNOWLEDGEMENTS

The authors gratefully acknowledge the support provided by the Council of Scientific and Industrial Research, Government of India through a fellowship to the first author.

7. REFERENCES

1. Henderson, F.M. : "Open Channel Flow". Macmillan and Co., New York, 1966, 522 pp.

2. Koussis, A.D. : "Comparison of Muskingum Method Difference Schemes". Journal of the Hydraulics Division, ASCE, Vol. 106, No. HY5, May 1980, pp. 925-929.

3. Miller, W.A. and Cunge, J.A. : "Simplified Equations of Unsteady Flow". Chapter 5 in Unsteady Flow in Open Channels, Water Resources Publications, Fort Collins, Colo., 1975, pp. 183-257.

4. Weinmann, P.E. : "Comparison of Flood Routing Method for Natural Rivers". Report No. 2/1977, Department of Civil Engineering, Monash University, Clayton, Victoria, Australia, 1980, pp. 182.

5. Weinmann, P.E. and Laurenson, E.M. : "Approximate Flood Routing Methods : A Review". Journal of the Hydraulics Division, ASCE, Vol. 105, No. HY12, Dec. 1979, pp. 1521-1536.

6. Wong, T.H.F. and Laurenson, E.M. : "Wave Speed-Discharge Relations in Natural Channels". Water Resources Research, Vol. 19, No. 3, June 1983, pp. 701-706.

Engineering Design, Maintenance and Operation of Schemes

PAPER M1

International Conference on
RIVER FLOOD HYDRAULICS
17-20 September, 1990

Groundwater Responses to Embanked River Flood Levels

D C Watkins

Hydraulics Research, Wallingford, UK.

ABSTRACT

When an embanked river contains a high water level, high pressures are transmitted to the groundwater in the flood plain aquifer. This may lead to groundwater problems such as ponding or loss of soil stability.

A description of the groundwater flow system is given. A method for making an approximate assessment of the degree of groundwater response to a given river hydrograph in a particular flood plain is described. The use of numerical models are discussed with particular reference to the representation of the river and the alluvial overburden. Remedial measures are discussed briefly.

INTRODUCTION

Embankments are often used to protect land on flood plains from river flooding. When a flood event passes down a river a high head of water is contained by the embankment, preventing the flood water from inundating the flood plain.

These flood plains are commonly built up of highly permeable river sand and gravel deposits, overlain by a low permeability overburden of silt and clay alluvium. There is a potential for groundwater flow to take place within the flood plain aquifer, beneath the embankment. This can lead to surface ponding due to exfiltration of groundwater within the protected area and also to problems associated with soil stability.

The hydraulics of such systems should be considered during the design of flood embankment schemes in order to identify areas at risk and to assess the true degree of flood protection provided. The purpose of this paper is to highlight the hydraulic features of the problem and to discuss some relevant aspects of numerical models that may be used to study particular situations in detail.

International Conference on River Flood Hydraulics, edited by W.R.White

THE GROUNDWATER FLOW SYSTEM

General Description

Figure 1 shows a cross-section through the type of system envisaged. The groundwater flow is initially in a steady condition, usually with a net flow of water to the river which acts to drain the flood plain (Figure 1a). With the onset of a flood event the water level in the river rises, reversing the direction of groundwater flow as the river recharges the aquifer (Figure 1b). When the river level recedes, the high groundwater heads dissipate and the groundwater drains back toward the river (Figure 1c).

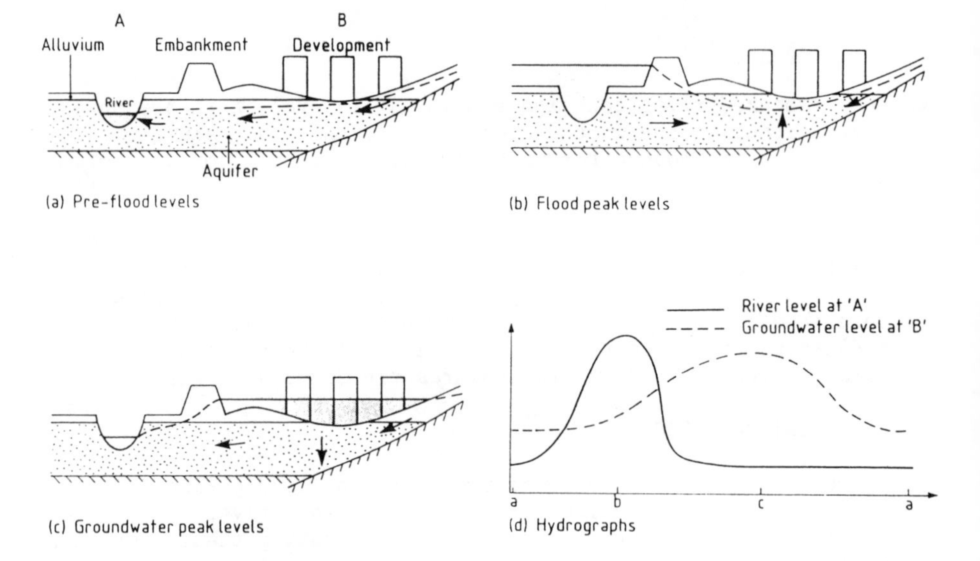

Fig 1 The groundwater flow system

The speed and degree of response of the groundwater system to the river flood event (Figure 1d) depends on the geo-hydraulic properties of the flood plain; the hydraulic conductivities and storage coefficients of the aquifer and overburden, and also on the geometry of the groundwater system; the thickness of aquifer and overburden and the width of the river valley.

Types of Aquifer

There are three basic types of aquifer that may be considered: unconfined, confined or semi-confined aquifers, depending on the degree of influence of the alluvial overburden. The unconfined, or phreatic, aquifer is one above which the overburden is absent or has negligible effect. In the confined case, the overburden is considered to be totally impermeable. These are the two extremes when considering the influence of the overburden. The most likely situation to occur naturally, however, is that of a low, but not negligible, permeability overburden which semi-confines the aquifer but may also transmit high porewater pressures and possibly allow seepage to the surface.

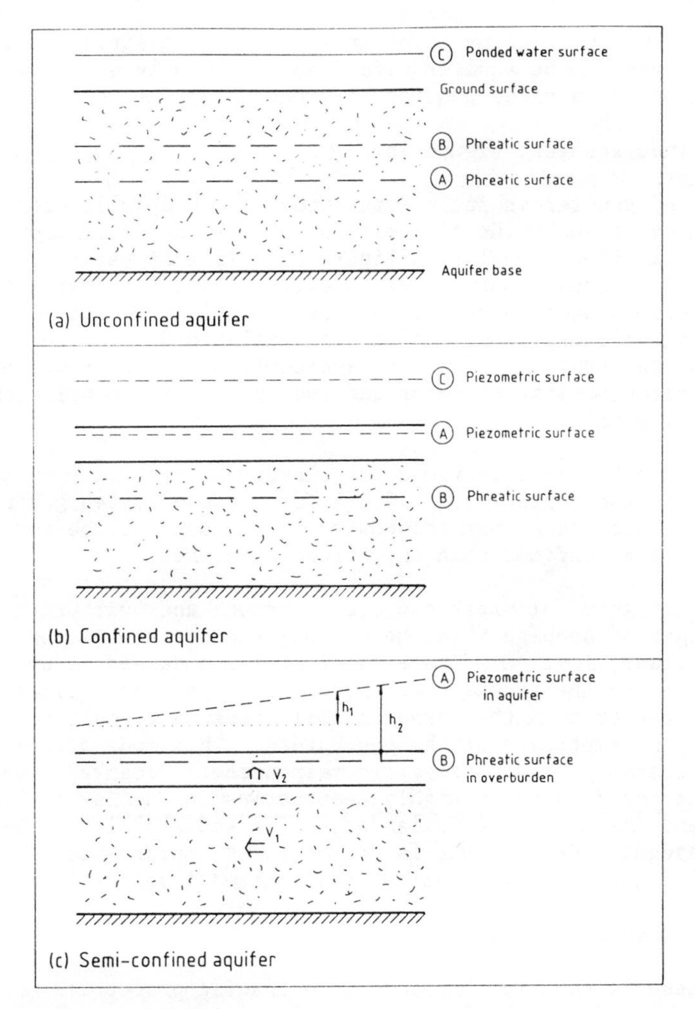

Fig 2 Types of aquifer

Each case is considered in a little more detail below:

(i) Unconfined aquifer, Figure 2a.

The unconfined aquifer contains a water table which reflects the hydraulic head elevation in the aquifer (phreatic surface). If a volume of water is added to the aquifer the water table will rise, say from level A to B in Figure 2a, in accordance with the available pore space or specific yield of the aquifer. This storage is the difference between the unsaturated and saturated moisture contents of the aquifer material. For an unconsolidated granular soil, the available storage may be in the region 15 - 35 % of aquifer volume, depending on the particle size grading.

As there is no restricting layer in an unconfined aquifer, if the hydraulic head in the aquifer rises above ground level, level C, exfiltration and surface ponding of groundwater will occur.

(ii) Confined aquifer, Figure 2b

The confined aquifer is fully saturated. The hydraulic head elevation is given by the piezometric surface, which is above the top of the aquifer, level A on Figure 2b. If this were not the case, an unconfined condition would exist, level B. There can therefore be no storage due to the specific yield of the soil. Instead, a small degree of storage is available due to the elastic storage of the aquifer. This storage coefficient incorporates the slight compressibility of water and the stress-strain relationship of the soil matrix.

In comparison to specific yield the elastic storage is very small, typically in the region 0.01 - 0.5 % for unconsolidated granular aquifers. This means that groundwater responses will be more pronounced for confined than unconfined aquifers.

As no exfiltration of water can occur through the overburden, there is no danger of seepage when the piezometric surface exceeds the ground surface, level C. There is, instead, a danger of uplift pressure due to the excess head above the top of the aquifer, becoming greater than the downward soil pressure, resulting in flotation and rupturing of the overburden. This mode of soil failure caused by high piezometric responses to embanked river floods was noted as being highly destructive in the Bay of Plenty, New Zealand (Raudkivi and Callander, 1976) and also in Ise Bay, Japan (Naguchi, 1989). This is an important aspect when considering the flood protection of urbanized flood plains.

(iii) Semi-confined aquifer, Figure 2c

In this case we need to consider the hydraulic properties of the overburden material as well as the aquifer, in order to take the hydraulic head in the overburden into account.

High uplift pressures may evolve similarly to confined aquifers but the excess head this time is due to the difference in head between levels A and B, Figure 2c. Another mode of soil failure that may occur in this situation is that of high groundwater heads evolving within the overburden. These high porewater pressures result in a lowering of the effective stress and subsequent loss of soil strength which can lead to subsidence around foundations.

An important point to note here is that in the aquifer, vertical gradients are very small and so the groundwater velocity is always predominantly horizontal; v_1, due to head difference h_1 in Figure 2c. The groundwater head changes much faster in the aquifer than in the overburden, due to the large difference in permeability between them. This generates predominantly vertical groundwater velocities in the overburden; v_2 due to head difference h_2 on Figure 2c.

Semi-confined aquifers present more complex modelling challenges than fully unconfined and confined aquifers. Models of these latter two types of aquifers may suffice in many situations. If soil stability calculations are to be performed, however, the response of groundwater pressure in the overburden material needs to be assessed in as much detail as possible.

APPROXIMATE ASSESSMENT

In their studies of baseflow recessions of stream-aquifer systems, Singh and Stall (1971) introduced the dimensionless constant, τ, to characterize aquifers whereby

$$\tau = \frac{Tt}{SL^2} \quad (1)$$

where T = aquifer transmissivity
S = aquifer storage coefficient
L = distance from river to catchment edge
t = time of recession

The transmissivity (product of hydraulic conductivity and depth of flow) and the storage coefficient may be found from conducting on-site pumping tests.

Watkins (1988) used equation (1) to characterize flood plain aquifers by substituting

t = period of flood cycle
L = width of flood plain

Using a simple river boundary condition (see later) and neglecting the overburden, the response to sinusoidal flood cycles was examined for various values of τ. When $\tau = 0.1$, groundwater responses are small. At $\tau = 1$, the response is considerable and groundwater problems are likely to occur. At $\tau = 10$, 99% of the river flood peak is transmitted to the aquifer location furthest from the river. Thus τ was used to assess the degree of response of the aquifer.

The parameter SL^2/T can be interpreted as the aquifer response time (Nutbrown and Downing, 1976). Designating the aquifer response time as t^*,

$$t^* = SL^2/T \quad (2)$$

and applying the values of τ considered above,

$$\tau = 0.1 \qquad t^* = 10\, t$$
$$\tau = 1 \qquad t^* = t$$
$$\tau = 10 \qquad t^* = 0.1\, t$$

The aquifer response time, t^*, may therefore be used to characterize the response of a flood plain aquifer to a flood event. If t^* is in the order of ten times the flood cycle period or more, then groundwater responses will be small. If t^* is in the region of the flood cycle period then groundwater responses may be considerable and are liable to cause problems. If t^* is around one tenth of the flood cycle period or less, the aquifer will respond fully to the flood hydrograph right across the valley.

Note that an order of magnitude is not a large variation when considering field measurements of T and S.

MODELLING ASPECTS

Combining the motion equation (from Darcy) with the continuity equation, the basic partial differential equation of transient groundwater motion may be written as[1]

$$K\nabla^2\phi = S\,\frac{\partial\phi}{\partial t} \tag{3}$$

where K = hydraulic conductivity
S = storage coefficient
t = time
ϕ = hydraulic head potential

This type of mathematical problem with complex boundary conditions can be solved conveniently using a numerical method based on finite difference or finite element techniques[2].

Taking account of the fact that groundwater flow in the aquifer is predominantly horizontal, equation (3) may be written as

$$T\left(\frac{\partial^2\phi}{\partial x^2} + \frac{\partial^2\phi}{\partial y^2}\right) = S\,\frac{\partial\phi}{\partial t} \tag{4}$$

Some aspects of incorporating the river boundary and the alluvial overburden into a numerical model to simulate groundwater responses to embanked river floods are discussed below.

The river boundary

The river flood hydrograph is the imposed condition that drives the

[1]See Bear 1972, for a rigorous derivation and assumptions.
[2]See Remson et al (1971) Verruit (1982) and others for applications of numerical models to groundwater flow problems.

groundwater flow. The embanked river flood hydrograph may itself by derived from other numerical modelling work.

Groundwater models often incorporate rivers simply by treating them as simple boundaries of specified head. This is done by setting the head potential in the aquifer immediately adjacent to the river, ϕ_a, equal to the head in the river, ϕ_r. This assumes that a perfect hydraulic connection exists between the river and aquifer. If a horizontal flow model is being used, it must be further assumed that the river fully penetrates the aquifer. This is shown diagrammatically on Figure 3.

In practice, perfect hydraulic connection is rarely achieved and the river usually only penetrates the uppermost portion of the aquifer. For a study of groundwater responses to river flows, however, an accurate representation of the river-aquifer interaction is required. This can be achieved by the introduction of more complex conditions at the river boundary.

By assuming a layer of material to be present on the bed of the river, the river-aquifer interaction may be described as leakage through the layer. The layer may be described in terms of a leakage resistance, c, given by

$$c = b'/K' \qquad (5)$$

where b' = thickness of layer
K' = hydraulic conductivity of layer

The representative value of c for the river is usually found by model calibration against field data. The leakage resistance has units of time and is typically in the range 50 - 500 days for British rivers but may be greater where siltation is present. The use of the river leakage resistance also accounts for errors due to the river only partially penetrating the aquifer.

In order to apply the leakage resistance, the relative elevations of ϕ_a, ϕ_r and the river bed level, z_r, are required. If the head in the aquifer exceeds the river bed level, the hydraulic gradient through the leaky layer is a function of the head difference between river and aquifer, $\phi_r - \phi_a$; complex type (i) on Figure 3. If the groundwater head is below the river bed, the leakage is independent of ϕ_a, the leakage depends on the depth of water in the river only, $\phi_r - z_r$; type (ii) on Figure 3. If there is no water in the river, then the river can have no effect on groundwater; type (iii) on Figure 3. This is not likely to be the case for the conditions considered here. The condition that applies to groundwater responses to river floods is the complex type (i) on Figure 3. This is a non-linear condition and so a suitable solution procedure is required in the model.

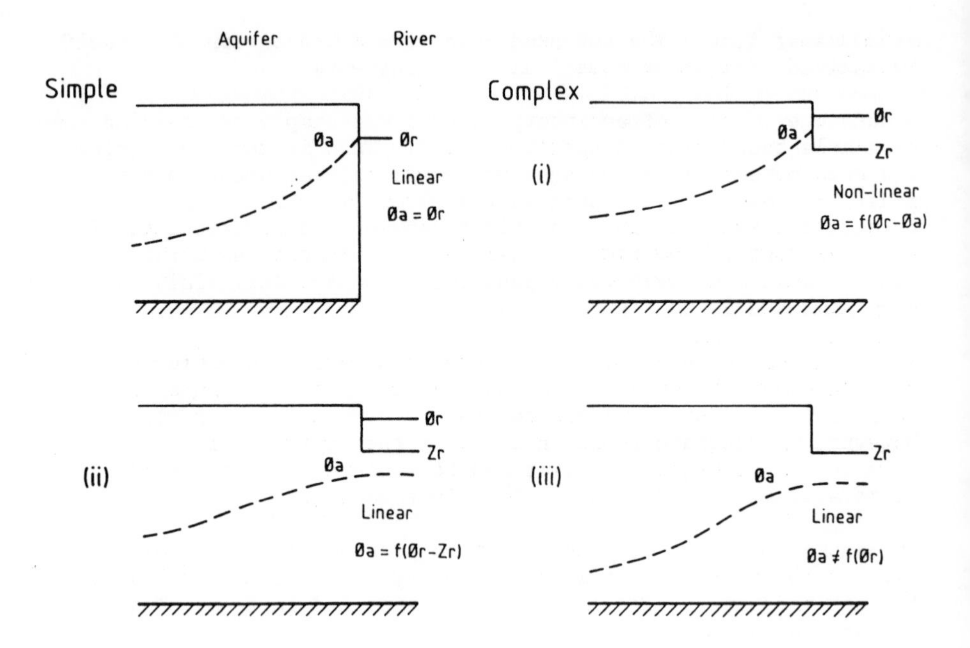

Fig 3 Types of river boundary

The overburden

The overburden may be incorporated in the model in a number of ways depending upon the accuracy of information required from the model. If groundwater heads in the aquifer and ponding rates are all that are required, the overburden may be modelled fairly simply. If porewater pressures and soil stability analyses in the overburden are required then more complex modelling procedures should be used. Three possible schemes are discussed below in order of increasing computational complexity.

(i) The overburden may be treated as a layer dividing two leaky aquifers. The flood plain aquifer may be designated as the lower aquifer and the upper aquifer is the space above ground level assigned a storage coefficient of unity and very high hydraulic conductivity. A leakage resistance, c, is found for the overburden layer by applying equation (5). Leakage from lower to upper aquifer, q_{12} is described by

$$q_{12} = \frac{\phi_1 - \phi_2}{c} \tag{6}$$

where subscripts 1 and 2 refer to the lower and upper aquifers respectively.

A difficulty arises when the head in the aquifer is below ground surface. The 'upper aquifer' then has no effect on the flow and the saturated thickness of overburden is unknown so equation (6) cannot be applied. One way round this is to assume that the overburden remains fully saturated and with all groundwater heads in the overburden equivalent to atmospheric pressure. The aquifer is then treated as fully confined while the piezometric level is below ground level and as leaky if it is greater.

(ii) A method developed by Nawalany and Plywaczyk (1985) provides more information about the hydraulic conditions in the overburden. By combining equations (5) and (6) and integrating, they developed an analytical equation which can be solved to calculate the phreatic head in the overburden at a given model time step.

The equation they use is

$$h_{(n)} - h_{(n-1)} + \phi_{a_{(n-1)}} \ln \left(1 - \frac{h_{(n)} - h_{(n-1)}}{\phi_{a_{(n-1)}} - h_{(n-1)}}\right) + \frac{K'}{S'} (t_{(n)} - t_{(n-1)}) = 0 \qquad (7)$$

where h = phreatic head in the overburden
K' = hydraulic conductivity overburden
S' = overburden storage coefficient
n = number of time step

This equation is non-linear so a solution procedure is required to solve for each time step.

(iii) A more thorough approach toward modelling the overburden is to treat it as a saturated-unsaturated system with the fully saturated aquifer flow system providing a boundary condition. The equation to solve numerically is the Richards equation:

$$\nabla (K \nabla \phi) + \frac{\partial K}{\partial z} = C \frac{\partial \phi}{\partial t} \qquad (8)$$

where $K = K(\phi)$
$C = \frac{\partial \theta}{\partial \phi}$
θ = volumetric moisture content

This equation resolves to equation (1) when the soil is fully saturated. The equation is highly non-linear because both hydraulic conductivity and moisture content are now functions of head potential.

Taking account of the fact that predominantly vertical flow occurs in the overburden, equation (8) may be written as

$$\frac{\partial}{\partial z} \left[K \left(\frac{\partial \phi}{\partial z} + 1\right)\right] = C \frac{\partial \phi}{\partial t} \qquad (9)$$

The base of the overburden is a boundary where the head is specified from the result of modelling the aquifer using equation

(4). Because the leakage is small in comparison to the flow in the aquifer, it may be ignored when computing ϕ_a. The two models do not need to be coupled and solved simultaneously. The extra effort required in modelling the overburden in such detail is justified if detailed calculations involving the porewater pressures in the overburden soil are to be performed.

REMEDIAL MEASURES

If a groundwater problem is identified then the question arises; what may be done to correct it ?

Vertical impermeable barriers constructed in the aquifer beneath the embankment may restrict groundwater recharge but will also affect groundwater discharge and impede the river draining the flood plain naturally. It may also be possible to construct partial barriers that impede groundwater responses enough on the time-scale of a flood event whilst still allowing relatively unimpeded steady-state drainage. The balance between the design of an effective and ineffective scheme, however, is delicate.

A more reliable method of controlling the groundwater responses is by pumped drainage. A drain situated at the inside toe of the embankment may be used to control groundwater within the protected area. Because the drain would be used when ambient groundwater and river levels are high, the discharge would need to be pumped. The feasibility of such a scheme, rate at which pumping would be required and design details may be studied by the application of numerical models.

CONCLUSIONS

The response of groundwater to embanked river flood levels may be modelled and predicted using numerical techniques. The groundwater flow system may be conceptualized and modelled in varying degrees of complexity. The choice of model design depends mainly on the detail and nature of the results required. Should detailed soil stability calculations in the overburden material be intended, then as much detail as possible is required in the model results. This involves solving complex, highly non-linear problems.

An approximate assessment of the likelihood of groundwater problems occurring on a particular flood plain may be gained from comparison of the aquifer response time, equation (2) with the flood cycle period.

Flow in the flood plain aquifer may be modelled suitably in two dimensions using equation (4).

The river boundary is best modelled as a non-linear boundary condition using a leakage resistance, equation (5).

The alluvial overburden may be incorporated in the model in a number of ways, the most sophisticated of which involves solving equation (9) numerically.

ACKNOWLEDGEMENTS

The author is grateful to the Ministry of Agriculture Fisheries and Food who funded the work at Hydraulics Research as part of a commission on River Flood Protection.

REFERENCES

Bear, J., 1979, Hydraulics of Groundwater, McGraw-Hill, New York.

Naguchi, M., 1989, Hydraulic and Hydrological Problems in Japan, Nagasaki University, Japan.

Nawalany, M. and Plywaczyk, L., 1985, The Numerical Model of a Combined Drainage System, Technische Hogeschool Delft.

Nutbrown, D.A. and Downing, R.A., 1976, Normal-Mode Analysis of the Structure of Baseflow Recession Curves, Journal of Hydrology, 30, pp327-340.

Raudkivi, A.J. and Callander, R.A., 1976, Analysis of Groundwater Flow, Edward Arnold, London.

Remson, I., Hornberger, G.M. and Molz, F.J., 1971, Numerical Methods in Subsurface Hydrology, J.Wiley and Sons, New York.

Singh, K.P. and Stall, J.B., 1971, Derivation of Baseflow Recession Curves and Parameters, Water Resources Research, 7(2), pp292-303.

Watkins, D.C., 1988, Groundwater Flow Beneath Flood Embankments, Hydraulics Research Report no. SR 169.

Verruit, A., 1982, Theory of Groundwater flow, Macmillan, London.

PAPER M2

International Conference on

RIVER FLOOD HYDRAULICS

17-20 September, 1990

REMOTE SENSING TO ASSESS VEGETATIVE COVER EFFECTS FOR FLOOD FORECASTING

N. Kouwen, E.D. Soulis, A. Pietroniro
Department of Civil Engineering, University of Waterloo
Waterloo, Ontario, Canada, N2L 3G1

R.A. Harrington
Conservation Authorities and Water Management Branch
Ontario Ministry of Natural Resources
Queen's Park, Toronto, Ontario, Canada, M7A 1W3

ABSTRACT

Remotely sensed data is used to classify the vegetative cover characteristics of a watershed for use in a distributed rainfall-runoff model. Model parameters were calibrated separately for each class. The results show that parameters determined by calibrating the model for one watershed can be successfully used to predict flows in a watershed that is physiographically similar but has a different mix of vegetative cover.

INTRODUCTION

It is generally known that vegetative cover directly affects the surface runoff characteristics of a watershed. As a result, the hydrologic response of a watershed to rainfall is to a large extent determined by the degree and characteristics of the cover. The vegetation affects the runoff in two distinct ways. First, the vegetation intercepts a certain amount of the rainfall and affects the surface roughness. Secondly, the vegetation modifies the permeability of the underlying soils simply through the nature of the vegetation's root structure and annual regeneration. Most basins of practical interest are covered by a mix of vegetation types and consequently one of the greatest problems in modelling the rainfall-runoff process has been the inability to evaluate, on a watershed scale, the various modelling parameters that affect the watershed's runoff characteristics. Thus transferring model parameters from one basin to another is generally unsuccessful and changes in runoff due to the changes in land use of a basin can only be approximated. Furthermore, determining the extent and location of various vegetation covers in a basin presents significant practical difficulties.

The availability of remotely sensed imagery of the earth surface is a solution to the land cover estimation problem and this paper describes a hydrologic model constructed to separately calculate the runoff for each type of land cover classification of hydrological significance as identified by the remotely sensed data. The rainfall-runoff process is modelled in a way that allows the model

International Conference on River Flood Hydraulics, edited by W.R.White

parameters to be calibrated separately for each of the different vegetative covers present in the watershed. The results show that the parameters are valid in a neighbouring watershed. Furthermore, using the calibrated parameter values and varying land cover data, a sensitivity study shows how the effect of land use changes on the peak flows resulting from rainfall events can be determined.

LAND COVER ESTIMATION

Figure 1 is a LANDSAT image of a portion of Southern Ontario, Canada. This image shows only the relative brightness in one of the four bands available but brightness is related to vegetation type and the figure serves to illustrate the great variation in the relative amounts of different vegetative covers. A portion of Lake Huron is shown on the western (left) side of the image and the Georgian Bay coast is shown to the north (top). The image is band 3 of the LANDSAT 2 Multi-Spectral Scanner (MSS) recorded on 22 May 1981.

The portion of the image containing the river basins of interest, the Grand and Saugeen, shows a variety of urban and rural land uses but for this study five hydrologically significant classes were used namely urban or barren, forested, cropland, wetland and water. Spectral signatures were developed using between 5 and 10 sites with known land cover and classified images were generated using a maximum likelihood classification scheme.

Raw LANDSAT data has inherent geometric distortions due to its orbit, the scanning angles, the curvature of the earth and a number of other factors. These distortions were corrected to make the image conform to the local UTM grid system. This involved the alignment of known ground control points, such as road intersections or coastal promontories, in both the image and the base map coordinate system and resampling the image. Digitized watershed boundaries, determined from topographic maps, were used to delineate the portions of the classified image within the river basin of interest. Table 1 lists the percentage of each land cover in each of the five sub-basins of the Saugeen River Watershed.

DISTRIBUTED HYDROLOGIC MODELLING

Although the runoff could be calculated for each pixel, there is actually no advantage in doing so because the spatial resolution of rainfall measurements is much coarser that the resolution of the LANDSAT data. The latter is available on a 79 m by 79 m grid while rainfall, if measured with radar, is commonly available on a two km by two km grid. If no radar data is available, raingauges are often widely spaced, with the consequence that a grid size smaller that 10 km by 10 km does not improve modelling runoff from rainfall. Also, previous research has shown that if a watershed is sub-divided into 25 to 50 computational units, the drainage pattern and variations in rainfall can be adequately represented (Garland, 1986).

The approach taken for this paper is to subdivide the watershed into a convenient number of sub-basins to correspond to gauging locations

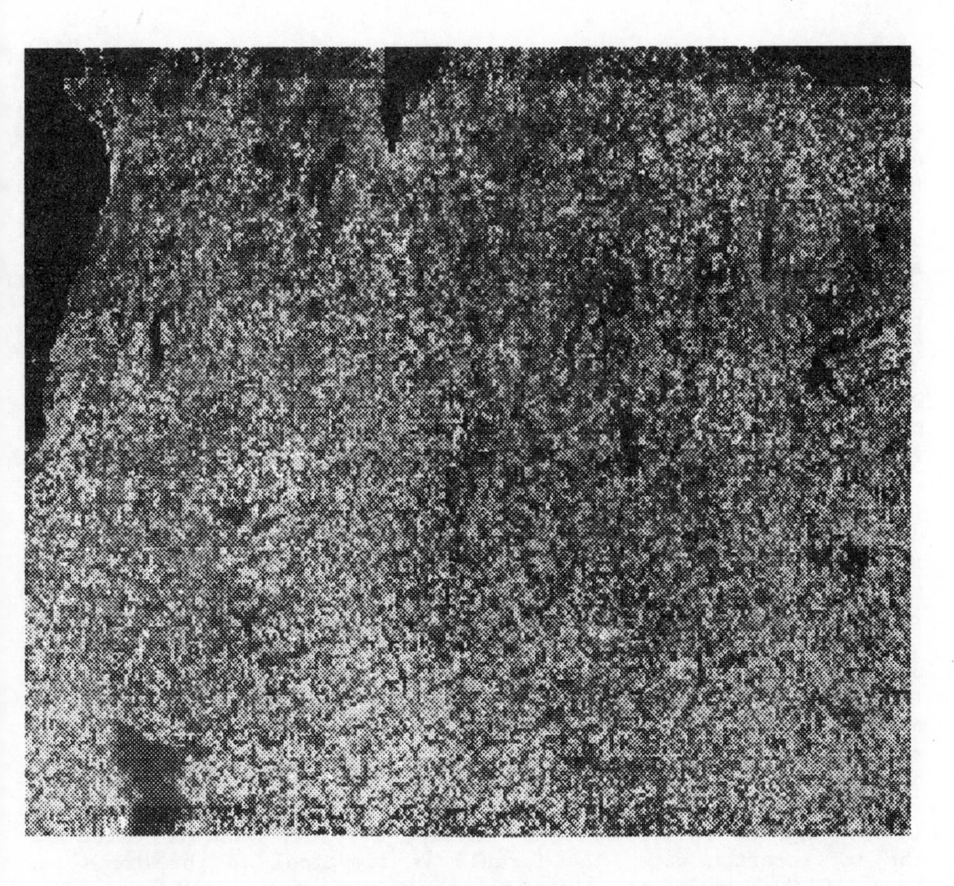

Figure 1 - LANDSAT image of the Saugeen River Watershed

TABLE 1 - Percent of Land Cover Classes on the Saugeen River Watershed

Basin Number	Barren %	Forest %	Cropland %	Wetland %	Water %
1	15	19	52	12	2
2	18	14	50	15	3
3	11	21	56	10	2
4	8	25	45	20	2
5	14	14	62	6	4

or major changes in basin physiography and then divide each sub-basin into square sub-basin elements so that the above conditions are met. Then, to account for the wide variations of the hydrologic response to rainfall for various vegetative covers in the watershed, and to account for the interspersed nature of the various covers, the depth of runoff is calculated separately for each cover class in a sub-basin element and multiplied by the area occupied by that cover to obtain its contribution to the flow from the sub-basin. The separate contributions are then added to obtain the total runoff from a sub-basin element, which is then routed using storage routing to the outlet of the basin. This modelling approach is the basis for the co-ordinate based hydrologic model called SIMPLE.

<u>Description of SIMPLE</u> - The following is a brief description of the hydrologic modelling algorithm used in SIMPLE. For more details, the reader is referred to Kouwen (1988).

The model does not reflect the whole rainfall-runoff process but does model the dominant short duration processes such as interception (the exponential relationship with accumulated precipitation in Linsley et al. 1949); infiltration (Green and Ampt, 1911; Philip 1954); depression storage (ASCE 1969); interflow (linear storage-discharge function); base flow (recession curve); overland flow (storage routing and Manning's formula); and channel flow (storage routing and Manning's formula). The exclusion of other factors such as snowmelt and evaporation has no significant effects on results in this paper since the model was tested using only rainfall-induced flood events in a moderate climate.

In SIMPLE, the Philip formula (Philip, 1954) is used to calculate the infiltration rate. The formula is identical to the Green and Ampt (1911) formula with the exception that surface ponding is added to the capillary potential to calculate the hydraulic gradient. As well, Philip provided a simple method to calculate the capillary potential as a function of soil permeability.

Two key processes, rainfall excess estimation and runoff routing, are modelled in a different way from other hydrologic models. In SIMPLE, runoff is calculated separately for each land cover class in each element, and the modelling parameters are identical throughout the whole watershed for a particular land cover class. As a result of this approach, SIMPLE is not very sensitive to grid size (Tao and Kouwen, 1989a). This is because up to six land cover classifications can be specified for each element, negating the requirement that each element has to represent a homogeneous hydrologic response classification.

The hourly rainfall input to SIMPLE is derived either from raingauges or from raingauges and radar. The reciprocal distance weighting technique is used to obtain the spatial distribution of the rainfall measured by raingauges. If radar is available, the Marshall-Palmer (Marshall and Palmer, 1948) Z-R relationship is used to determine the rainfall intensity, R, from the reflected power, Z.

Brandes' technique (Brandes 1975) is applied to adjust radar rainfall data based on the "ground truth" raingauge rainfall measurements.

It is generally agreed that radar rainfall data has to be adjusted with ground-based rainfall observations (Browning and Collier, 1989). The calibration of the model for the events modelled in this paper relied on adjusted radar precipitation measurements exclusively, since these rainfall estimates were found to be more accurate than estimates based on radar or gauge measurements alone (Cooper, 1988).

The topographic and physiographic information needed by SIMPLE is obtained from topographic maps, LANDSAT imagery, and other sources. For each sub-basin element the channel elevation, land surface slope, land cover characteristics, flow direction, and the number of channels traversing it are required. In addition, the area of each element within a given sub-basin is needed.

Parameter Optimization - As with all physically based models, SIMPLE requires a lengthy list of parameters. Some of them, such as a channel meandering factor and a base flow recession constant, are shared by all elements in the basins. The channel roughness and velocity factors for channels are assigned by sub-basin. The remainder, namely the interflow recession constant, maximum depression storage, maximum interception storage, soil permeability, overland roughness, and impervious area roughness are associated with types of land cover only and are the same throughout the basin. Any combination of these parameters can be programmed to pass through an optimization process. The automatic pattern search optimization algorithm, first introduced by Hooke and Jeeves (1961), and later programmed by Monro (1971), is used for the optimization. The objective of optimization is to minimize the root mean squared differences between observed flood flows and simulated ones. The simulated flows are compared to measured flows at streamflow gauging stations.

The parameters selected for optimization in this study were: soil permeability, interflow coefficient, overland roughness, and channel roughness. The remaining parameters were assigned values through physical reasoning. The soil permeability, the interflow coefficient and overland flow roughness were optimized separately for each of four types of land cover (urban/barren area, forest area, farmland and wetland). Thus, for instance, for forested areas, the permeability, interflow and overland flow roughness parameters were kept the same over the entire study basin. The channel roughness values were optimized separately by sub-basin.

METHODOLOGY AND RESULTS

The model parameters were first optimized using three events on the Grand River watershed in Ontario, Canada. The basin area is approximately 3500 square kilometers and the terrain is composed of varied landforms and soils left by receding glaciers. The watershed is well instrumented and covered by a weather radar near Toronto, Ontario. There is a substantial amount of urbanization in the lower sections of the watershed. Five land cover classes were delineated from LANDSAT imagery as described above and parameters fitted to each class.

Next the model was configured for the Saugeen watershed which is located adjacent and to the north-west. The Saugeen drains 4000 square kilometers into Lake Huron. The Saugeen watershed generally has similar terrain and climate as the Grand River watershed but it is more forested. All parameter values determined from the Grand River were used except those representing river roughness. Because these parameters cannot be linked to remotely sensed watershed characteristics, the river roughness was optimized using the same three rainfall events that were used to determine the parameters for the Grand River.

SIMPLE was then used to simulate seven separate events as a validation in space of the model and its parameters. Figure 2 is a plot of the modelling results. The measured peak flows are plotted along the horizontal axis while the computed peak flows are plotted along the vertical axis. If a point falls on the diagonal line, the calculated flow exactly equals the measured flow. The plus signs are for the calibration run with three events compared at eight streamflow gauges on the Grand River. The boxes represent the validation points for the Saugeen River for seven events with comparisons at seven streamflow gauges.

The closeness of the validation points to the diagonal line indicates that the parameter values optimized on the Grand River Watershed are also applicable to the Saugeen River Watershed.

A set of parameters that are directly related to specific land cover classes allows a sensitivity analysis to be carried out on the effects of changes in the land cover mix in the watershed. For example, all barren and cropped areas were (computationally) converted back to the original forested state of the watershed and the peak flows computed for the same rainfall events. Figure 3 is a plot of the peak flows for the current land cover mix versus the peak flows that would result if all deforested land was returned to forested land. This condition of course would not revert conditions back to pre-settlement times because much of the area that is now covered by forest was logged in the past and changed by man to some degree. These changes are reflected in the optimized parameters. Nevertheless, Figure 3 indicates how the peak flows may have changed due to the present deforestation of the watershed. The results suggest that on the average, if barren and cropped land were to be converted back to forested land, the peak flows would drop between 22 and 50 percent, with an average drop of 19 percent. Most of this drop is due to the elimination of the barren land.

Similarly, Figure 4 shows what would happen if all the forest and bare land were replaced by cropped land. Again the peak flows would be reduced. In this case, the increase of the flow from the previously forested land would be more than offset by the decrease of the previously bare land. The peak flows are lower by 5 to 50 percent, with an average of 26 percent.

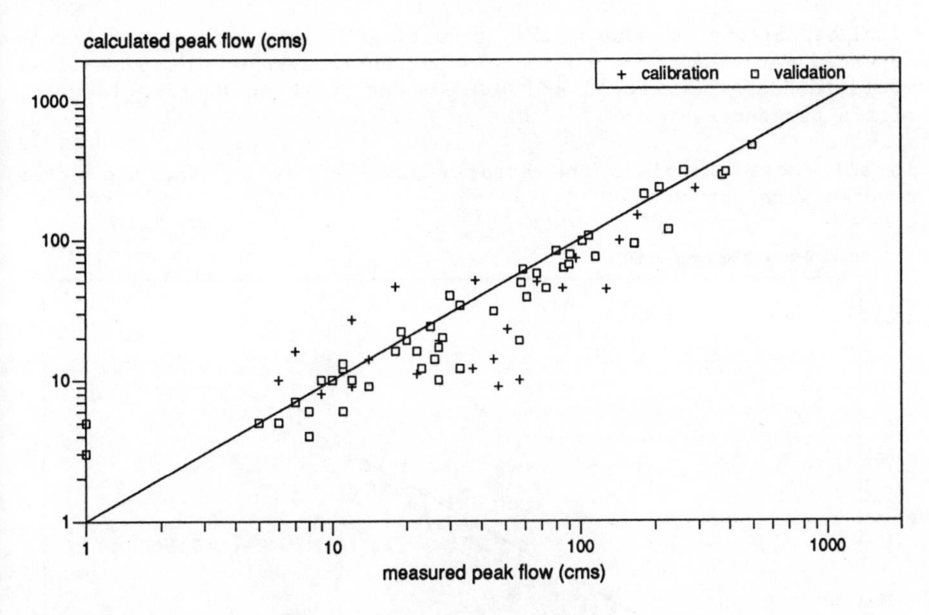

Figure 2 - Validation in Space for the Saugeen River Watershed

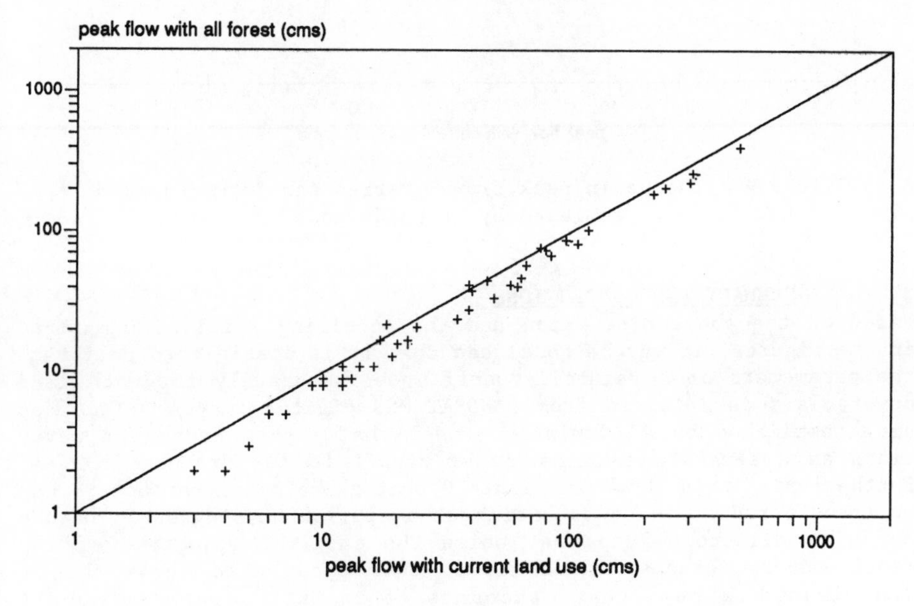

Figure 3 - Change in peak flows: barren and cropped land replaced by forest

Figure 5 shows the change if forested land and cropped land are replaced by barren land. The peak flows would increase by 24 to 233 percent with an average increase of 105 percent over the peak flows resulting from the current land cover mix.

Finally, Figure 6 shows the result of comparing a completely forested watershed to a completely barren watershed. The peak flows would increase between 18 and 400 percent, with an average increase of 166 percent.

In all these examples, the areas classified as wetland and water covered were not changed.

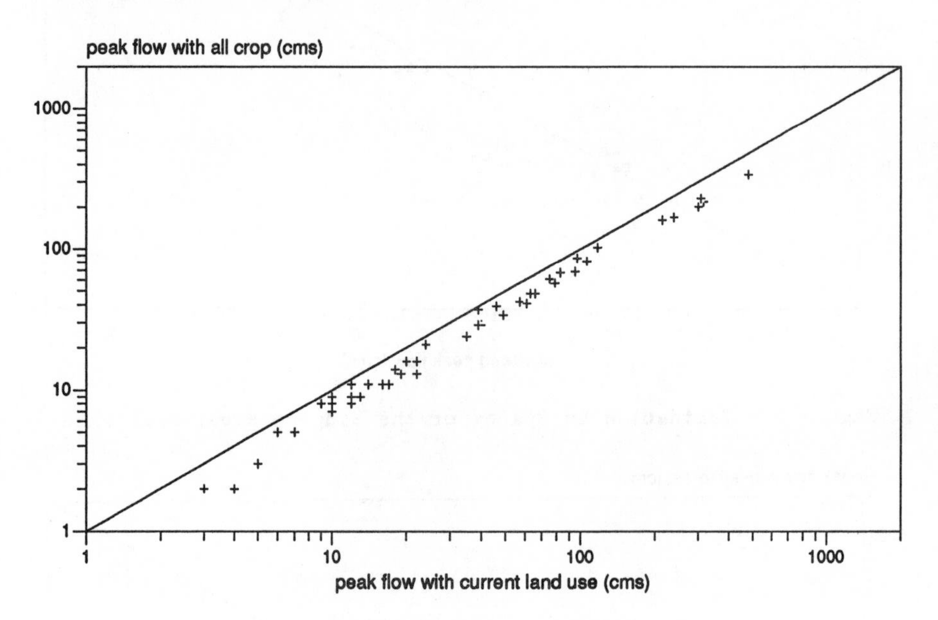

Figure 4 - Change in peak flows: Barren and forested land replaced by cropped land

SUMMARY AND CONCLUSIONS

Based on the above discussion and the modelling results summarized in the figures, it may be concluded that it is possible to calibrate the parameters of a rainfall-runoff model separately for each land cover class as inferred from LANDSAT MSS digital imagery. This can be accomplished by a simulation model that treats each land cover class as a separate contributor of runoff to the drainage system. Furthermore, it is shown in Figure 2 that these model parameters can be transferred at least to basins of a similar physiographic nature but with different land use. While the original objective of the model was to forecast flood flows, this paper also shows that a distributed model that accounts for the separate runoff contributions can be used to show the impact of changing watershed conditions.

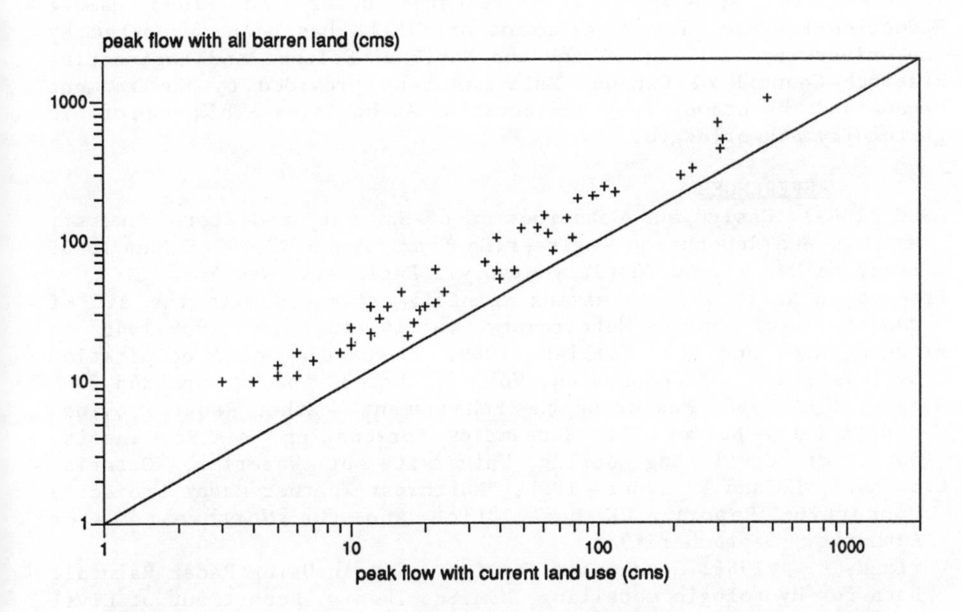

Figure 5 - Change in peak flows: Cropped and forested land replaced by barren land

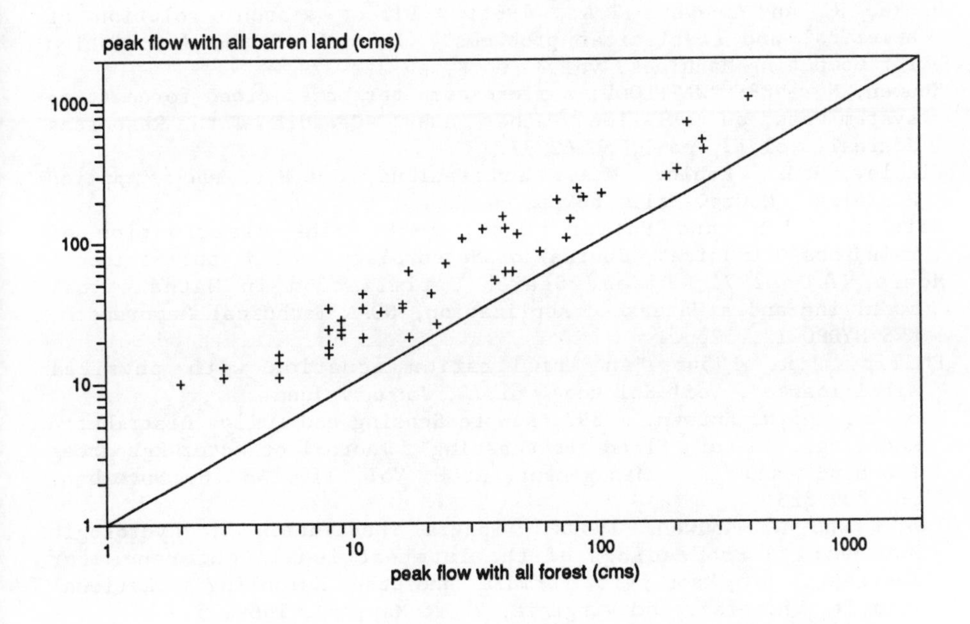

Figure 6 - Change in peak flows: Forest replaced by cropped land

ACKNOWLEDGMENTS

The writers would like to thank the Ontario Ministry of Natural Resources for sponsoring this research under the Flood Damage Reduction Program. The development of SIMPLE has been supported by the University of Waterloo and the National Science and Engineering Research Council of Canada. Data has been provided by Environment Canada and the Grand River Conservation Authorities. This support is gratefully acknowledged.

REFERENCES

ASCE (1969) "Design and Construction of Sanitary and Storm Sewers", Manuals and Reports on Engineering Practice-No 37 (WFCF Manual of Practice No. 9), Am. Society of Civil Engineers, New York, NY.

Brandes, E.A. 1975: "Optimizing rainfall estimates with the aid of radar", J. of Applied Meteorology, vol.14, no.10, pp.1339-1345.

Browning K.A. and C.G. Collier, 1989, "Nowcasting of Precipitation Systems", Rev. of Geophysics, Vol. 27, No. 3, August, pp. 345-370

Cooper, T.E. 1988: Measuring the Enhancement Weather Radar Provides a Rain Gauge Network for Streamflow Forecasting, M.A.Sc. Thesis, Dept. of Civil Engineering, University of Waterloo, Ontario.

Crowther , L. and P. Ryder, 1985, "Northwest Weather Radar Project", Consortium Report, UK Met Office and the Northwest Water Authority, September 1985.

Garland, A.G. 1986: Resolution Consideration in Using Radar Rainfall Data for Hydrologic modelling, M.A.Sc. Thesis, Department of Civil Engineering, University of Waterloo, Ontario, 248pp.

Green, W.H., and Ampt, G.A., 1911, "Studies in Soil Physics, 1, The Flow of Air and Water through Soils", Journal of Agricultural Science, Vol. 4, pp. 1-24.

Hooke, R. and Jeeves, T.A., 1961: "'Direct search' solution of numerical and statistical problems", Journal of the Association for Computing Machines, vol.8, no.2, pp.212-229.

Kouwen, N. 1988: "WATFLOOD: a micro-computer based flood forecasting system based on real-time weather radar", Canadian Water Resources Journal, vol.13, no.1, pp.62-77.

Linsley, R.K., Kohler, M.A., and Paulhus, J.L.H., 1949: Applied Hydrology, McGraw-Hill, 689pp.

Marshall, J.S. and Palmer, W.M., 1948: "The distribution of raindrops with size", Journal of Meteorology, vol.5, pp.165-166.

Monro, J.C. 1971: Direct Search Optimization in Mathematical modelling and a Watershed Application, NOAA Technical Memorandum, NWS HYDRO-12, 52pp.

Philip, J.R. 1954: "An infiltration equation with physical significance", Soil Science, vol.77, January-June.

Tao T., and N. Kouwen, 1989, "Remote Sensing and Fully Distributed Modeling for Flood Forecasting", Journal of Water Resources Planning and Management, ASCE, Vol. 115, No. 6, November, pp. 809-823.

Tao T and N. Kouwen, 1989a, "Spatial Resolution in Hydrologic Modelling", Proceedings of the Internatgional Conference for Centennial of Manning's Formula and the Kuichling's Rational Formula, University od Virginia, 22-26 May, pp. 166-175.

PAPER M3

International Conference on
RIVER FLOOD HYDRAULICS
17-20 September, 1990

THE RIVER THAMES STRATEGIC FLOOD DEFENCE INITIATIVE PLANNING, A MODEL INFLUENCE

John L. Gardiner, FICE, FIWEM
Technical Planning Manager, NRA-Thames Region

SYNOPSIS

This paper updates "River Thames Flood Defence, A Strategic Initiative", (Gardiner, 1988a) which dealt with the techniques and method of approach in the evolving Thames catchment planning process. Management of flood plains creates the "downstream condition" of a Thames Catchment Plan, nowhere more so than the River Thames itself. The strategic initiative is now in its fifth year. The power of environmental assessment backed by deterministic and dynamic modelling is now enabling the NRA to engineer a stronger policy role in Town and Country planning; the paper concentrates on this new development.

INTRODUCTION

The River Thames, the "Royal River" of Britain, achieved international fame in the scientific community recently, because of the success of the campaign to restore river quality and fish - especially salmon, to a river notoriously polluted for a century or more. But husbandry of rivers, and of the special landscapes of river corridors, goes far beyond pollution control. Society, which for so long has turned its back on the Thames and many of its tributaries, is now becoming aware of the lost opportunities and concerned to regain what is commonly regarded as a national heritage.

Among the many "green" changes wrought in the 1980's was the formation of the National Rivers Authority (NRA) as the "guardian of the water environment". Formed officially by the Water Act on Vesting Day, 1st September 1989, the NRA took over from the water authorities their functions of flood defence, recreation and navigation. It is the NRA's intention to develop its influence over land use change and management in the catchment, in order to play a full role as guardian of the water environment.

The overall well-being of river corridors is dictated by the quality and quantity of surface water run-off from catchment development. It follows that control of such development through the local authority planning system is needed to sustain the integrity of all NRA investment. The need for an integrated plan focusing on the catchment's surface water and associated land use is clear.

International Conference on River Flood Hydraulics, edited by W.R.White

This has also been the conclusion of major project appraisal, in which there is now a requirement for environmental assessment procedure supported by the tools of new technology (Gardiner 1988b). Just such a procedure is essential to a catchment planning method integrating economic, environmental, social and local authority planning influences. Investment in good data-handling with adaptable, distributed hydrological modelling and computational river modelling capability is needed to cope with analysis of urban catchments. A joint approach is thereby facilitated with local authorities, environmental interests, landowners and the public, to the complex issues of land use change and achievement of a number of common aims and strategies. NRA investment can then be designed to support sustainable development through achieving environmental well-being.

The programme for catchment planning has two essential elements, the flood plain and the rest of the river catchment. Clearly, it is vital to establish the "baseline" hydrological capacity of the former, compatible with land use plans for both the natural and built environments. The River Thames provides the downstream condition for all its tributaries; knowledge of its capacity, allowing for flood alleviation schemes, is a vital ingredient of the Thames Catchment Plan (Thames Region, 1989).

Even in the supposedly stable soils of lowland Britain, no plan for a river catchment should be attempted without geomorphological input (Newson, 1986). This guides the function and location of investment at catchment scale, then interprets the catchment plan in the way the function is achieved at reach scale, and finally helps to detail local works (Brookes, 1988).

INVESTMENT

The expenditure profile for the six highest-spending regions in flood defence inherited by the NRA in 1989, was as follows (000's, 1989/90 prices):

	NRA TOTAL	THAMES	ANGLIAN	SEVERN -TRENT	NORTH -WEST	S'THERN	YORK-SHIRE
Flood Defence	158,470	42,440	35,959	17,600	16,262	14,020	10,599
Water Resources	52,417	3,007	5,850	8,410	2,222	3,463	2,449
Water Quality	39,391	4,537	5,885	5,940	4,200	3,056	3,145
Fish-eries	12,328	1,017	1,102	1,770	2,374	742	817
Rec. & Amenity	2,244	1,274	398	200	-	103	112
Naviga-tion	4,999	3,742	685	-	-	572	-
TOTAL EXPEND*	269,849	56,017	49,879	33,920	25,058	21,956	17,122

*Welsh 24,382; Northumbria 18,822; Wessex 12,421; South-West 10,272

The table shows the high spend on flood defence in relation to other functions, reflected in most regions of the NRA; the vast majority of this expenditure is on capital or revenue works. However, investment in planning, project appraisal and post-completion appraisal is increasing in response to a widespread change in attitude among river engineers heavily criticised over the last decade for environmental insensitivity.

Legislation has encouraged such change, and the NRA recognises the need to become more accountable in environmental terms for its development-like activities such as flood defence. As might be expected from the table, a very considerable contribution has been made by a strong programme of strategic studies since 1984 in furthering flood defence interests in the Thames catchment, in several ways:

a) formulating sustainable river catchment plans;
b) defining the approach to acceptable flood defence schemes;
c) facilitating efficient implementation of major schemes;
d) improving predictability of catchment response to rainfall;
e) improving public perception of the NRA;
f) improving data management.

The approach, rooted in the Lower Colne Study method (Gardiner et al, 1987), requires various analytical tools to achieve cost-effective environmental sensitivity. Hydrological and river models, econometric and digital ground models and a geographic information system are being steadily integrated with each other (Fig. 1) and into the approach (Jones and Mills, 1988).

The demands of the Thames capital programme and feedback from it have driven such development and underlined the requirement for catchment planning. The ability to handle data and provide consistent, predictive analysis underpins the improved planning capability. Pioneer work in this field will prove of major benefit to the NRA.

Continuing increase in software capability and the computational power is opening many doors - not only in improving present methods, but in bridging the divide between different disciplines and functions in the NRA, local authorities and environmental interests. The land use planning implications of a similar model and GIS-related development have been recognised in the NERC/ESRC Land Use Strategy Programme announced in December 1989.

Thames Region's predecessor pioneered the partnership approach with Local Authorities (Gardiner and Phillips, 1988); the drive now is to include suitable Policies within the Local Plans. Nationwide, awareness of the NRA's lead role in caring for community interests on a catchment scale will be greatly enhanced. To play this lead role, the NRA will need to build on the technological advance underpinning the new standards of river catchment planning (Thames Region, 1990).

Two most valuable investment lessons learned concern firstly, the need for investment in specialist, in-house modelling staff, who not only mastermind the core activities but also develop and maintain the vital quality assurance system, and secondly the benefit of the "extended family" concept, which acknowledges the value for money to be derived from continuity in sharing mutual interests with other organisations committed to similar goals.

HYDRAULIC MASTER PLAN

Although preceded by initial work on the Maidenhead Study, the Strategic Initiative was conceived in 1986 with mathematical modelling of the Tidal Thames, from Teddington to Southend. This involved the river model ONDA and complex combined probability analysis of tides and river flows with the Thames Barrier operating rules superimposed. The second phase comprised the detailed appraisal of the various options for Maidenhead, together with preliminary appraisal of the Windsor to Chertsey reaches (see map).

Concurrently, completion of the non-tidal, in-bank Thames Model (from Lechlade to Teddington) provided a clear pathway toward the backbone of the Thames River Catchment Plan, with its possible flood alleviation strategies. The Thames flood plain was physically modelled in the complex Maidenhead area, and mathematically modelled initially from Cookham to Windsor and then on to Walton Bridge (Palmer and Harpin, 1988). Following reconciliation of results between the physcial model of the Maidenhead flood plain and the mathematical model, improved planning strategies have been developed for the Maidenhead, Windsor and Eton area in close liaison with the Royal Borough of Windsor and Maidenhead.

A similar process is being introduced downstream, taking advantage of the current Runnymede Local Plan revision. Once these policies and specific strategies have been expanded into floodplain plans based on modelled and agreed flood plain zones, the process can be extended progressively to cover the entire Thames flood plain.

Complementary to the planning control element of the initiative is the proposed major capital investment to achieve a 1-in-65 year minimum standard of flood protection for Maidenhead, Windsor and Eton. Planning application is scheduled for 1990, and it is important for its success to establish this scheme's credentials as part of the strategic initiative aiming to provide a similar standard downstream. Attenuation of any residual worsening, however negligible, at the downstream end of the proposed Maidenhead, Windsor and Eton scheme is of known concern to Royal Borough Councillors who represent Datchet and Wraysbury.

DEVELOPMENT INFLUENCE

The pressure for development on the Thames floodplain is unremitting, owing to its location in the South-East and the recent phenomenon of "Silicon Valley", caused by the M4 Motorway and Heathrow, the world's busiest airport. Local Authorities are therefore welcoming a more systematic approach to the creation or confirmation of consistent planning policies based on model predictions, especially when they reinforce land use constraints such as Green Belt designation.

The opportunity for a structured dialogue over agreed land-use change within the existing floodplain such as might arise from a major scheme, has been welcomed by local authority planners in connection with the Maidenhead, Windsor and Eton Scheme, and then by planners, landowners and developers alike in the Datchet to Walton Bridge area immediately downstream.

Discussions with these various interests, following the analysis provided by the initial 1986 ARC (Wraysbury) study, has so far shown that:

a) a feasible corridor for a flood alleviation channel currently exists, the criteria being that of avoiding singificant property demolition and Sites of Special Scientific Interest;
b) some activities and plans for development could be modified by agreement to facilitate if not construct the relief channel required to match the standard of protection proposed upstream;
c) in contrast to the preceding item, which has clear financial benefit (of sizeable proportions) to the community, there are known current activities and plans likely to prejudice a major scheme significantly. These range from loss of access to pit-filling with domestic waste and property development across possible routes.

It is apparent that continuing discussions with the local authorities and the relatively few landowners and other interested parties are needed to keep the Authority's options open and minimise the costs of any future scheme. So far there is little doubt, however, that the third major element in the strategic initiative after the Tidal Thames and the Maidenhead, Windsor and Eton scheme is both appropriate and achievable.

PLANNING POLICY

It can be successfully argued that the root cause of any damage caused by flooding can be found in development planning decisions. The argument for development in flood-risk areas is usually centred on the overriding benefits to local economic development, employment, housing and infrastructure (e.g. transport) needs. What is frequently missed is the fact that all the latter reasons lie within the remit of the Local Plan, whereas the flooding aspects may not. NRA advice therefore lacks the strength of Local Plan policies, and are not "material considerations" for the planning committee.

The opportunity for change is this situation is being brought about by a steady shift in government focus towards care for the environment as a basis for sustainable development. Since this is a new emphasis, and somewhat removed from housing and highways, planners can be forgiven for a degree of uncertainty in interpretation.

The NRA can benefit from this change by demonstrating to local authorities an approach which is in tune with the new thinking and offers an interpretation of how to proceed. Offered in the spirit of partnership, the approach has so far had a warm reception from local authorities, and has centred on the following (draft) policies:

Policy 1: In the areas at risk from flooding as defined on the floodplain map held by the NRA there will be a general presumption against new development or the intensification of existing development.

Policy 2: Appropriate flood protection will generally be required where the redevelopment of existing developed areas is permitted in areas at risk from flooding. The flood protection requirements for such redevelopments will be defined by the Council in consultation with the NRA.

Policy 3: Planning permission will not normally be granted for new development or redevelopment of existing urban areas if such development would result in an increased flood risk in areas downstream due to additional surface water run-off. Consequently, the Council will consult the NRA and adjacent Boroughs to assess the impact of any proposals on its area which appear likely to have significant surface water run-off consequences, prior to the granting of planning permission.

Policy 4: Where development is permitted which is likely to increase the risk of flooding, it must include appopriate attenuation measures defined by the Council in consultation with the NRA.

Policy 5: There will be a general presumption against development which would adversely affect the integrity of the tidal defences.

Policy 6: Where development relating to the tidal defences is permitted, the Council will, in consultation with appropriate bodies including the NRA, require appropriate measures to be incorporated to protect the integrity of the defences.

Policy 7: Where appropriate the Council will, in consultation with the NRA, follow the Thames-side Guidelines.

Policy 8: The Council, in consultation with the NRA, will seek to promote river corridors as important areas of open land both within the borough and, where relevant, across the borough boundary by:
- conserving existing areas of value within river corridors and, wherever possible, seeking to restore and enhance the natural elements of the river environment;
- supporting initiatives which will result in improvements to water quality;
- where appropriate promoting public access in river corridors; and
- identifying appopriate locations for water-related recreation along river corridors.

Policy 9: There will be a general presumption against any development which will have an adverse impact on the water environment, particularly in relation to rivers, ponds, wetlands, public access in river corrdiors, and water-related recreation.

Policy 10: The Council, in consultation with the NRA, will seek to ensure that all works in, under, over and adjacent to watercourses are appropriately designed and implemented. When acting as the Drainage Authority, the Council, in consultation with the NRA Thames Region, will consider the likely impacts of drainage proposals in accordance with the provisions of Statutory Instrument 1988 No. 1217 "The Land Drainage Improvement Works (Assessment of Environmental Effects) Regulations 1988. Where works are proposed by an interested party which is not the drainage authority, the Council, in consultation with the interested party, will consider the likely impacts of drainage proposals in accordance with the same regulations.

Policy 11: The Council will consult the appropriate NRA region on all relevant matters in accordance with the procedures formulated by that NRA region.

THE FLOODPLAIN MANAGEMENT STRATEGY

In the same way that a local plan is supported in the public consultation process by a succinct document outlining the plan and its key issues, the floodplain element of the catchment plan must have a supporting document - especially if it is to form part of the local Plan.

Naturally, any capital works proposed as part of the local plan strategy will undergo the normal process of consultation leading to the adoption of the plan; there is no reason why flood alleviation works should be excluded in principle, and every reason (especially in terms of cost-effective use of ratepayers' money) why such infrastructure works should be included.

In order to prove acceptable for use in the local planning procedure, the document should include:

a) Objectives of the Floodplain Management Strategy
   - the legislative responsibilities of the NRA Thames Region
   - the level of protection for property
   - the environmental objectives.

b) Summary of Constraints and Opportunities
   - the conclusions of the Technical Report
   - a statement of the constraints and opportunities likely to influence the formulation of the management strategy.

c) Review of the Options
   - their evaluation against the constraints and opportunities.

d) - The Preferred Management Option
   - description of the preferred option, including the rationale for its selection

- explanation of its main components (structural and non-structural components such as landscape enhancement and habitat creation).

e) Implementation and Monitoring
   - arrangements for monitoring implementation of the strategy
   - arrangements for ongoing consultation with all interested parties.

REGIONAL EQUITY

The inclusion of those community interests for which the NRA is responsible within the local authority planning system is a logical step in establishing regional equity in terms of level of service. This is not only important in its own right, especially when the significance of the Community Charge is considered, but has considerable impact on the socio-political acceptability of capital investment plans which cross local authority boundaries.

So far, the strategic initiative has extended from the Thames Barrier to Cookham (immediately upstream of Maidenhead), with the exception of the stretch from Teddington to Walton Bridge (currently thought to have a good level of protection). Lessons learned on the Maidenhead, Windsor and Eton (MW&E) study have been of direct relevance to the Datchet, Wraysbury, Staines and Chertsey (DWS&C) study (Gardiner, 1988c). For example, opponents of any major flood alleviation scheme will exploit any environmental, social or political points in the proposals thought to be sensitive. The major examples to date have been:

a) gravel-winning;
b) worsening of downstream conditions (cf. Hydraulic Master Plan);
c) equity in the standard of protection (S.O.P) achieved by any scheme;
   the idea that everyone (especially in the same Local Authority) contributes to the rates and has a right to enjoy the minimum standard of protection claimed for the scheme.

At many of the 25 meetings held during the public consultation phase of the Maidenhead Study, the question of equity was raised by Councillors of the Royal Borough at every opportunity, and must be addressed with care. The scheme has a variable S.O.P., even within Maidenhead. Effectively, the scheme (a new East Bank channel with West Bank channel improvements and embankments) provides a minimum S.O.P. of 1-in-65 years to those areas which currently have a 1-in-2 year risk. Most properties will enjoy a far higher standard.

It can therefore be argued that a minimum S.O.P. should be identified as a regional target, even if it is only to be achieved by protecting individual properties in some cases (as is likely in Wraysbury). A logical extension to the argument is that strategic methods of protection, such as new channels, dredging and long embankments may need to achieve less than the minimum if the properties most at risk can be individually protected to the minimum S.O.P. This leads directly to the principle of utilising a range of strategies for alleviation, and the need to look in some detail at the potential not only for strategic elements such as new channels, but for effective localised works, from the start.

EXTENDED SCHEME BENEFITS

Although the area covered by the DWS&C study is somewhat larger than the MW&E study area, the opportunities for works are considered to be far more straightforward and less controversial. As the area of interest grows so does the potential for regional enhancement of benefits, because of the following:-

a) work to date indicates that potential damages arising from the flooding are likely to be substantial, and the same mechanism which has provided a large proportion of the Maidenhead benefits is likely to provide greater benefits in the Staines area;

b) the regional-scale flood will have an adverse multiplier effect throughout the local economy (not currently being studied);

c) the investment of a large sum of money in a regional scheme may have a beneficial multiplier effect in creating further employment within the area;

d) there are likely to be very signficant recreation benefits if they are built-in to regional water/river recreational strategy (particularly true of the Datchet-Chertsey reach, which has large areas of poor-quality environment);

e) the economic and social effects of a regional-scale flood in terms of evacuation costs and associated implications are of a different order of magnitude, and only assessed before in this county in the case of the York floods of 1982.

OPPORTUNITY, CONTINUITY AND RESULT

The likelihood of Thameside towns achieving a good standard of protection at acceptable cost (in financial, environmental and social terms) is probably at a maximum at the present time. From what is known to date, there is every reason to believe that such a standard is not only possible, but practical to achieve in all respects. There is also a great opportunity to enhance a large area of the Thames flood plain environmentally, and test the techniques of habitat creation and restoration on a major scale. Significant progress has been made in achieving the aims of the River Thames Strategic Flood Defence Initiative with the methods and techniques developed on the Lower Colne and Maidenhead studies (Thames Region 1990). Once the first major Thames scheme is underway, the continuity in experience, personnel, methodology and programme should give the Initiative a momentum and political acceptability of incalculable benefit for any future Thameside study area with a less favourable benefit/cost ratio.

Even if the capital investment aspect of the Strategic Initiative should prove difficult to implement, the flood plain management strategy based on the policies firmly lodged in the Local Plans will provide a new consistency and strength to the NRA's advance towards its functional and catchment planning objectives.

The principles and policies are being tried not only within the Thames flood plain area, but throughout London's Boroughs as the Unitary Development Plan programme proceeds. A complementary Catchment Plan programme is in progress, designed to provide the data and strategies required for the NRA's new role in the development planning process.

BIBLIOGRAPHY

Brookes, A. 1988: "Channelised Rivers: Perspectives for Environmental Management", John Wiley and Sons 342 pp.

Gardiner, J.L., Dearsley, A.F. and Woolnough, J.R. 1987: "The Appraisal of Environmentally Sensitive Options for Flood Alleviation using Mathematical Modelling", J. IWEM, 1(2), 171-184.

Gardiner, J.L. and Phillips, S. 1988: "Planning for the River Catchment", Planning Magazine (798).

Gardiner, J.L. 1988a: "River Thames Flood Defence: A Strategic Initiative", paper given to IWEM Central Southern Branch meeting, Wallingford.

Gardiner, J.L. 1988b: "Environmentally Sensitive River Engineering: Examples from the Thames Catchment", in Petts, G. (Ed): Regulated Rivers: Research and Management", Vol.2, John Wiley and Sons.

Gardiner, J.L. 1988c: "Promoting a Risk Reduction Project: Experience in Thames Water", in Handmer, J.W. and Penning-Rowsell, E.C. (Eds): "Risk Communication and Response", Gower Technical Press, Aldershot.

Jones, L.D. and Mills, D.N.M. 1989: "THAMESIS - A geographic information system" in Computer Bulletin, Dec. 1988 p14.

Newson, M.D. 1986: "River Basin Engineering - Fluvial Geomorphology", JIWES, 40(4), 307-324.

Palmer , J. and Harpin, R. 1988: "River Thames Flood Defence - The Mathematical Modelling Contribution", paper given at IWEM Central Southern Branch meeting, Wallingford.

Thames Region, NRA 1989: "Flood Defence and Environment Catchment Plan: Implementation Guidelines Report", Reading.

Thames Region, NRA 1990: "River Corridor Conservation: A Manual for Project Appraisal", John Wiley and Sons (in press).

NOTE: The views expressed in this paper are those of the Author, and may not necessarily be shared by NRA-Thames region.

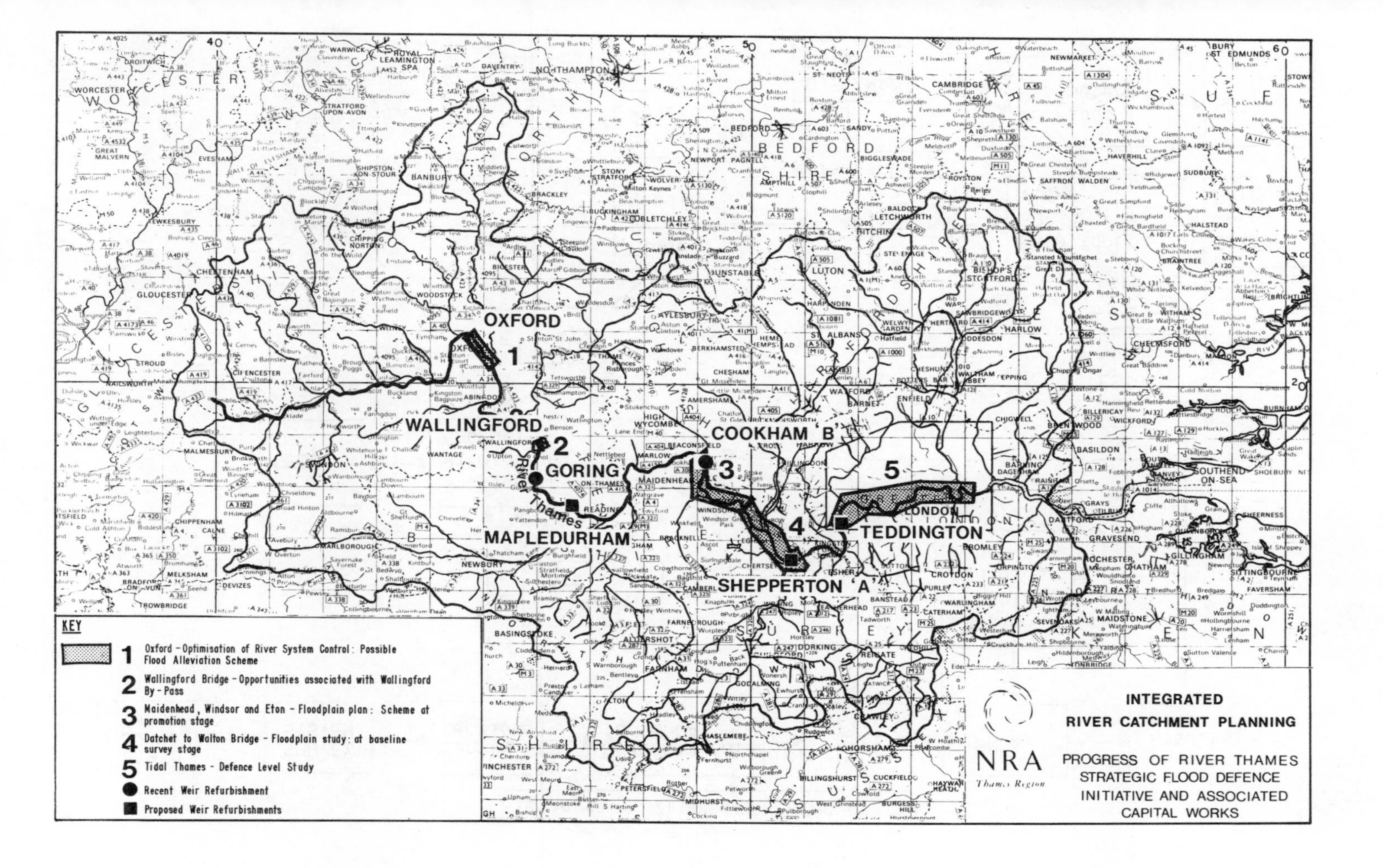
OXFORD
WALLINGFORD
GORING
River Thames
MAPLEDURHAM
COOKHAM 'B'
SHEPPERTON 'A'
TEDDINGTON
LONDON
1
2
3
4
5
KEY
1 Oxford - Optimisation of River System Control: Possible Flood Alleviation Scheme
2 Wallingford Bridge - Opportunities associated with Wallingford By-Pass
3 Maidenhead, Windsor and Eton - Floodplain plan: Scheme at promotion stage
4 Datchet to Walton Bridge - Floodplain study: at baseline survey stage
5 Tidal Thames - Defence Level Study
Recent Weir Refurbishment
Proposed Weir Refurbishments
NRA
Thames Region
INTEGRATED
RIVER CATCHMENT PLANNING
PROGRESS OF RIVER THAMES
STRATEGIC FLOOD DEFENCE
INITIATIVE AND ASSOCIATED
CAPITAL WORKS

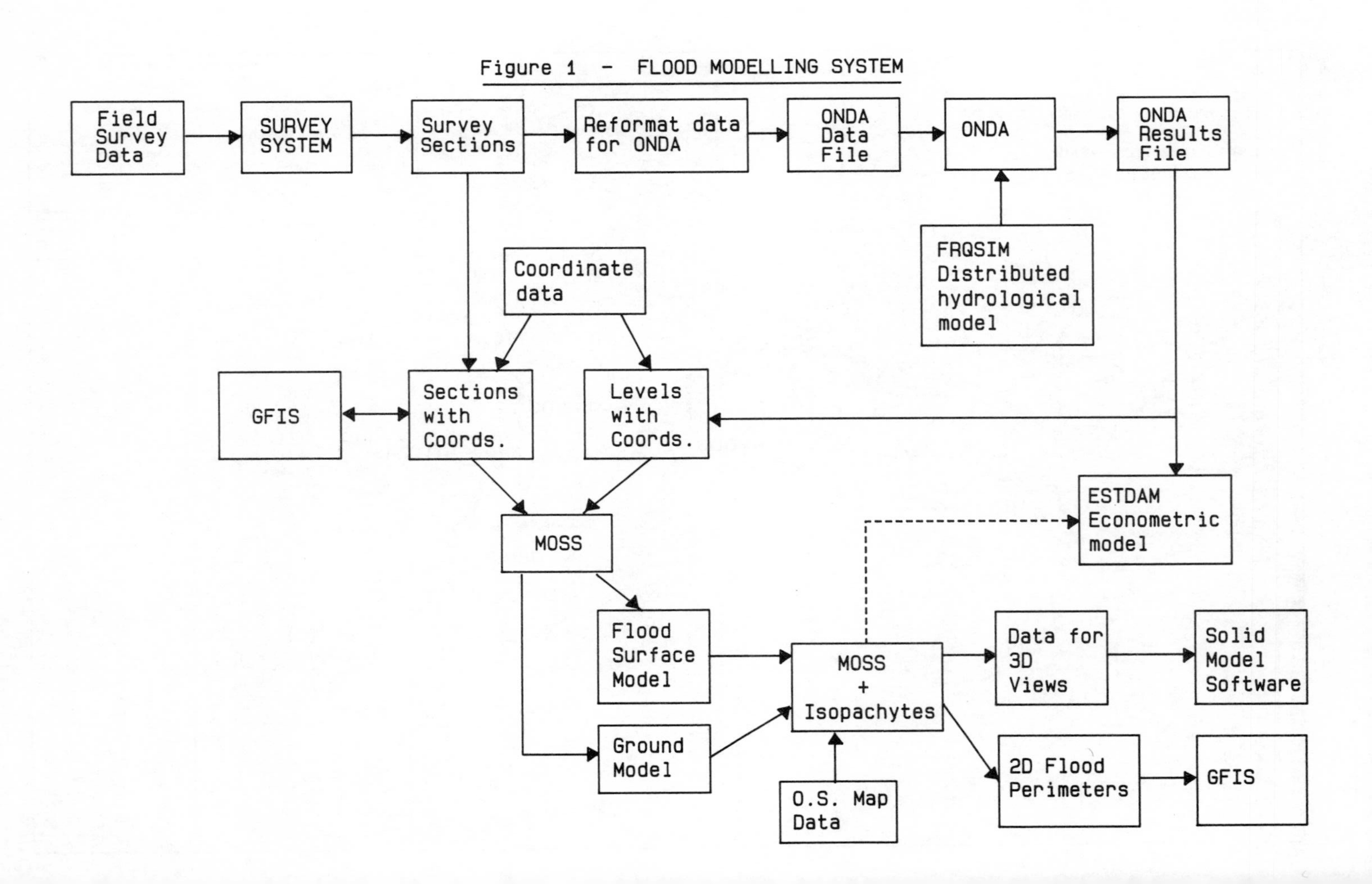

Figure 1 - FLOOD MODELLING SYSTEM

International Conference on
RIVER FLOOD HYDRAULICS
17-20 September, 1990

THE RIVER AVON: STRATFORD TO TEWKESBURY
A CASE STUDY OF THE SURVEY AND ASSESSMENT OF ANCIENT WEIR STRUCTURES

R.J. Mains-Smith — Principal Engineer Policy and Planning, National Rivers Authority, Severn-Trent Region

P. Treadgold — Partner, Flynn and Rothwell

THE RIVER AVON

The River Avon is navigable for 74km between Tewkesbury and Alveston which is 6km upstream of Stratford-upon-Avon. The Lower Avon Navigation Trust is responsible for Navigation from Tewkesbury to Evesham and Upper Avon Navigation Trust from Evesham to Alveston. The navigation has 17 impounded reaches with a total level difference of 26m. A map and long section between Stratford and Tewkesbury are given in Figures 1 and 2 respectively.

Apart from its obvious land drainage function, the river is also widely used for recreational purposes. It is an important coarse fishery with virtually every metre of bank let to fishing clubs. Lastly, the importance of the river as a habitat for wildlife cannot be overstressed. In particular, it is the only breeding area in Britain for the Marsh Warbler.

HISTORY AND DEVELOPMENTS OF THE MILLS, WEIRS AND NAVIGATION

Some weirs were originally developed for mills over a long period of time and at Pershore, Wyre, Fladbury, Cropthorne, Chadbury, Evesham and Harvington, they are mentioned in the Domesday Book (1086). Subsequently there were mills at Tewkesbury, Strensham, Eckington, Nafford, Welford and Stratford. There are no longer any working mills but the buildings still remain although largely converted for domestic use. The mill at Pershore was the last water driven mill, production ceasing when it was destroyed by fire in the late sixties.

In 1653, William Sandys of Fladbury received Royal Letters Patent from Charles I to make the River Avon navigable from Tewkesbury to near Coventry. Work was carried out from 1636 to 1639 making the River navigable by barge up to Stratford. The navigation was divided in 1717 into Upper and Lower sections at Evesham. The Avon Navigation Act of 1751 laid down tolls etc, and around 400, 30-ton barges used the river each year.

The Upper Avon Navigation declined from 1845 and traffic ceased in 1875 when the Great Western Railway, who owned the navigation, refused tolls and were therefore not required to carry out maintenance under the 1751 Act. Meanwhile, the Lower Avon Navigation remained in private hands until the Lower Avon Navigation Company

International Conference on River Flood Hydraulics, edited by W.R.White

bought the navigation rights in 1924 and repair work was carried out between 1924 and 1930.

During the Second World War the River Avon was not navigable above Pershore. In 1945 the Lower Avon Navigation was bought by John Whitehouse and in 1950 the navigation rights passed to the Lower Avon Navigation Trust, a registered Charity, and Douglas Barwell set about restoring the navigation. In the period 1951 to 1954 the locks between Tewkesbury and Evesham were restored allowing navigation to Offenham upstream of Evesham.

The Stratford Canal was restored between 1961 and 1964, and restoration of the connecting Upper Avon was the next obvious step to complete a navigable ring route. On the Upper Avon all but two of the weirs had collapsed or had been lowered and all the locks were beyond repair. In 1965 the Upper Avon Navigation Trust was formed as a Charity. After four years of surveys and investigations, followed by restoration over a five year period, the Upper Avon Navigation was opened in 1974. Thus the Midlands Circuit was completed as shown in Figure 3.

FLOODS AND WEIR FAILURES

Since the second World War, there have been 3 notable floods on the Lower Avon. These were approximately 1 in 50 year events in March 1947 and July 1968 and a 1 in 10 year event in January 1959 where peak flows at Evesham were around 360cu m/s and 240cu m/s respectively.

Most of the old weirs have masonry glacis (sloping face). Dislodgement of these masonry blocks rapidly leads to scouring of the fill material underneath and of adjacent blocks. Evesham weir for example has been repaired in 1957, 1968, 1970, 1973 and has had various minor repairs since. During the last decade, Welford Weir had major repairs in 1980, the Fish and Anchor Ford at Offenham was repaired in 1983, Pershore Weir was repaired in 1984 and finally Wyre Mill Weir was repaired in 1987 following a partial collapse. Many emergency repair situations have arisen, fortunately not during winter months, when a flood could have destroyed the whole of a damaged weir.

There are a number of weirs, mainly downstream of Evesham, of similar age to those that have suffered from damage and partial collapse and these problems are therefore indicative of future problems on these structures. Due to the long history of weirs on the River Avon, the cessation of milling and the several navigation restoration schemes, several of the weirs are now of unknown or uncertain ownership.

EARLY PROJECTS

The first Lower Avon Improvement Scheme was started in 1939 and was eventually completed in 1952. This involved the resectioning of the river between Tewkesbury and Pershore to provide in-bank capacity of around 110 cumecs which was still below the Mean Annual Flood discharge of 160 cumecs. The other major works involved the impounding structures either repairing, rebuilding or replacing sluices or weirs.

Severn-Trent Water Authority, predecessor to NRA, was pressured by the Local Farming Community to provide flood protection so that the full potential of the fertile land could be realised. It was decided in 1977 to undertake an investigation of the flooding problems downstream of Evesham to determine the feasibility of carrying out major improvement works.

The completion of the feasibility study coincided with a change in the Ministry of Agriculture, Fisheries and Food priorities for capital expenditure on land drainage works whereby the lowest priority was assigned to schemes primarily for agricultural benefit. Initial studies raised concerns over the loss of habitat for the Marsh Warbler, and this together with the changing priorities meant that the detailed design of an improvement scheme never started.

PROGRESS BY THE NRA AND ITS PREDECESSORS

Initial Appraisals In January 1983, the Authority published a report on the 40 river structures between Tewkesbury and Stratford-upon-Avon of which 10 are owned by the NRA. The underwater survey was carried out by a specialist firm of divers, Keliston Marine Ltd. between October 1981 and March 1982. The report detailed the visual structural defects, ownership, responsibility for maintenance and required repair costs. The River Avon Steering Group met for the first time in October 1983 to consider this Report. The Group comprised the Chairmen of the Severn Local Land Drainage Committee, Regional Land Drainage Committee, WARF, officers of Severn-Trent Water Authority and the two Navigation Trusts.

Structures owned by the NRA A further condition survey was carried out in 1985 by Shoreline Engineering on Authority owned structures and the Stratford area. The Contractor identified and carried out minor repair works such as underwater concrete bagging and some pointing work for approximately £4,000.

The Authority later commissioned Morgan Horne to carry out a full feasibility study on 7 sluices and 3 weirs owned by the Authority. The study was carried out between May and August 1988 and recommended rebuilding of Eckington Sluice and Standchard Pit Weir as a labyrinth weir and remedial works to the other eight structures.

Following an in-house benefit assessment which showed a benefit/cost ratio of 4, a £2.9m refurbishment scheme was approved in principle by MAFF for grant aid. A Consultant was commissioned in January 1990 for the design and supervision, and construction is phased between June 1990 and March 1995. This major expenditure will prolong the life of the structures and reduce the risk of partial or total collapse.

Structures Owned by Others It was the partial collapse of Wyre Mill Weir which led to the reconvening of the River Avon Steering Group in January 1988. The membership was widened to include riparian

District. Borough and County Councils, the Nature Conservancy Council, the Countryside Commission and private owners. The consequences of a total collapse were discussed and there was agreement that a preventive maintenance policy was required to minimise overall costs. The Authority offered to arrange a joint investigation into the condition of 10 weirs and 1 sluice. none of which it owned, subject to a 50% contribution.

Eight contributions were received in the subsequent months and a brief was awarded to Flynn and Rothwell in April 1989 which culminated in a detailed report in August 1989. Upper Avon Navigation Trust preferred to carry out their own survey of 4 weirs in their ownership to the same format, and their report was available in December 1989. The River Avon Steering Group met again in January 1990 to consider the implications of these reports and to discuss future funding.

The following sections describe the work involved in surveying, assessing stability, and determining remedial work to old structures.

OBJECTIVES OF THE STUDY

Previous diving surveys had identified urgent work and provided a record for comparison with subsequent updates. The record format generally had been single sheet sketches and asset listings. Assessments and costings reflected an 'order of magnitude' approach.

The appraisal of the structures undertaken for the River Avon Steering Group provided sufficient information to indicate urgent works and also to provide a basis for raising funds from the owners of the structures. It had previously been determined that a policy of planned refurbishment would be adopted rather than the historical approach of patching and emergency repair.

The brief for the study included:

- Survey of structures by boat and diver and the presentation of detailed drawings showing geometry, construction finishing materials and any visible defects.
- In preference to detailed site investigations, the ground conditions, history of the structures and foundation/construction to be determined by literature and desk study.
- Investigation of the stability of the structures under a range of flood conditions.
- The assessment of residual design lives and, where these fail to meet defined levels, the presentation of proposals for remedial works and costs estimates.

SURVEY

Geological This is the only available and relatively cheap method of establishing the ground conditions. Whilst geological maps give limited information on the surface deposits, drift mapping will indicate the nature and approximate thickness of the foundation strata, and there may be further clues within individual borehole records. Geological mapping can also trace faults, wells and landslips. Bed material may also be inferred from bank erosions evident upstream of the site.

In the case of mapping in the Avon Valley, the records used were dated from 1856 to 1974. Although there has been no significant habitation development and the watercourse has remained subtantially unaltered, there has been some dredging and blasting to provide adequate draft in the navigation.

Diving and Topographic As the depth of water was not great (rarely more than 3m) survey could be undertaken by a wet-suited diver, using 'Scooba' underwater apparatus for the deeper areas. Although flows were low throughout the survey period, poor visibility required all underwater 'inspection' to be done by touch.

A common-sense approach was taken to the precision of plotting on the plans. Given that the navigation would be drained down locally prior to any repair works, defects were located to only approximately 0.25m in plan with bed levels being to plus/minus 100mm. As any repairs would be on a schedule of works basis it was more important to derive an accurate extent of the works rather than precise survey and locational information. The accurate assessment of repair was assured by using a Chartered Civil Engineer Diver.

The survey was difficult because there are sluices at only three of the weirs (Nafford, Pershore and Stratford, see Figure 1). For this reason, all survey was first done wet, and then on one occasion only, the pounds were drawn down to permit the inspection of the glacis of Pershore, Nafford and Berwick Brook weirs. This was done during an evening and early the following morning, minimising inconvenience to boat traffic.

Land survey was undertaken simultaneously to show all adjacent features within the 'zone of influence' of the weirs. This gave a precise locational and detail survey, and also defined areas of scour in the bed and at the bank.

Structure Testing There was concern that voids may have formed within the weir structures. These could have arisen from scour, piping or simply be construction defects. More importantly, as there was no information on the construction materials except where the weirs had failed, it was decided to investigate the use of non-destructive testing of the structures to establish their integrity.

Structure Testing Services Limited carried out a limited trial programme using a GSS SIR-3 ground probing radar system. Operating on the glacis of a weir that has been dried as far as possible, the system uses an impulse technique, where short duration electro-magnetic radiation impulses are propogated by a slowly moving antenna and reflections of these impulses from sub-surface features, are received by the same antenna. Reflections are produced where there is a change in the di-electric constant ie: where the material changes.

The results were constrained by time limitations and the sheet water on the glacis. However, the changes in material were clearly detected for a depth of some 2-4 metres below the surface of the weir. It has been recommended that this method be used when the weirs have been dried by damming-off during repair contracts.

Interviewing Each of the weir structures has existed for a long time. They have often failed, or at least have been maintained extensively. Interviews were conducted with current and previous river engineers to gain information on, inter alia: construction materials, typical cross-section, foundation levels, and incidence of failure.

The success of this process was mixed and whilst general guidance could be obtained on fill material, modes of failure and repair techniques, definitive information about the sub-surface geometry could not be obtained.

ANALYSIS

Features and General Description It is thought that the weirs were originally built at a 'ford' or firm bed feature, often at a rock incline where the progress of a river meander had been halted. Using a mix of clay and boulders as fill, they were built up and a stone pitching added to stabilize the crest and glacis.

Figure 4 shows a typical cross-section. Some weirs may have an upstream and/or downstream stone wall 'cut-off' to minimise scour, though there are no records of depth. Piling has been added to some weirs to secure the toe and in the case of Stratford weir both the upstream and downstream faces of the weir have been piled and tied together, and the weir reconstructed with a stepped concrete glacis. Clearly, if funding were to be available, it would be preferable (though expensive) to undertake similar repairs to all the weirs.

Some of the weir glacis had been concreted over in addition to stone patching. This is important when considering localised 'bursting' of the structure.

Modes of Failure Phenomena such as sliding and rotating are unlikely, given the cross section in Figure 4. Analysis was restricted to the following:

- Bulk Uplift: This is a function of the weight of the weir and can only be accurately determined when the thickness of surfacing elements has been established by site investigation. However by making conservative assumptions of weir mass and comparing this with uplift forces computed using electrical analogue techniques, the bulk factors of safety of the existing weirs were found to vary from about 1.2 to 1.8.
- Local Uplift: The bulk uplift factor of safety could be reduced locally where there is potential for high local pressure as a result of the particular geometry, eg: Nafford Weir where a steeply sloping glacis is joined to a horizontal apron. At the join, there is the possibility of high uplift pressure. This

effect would be made more severe by any lenses of porous material within the body of the weir.

- Hydrodynamic Forces: Water flowing over the weir will generally impose hydrostatic pressure on the surface of the glacis and increase the effective weight of the weir and so further reduce the likelihood of bulk uplift failure. However, if an area of stone pitching becomes displaced, there will be hydrodyanmic forces applied to the exposed surface. It is unlikely that under normal conditions, pitched stone could be displaced upwards adequately to promote such a failure.
- Bursting Failure: This could occur through a high localised internal pressure giving upwards displacement to a block that is subsequently removed by the additional hydrodynamic force on the exposed surface. Essentially, this is a combination of the uplift and hydrodynamic failure modes outlined above. This mode of failure was supported in interviews with the river engineers.
- Piping Failure: This mechanism was difficult to analyse because the depth of downstream cut-off was unknown and the sub-grade material had not been analysed to establish a transmission constant.

Results Analysis generally indicated that weirs without additional over-slabbing (weight coat) and downstream toe-piling are fundamentally unstable. Many of the weirs have evidence of downstream scour and undermining and this would support the need for toe-piling.

Piping failure was shown to be generally unlikely. However, small changes in soil grading under the weir can have a significant effect on the factor of safety. Without further testing of soil properties and without knowing the particular sub-surface geometry of the weirs, this mode of failure cannot be dismissed.

A GENERAL REHABILITATION SCHEME

Each weir on this reach has been constructed and repaired using similar techniques. However, they are all different in specific cross-section and have been repaired to a variable extent.

From the analysis, it was possible to derive a typical rehabilitation philosophy. This consists of:

- downstream piling to the toe to reduce piping and scour/ undermining.
- application of a surface weight-coat with nominal reinforcement.
- using broken-out concrete and pitching supplemented with imported rock-fill to stabilize the upstream face. This material will become 'bonded' by deposited sediment in time, and is cheaper than piling.

These principles are shown on Figure 4.
Much of the final design can only be conducted once boreholes, coring through the weir, and bed samples have been taken.

STRUCTURE OF THE REPORT

In this particular project there was a clear need for a rational and structured approach to reporting, and the final document was a compilation of discrete and separate reports for each structure with a summary interpretive report. An identical format was used for each report. This gave easy access to information for future cross-referencing, and minimised 'learning' for any prospective user of the information. It also allowed easy sub-division so that individual reports could be distributed to the owners of the respective structures, minimising the unnecessary transfer of information.

COSTINGS AND PRIORITISING

Given that the River Avon Steering Group is comprised of a number of Trusts, Authorities and individuals, all of whom have limited immediate funds, the appraisal of remedial work concentrated on spreading the work over an extended time scale by ranking the urgency of work at particular sites and allocating costs as 'short-term' and 'long-term'. By spreading works across several years, a cash-flow profile was devised to match, as far as practicable, the anticipated flow of funds from the various sources.

If funds were available now, virtually all the works would be undertaken in the short-term. Spreading the works over several years is simply a realistic response to cash constraints. The sites that feature in the later years of the programme are those where failures are more likely to be contained and localised, and without catastrophic consequences.

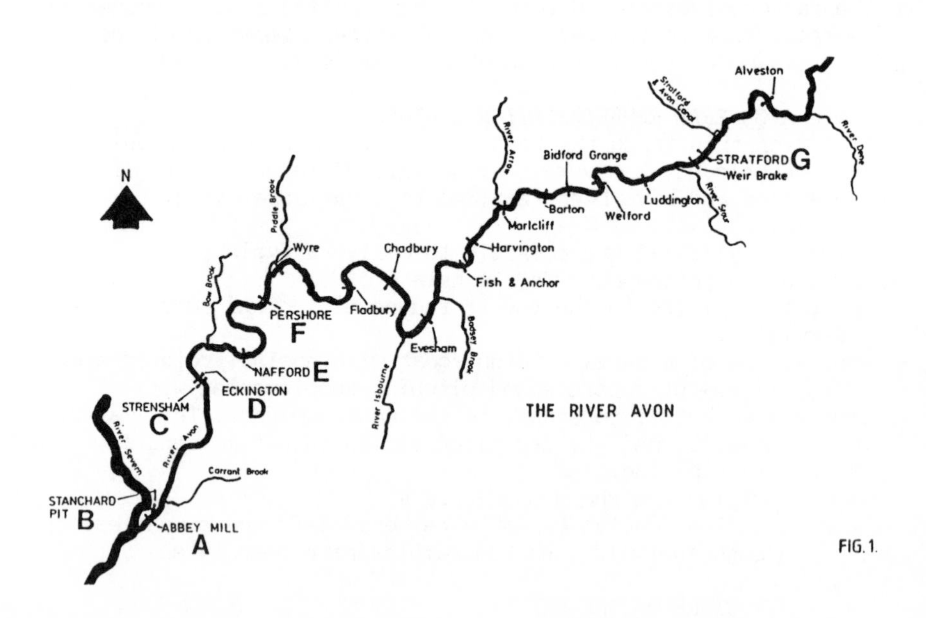

FIG. 1.

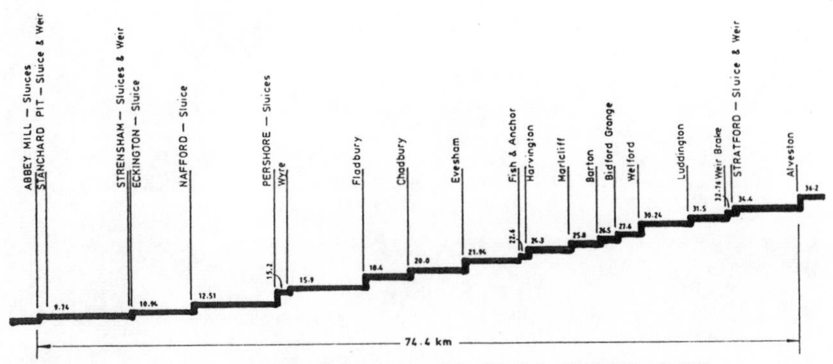

LONG SECTION THROUGH THE RIVER AVON SHOWING IMPOUNDED REACHES

FIG. 2.

THE MIDLANDS CIRCUIT

FIG. 3.

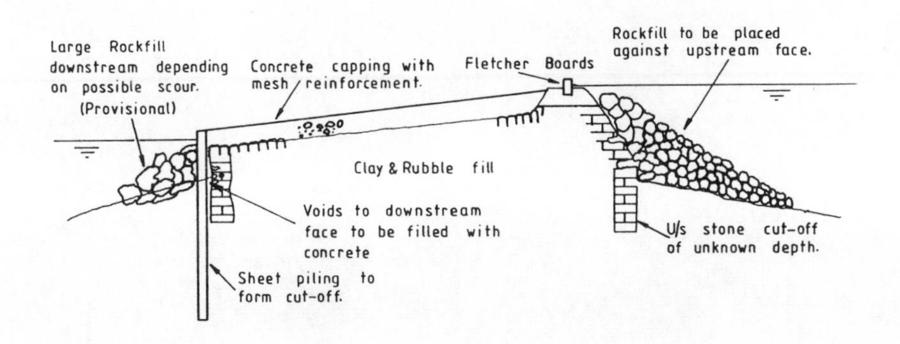

OUTLINE OF TYPICAL WEIR AND REMEDIAL WORK

FIG. 4.

PAPER M5

International Conference on
RIVER FLOOD HYDRAULICS
17-20 September, 1990

INTEGRATED REAL TIME DATA RETRIEVAL AND FLOOD FORECASTING USING CONCEPTUAL MODELS

C Dobson and G P Davies

National Rivers Authority, Severn Trent Region, UK

ABSTRACT

This paper describes the development and implementation of an improved minicomputer-based flood forecasting system for the Severn-Trent region. Data are telemetered over telephone lines from a network of rainfall, climate, river level and flow gauges to a central minicomputer. There they are processed and provide input to conceptual models, incorporating rainfall-runoff and flow routing routines. Data and forecasts are disseminated to flood duty officers who may be based either locally, at area offices, or at home. The transferred information which includes rainfall radar images, raingauge data maps, river level and flow hydrographs can be examined offline, and used by the hydrologists and river engineers to prepare new forecasts and issue flood warnings. The aim of this paper is to describe how this integrated system has been developed and to illustrate the principal features.

Key Words:

Real-time forecasting, Hydrometric network, Data loggers, Alarms, Stage/discharge, Conceptual models, Rainfall/runoff, Flow routing, Error correction, Snowmelt, Remote users, Microcomputer integration, Rainfall radar, Intelligent graphics displays.

INTRODUCTION

The Severn-Trent region of the National Rivers Authority covers an area of 21,000 sq.kms. and includes major industrial conurbations, extensive agricultural plains, upland headwaters and large estuaries. It is an area of contrasting climate and geology. Flooding may result from heavy rainfall and/or snowmelt, from high tides, or from a combination of both factors. The effect of floods is mitigated by embankments, reservoirs, and sluices in many areas. However, there are several urban areas and expanses of riparian agricultural land which are at risk from flooding. The National Rivers Authority provides a forecasting and warning service to reduce the losses associated with flooding in a large part of the main river network of the area. Flood forecasting has evolved step-by-step during the past ten years culminating in a

International Conference on River Flood Hydraulics, edited by W.R.White

period of development activity over 1988/9 with the commissioning of the new system in April 1989.

SYSTEM DESIGN AND DEVELOPMENT

The system was developed jointly by the Severn-Trent Region of the National Rivers Authority and Software Sciences Limited. This approach has enabled the incorporation of a wealth of flow forecasting experience with professional computing expertise, to ensure a robust and reliable system relevant to the needs of the user. The system is fully integrated to manage all aspects of data collection, hydrological modelling and dissemination of data. It has been designed in a structured yet flexible way. This modular approach will ensure that future developments and enhancements can be easily implemented. Particular attention has been paid to allow the system to operate automatically, triggered by incoming outstation alarms to provide rapid forecasts to duty officers.

The key components of the system are shown in figure 1.

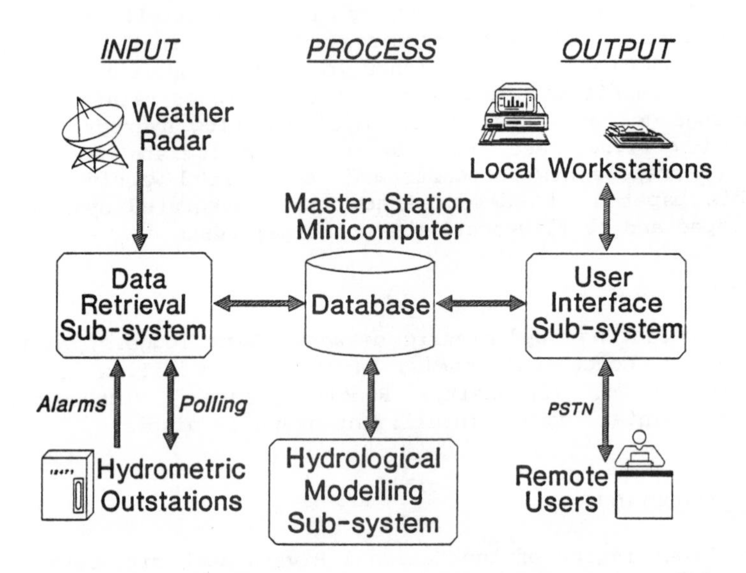

Figure 1 Flow Forecasting System Outline

The heart of the system is a DEC Microvax II minicomputer based at the regional headquarters in Solihull. There are the usual local display and printing facilities. Standard telephone lines are used for data collection, receipt of outstation alarms, and for communication with remote users. Weather radar is included as a continuous data source and is available for display and integration into the forecasting system. Forecast products are disseminated to both local and remote users who are equipped with powerful office microcomputers or portable laptop systems.

DATA COLLECTION

The hydrometric network comprises rainfall, climatological, river level and flow outstations all equipped with a standard TG1150 interrogable data logger manufactured by Delta Technical Services Ltd. The accuracy of the sensors and the reliability of telemetry has been crucial to the success of the project. The system can handle multi-parameter data from a single location. Typically up to 30 days data are held in memory on site so that outstation polling by the master station can be kept to a minimum.

Alarms generated by outstations are continuously monitored and logged on receipt. They can automatically start a data collection cycle and also be retransmitted to duty officers. Alternatively the flexible polling system allows data collection to be started at predetermined time intervals or on demand at any time. It takes less than 20 minutes to complete a polling cycle of the entire network of over 200 stations. All data are subject to automatic quality control before posting to the sensor database which extends back 35 days.

DATA PROCESSING AND FORECAST PRODUCTION

Quality controlled data from the comprehensive network of rainfall and river monitors is used to produce forecasts as shown on fig.2.

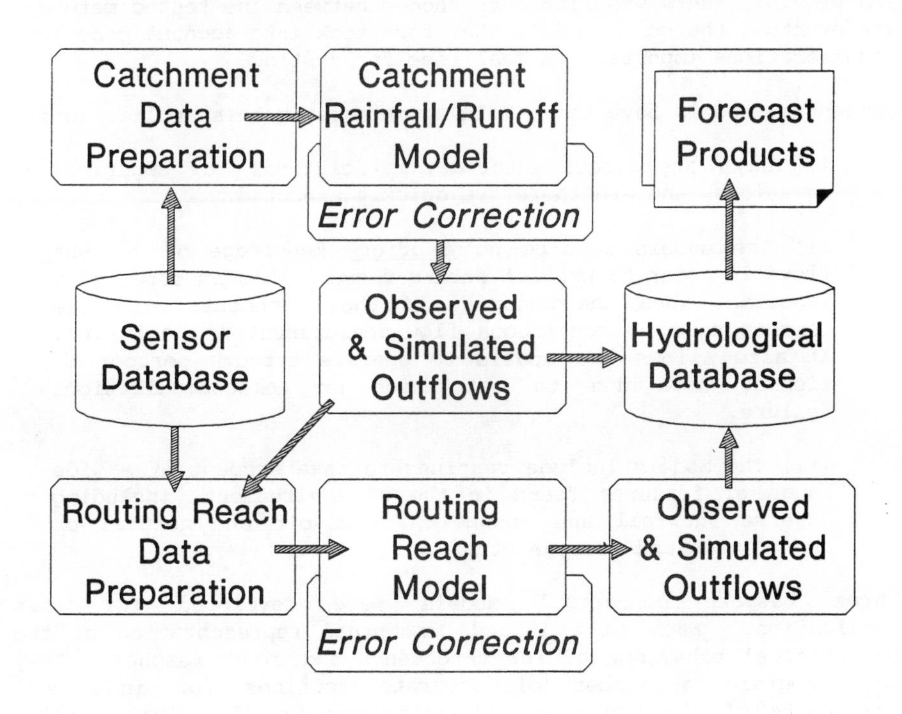

Figure 2 Processing Sensor Data for Hydrological Forecasts

The catchment data preparation routine combines point rainfall at up to six locations to produce estimates of areal precipitation. Air temperature from the closest available sensor is modified to take account of altitude etc., to provide mean catchment temperature for snowfall and snowmelt assessment.

If the catchment outflow is monitored, then river levels are converted to flow using a stage/discharge formula. At a few locations river flows are measured directly, because there is a variable stage/discharge relationship.

If there is significant reservoir storage in the catchment, then reservoir levels and outflow data are assessed.

The reach data preparation routine assembles all of the inflows to the reach, whether they are gauged flows, or estimates from the catchment model. If the reach outflow is monitored, then river flow is calculated as described above.

CHOICE OF FORECASTING MODELS

Conceptual models of moderate complexity were chosen for use in the system, following a comparative study of mathematical techniques in common use for hydrological simulation (Simpson et al 1980). That study showed that with perfectly prepared data sets for calibration and proving, there was little to choose between the tested methods. The eventual choice of model, therefore took into account practical considerations important in real time forecasting.

Conceptual models have three main advantages in this application:

i) They are direct mathematical solutions of empirical equations, and are therefore quickly executed.

ii) The models require no a priori knowledge of current flows in order to predict future flows. This is especially important when the majority of the catchments and some reaches have no continuous flow measurement in real time. It also allows the models to operate through periods of missing data due to outstation or telecommunications failure.

iii) The models include routines to take account of a wide range of features found in the UK environment, including diverse snowfall and snowmelt, reservoir and natural or bunded washland storage etc.

Three bespoke conceptual models were developed for this application. Each is a lumped conceptual representation of the hydrological behaviour of the catchments and river reaches. They each contain a number of separate routines for individual components of the hydrological cycle, and are described briefly below.

The rainfall-runoff catchment model was adapted for real time application from a more detailed simulation model (Bailey & Dobson 1981). Areal rainfall, supplemented if necessary by rainfall radar measurements, is the fundamental input data. A simple snowpack model uses air temperature and wind run data.

Rainfall and snowmelt are applied to a simple soil store model, after interception and direct evaporation have been estimated. Runoff from the soil store, as rapid runoff and interflow, is based on estimated catchment wetness. Percolation to groundwater, and outflow as baseflow, are modelled.

Runoff and baseflow within the catchment are attenuated using a cascade of two non-linear reservoirs, one each for the in-bank and out of bank components. If there is significant static floodplain storage within the catchment, this is modelled separately; in the same way as described for the flow routing model below.

This simple model was calibrated in the 40 gauged catchments in the Severn and Trent basins, and indirect parameter estimation used to allow the model to be applied to 70 ungauged catchments (mostly small lateral inflow streams). Calibration needs to be monitored periodically to ensure model performance is not compromised by changes to the catchment response. This is a penalty of a conceptual approach.

The river reach flow routing model was developed specifically for this application (Douglas & Dobson 1987). It takes a very simple approach to flood routing, by treating lag and attenuation as separate parts of the problem. All of the upstream inflows, and half of the lateral inflow are lagged; the degree of lagging is a function of the magnitude of the inflow. The inflow is then attenuated in three ways.

In-bank flows are attenuated separately, using a simple inflow-storage-outflow relationship. Any inflows in excess of bankfull discharge are available to enter static floodplain storage. These may be as natural or bunded floodplain storage, or as designed offline storage reservoirs filled by gates, sluices, or weirs. When static storage has been filled, dynamic floodplain flow is attenuated in the same way as the in-bank flows. Floodplain storage is evacuated using a simple drainage function, once the flood peak has subsided.

Downstream inflows, plus the remaining half of any lateral inflow, are added to routed upstream inflows, to produce the total outflow hydrograph.

The error correction (updating) model is applied only to gauged catchments and reaches, and forms an important adjunct to the two hydrologial models. It is an empirical and direct conceptual method, but it differs from the hydrological models because it "learns" how to work for each individual catchment or reach. The procedure examines the latest few hours of recorded data, and compares the difference between the model simulation and the gauged (observed) flows.

If the error pattern is relatively small and consistent, the model will predict a future error pattern, and apply this to the raw forecast to improve its accuracy for up to 48 hours ahead. If the pattern is complex, or the error is large, the model will attempt to improve for only a few hours ahead. This problem sometimes occurs in the earliest forecasts, when timing errors between observed and simulated flows are most likely to be apparent.

EVALUATION OF MODEL PERFORMANCE

The models described above are applied to a wide range of catchments and reaches in the Severn and Trent basins. The size and diversity of the application makes general statements about model accuracy rather difficult. The objective in real time forecasting is not to achieve a perfect match between "observed" and "simulated" flows, but to predict the exceedence of significant flow or level thresholds in order to issue advice and warnings to the public.

Measuring the accuracy of the models would require certain assumptions about the reliability, for instance, of the "observed" flows at any location. Since these are usually based on the estimation of flow at a river level gauge (using some form of rating equation), the observed flows have their own sampling error. This error may be seasonal.

Use of "observed" data from one location as the input to a downstream location can improve the model's performance if the observations are reliable, but if they are not, can lead to a degradation of results.

Further difficulties in the assessment of forecast accuracy arise because forecasts will be produced at frequent intervals during an event. To give as much lead time for warnings as possible, for the most upstream locations in a basin, models will be run before the end of the rainstorm. Clearly these early forecasts, heavily reliant on the rainfall-runoff model, will be less reliable than forecasts produced later in the event, for more downstream reaches. Here the results will be based on the flow routing formulation, with a higher proportion of the inputs to the system measured at river gauging stations, and a low reliance on rainfall runoff simulation.

Some results for complete events are presented on figures 3 and 4. These show the typical results for a significant flood event in the Severn Basin, with examples for a single upland catchment with a very short response time, and a middle reach of the river.

The degree of model error is significantly greater for the rapid response catchments which rely on rainfall - runoff models, and can vary from one event to the next. This can often be attributed to difficult meteorological conditions, especially variable orographic effects which may be poorly represented by the network of raingauges, or when marginal snowfall and snowmelt occurs. The difficulty in achieving consistent results from even well-calibrated rainfall-runoff models, means that wherever possible they do not form the sole basis for a flood warning, but provide an important extension of lead time for the upland reaches.

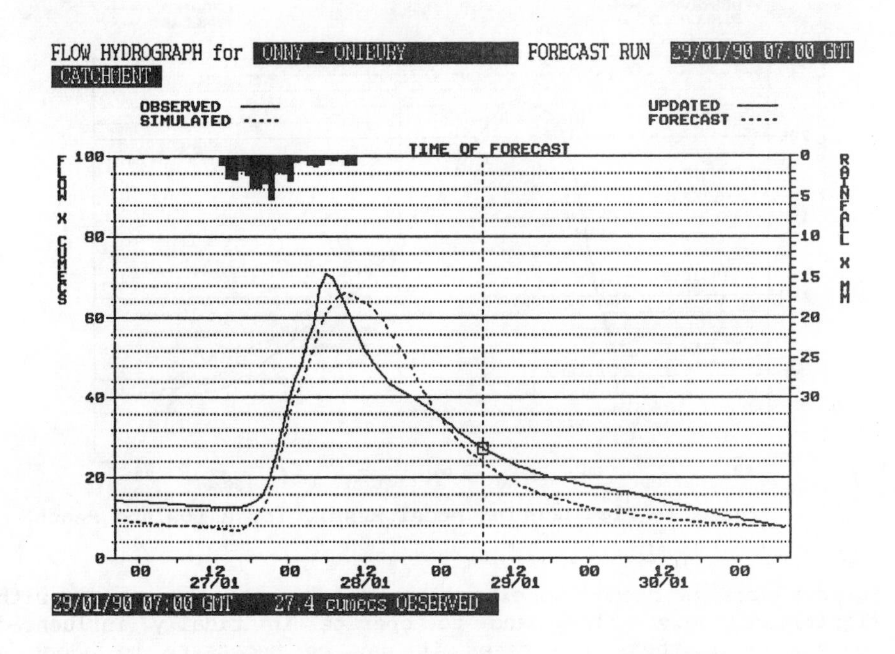

Figure 3 Rainfall-Runoff Model Result for an Upland Catchment

Results from the flow routing model are much more dependable, and are the basis for most of the flood warnings. This is to be expected, since each time a routing reach model can use data from a river gauge as its inflow, it can make a correction for any model errors resulting from the upstream reach. In addition, the flow routing model has a more modest task to perform, with far fewer losses and storages to consider. It is possible to provide proficient forecasts with at least 6 hours lead time for the majority of river reaches in the Severn and Trent basins.

Notable exceptions are when the relationship between river level and flow at a gauging station is affected by variable control or backwater effects. Here it is possible for the "observed" outflow to be incorrect, and the model simulation of flow may then be closer to reality. This type of error can then be carried on to the downstream reach, thus compounding the difficulty for the hydrologist. Other problems are experienced when static washland storage is emptying, and a second peak following renewed rainfall causes storage to refill. These two situations are being tackled by improved monitoring of the river and washlands, including direct flow measurement using ultrasonic and electromagnetic methods at difficult river gauging sites.

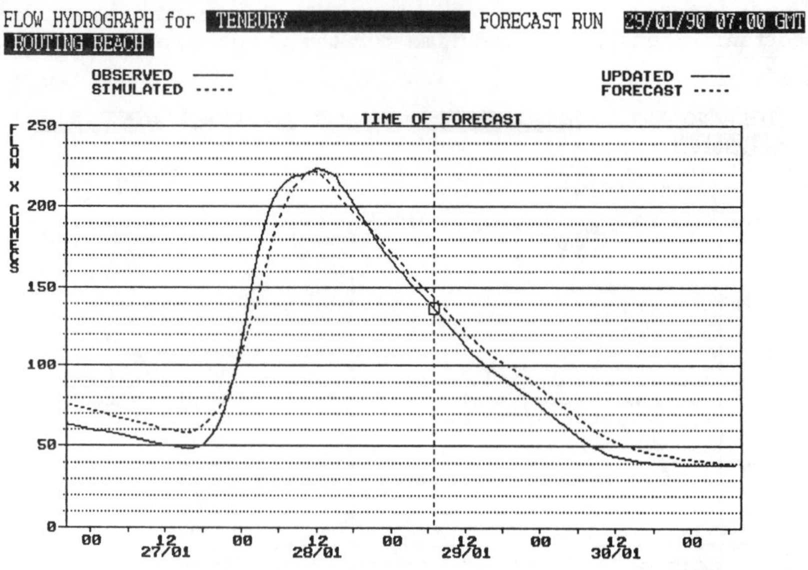

Figure 4 Flow Routing Model Result for a Lowland Reach

Further work is needed to extend the models into urban areas with significant sewer flow, and to operate in tidally influenced reaches. In these two cases it may be necessary to adopt a different modelling approach, because of the difficulty of devising and calibrating a suitable conceptual model.

DISSEMINATION OF DATA AND FORECASTS TO REMOTE USERS

Forecasts for over 100 catchments and reaches are produced in about 2 minutes, and significant forecast exceedences are transmitted via an alarm to the Duty Officer. Hydrologists and river engineers can access the data locally or remotely using standard IBM PC micro computers (or portable laptop compatibles). These powerful machines are connected to the master station by asynchronous links (mainly dial-up modems).

Users can control the master station using these local or remote terminals to amend polling or alarm strategies, and to roam around the basic sensor data to produce summary reports. To review the weather radar data and the forecast hydrographs, the system is more streamlined. Each remote terminal is configured to the precise requirements of its owner, so he can decant the data required for display as a bulk transfer (see fig.5).

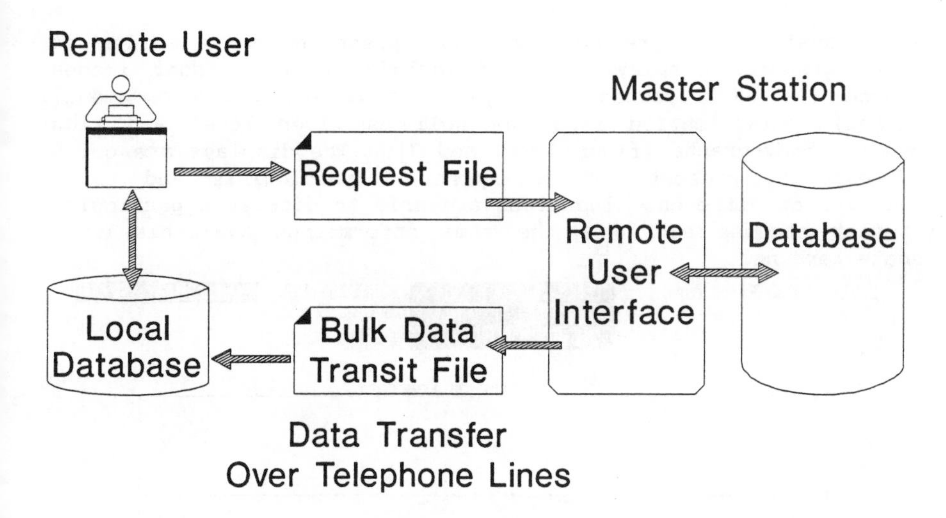

Figure 5 Integration of Intelligent Remote Terminals

Easy menus allow the user to compile a simple request for categories of data, which is transmitted to the master station. The master station will interpret the user's request, and extract only those data necessary to bring the user up to date. The data are compacted to speed up return transmission to the remote user. This way a user can transfer a large quantity of information quickly and easily for storage on the database of the remote terminal.

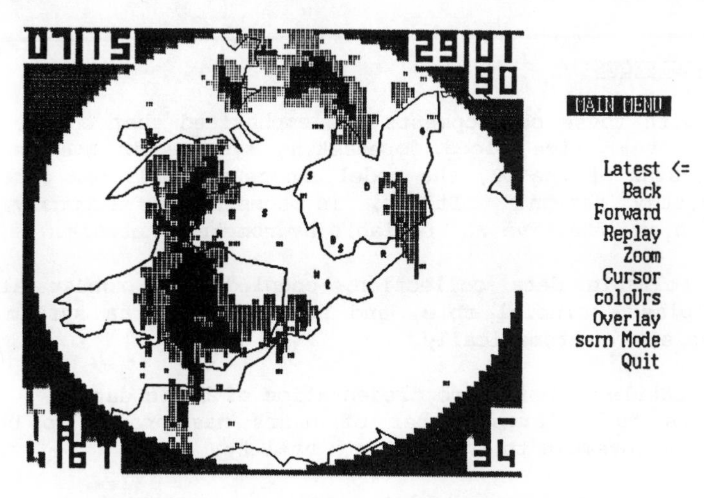

Figure 6 Rainfall Radar Image Display

Data transferred to remote users are presented on a series of active graphics displays. These include rainfall radar images (figure 6), with sequential replay to depict storm movement, rainfall distribution maps, as well as river level and flow forecast hydrographs (figures 3,4 and 7). The displays are quick and easy to present and interpret. Hydrologists and river engineers at different locations are able to discuss a particular forecast because each has the same information available on a remote terminal.

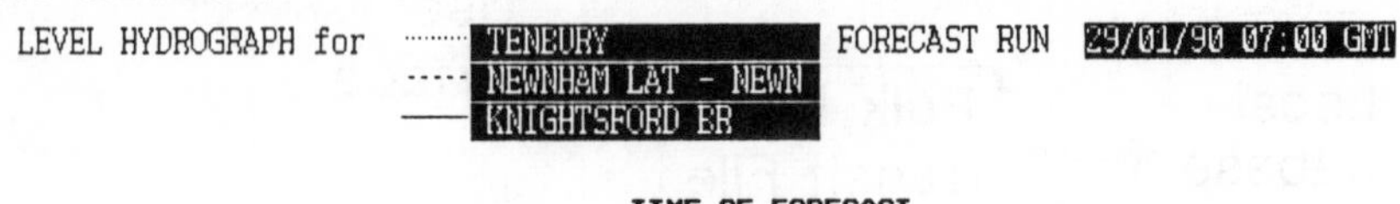

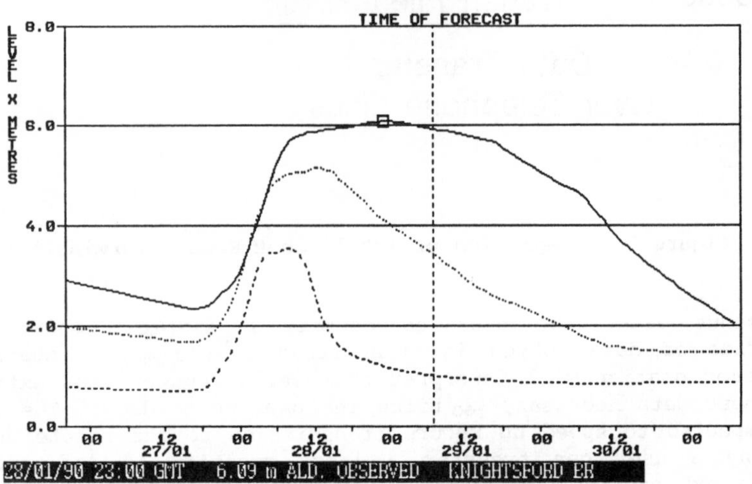

Figure 7 Level Forecasts for the Lower Severn Basin

CONCLUSIONS

Experience with these developments has emphasised that to provide an effective real time flood forecasting system for the Severn and Trent basins of the UK, the model choice was only one part of a total system design. It is, in some ways secondary in importance to an effective and reliable hydrometric network.

Rapid and reliable data collection, coupled with robust alarm strategies play a crucial role, and have allowed the system to operate completely automatically.

Easy and versatile transfer and presentation of basic data and forecasts to a large number of users has proved to be a significant improvement to the system's utility.

All of these factors have helped to produce a system which allows a very widespread flood forecasting and warning service to be provided 24 hours a day to riverside communities throughout the UK Midlands.

However, the system needs to produce reliable forecasts to command respect from the public and the emergency services. The versatility of the conceptual models chosen is considered to offer speed and reliability to an acceptable level of accuracy. They have been designed to operate using data that are available reliably and at low cost. They are resilient to data loss in real time, and are flexible enough to represent adequately the varying hydrological regimes in the Severn and Trent basins.

Future developments to the system will concentrate on extending the service into the headwaters, and urban areas. Forecasting in tidally influenced reaches will be researched, with a view to indentifying a model suitable for use in conjunction with those described above.

Improved real time error identification and forecast refinement, possibly using recursive optimisation in the gauged catchments and reaches, is also being considered.

ACKNOWLEDGMENT

The authors wish to thank Dr. Geoff Mance, Regional General Manager, National Rivers Authority, Severn Trent Region, for permission to publish this paper.

REFERENCES

Bailey R.A & Dobson C. (1981) Forecasting for floods in the Severn Catchment. J. Inst. Water Engrs. Sci, Vol 35(2), pp 168-178.

Douglas J.R & Dobson C. (1987) Real-time flood forecasting in diverse drainage basins. In Weather Radar and Flood Forecasting, J.Wiley & Sons, London. pp 153-169.

Simpson R.J, Wood T.R, and Hamlin M.J. (1980) Simple self correcting models for forecasting flows on small basins in real time. Proc. Oxford Symposium, IAHS Publication.No.129. pp 433-443.

International Conference on
RIVER FLOOD HYDRAULICS
17-20 September, 1990

RIVER FLOOD HYDRAULICS IN THE RIFT VALLEY IN MALAWI

M J LeGouais, Scott Wilson Kirkpatrick
L G Williams, Scott Wilson Kirkpatrick

ABSTRACT: This paper examines the adverse effects of river flood hydraulics on a highway in the Rift Valley in Malawi and describes measures proposed to alleviate these effects.

The location of the road across high energy streams is a primary cause of most of these problems and this is discussed. Other contributory factors include geologically recent movements of the land mass and fluctuations in the level of Lake Malawi. There is also a railway line in close proximity, parallel to and downstream of the road whose watercourse crossings have introduced a further influence on the natural morphological processes.

The paper concludes by describing the simple low cost measures which are being employed to correct and arrest the problems described and thereby minimise the cost and maximise the effectiveness of the rehabilitation works. The measures include use of gabions for river training works such as groynes, check weirs and stilling basins.

1 INTRODUCTION

Constructed in 1972 the Salima Balaka Road runs for 143km along the floor of the Rift Valley and over much of its length is confined between the western escarpment of the valley and the shore of Lake Malawi (see Figure 1.1). Many of the water courses crossing the road have caused serious maintenance problems arising from bed scour, meander progression, channel movement and accretion, leading to overtopping and erosion of the road surface and embankment, and the collapse or threatened collapse of culverts and bridges.

A railway line runs adjacent to the road on the downstream side. The railway was constructed in the 1930's and also has a history of washed out bridges and collapsed culverts.

By early 1986 the road and watercourse crossings had deteriorated to such an extent that major rehabilitation works were required, the design of which provides the basis of this paper.

2 THE SETTING

2.1 Topography and Geomorphology The shore of Lake Malawi is at an elevation of about 500m whereas the area to the west of the escarpment is at an elevation of about 1500m. However the escarpment is not a single defined change in level because complex faulting has produced a series of differential block movements. As a

International Conference on River Flood Hydraulics, edited by W.R.White

consequence the Dedza Massif which rises to an elevation of 2259m forms a watershed which runs along the crest of the escarpment west of the road. Over much of the southern half of the road there is an intermediate plateau, known as the Livulezi Shelf, at an elevation of about 900m and the eastern fault scarp at this shelf which marks the northward extension of the Bilila Fault, shows signs of recent rejuvenation (Dawson and Kirkpatrick).

In the north, the road runs some 12 to 15km from the foot of the escarpment but travelling south, the two converge until at the River Nadzipulu, the road runs 2km from the foot of the escarpment.

In the centre section of the road, both the road and railway run on a terrace of alluvium and colluvium which consists of the outwash fans and other talus deposited at the base of the escarpment slope but which also corresponds to an erosion level of 510 to 515 metres which has been identified in the central peninsula of Lake Malawi (Dawson and Kirkpatrick).

2.2 Drainage Pattern The road crosses 180 defined watercourses which usually flow from west to east. The catchments range in size from about 1km^2 up to 8180km^2. The larger catchments are located partly on the plateau, the mountains which follow the western fault line of the valley and on the escarpment. The catchments of the streams and rivers which have caused most problems for the road range up to 490km^2 in area.

Away from the lake shore the streams are frequently incised. Sand beds predominate but soils also have a cohesive fraction and high vertical banks are characteristic of many of the watercourses.

2.3 Hydrology Malawi is within the influence of the Inter-Tropical Convergence Zone (ITCZ) and has distinct dry and rainy seasons. The rainy season generally runs from November to April with the heaviest rain from January to March. The rugged relief means that rainfall is orographic, the Indian Ocean and the Lake Malawi being the sources of moist air. Over the catchments which cross the road the range of annual rainfall is 800mm to 1000mm with the rainfall tending to increase with altitude and distance from the Lake.

Malawi has a good network of hydrometric stations which are efficiently managed by the Hydrology Section of the Department of Water. For design purposes estimates of flood flows were based on regional flood frequency curves, initially based on papers by Pike (1964) and Drayton et al (1980).

During the project period further papers based on additional data were published by Laisi (1987) and Krishnamurthy (1987) which in general indicated higher flood discharges than the earlier papers, and the designs were reviewed to take account of this.

3 OVERVIEW OF THE PROBLEMS

3.1 Summary of the Problems The problems encountered on the watercourse crossings fall into the following categories:

a) Bed scour progressing upstream (degrading)
b) Meander progression - erosion of river bank and road embankment
c) Local bed scour at culvert outlet
d) Inadequate downstream channel capacity
e) Inadequate bridge or culvert capacity
f) Accretion/silting up of culverts (aggrading)
g) Movement of upstream channel
h) Overtopping of road embankment

In many cases, two, three or even four of these problems may occur on one watercourse, particularly d) to h), which are often interrelated problems.

3.2 Morphology The explanation for most of these problems can be traced to the location of the road in a narrow strip of land between the escarpment and the Lake.

A generalised cross section of the valley is shown in Figure 1.1. The watercourses flowing into the Lake can be classified as the young upper courses of the much larger Shire/Zambezi river basin. The transition from the mountains and escarpment onto the relatively flat valley floor is abrupt, and a terrace has been formed by outwash fans of sediment brought down from the higher ground and by talus from the scarp slope.

Streams which flow across these outwash fans will deposit sediments in their bed and therefore have poorly defined channels so that during times of flood avulsion may occur with the result that a new drainage path will be formed. Thus locating a bridge or culvert across areas of active outwash fans risks problems of silting and migration of the channel.

Relatively recent uplift or a drop in the Lake from an ancient level have been reported (Dawson and Kirkpatrick). Following such changes the tendency of rivers to approach an equilibrium bed profile will be accelerated and if the bed material is an unconsolidated sediment the rate of degradation can be very rapid indeed.

Many of the factors believed to influence the formation of meanders are also present for these watercourses; eg

an unconstrained flat area
a layer of unconsolidated generally non cohesive sediments
regime slopes less than the longitudinal ground slope
large sediment loads

3.3 Malawi Railways The Malawi Railway line was built about 40 years earlier than the road and has exercised a significiant influence on the watercourses, including fixing vertical and horizontal constraints causing accretion by constraining flood discharge through inadequate waterway and cutting off emphemeral drainage channels.

When the road was built the influence the railway had exercised on the water courses was perhaps not recognised. The effect of the railway on the road is described in 4.1 ii) below.

3.4 Location of the Road The route followed by the road is very similar to that adopted by the railway and very little account was taken of the river morphology in either case. It is understandable that the road and railway engineers should have gratefully accepted for their alignment the heaven-sent terrace of granular material between the inhospitable rocky scarp slope and the marshy fringes of the lake !

4 SPECIFIC PROBLEMS

4.1 Bed Scour Progressing Upstream This is the most serious of the problems and has caused the collapse of a number of culverts and bridges on the railway and of at least one major culvert on the road. A programme of maintenance has so far prevented a bridge collapse on the road, although at the time of writing two bridges are very seriously at risk.

Severe bed scour is occurring on the rivers Nakaingwa, Nadzipokwe, Naminkokwe, and Ngoni and on a number of smaller watercourses. As a result, bridge foundations and abutments are being attacked and would have been undermined but for the protective gabion work carried out by the Ministry of Works.

There are a number of possible reasons for this phenomenon but it is difficult to show conclusively the particular cause in each case without considerable further studies. Since the remedial measures would be the same in each case such studies are not justified. Most of the watercourses are sand-bed rivers with high bed-material loads and, even if in regime, would be sensitive to channel modifications, due to engineering works or other causes.

i) The possible reasons are as follows:

   Where the rivers flow off the escarpment across a 'terrace' before falling again on to the valley floor, it seems likely that the rivers are cutting down to establish a smooth equilibrium profile (see Figure 4.1a) and this is the area of greatest scour attack.

ii) A second possible reason, a variation of i) above, arises from the fact that the road was built upstream of the railway and some 40 years later.

   If the railway bridge provided a flow constriction, it would have caused accretion upstream and some scour downstream (see Figure 4.1b). Thus the road bridge was built to suit the river level resulting from 40 years accretion, and the railway would have constituted a form of scour check downstream of the road bridge. If the railway bridge then collapsed and was re-built with a larger waterway, the river would cut down to re-establish a smooth equilibrium profile.

iii) In one case, the River Nakaingwa flows into the River Nadzipulu about 1km downstream of the road crossing. In 1970 both rivers were strongly meandering between the road and their confluence, but, due to meander progression, the River Nadzipulu has since 'captured' the River Nakaingwa further upstream and cut off meanders in both rivers (see Figure 4.1c). Both river gradients have thus steepened but particularly the Nakaingwa since its gradient in this reach is greater than that of the Nadzipulu. The Nadzipulu bridges are founded on rock but severe scour is occurring on the Nakaingwa and both the road and rail crossings have collapsed and have had to be rebuilt, but are still under attack.

iv) Inadequate width of bridge opening. Where scour is occurring, the lowering of the bed level reduces the bed width (since the sides are sloping). This increases velocity of flow and thus accelerates the scour.

v) Increased flow due to changed land use. The clearance and cultivation of land often causes higher and faster run-off and hence greater flood flows. However an assessment of the extent and effect of changing land use was not within the scope of the study.

4.2 Meander Progression This phenomenon is causing problems on the River Lifisi and River Ngodzi and is likely soon to cause problems on the River Luwadzi and the River Nadzipokwe.

The effect of meander progression is that the approach to the bridge or culvert becomes very skewed, increasing the afflux or head-loss through the bridge and eventually attacking the road embankment. This is already happening on the River Lifisi and River Ngodzi and existing remedial works consist of gabion wing walls and rockfill groynes, stabilised with timber piles and woven timber retaining walls. The latter are a clever and cost-effective solution but have a limited life and need to be supplemented by more permanent measures.

4.3 Local Bed Scour at Culvert Outlets Local scour holes have formed at a number of culvert outlets, usually small pipe culverts, due to locally high velocities. The scour hole extends only for a few metres, and this form of scour is clearly distinguished from scour progressing upstream (degradation).

4.4 Inadequate Downstream Channel Capacity This occurs on a number of culverts, although it is not apparent on any bridges. It can lead to overtopping and to silting up of the culvert. It may be due to vegetation growing in the channel, channel diversions by farmers, inadequate capacity of the railway culvert or non-alignment/lack of connecting channel between the road and rail culverts.

4.5 Inadequate Bridge or Culvert Capacity No bridge was so substantially undersized as to warrant its reconstruction since they had all been in operation without overtopping for 14 years but some culverts required reconstruction at an increased size.

4.6 Accretion or Silting up of Culverts This occurs on a small number of culverts and is usually due either to inadequate capacity of the downstream channel or location of the road across active outwash fans.

4.7 Movement of Upstream Channel In several cases, the channel has changed its course upstream of the road, and meets the road two or three hundred metres away from its allotted culvert. This may be caused by factors such as avulsion of flood discharge over an active outwash fan or by farmers diverting watercourses for irrigation or drainage.

4.8 Overtopping of Road Embankments Where overtopping of the road embankment occurs, it is usually due to one of the problems set out in paragraphs 4.4 to 4.7.

5 ALLEVIATION MEASURES

A number of important factors had to be considered in the choice of alleviation measures for rehabilitation of the road.

Firstly the alignment was fixed; funds were simply not available to reroute the road and even if this were possible there was no guarantee that totally secure watercourse crossings could be provided everywhere within the corridor.

Secondly the measures taken could not be regarded in any way as permanent. They could reduce and control the problems but could not wholly eliminate them, especially in the long term.

Thirdly, to keep costs low it was essential as far as possible to use locally available materials and skills and to minimise the imported content. It was also necessary that the measures taken could be maintained by the local highway maintenance unit.

For these reasons gabions were chosen as the primary material for construction of river training works. Vegetative solutions were not appropriate because the river banks cannot sustain adequate cover either through the dry season or against the ravages of the large population of domesticated animals which are a consequence of the densely populated rural areas bordering Lake Malawi.

The training works were used to deal with specific problems as follows.

5.1 Bed Scour Progressing Upstream There are two possible approaches to deal with the problem of bed scour as follows:

i) To reconstruct the threatened bridges and culverts with lower invert and foundation levels. It is unlikely that they could be constructed sufficiently low to eliminate all threat of damage from future bed scour, and this would probably also involve lowering of the vertical road alignment with considerable disruption to traffic.

ii) To protect the existing culverts and bridges by means of suitable drop-structures or aprons and to control further scour by means of scour-checks or sills in the downstream bed. The scour-checks act as energy dissipators and upstream a stable, non-scouring gradient is established. The scour checks consist of weirs (vertical or stepped on streams, sloping on rivers) with downstream aprons and counter-weirs or steps to contain the hydraulic jump. The structures are much more expensive than simple sills and aprons but can be designed for a fall of up to 5 metres. They can also be used to restore (at least partly) the bed and hence the bed width at a bridge.

Alternative ii) was adopted and a substantial scour check consisting of a gabion weir and apron was proposed just downstream of each problem bridge. A typical example is shown in Figure 5.1.

5.2 Meander Progression The remedial measures for meander progression can be based on two approaches, which may be combined ie:

a) to improve the erosion resistance of the outside bank (structural);
b) to modify the bed morphology so as to reduce secondary circulation currents and bed shear stresses (hydraulic).

The training of river meanders should also take account of the following:

a)
b) that meanders further upstream may also be progressing and
that the channel should not be straightened but trained in a meander whose length and curvature match those of the natural river.

Gabions were used for a structural solution in the form of a stepped river training wall or a sloping gabion mattress revetment. In both instances a gabion mattress apron was provided to prevent damage by scour at the toe of the bank with stub groynes as further protection in some cases.

The hydraulic solution was appropriate to the larger rivers. The groynes have a stepped cross section and the heads of the groynes are protected by gabion aprons. Groynes are used on the outside of the bend and the spacing is in the range 1.5 to 4 times the groyne length and not more than the desired width of the channel.

Generally the training walls and groynes were taken 3.0m above general bank level. This was sufficient for a large range of discharges and the risk of damage from overtopping by extreme floods was judged acceptable.

5.3 Inadequate Downstream Channel Capacity The proposed remedial
i) measures comprised the following as appropriate.

ii) Clearance of vegetation.

Construction of a new connecting channel between the road and rail culverts with the road embankment and culvert raised as necessary.

iii) Where the railway culvert is smaller than the road culvert and this is causing silting up and/or overtopping, the road embankment to be raised and new road culverts installed adjacent to but slightly lower than the old, (which will be retained) against the possibility of failure or enlargement of the railway culvert, in which case the bed will scour back to its original level.

5.4 Quality of Gabion Work The gabion work carried out previously as remedial maintenance measures has had a limited life and in order to ensure that the gabion works which were proposed should have an adequate life a detailed specification was prepared. This took account of the conditions that would be encountered during construction and service and followed the recommendations of gabion manufacturers. Particular attention was paid to the quality and diameter of gabion wire, to the construction of the gabions and to the wire mesh and stone sizes to be used in specific locations. Where gabions were to be placed in areas of the river bed subject to high flow velocity the gabions were stabilised and protected with a bituminous sand mastic grout.

6 CONCLUSIONS

The history of the Salima Balaka Road illustrates that an appreciation of river flood hydraulics and morphological processes can be of vital importance to the success of a highway project.

7 ACKNOWLEDGEMENTS

We are grateful to the Secretary for Works of the Government of Malawi for permission to publish this paper.

8 REFERENCES

Dawson A L and Kirkpatrick I M, The geology of Cape Maclear Peninsula and Lower Bwanje Valley, Bulletin No 28, Malawi Minstry of Natural Resources - Geological Survey Department.

Drayton R S, Kidd G H R, Mandeville A N and Miller J B, 1980, A regional analysis of river floods and low floods in Malawi, Institute of Hydrology Report No 72 and Malawi Water Resources Div Report No TP8.

Krishnamurthy K, 1987, Guidelines for peak flood estimation for design of culverts and bridges and design of dam spillways, UNDP and Malawi Dept of Water, Ministry of Works and Supplies WR No TP12.

Laisi E Z, 1987, Flood frequencies in Malawi: a basis for design, Water Resources Branch, WRB No TP14.

Pike J G, 1964, The estimation of flood frequencies in Malawi, Malawi Ministry of Works and Supplies, Professional Paper No 3.

Fig 1.1 Location Plan And Section

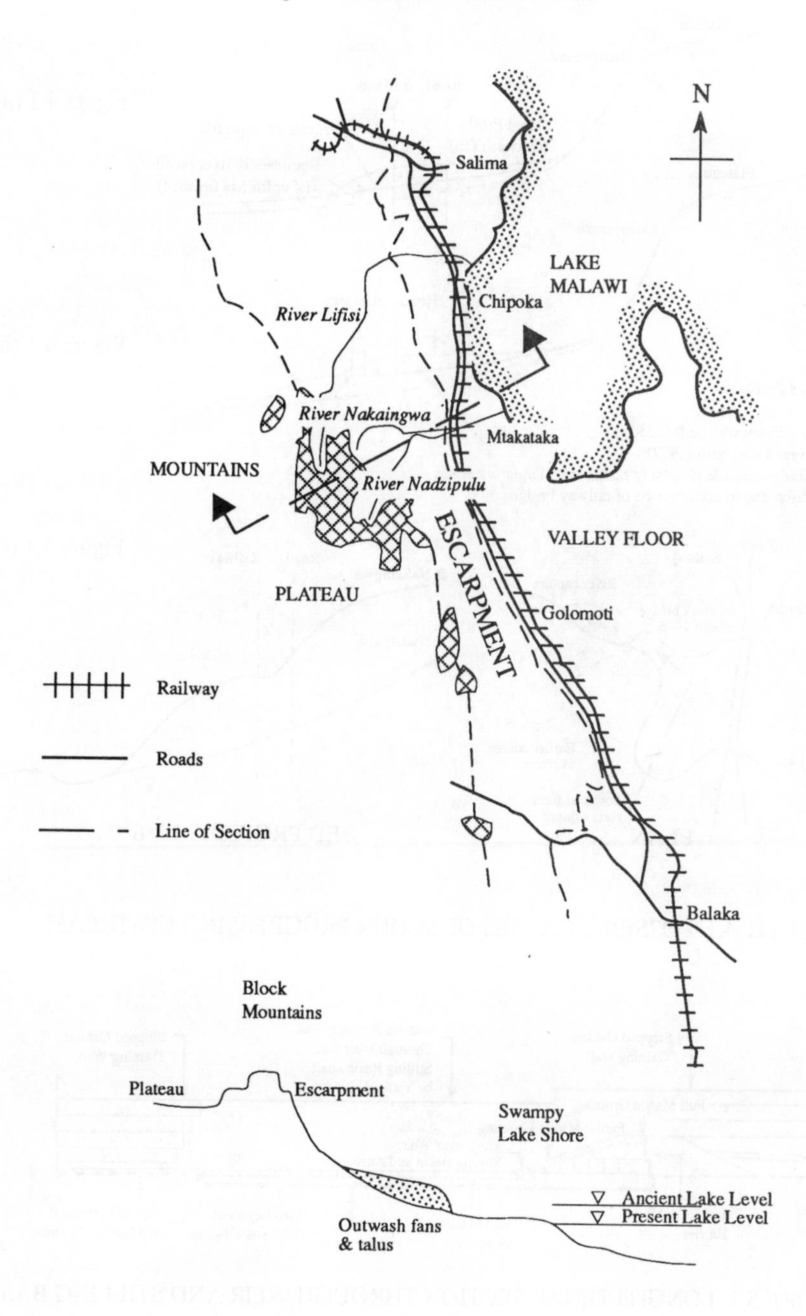

Typical Section

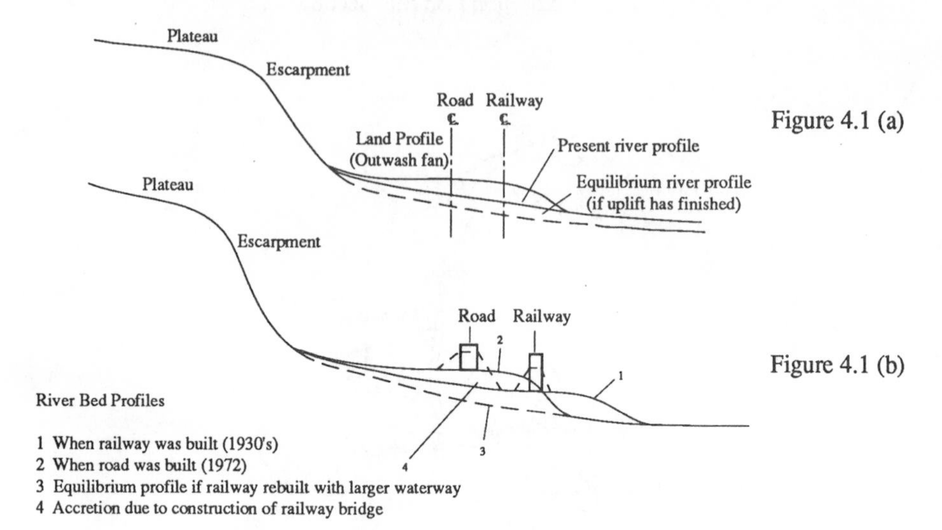

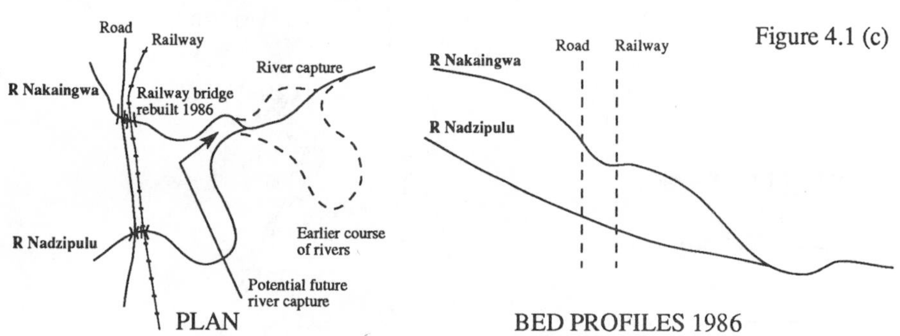

FIGURE 4.1 POSSIBLE CAUSES OF SCOUR PROGRESSING UPSTREAM

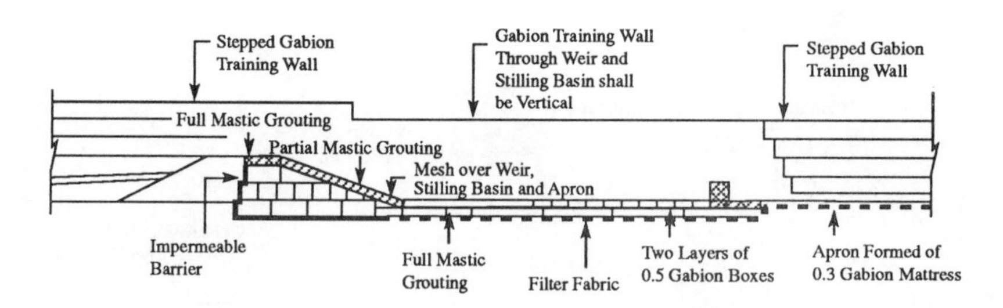

FIGURE 5.1 LONGITUDINAL SECTION THROUGH WEIR AND STILLING BASIN

PAPER N2

International Conference on
RIVER FLOOD HYDRAULICS
17-20 September, 1990

AYLESBURY FLOOD ALLEVIATION STRATEGY AND SCHEME

AUTHORS AND AFFILIATIONS:

G.P.G. Johnson Bsc (Hons) C.Eng. M.I.C.E. M.I.W.E.M.
Projects Manager, National Rivers Authority (Thames Region) U.K.
S.C. Capel-Davies Bsc (Hons) C.Eng. M.I.C.E. M.I.W.E.M.
Principal Engineer, Peter Brett Associates, U.K. (formerly National Rivers Authority (Thames Region) U.K.

ABSTRACT

Aylesbury, a rapidly expanding town, has suffered from flooding at various times in the past. The NRA Thames Region has initiated a study to establish the extent of flooding and to examine ways of alleviating flooding in the future.

The study has centred on a hydraulic mathematical model covering a reach of the River Thame and several of its tributaries draining the town and its environs. The model has been used to produce flood envelopes for a range of events covering existing and foreseeable future development. The preferred strategy is based upon upstream storage, combined with minor works in the town.

The NRA has worked closely with the District Council during the study, and this paper will examine not only the engineering, environmental and economic assessments, but also the problems experienced in promoting a strategy based on upstream storage and the consequential difficulties with change of land use and continuing urban expansion.

INTRODUCTION

Aylesbury, the administrative centre of Buckinghamshire, is situated about sixty-five kilometres north-west of London (Fig.1). The population has doubled since 1960 and continuing expansion is creating pressure on the local river system which in turn has led to an increased risk of flooding.

The town is bounded to the north and west by the River Thame (a tributary of the Thames). The major tributary, the Bear Brook, runs through the town from east to west. It drains a largely rural catchment of about 60 square km, the predominant soils being chalk hills with clay valleys. The brook is also fed by several small tributaries rising close to the town.

Local improvement works have been carried out over the years but have had little effect on major floods which have occurred some six times since 1947, when some 150 properties were directly affected, the most recent event occurring in 1987.

In the early 1980's an investigation had been carried out into the flooding problem using mainly manual techniques for flow analysis. This proved to be a significant limitation bearing in mind the complex mechanism of flooding which takes place.

Several schemes were considered including transferring headwaters into the upstream section of the Thame by enlarged natural channels; a tunnel; upstream flood storage; and enlargement of channels through the town. At that stage, it was considered that no scheme was cost-beneficial and although the tunnel was preferred, it had more recently been discounted on cost and other grounds.

However, Thames Water Rivers Division, the National Rivers Authority-Thames Region's predecessor, had been aware of the growing problem and hence initiated a further detailed study in 1987. The principle aim was to prepare a comprehensive strategic drainage plan for all the watercourses in Aylesbury which would recommend measures to alleviate existing flooding and the problems resulting from foreseeable future developments.

CONSTRAINTS

It had always been a major concern prior to the start of the Study that there were significant drainage constraints restricting expansion and redevelopment of the Town. How could this be adequately addressed within the complicated legislative and administrative framework?

Aylesbury Vale District Council (AVDC) supplied plans indicating likely development upto 1996 from which the effects such as a ring road and areas of likely increased runoff could be assessed.

The town is situated close to the headwaters of the River Thame which itself had been extensively studied in 1982/3. The conclusions were that, although flooding was significant the effect was on agricultural land and any scheme would not be cost-beneficial. Thus any potential solution to the flooding of Aylesbury must not cause significant effects downstream.

In addition to alleviating flooding any resultant engineering work should cause minimum environmental impact and where possible opportunities for enhancement pursued.

Most of the rivers are designated as "main river" for which the NRA has permissive powers to carry out maintenance and improvement works. Some of the smaller watercourses, particularly the Stocklake Brook and some in the town, are not so designated but are covered by similar powers possessed by AVDC. The canal comes under the jurisdiction of the British Waterways Board. This split in powers necessitated close liaison to ensure a workable comprehensive solution for both the present and future drainage circumstances.

STUDY STRUCTURE

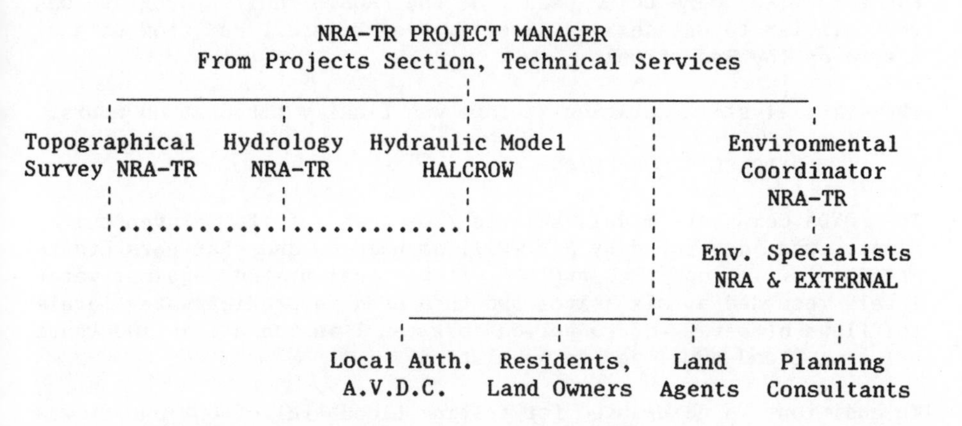

HYDROLOGY

In common with most sites there was little long term useful hydrometric data available and so six water level loggers and three rain gauges were installed. Fortunately (for us anyway) three significant rainfall and corresponding flood events occurred allowing reasonable depth-discharge courses to be established. Other valuable data on the mechanism of flooding and damages was also collected.

The catchment was intially modelled using the UNIHYD and FRQSIM (frequency simulation) programmes initially developed by the Greater London Council for urban catchments in London but upgraded by NRA-TR. It is a sophisticated time-area model which takes into account the degree of urbanisation and the paved percentage of each node area.

The whole catchment was divided into 30 areas and rainfall profiles were calculated using methods outlined in the Flood Studies Report (FSR) the 10.5 hr storm duration being critical. This provided the basis of the input to the hydraulic model either as direct input hydrographs or by producing combined routed inputs from the upstream areas.

For the modelling of the storage ponds storms having durations of 7.5 to 90 hours were examined to establish volume requirements rather than peak flows. However, it was found that as set up the volumes increased as did the peak flows which was not realistic. Examination of the problem revealed that it was caused by a combination of long unit hydrographs used to model the runoff from the large rural catchments combined with the rainfall loss model used in the FRQSIM program for rural areas.

In agreement with the designated Construction Engineer (required as the main storage pond will be covered by The Reservoirs Act), it was agreed to model these areas as closely as possible to FSR methods. Modifications were mainly needed on the loss model since FSR rainfalls were being used and the FRQSIM unit hydrograph was very similar to one derived directly from rainfall and flow data at a site on the Bear Brook.

The critical storm duration storage was finally fixed at 60 hours.

HYDRAULIC MODELLING

The ONDA Computer model, selected because of its proven suitability, was developed by Sir William Halcrow and Partners Ltd to model flow in open channels. It was calibrated against water levels recorded at six sites and then used to predict water levels for flows of seven return periods between 1 in 5 and 1 in 100 years allowing flood envelopes to be plotted.

In addition to being used for testing flood relief options it was also used to test for sensitivity to blockage at structures and modifications resulting from planning applications, it eventually being retained by NRA-TR as part of a catchment planning tool.

Initial boundary limits were set as downstream of Eythrope, on the River Thame and upstream as Broughton Lane on the Bear Brook. The model was complex having over 400 nodes covering 20 km of channel. Small tributaries were either only partially modelled or treated as point inputs, although the depth of detail had to be increased during the study.

Because of heavy weed growth selection of a suitable value for Manning's 'n' was difficult and calibration was based mainly on the event of November 1987, a value of 0.060 being adopted. Two other events were tested, discrepancies being accounted for by differences in vegetation and baseflow.

Flooded areas subsequently generated, covering the various return periods for existing conditions, and were compared with areas known to have flooded in the past. However, for the rarer events e.g. 1 in 50 to 1 in 100 the areas became more predictive.

Having established existing conditions the model was used to predict flooded areas for the 1996 developed state and hence to investigate options for alleviation. It became clear that to alleviate flooding the only viable scheme would consist of providing upstream floodwater storage, combined with the removal or bypassing of bottlenecks, such as occur at old mills and bridges, within the town. Major works within the congested area were discounted, along with the other options on cost, environmental or hydraulic grounds.

Potential sites on the Bear and Stocklake Brooks were identified. The storage capacities were assessed as 90,000 m3 and 10,000 m3 respectively with the outflows being limited to 3 m3/s and 1 m3/s. At this stage in the study, the way forward seemed clear and it only remained to expand the proposals, in particular, the details of storage requirements.

As previously mentioned, the eastward cut off point was originally fixed as Broughton Lane, the area upstream being represented by a single hydrograph. To study the area in greater depth required extending the model, thus needing further survey and hydrology inputs.

Unfortunately, connecting the newly modelled areas onto the original model produced significantly different results with increased storage requirements. These differences had the potential to affect the levels and flooded areas for existing, 1996 development, and post scheme conditions each for seven return periods.

The differences were found to lie in initially interpolating between Ordnance Survey spot levels which turned out to be nearly 1 metre too high and problems with the hydrology. The first problem was resolved by further extensive surveying, the second was tied up to the way 'losses' were represented, as already detailed.

By the time problems had been resolved numerous ONDA runs had been made for the different storm durations/return periods for the various conditions. Fortunately the ONDA model did not need recalibrating and the final enlarged model did not produce significantly different water levels and associated flooded areas.

The final strategy evolved was one of upstream flood storage, at points which would intercept maximum flood flows, combined with limited works within the town such as the removal of bottlenecks at old mills.

ENVIRONMENTAL ASPECTS

For several years efforts have consciously been made to ensure that river works carried out by this Authority and its predecessor have had minimum impact on the environment. With the introduction of further legislation in 1988 this authority introduced certain procedures to formally ensure not only that impact was kept to a minimum but to encourage, where possible, enhancement. It is generally hoped that by close liaison with interested parties potential conflict could be 'designed out' of a scheme and hence avoid the need for preparing full Environmental Statements.

To assist in supplying base data the Berkshire, Buckinghamshire and Oxfordshire Naturalist Trust (B.B.O.N.T.) were employed in 1987 to carry out an ecological survey of the streams. The results indicated six small locally important sites on the north-east fringes of the developed area and also highlighted many areas for possible enhancement.

Assessment was also carried out for the following disciplines:

Agriculture (AVDC)
Amenity (AVDC)
Angling
Aquatic Biology
Archaeology
Fisheries
Geomorphology
Human Impact
Landscape
Planning (AVDC)
Recreation
River Maintenance
Water Quality
Wildlife

Most of the assessment was carried out by NRA-TR's in-house environmental specialists with information supplied by Aylesbury Vale District Council as indicated.

This data proved invaluable in considering and finally proposing the various aspects of a flood relief scheme.

SCHEME FINANCE

Potential benefits were assessed using the methods described in 'The Benefits of Flood Alleviation - a manual of Assessment Technqiues' by Penning-Rowsell and Chatterton, flood levels being as predicted by the ONDA model. Direct damages were also taken for industrial areas which were affected by the 1987 flood.

With a discount rate of 6% and an assumed scheme life of 50 years, the discounted benefits for the 1 in 100 year return period, the adopted optimum level of protection, was estimated at 2.18 million. The estimated cost of the scheme is 0.9 m (1989 prices) giving a substantial benefit/cost ratio of 2.4. In view of this, no allowance was made for intangible benefits.

Although AVDC will be financing sections of the scheme it has been agreed that the NRA will undertake the design on a rechargeable basis. An application will also be made to the Ministry of Agriculture Fisheries and Foods for grant aid with the scheme considered as a whole, although the individual authorities will make separate detailed claims as they attract different rates of grant.

SCHEME PROMOTION

AVDC have powers to carry out improvement works over some of the town's watercourses and as such they have a keen interest and helped finance the study. Additionally, they are the Planning Authority and also a major landowner.

Regular monthly meetings were held to review progress on all fronts of the study. Provisional timetables had been worked out prior to the study but additional impetus was given by flooding which occurred in 1987 creating much local interest.

Occasional newsletters were issued to keep people informed of progress with formal presentations being made to the elected Members of AVDC. Approval of the strategy was sought as one of the storage sites was on non-main river which would incur the Council in expense.

Mention has been made of the Aylesbury Proposed Local Plan which, coincidentally, was in the public consultation stage in 1989/90. In particular the area required for the Bear Brook flood water storage was shown as having development potential if the flooding constraints were to be removed. The plans would not significantly extend the area liable to flood but would increase the depth and duration and with 11 Ha of land at stake there was a potential conflict with future developers.

To give the scheme greater standing it was considered desirable to be able to identify the actual areas required for storage and include this in the Draft Local Plan. Time was short but best estimates were supplied in December 1989 which were approved by AVDC for inclusion in the final amendments to the Draft Plan. The amendments also included a clause which left a way open for a developer to find an alternative scheme providing all requirements of the NRA and AVDC could be satisfied.

With the high cost of development land it was thought that objections and alternatives could well be forthcoming. An option which the NRA considered was to join forces with a developer to promote a joint scheme. This was discounted, however, because of wanting to keep to the original programme and not wanting to be intimately associated with a scheme which may be less than environmentally sensitive. The development of the site would not be straightforward and would probably take several years to progress, there being changes likely to the alignment and size of the proposed ring road which also crosses the site.

Local landowners had been approached and had had the elements of the scheme explained but with the Public Inquiry into the Local Plan due to be held in March 1990 it was considered desirable that the wider public be made fully aware of the NRA scheme and be able to comment on the proposals. Consequently, the decision was taken in late December to hold an exhibition in early February 1990. To produce full details of the scheme including future landscaping and conservation measures required a major input to rapidly coordinate the detailed views representing the various disciplines. There is no doubt that the production of the environmental database in the early stages of the study combined with regular liaison meetings with AVDC greatly eased the process and made the chances of reaching the targets possible.

THE FUTURE

A planning application for the flood storage areas and associated structures will be made as soon after the exhibition as possible but at this stage, January 1990, it is not known how it will be treated by the Members of AVDC because of the possible effect of the Local Public Inquiry.

Although no timetables are able to be published on the outcome of the Inquiry (the time taken to publication being dependent on the Inspector) it is unlikely to be before September 1990. This would make formal adoption of the Local Plan by AVDC unlikely before the end of 1990 which could be the earliest date any application could be considered. Issues of land acquisition, leasing and compensation will also have to be resolved. However, with many Members of AVDC wanting river flood relief in some form and drainage constraints on the town expansion removed, construction had been programmed for commencement in late 1990, and completion in 1992. These targets are still possible as work could start on the less controversial works within the town, however, some of these may well be affected by development proposals, but that is another story.

CONCLUSIONS

River engineering is not only about producing technically and environmentally sound solutions. It is also about producing publicly acceptable schemes that can be economically implemented within the planning framework.

The latter is not static and can not always be predicted. One thing that can be said however, is that development pressures will become intense with the technical, administrative and promotional problems encountered at Aylesbury being rather more typical than exceptional.

ACKNOWLEDGEMENTS

I would like to thank my colleagues in the NRA-Thames Region both former and present, members of staff of Aylesbury Vale District Council, Sir William Halcrow and Partners and Peter Brett Associates who have assisted with this study and scheme promotion.

REFERENCES

National Rivers Authority, Thames Region
'Aylesbury Arterial Drainage Study - Final Report 1990'.

National Rivers Authority, Thames Region,
'Aylesbury Arterial Drainage Study - Technical Annexe No. 1, Hydraulic Modelling Report 1990'.

Aylesbury Vale District Council
'Aylesbury Local Plan - Adoption Draft May 1989'.

Penning Rowsell, E.C. and Chatterton J.B.
'The Benefits of Flood Alleviation - a manual of Assessment Techniques, 1977'.

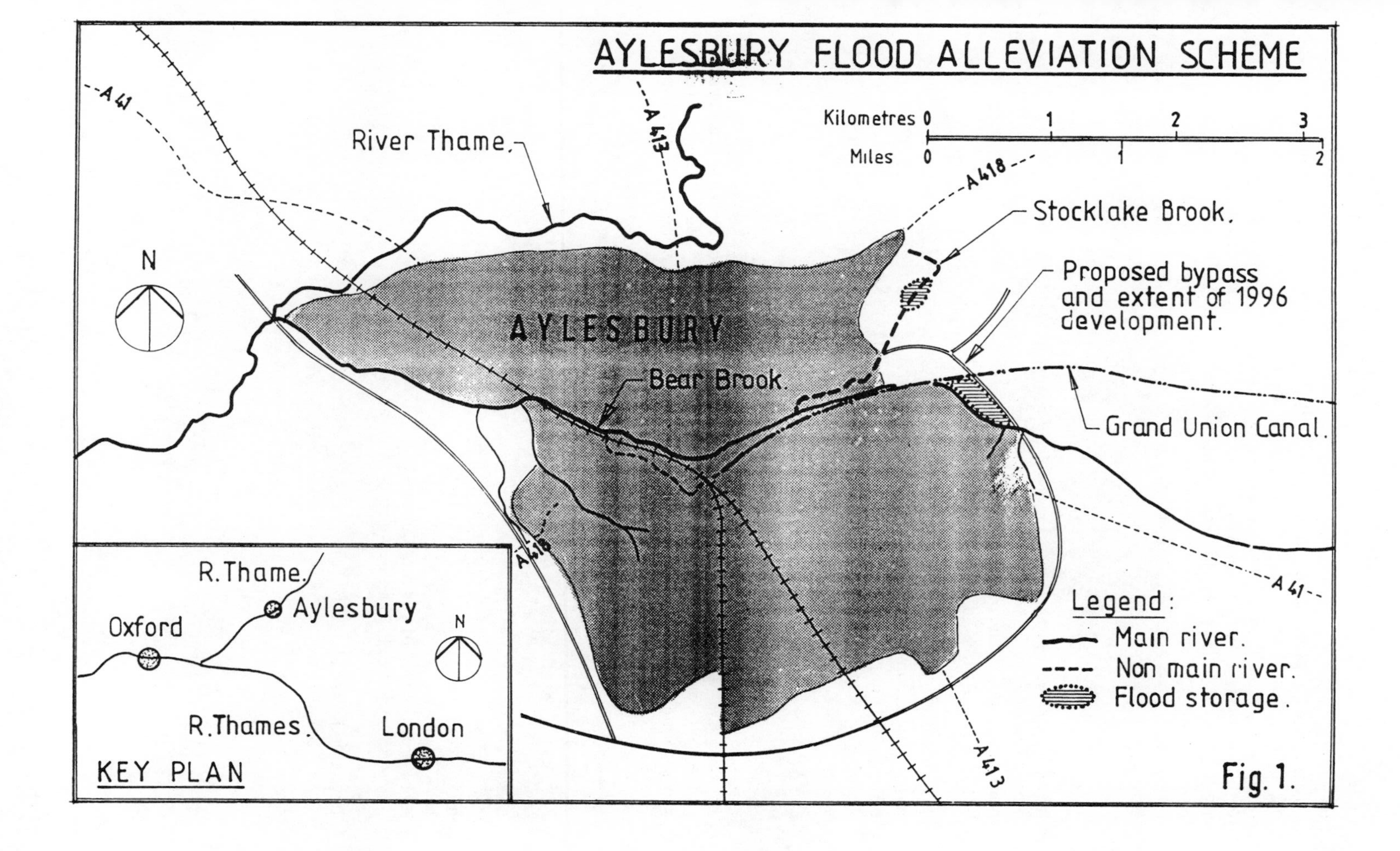

AYLESBURY FLOOD ALLEVIATION SCHEME
Kilometres 0 1 2 3
Miles 0 1 2
River Thame.
A 41
A 413
A 418
Stocklake Brook.
Proposed bypass and extent of 1996 development.
AYLESBURY
Bear Brook.
Grand Union Canal.
N
Legend:
Main river.
Non main river.
Flood storage.
R.Thame.
Aylesbury
Oxford
N
R.Thames.
London
KEY PLAN

Fig. 1.

PAPER N3

International Conference on
RIVER FLOOD HYDRAULICS
17-20 September, 1990

THE VAL POLA (ITALY) ROCKSLIDE: MANAGEMENT PROBLEMS OF HYDRAULIC EMERGENCY

U. Maione
Istituto di Idraulica, Politecnico di Milano
Piazza Leonardo da Vinci, 32
20133 Milano - Italy

ABSTRACT

On July 28th 1987, early in the morning, falling from a mountain located in a valley of Northern Italy (Alta Valtellina), a big mass of rock destroyed two villages, causing the death of several people.
The slide dammed the Adda river creating upstream a lake.
The paper describes the procedures adopted in facing this emergency.

INTRODUCTION

On July 28th 1987, after a long period of heavy rains and a severe inundation of the entire Valtellina, Northern Italy (Fig.1), a rockslide fell down from the Val Pola into the Adda river valley. The slide dammed the course of the Adda river creating behind an impoundment with a potential capacity of about $20 \cdot 10^6$ m^3. Two villages were destroyed and 27 people died. The rockslide occurred in a highly populated Alpine region with villages located in the plain close to the Adda river.

CHARACTERISTICS OF THE NATURAL DAM AND PROBLEMS RELATED WITH THE PRESENCE OF THE LAKE

The rock avalanche (Fig.2)($40 \cdot 10^6$ m^3) fell down from a 1200 m. height above the valley level (Fig.3) creating a dam of loose rock about 90 m high and 3000 m long.
Debris spread out in a heterogeneous way: from place to place materials such as fine debris and mud as well as coarse blocks of big dimension were found. The largest impounding volume upstream the dam, before the top was artificially lowered as described in the following, was about $20 \cdot 10^6$ m^3.
The catchment area upstream the slide location was 538 km^2 wide, 38 km^2 of which directly draining to the artificial dams of Cancano and S. Giacomo and 440 km^2 collected by hydroelectric diversion channels placed along the Adda river and its tributaries (Fig.4).
Glaciers in the basin are 40 Km^2 wide.
Large portions of the Adda catchment were involved in existing and potential landsliding phenomena.
The estimated flood discharge at the landslide dam section, for a

International Conference on River Flood Hydraulics, edited by W.R.White

100 years return period, is about 400 m^3/s.

These few data clearly point out the risks connected with this situation the main of which are:
- dam failure and consequent flood inundation of the downstream valley area;
- splashing of additional landslides into the lake, when filled, producing a wave similar to that occurred in the Vajont tragedy.

The day after the accident, a special Commission formed by the Civil Protection decided the following emergency program:
- emptying of the lake by means of a pump station; the plant had to be built in no more than 50/60 days in order to avoid the filling of the lake by the water incoming from the Adda river, even if in normal condition;
- construction of a by-pass tunnel before the following rainy season (from April to November);
- stabilization of the downstream face of the natural dam in order to avoid failure in case of overtopping;
- monitoring of the highly instable zones in the scar head of the landslide and in the surrounding areas. This measure was considered fundamental in order to foresee other landslide falls and consequently to allow working on the dam in security conditions;
- rainfall and flow monitoring in the upstream catchment for real time flood forecasting.

In the same days a scientific collaboration was started with C.R.I.S. and I.S.M.E.S. (Research Centers of the National Organization for Electric Energy) in order to perform physical modelling and monitoring.

LAKE EMPTYING

On the basis of the available historical data the average discharge flowing into the lake, during dry weather from August to November, was estimated in 1-2 m^3/s. Only the 62 km^2 basin immediately upstream the dam conveyed the water directly into the lake; the other portions of the catchment were drained by a network of artificial channels and by-passed the dam site in a tunnel placed into the right abutment, reaching an hydroelectric power plant (Fig.4).
Then it was decided to build a pumping station with design discharge of 6 m^3/s, enough for emptying the lake in 46 days, provided that no floods occurred in that period.

During the plant building it was realized that the inflow never fell below 6-7 m^3/s, probably due to the saturation of the soil after the heavy rains of the previous July (250 mm from July 15th to 22th). Therefore it was decided to add a second pumping plant with a 3 m^3/s discharge capacity and, subsequently, a third one of 6 m^3/s.

The last plant conveyed the waters to the a.m. existing hydroelectric tunnel up to its maximum capacity, taking advantage of an existing window in the neighbouring of the lake (Fig.5).
On September 19th the first pumping station was ended and two days later it started working, even if at a reduced rate. The second plant was finished on September 17th, the third one on September 28th (Fig.5). The emptying of the lake was completed on October 27th (Fig.6) but, before this date, two significant floods occurred requiring the management of the emergency situation.

CONTROLLED OVERTOPPING

As previously mentioned, one of the first objectives of the emergency management was to avoid an overtopping of the dam. It was clear in everybody's mind the recent tragedy of Mayun Marca landslide (Mantaro river, Peru') where, under analogous circumstances, the dam collapsed after the overtopping and produced a tremendous flood wave downstream. Also a literature review (Schuster, 1986) showed that in many cases the overtopping had provoked the failure of the natural dam.
The risks connected to the overtopping are so high that all the Countries have very strict rules and regulations on the matter of planning and building spillways on the abutments of dams in coarse materials, just in order to avoid the overtopping, which is never admitted.

Studies carried on during that weeks by means of dam-erosion and flood-propagation mathematical models at C.R.I.S. (Bertacchi et al, 1988) confirmed such hazard. Results of mathematical simulation showed that a peak discharge of about 1600 m^3/s (4-5 times bigger than that occurred on July 1987, which had already caused so many damages in the same area) have to be expected immediately downstream the dam, in case of overflow and subsequent fast erosion of the top.

On August 19th, results obtained by means of a physical model built in only twenty days by C.R.I.S. confirmed substantially those of the mathematical model. In fact, even with a small overflow discharge, the physical model showed that the overtopping of the dam would give rise to an erosional process, at first slow and afterward fast, with a peak flood discharge of about 1400-1500 m^3/s. But the model showed also that the lowering of the top height of about 8-10 m (from 1108 to 1100-1098 m above s.l.) would lead to a very significant reduction of the peak discharge from 1400-1500 m^3/s to 150 m^3/s (Fig.7). This result has to be related to the peculiar shape of the top of the blockage, something like a trapezoidal heap about 10 m high and 100 m long in the valley direction (Fig.8). About 10^7 m^3 of water could be retained upstream. Moreover, the compound of this natural ridge made it very weak to the erosional and mechanical stresses so that it would be worn away quickly during overflow; the fast emptying of the lake would then give rise to a peak discharge of just 1400-1500 m^3/s.

Below this ridge, about 1096-1098 m above s.l., the dam body enlarged in the direction of the valley (Fig.8), making it much more resistant to the erosional process. Therefore, by lowering the top, the erosion would be gradual and the maximum peak discharge would be reduced up to about 150 m^3/s.

The experiments on the physical model were just finished when a big flood occurred on August 24th. The flood volume coming into the lake was about $4.5 \cdot 10^6$ m^3 with a peak discharge of 175 m^3/s. The rate of growing of the water level in the lake rose up to 1 m/h, suggesting the immediate evacuation of the 30,000 people living in the downstream villages. At the end of the flood the water level in the lake reached 1098 m above s.l.

On the basis of the results obtained by means of the physical and mathematical models, being by that time impossible to avoid the filling of the lake, it was decided to dig a channel through the body of the dam, with bottom intake at 1098-1100 m above s.l.
Furthermore, it was decided to anticipate the natural overtopping by means of the inflow of a 40 m^3/s constant discharge, coming from that normally diverted by the hydroelectric channels (Fig.4). The main aim of this measure was to increase the erosional capacity of the discharge, too weak in normal flow conditions, in order to model in a controlled way the channel, lowering the intake height and preparing the bed to heavier flow conditions.
On August 24th it was started to build a channel across the landslide dam. At the day of the overtopping the channel was about 300 m long and 10 m wide, with a bed slope of 1%. The intake bottom was 8 m lower than the original ridge height, with a reduction of the potential impoundment behind the blockage of 10^7 m^3.
On August 29th it was started to fill the lake with the increased discharges. The overtopping started at 9:00 a.m. on August 30th. At 3:00 a.m. on August 31st, about a month after the rockslide occurrence, the Adda river started flowing again. The inflow of water from the hydroelectric diversions was stopped a little later.
It was noticed that the water had moderately eroded the intake of the channel. On the contrary, in the downstream edge the channel was significantly lowered (5-6 meters). On the basis of this experience, the maximum discharge allowed to flow through the dam without any damage was estimated in 100 m^3/s or more.
The discharge coming into the lake never fell below 6-7 m^3/s until, on 26th September, another flood occurs in the upstream catchment. The discharge at the lake, just filled, rose up to 120 m^3/s but no problems were noticed in the landslide stability; the water in the outlet channel flowed regularly without any other significant erosion.

The flood evolution was continuously monitored in real time by means of the information coming from some rain-gauges placed inside the catchment and two recorders measuring water levels in the lake and in the downstream channel. All the information was

sent to a central office located in S. Bartolomeo (Fig.4) just in front of the slide site. Here it was collected and processed by means of a real-time hydrological model in order to forecast the discharges expected two-three hours later into the lake (Brath et al., 1988).
This procedure made possible to avoid a further evacuation of about 30,000 people living in the downstream villages.

DIVERSION WORKS OF THE ADDA RIVER

The emergency program included the construction of a by-pass tunnel, to be built in the first months of 1988 on the left bedrock abutment (Fig.5), in order to drive away from the lake the floods during the rainy period (Spring and Summer). During this seasons the expected discharges were, in fact, very much greater than those conveyable by the pump stations, in spite of the hydroelectric diversions.

The tunnel solution was preferred to a channel through the natural dam since the risk of new landslides falling into the lake advised against keeping high the water level. The same reason, as previously mentioned, had suggested, in the first days of the emergency, to completely empty the lake, as faster as possible, by means of pumping stations.

Problems related to the practical construction of the diversion led to the excavation of two tunnels, one of 4.20 m and the other of 6.00 m diameter, with a total conveyance of 350-400 m^3/s. This value corresponds to an almost 100 years return period discharge at the dam site. Such design discharge was regarded of high safety considering:

a) the storage available into the emptied lake and the routing of the flood wave above the intake level; that means, with the same discharge as outlet, a return period of the incoming discharge higher than 100 year;
b) the temporary nature of the diversion so that an event of such a return period has a low probability to realize during the operation time. This period was estimated long enough to allow the final arrangement of the landslide area, i.e. 5-10 years at most.

Anyway, to ensure a better degree of security, the channel on the body of the natural dam was enlarged and lowered to convey about 250 m^3/s. On the right side an earth embankment was raised, in order to shelter the channel from the debris flows coming, continuously, from the scar head of the slide.

STABILIZATION OF THE DOWNSTREAM FACE OF THE NATURAL DAM

Besides the construction of the channel and of the tunnels, the stabilization of the downstream face of the natural dam was performed to ensure a good resistance even in the case of high spilling discharges.
A series of check dams, placed at the end of the downstream face

of the blockage (Fig.5), were designed to hold the earth thrust and the erosion effects of the high velocity outlet flows. The central part of the check dams is shaped to allow the continuity of the outlet spillway channel.

CONCLUSIONS

The paper describes the solutions adopted in facing the very serious hydrogeological emergency which took place in August-September 1987, after the falling of a big rockslide in Valtellina (Northern Italy) and the damming of the Adda river.

It must be stressed the fundamental contribution given by many researchers from Universities and public bodies (C.R.I.S. and I.S.M.E.S. mainly), which I want to warmly thank once again. The definition and the execution, in very few weeks, of a scientific research program allowed the Commission to choose the emergency measures in the best way.

In particular I refer to the fundamental results given by the mathematical and physical models of the dam collapse, the generation and routing of the downstream dam-break wave, the impact of a landslide fall in the lake, the seepage through the dam, all realized in very short time by C.R.I.S.. Very useful were also the studies on probability distribution of the flood events in Valtellina and the flood forecasting models carried out by the researchers of the Institute of Hydraulics of the Polytechnic of Milan.

The soil mechanics measurement program on the natural dam, on the scar head of the slide and the model of the rock fall, all conducted by I.S.M.E.S., were another essential contribution to the settlement of the interventions.

REFERENCES

Bertacchi P., M. Fanelli and U. Maione, An overall approach to the emergency hydraulic problems arisen from the natural dam and lake formed by the Val Pola rock-slide, XVI Congress CIGB-ICOLD, S. Francisco, 1988.

Brath A., M. Mancini, P. Mignosa and M. G. Tanda, Curve segnalatrici di rischio idrologico, XXI Congress of Hydraulics and Hydraulic Construction, L'Aquila, 1988.

Maione U, L'emergenza in val di Pola, Politecnico, Vol.1, N.4, December 1988.

Schuster R. L., Landslide dams: processes, risk and mitigation, Geotechnical Special Publication N.3, ASCE, Robert L. Schuster Ed., 1986.

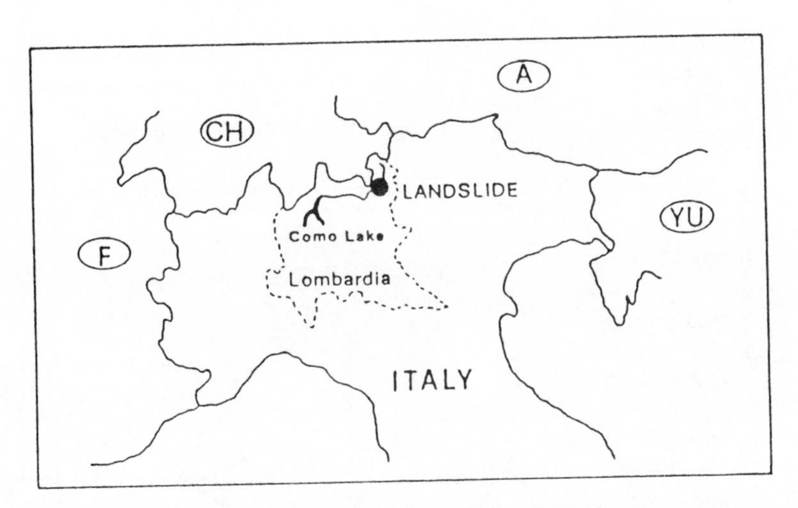

Fig.1 Location of the landslide.

Fig.2 View of the rockslide (one month after its occurrence).

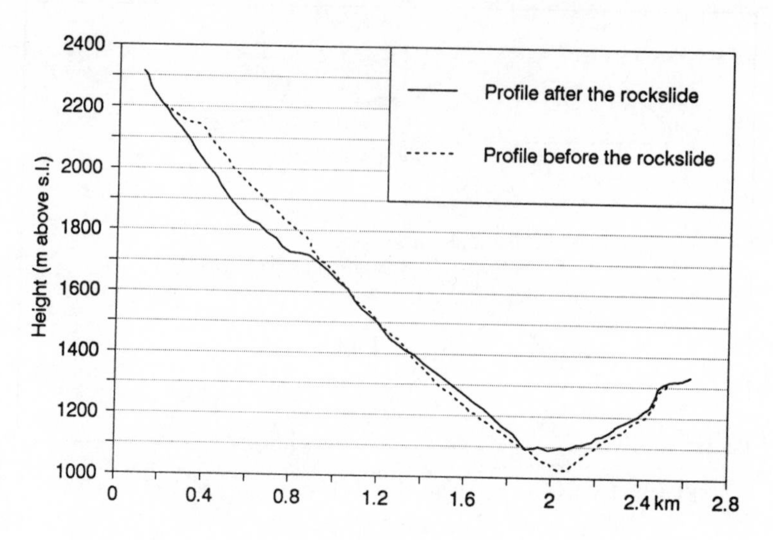

Fig.3 Cross section of the valley before and after the rockslide occurrence.

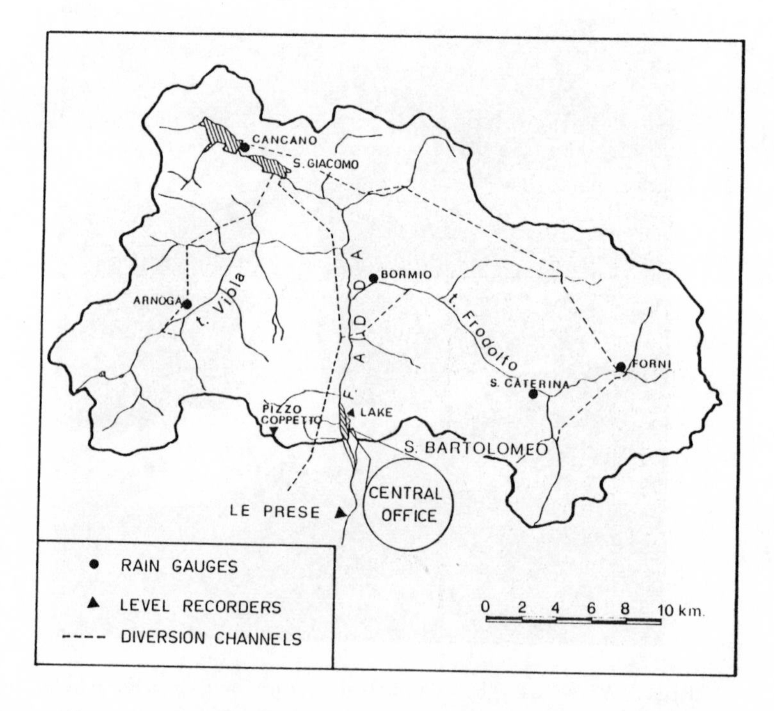

Fig.4 Characteristics of the upstream catchment, with the diversion channels and the instrumentation set up.

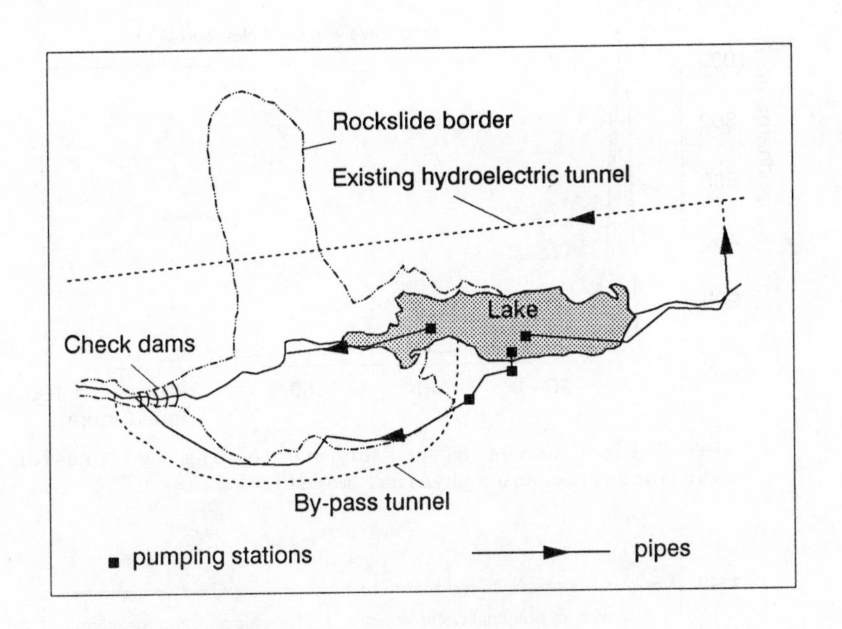

Fig.5 Pumping plants, diversion tunnel and stabilization works in the landslide location.

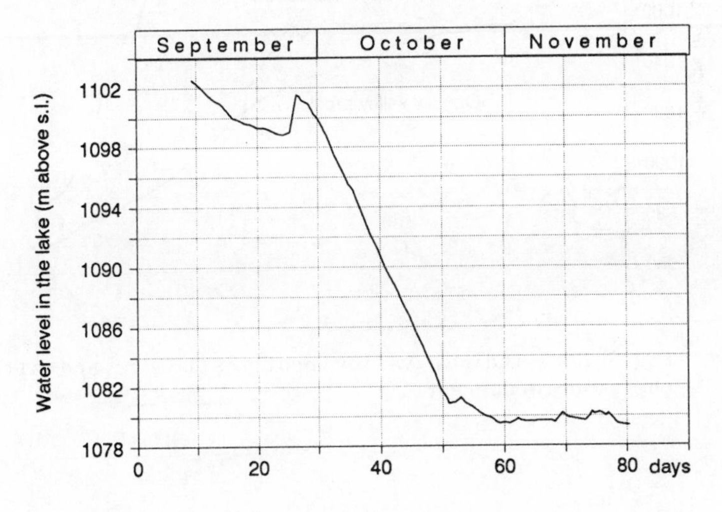

Fig.6 Water level history in the lake from September 9th to November 20th.

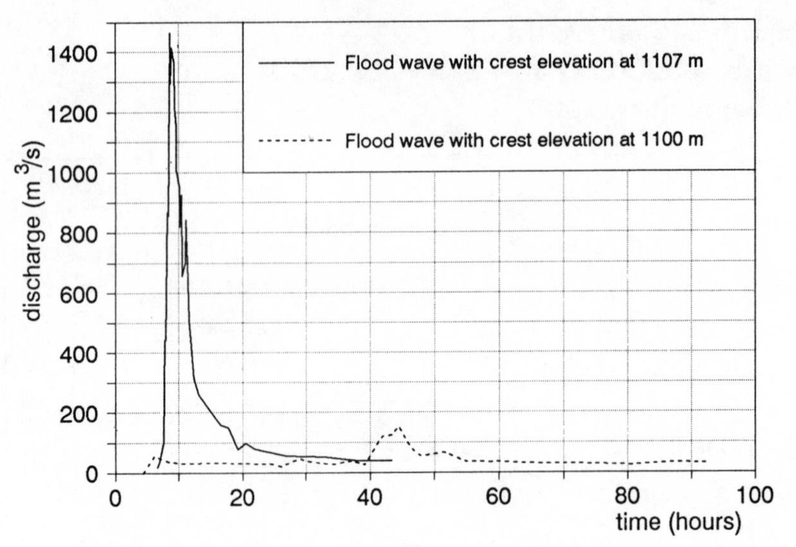

Fig.7 Flood waves after the overtopping and erosion of the landslide dam (physical model).

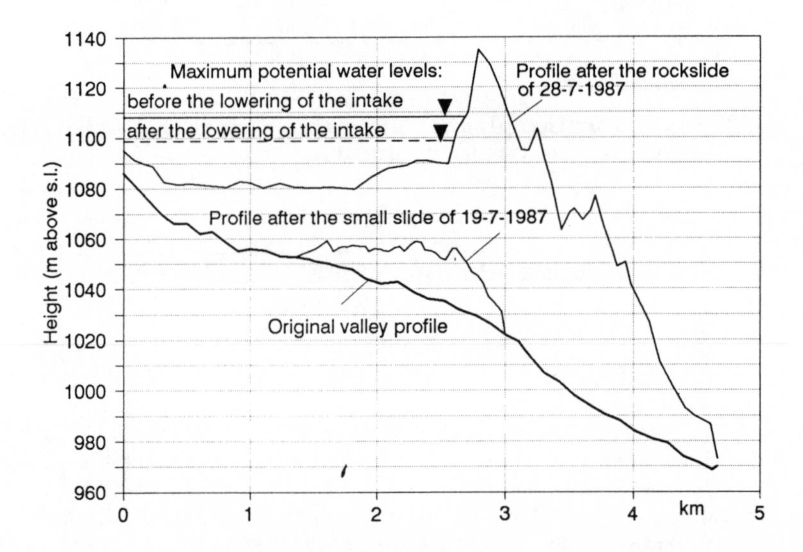

Fig.8 Longitudinal valley profiles before and after the rockslide occurrence.

PAPER N4

International Conference on
RIVER FLOOD HYDRAULICS
17-20 September, 1990

VILLAGE FLOOD PROTECTION IN HONG KONG - A CASE STUDY

J.M.Bartlett, Senior Hydraulics Engineer, Binnie & Partners
N.R.Townsend, Chief Engineer, Binnie Consultants Ltd
(formerly Binnie & Partners (Hong Kong))

SUMMARY

Development pressures in the North West New Territories of Hong Kong have resulted in the deterioration of the main drainage networks, resulting in frequent flooding of historic villages. Five catchment computer models have been constructed, taking into account both fluvial flooding and extreme sea levels from typhoon surges. Results from the models have provided design flood levels in the villages and a programme of flood protection measures has been drawn up.

INTRODUCTION

The North West New Territories of Hong Kong (NWNT) belie the popular image of mountainous, urban Hong Kong. Much of the area is surprisingly low-lying and was, until recent years, rural in character. Figure 1 shows the location of the area. There are five main catchments within the area ranging in size from 5 to 40 km^2. The topography is similar for all catchments, with a low-lying coastal strip, an extremely flat fluvial flood plain extending inland and a ring of steep hills at the head of the catchment.

The natural deterioration of drainage in the area has been accelerated by man's influence. Change in land use from agriculture to formal or informal developments has resulted in the loss of flood storage and increased flooding in the historic established villages. In 1988, Binnie & Partners (Hong Kong) were commissioned by the Hong Kong Government Territory Development Department to examine the flooding problems in the 204 established villages in the NWNT, and to propose the most economical, socially acceptable, means of providing protection to the flood prone villages.

In order to examine flooding in the villages, it was necessary to consider the flood hydraulics catchment-wide, and catchment computer models were therefore constructed. For the low-lying coastal areas, there was the particular problem of analyzing the combined probability of fluvial floods and extreme sea levels due to typhoon surges. A method was used that made allowance for a degree of dependency between rainfall and typhoon surge. The analyses carried

International Conference on River Flood Hydraulics, edited by W.R.White

out enabled broad drainage strategies to be drawn up for the NWNT, and outline designs to be produced for individual village flood protection schemes.

REASONS FOR FLOODING IN THE NWNT

The land use within the low-lying areas of the NWNT has changed radically over the last 40 years. Immediately post-war, these areas were mainly paddy, fringed by mangrove swamps. Most established villages lay inland, at an elevation such as to avoid inundation from all but the most severe fluvial flood or typhoon surge.

During the 1960's and 70's cultivation declined in the study area, and much of the paddy and marshland was bunded to form more profitable fish ponds. This reduced the areas of flood storage available. During the 1980's extensive planned urban development has occurred and continues in the new towns of Yuen Long and Tin Shui Wai. There has also been an unplanned growth of semi-urban areas. Many fish ponds have now been filled to form storage yards. The resulting loss of flood storage and increase in run-off quantities has resulted in increased flooding in the established villages in the NWNT. Some of these villages flood to some extent with any significant rainfall. One village investigated during the study flooded through the village latrine during every higher than normal tide.

A consequential but important factor brought about by the changes in land use, is the resulting reduction in maintenance of the watercourses. With the decline of irrigation requirements, the perceived need for maintenance has also declined. Some watercourses have even been blocked by casual filling of land for use for storage. Many of these watercourses are in private ownership and attempts by Government Departments to gain access for maintenance are often thwarted by the occupiers requests for compensation.

Natural deterioration of the river networks of the NWNT, is also evidenced by the siltation of Deep Bay and the gradual advance of the foreshore. However, this effect is small compared with man's influence, due to the changes in land use and lack of maintenance of watercourses described above.

ANALYTICAL TOOLS FOR CATCHMENT MODELLING

A review of hydrological and hydraulic software was carried out to determine the most appropriate computer models for use in the NWNT. Previous Binnie & Partners studies in the area had used the unit hydrograph method for catchment floods and their in-house transient flow 1-D hydraulic model STIDE for hydraulic analysis.

For the present study, the choice of hydrological software was the

RORB program (Mein et al. 1974), extensively used in Australia, and with growing application outside. RORB is an interactive, single event, streamflow routing model, that is extremely user friendly when mounted on an IBM-PC compatible computer. It is easy to adjust catchment characteristics within the model to represent changes in development or drainage.

Within RORB, rainfall is operated on by a loss model to produce rainfall-excess. The rainfall-excess is operated on by a catchment storage model representing the effects of overland flow storage and channel storage to produce the surface runoff hydrograph. The program is general and may be used for any stream network. Runoff routing omits the concept of a standard catchment response to a given input. It estimates the hydrograph directly by routing the rainfall-excess through a conceptual model of the catchment storage, modelled by a series of concentrated non-linear storages, with the relationship:

$$S = Kd_iQ^m$$

where K and m are catchment parameters determined by trial and error fitting, d_i is the relative delay time of a storage based on topographic properties and Q is the outflow discharge. Empirical expressions have been developed for K and m for ungauged catchments. These expressions, developed under Australian conditions, were found to offer good calibration for the NWNT catchments modelled.

The hydraulic model used was the Binnie & Partners in-house FWAVE model, a quasi 2-dimensional version of the STIDE program already used successfully in the NWNT. It uses Priesmann's solution of the St Venant unsteady flow equations within a simply connected tree channel network. Flood blocks and reaches of blocks can be modelled with interconnecting channels or levees. Hydraulic structures are included within the program, and optional subroutines have been written for applications including barrages, tidal power, and water quality.

Five catchment models were constructed, using the RORB model for the upland areas, and the FWAVE model for the tidally influenced downstream areas. Two of the catchment RORB models were calibrated for three historic flood events against recorded rainfall and flow data at three flow gauging stations. One of the hydraulic FWAVE models was calibrated against recorded flood levels through a major event. In all cases good calibrations were achieved, that allowed transfer of the calibration parameters to the models for adjacent catchments. A typical RORB calibration is shown in Figure 2.

COMBINED PROBABILITY

The sub-tropical climate of Hong Kong gives intense rainstorms and hence large volumes of run-off. The low-lying coastal areas of the NWNT are also influenced by typhoons, with tidal surges being produced by the associated high wind and low atmospheric pressures. When these combine in tidal watercourses, the flood levels are raised well above the levels caused by rain or surge alone. A combined probability method was therefore required to analyze flooding in the study ares catchments.

The method used was based on the matrix method developed by Binnie & Partners for use in the design of flood defences of the River Ancholme, UK (Thompson & Law, 1983). The catchment models constructed allowed peak flood levels to be determined for a given combination of rainfall and tidal conditions of known probability. For any one layout a probability matrix can be drawn for each location. On this matrix the peak flood level reached can be plotted against the probability of rainfall being exceeded, as shown in Figure 3. This is presented as statistical probability rather than the more usual return period, using a logarithmic scale to obtain a sufficiently accurate result for high, rare floods. It is unnecessary to carry out every possible computer simulation to define flood levels throughout the matrix, attention being concentrated where the critical levels occur.

The above method assumes that sea levels and rainstorm events are sufficiently independent for any connection between the natural processes causing them to be ignored. In Hong Kong, however, there is correlation between extreme sea level and rainfall during typhoons. During this and earlier Binnie & Partners studies, the correlation was investigated in detail, but work was limited by the relative rarity of major typhoon events. An attempt was made to produce two sets of rainfall events from the total set of rainfall data available in Hong Kong. One would only be associated with normal tide levels. The second set would be of typhoon events that would always have an associated extreme sea level; the magnitude of surge and rainfall would, however, be independent. This task was, however, not completed due to the difficulty of defining a typhoon event. Heywood (1950) makes no definition. Kwong Woon-Pui (1974) arbitrarily defines it as the rainfall amount recorded at the Hong Kong Royal Observatory from the first day a typhoon enters within 300 nautical miles of Hong Kong, until three days after it leaves the area. Binnie & Partners earlier studies arbitrarily defined it as rainfall in the 12 hours before and after the peak surge level. It was reluctantly concluded that the available information offered no definitive information for the division of Hong Kong rainfall into two sets, and that such a division would require a complete re-analysis of the Hong Kong rainfall records.

All sources did, however, give clear qualitative information on the nature of typhoon rainfall. The most extreme rainfalls come from short duration convective thunderstorms. Typhoon rainfalls are lower than non-cyclonic rainfalls for all durations and return periods. Typhoon rainfalls often coincide with, or are close to, peak sea levels caused by surge. Recent Japanese papers by Michio Hashino (1985) give supporting evidence to these conclusions.

For the present study, the dependency between rainfall and sea level was incorporated by an empirical method. By comparing historic typhoon events with equivalent independent events for the period of typhoon record, it was found that extreme water levels occurred more often than indicated by independent events analysis. This offset of the historic event line is shown in Figure 4. The dependency factor varies as one moves inland in the drainage system. Obviously the factor is zero at the river outfall, with complete dependency on sea level. Towards the limit of tidal influence, the dependency factor again returns to zero, levels being solely dependent on fluvial floods. However, for much of the tidal area the factor was found to be close to 1.5. This value was found to hold for a number of Hong Kong catchments and for a range of drainage improvement options within that catchment, and thus could be used as a factor on the independent analysis frequencies for design purposes. Typical results of the analysis, comparing matrix results with those from a fluvial flood are shown in Figure 5. The use of this matrix method meant that the limited historic typhoon data for the NWNT could be supplemented by the much longer rainfall and water level records available for Hong Kong.

FLOOD PROTECTION METHODS

The study Brief required that a comprehensive review was made of both structural and non-structural flood mitigation measures. In the past, such measures in Hong Kong have always been structural in nature, typically involving channel improvements, levees and bunded flood pumping schemes. The review considered a wider range of options, especially non-structural measures such as development controls and the designation and preservation of flood plain areas.

Within Hong Kong, only limited legislation presently exists to control development in rural areas such as the NWNT. In particular, the Government is unable to prevent the filling and raising of the flood plain, and has limited powers to ensure the maintenance of watercourses. Although there are moves to impose more stringent development controls, much damage to the flood plain in terms of loss of flood storage and encroachment into streams has already occurred. It was therefore concluded that the traditional structural measures offered the only viable means of flood mitigation. Further, the extremely high value of land in Hong Kong makes any options which require a large land take economically unattractive. These factors made flood storage options, where washlands are preserved as low-grade agricultural land or playing fields, extremely expensive to implement. New or improved catchment drainage channels therefore proved the only viable approach to flood mitigation.

OUTLINE SCHEMES

Outline flood mitigation schemes were proposed for all villages with an identified flooding problem. These schemes included recommendations for improvements to the main catchment drainage channels (outside the scope of the study, but essential to improve the drainage of the area) local drainage network improvements, and for some villages bunded and pumped flood defences. A typical scheme is shown in Figure 6.

Simple cost benefit analyses, based on the cost per regularly flooded household, were used to establish the most economic scheme for each village and to draw up a programme for the improvements. Improvements have already been implemented as part of other on-going projects. It became apparent that costs of schemes often far exceeded the direct benefits to the inhabitants of the villages. The need for most of the schemes has arisen because of land use changes in the catchments. The benefits of these changes should therefore be reflected in the analyses if a cost benefit approach is going to be used to determine whether or not to proceed with a scheme.

CONCLUSIONS

This paper illustrates a practical application of river flood hydraulics for flood mitigation work in tidal areas. The use of combined probability methods offers increased confidence in predicting flood levels in such areas. This paper also highlights the problem of such analyses where sea level and rainfall are not truly independent. An empirical approach to such an analysis has been presented, but there remains room for development of a more rigorous method of assessing the correlation between rainfall and typhoon surges.

The flood mitigation solutions adopted illustrate the fact that a high demand for land, and limited development controls, restrict the choice of solution to structural measures, rather than a flood plain management approach. In assessing such measures, cost benefit analysis must be used with care, not as a final arbiter of schemes, but as a method of ranking their priority.

ACKNOWLEDGEMENTS

The authors are grateful to the Hong Kong Government Territory Development Department for their permission to present this paper.

REFERENCES

G.S.P.Heywood, 1950. Hong Kong Typhoons. Royal Observatory Technical Memoir No. 3.

Kwong Woon-Pui, 1974. Tropical Cyclone Rainfall in Hong Kong. Royal Observatory Technical Note No. 3.

R.G.Mein, E.M.Laurenson & T.A.McMahon, 1974. Simple Non-Linear Model for Flood Estimation. ASCE Journal of the Hydraulics Div., Vol 100.

Michio Hashino, 1985. Formulation of the Joint Return Period of Two Hydrologic Variate associated with a Poisson Process. Journal of Hydroscience and Hydraulic Engineering, Volume 3, No. 2.

Michio Hashino, 1985. Characteristics of Concurrence of Rainfall, Flood and Storm Surge associated with Typhoon. Journal of Hydroscience and Hydraulic Engineering, Volume 3, No. 2.

G.Thompson & F.M.Law, 1983. An Assessment of the Fluvial Tidal Flooding Problem of the River Ancholme, UK. IUGG Symposium on Assessment of Natural Hazards, Hamburg.

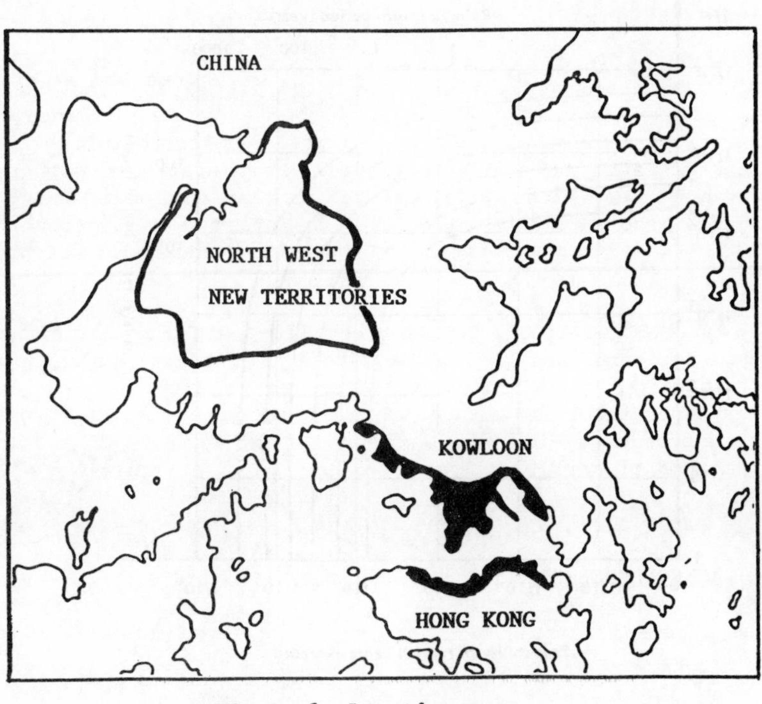

Figure 1: Location map

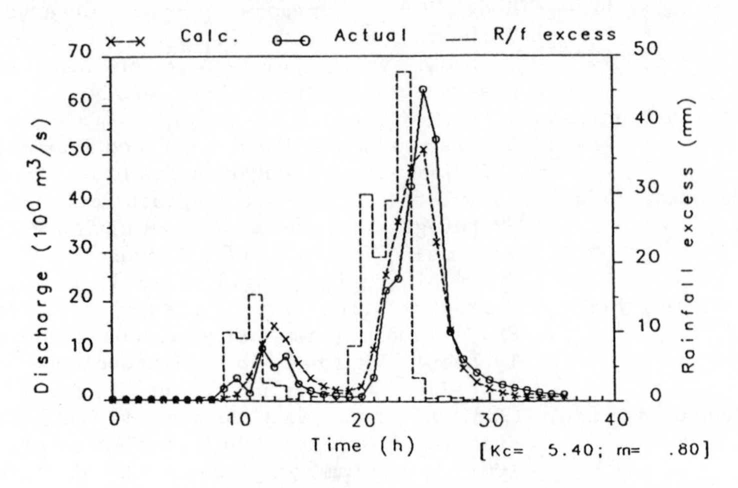

Figure 2: Typical RORB model calibration

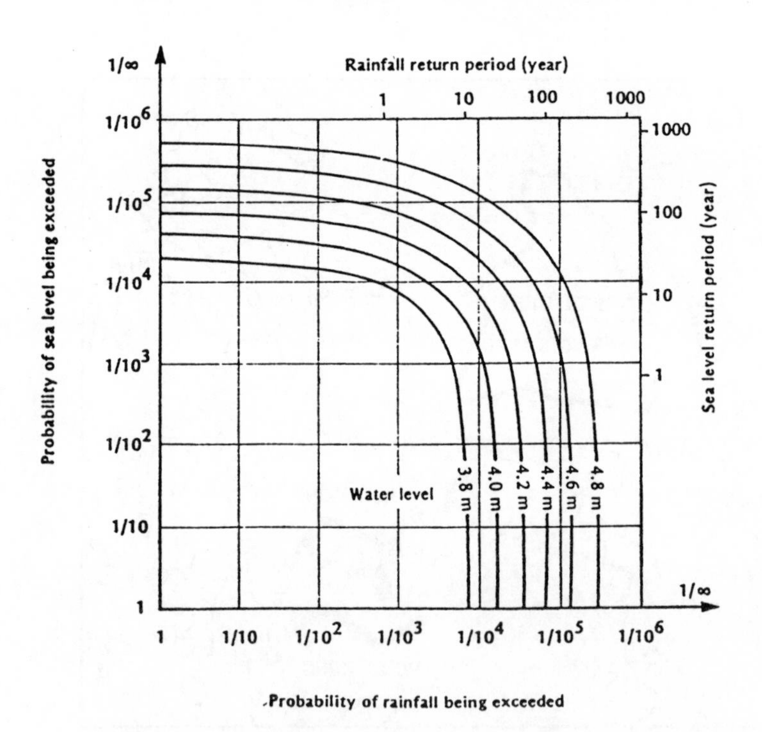

Figure 3: Flood level matrix

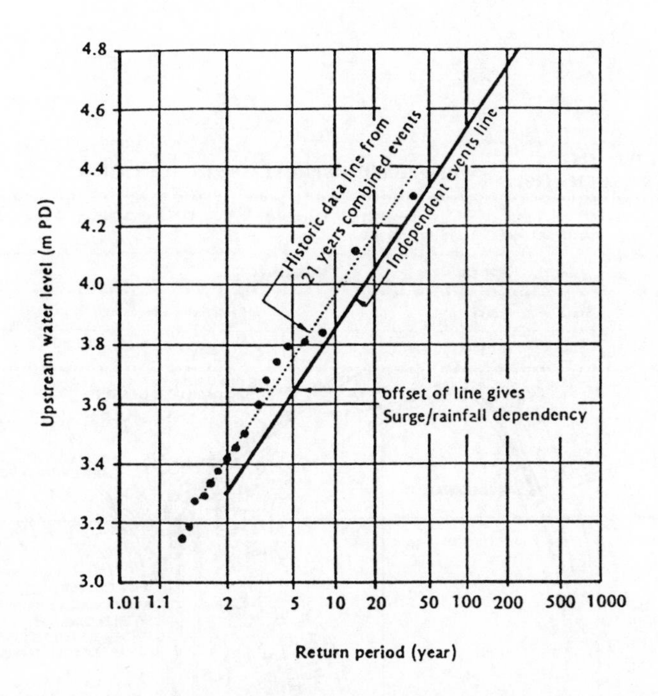

Figure 4: Calculation of dependency factor

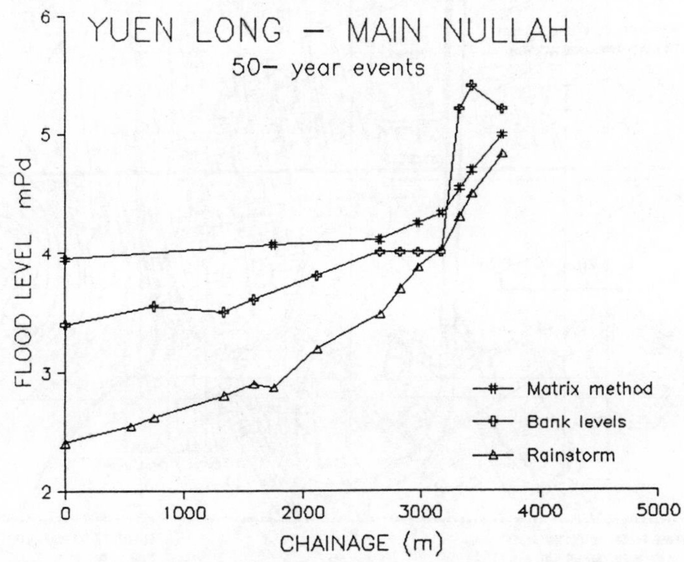

Figure 5: Typical model results, comparing fluvial flood and dependent combined probability water levels

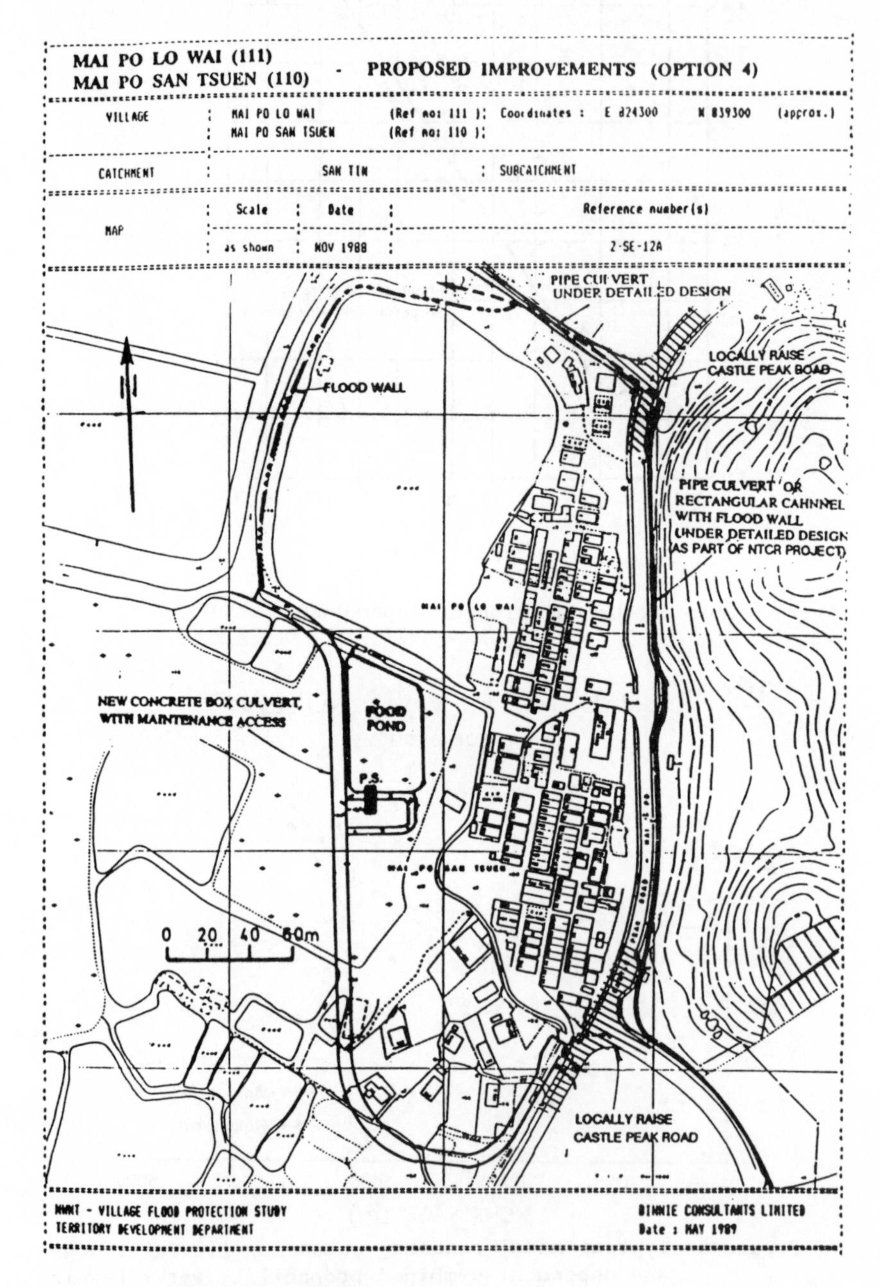
MAI PO LO WAI (111)
MAI PO SAN TSUEN (110)
- PROPOSED IMPROVEMENTS (OPTION 4)
VILLAGE
MAI PO LO WAI
(Ref no: 111)
MAI PO SAN TSUEN
(Ref no: 110)
Coordinates : E 824300 N 839300 (approx.)
CATCHMENT
SAN TIN
SUBCATCHMENT
MAP
Scale
Date
Reference number(s)
as shown
NOV 1988
2-SE-12A
PIPE CULVERT
UNDER DETAILED DESIGN
LOCALLY RAISE
CASTLE PEAK ROAD
FLOOD WALL
PIPE CULVERT OR
RECTANGULAR CAHNNEL
WITH FLOOD WALL
UNDER DETAILED DESIGN
(AS PART OF NTCR PROJECT)
MAI PO LO WAI
NEW CONCRETE BOX CULVERT,
WITH MAINTENANCE ACCESS
FLOOD
POND
P.S.
MAI PO SAN TSUEN
0 20 40 60m
LOCALLY RAISE
CASTLE PEAK ROAD
NWNT - VILLAGE FLOOD PROTECTION STUDY
TERRITORY DEVELOPMENT DEPARTMENT
BINNIE CONSULTANTS LIMITED
Date : MAY 1989

Figure 6: Village flood protection scheme